Geoffrey Akst • Sadie Bragg

Basic Mathematics

Fourth Custom Edition for
Borough of Manhattan Community College

Taken from:

Basic College Mathematics through Applications, Fifth Edition
by Geoffrey Akst and Sadie Bragg

Introductory Algebra through Applications, Third Edition
by Geoffrey Akst and Sadie Bragg

Taken from:

Basic College Mathematics through Applications, Fifth Edition
by Geoffrey Akst and Sadie Bragg
Copyright © 2013 by Pearson Education, Inc.
Boston, Massachusetts 02116

Introductory Algebra through Applications, Third Edition
by Geoffrey Akst and Sadie Bragg
Copyright © 2013 by Pearson Education, Inc.
Boston, Massachusetts 02116

This special edition published in cooperation with Pearson Learning Solutions.

All trademarks, service marks, registered trademarks, and registered service marks are the property of their respective owners and are used herein for identification purposes only.

Pearson Learning Solutions, 501 Boylston Street, Suite 900, Boston, MA 02116
A Pearson Education Company
www.pearsoned.com

Printed in the United States of America

7 8 9 10 V0UD 18 17 16 15 14

000200010271666080

TF

ISBN 10: 1-256-78452-4
ISBN 13: 978-1-256-78452-4

Contents

Preface vii
Index of Applications xiii
Photo Credits xviii

1. Whole Numbers 1

Pretest 2
1.1 Introduction to Whole Numbers 3
1.2 Adding and Subtracting Whole Numbers 14
1.3 Multiplying Whole Numbers 32
1.4 Dividing Whole Numbers 44
1.5 Exponents, Order of Operations, and Averages 55
1.6 More on Solving Word Problems 66
Key Concepts and Skills 72
Review Exercises 75
Posttest 80

2. Fractions 81

Pretest 82
2.1 Factors and Prime Numbers 83
2.2 Introduction to Fractions 93
2.3 Adding and Subtracting Fractions 109
2.4 Multiplying and Dividing Fractions 130
Key Concepts and Skills 145
Review Exercises 148
Posttest 155
Cumulative Review Exercises 156

3. Decimals 157

Pretest 158
3.1 Introduction to Decimals 159
3.2 Adding and Subtracting Decimals 173
3.3 Multiplying Decimals 183
3.4 Dividing Decimals 192
Key Concepts and Skills 205
Review Exercises 207
Posttest 211
Cumulative Review Exercises 212

4. Basic Algebra: Solving Simple Equations 213

Pretest 214
4.1 Introduction to Basic Algebra 215
4.2 Solving Addition and Subtraction Equations 223
4.3 Solving Multiplication and Division Equations 232
Key Concepts and Skills 242
Review Exercises 243
Posttest 246
Cumulative Review Exercises 247

5. Ratio and Proportion 249

Pretest 250
5.1 Introduction to Ratios 251
5.2 Solving Proportions 261
Key Concepts and Skills 270
Review Exercises 271
Posttest 273
Cumulative Review Exercises 274

6. Percents 275

Pretest 276
6.1 Introduction to Percents 277
6.2 Solving Percent Problems 290
6.3 More on Percents 302
Key Concepts and Skills 313
Review Exercises 315
Posttest 319
Cumulative Review Exercises 320

7. Signed Numbers 321

Pretest 322
7.1 Introduction to
     Signed Numbers 323
7.2 Adding Signed Numbers 333
7.3 Subtracting Signed Numbers 340
7.4 Multiplying Signed Numbers 346
7.5 Dividing Signed Numbers 352
Key Concepts and Skills 358
Review Exercises 359
Posttest 362
Cumulative Review Exercises 363

8. Basic Statistics 364

Pretest 365
8.1 Introduction to Basic Statistics 368
8.2 Tables and Graphs 376
Key Concepts and Skills 390
Review Exercises 392
Posttest 396
Cumulative Review Exercises 398

11. Basic Geometry

11.6 Square Roots and the
     Pythagorean Theorem 515
Review Exercises 531
5.2 More Laws of Exponents and
     Scientific Notation 360

Appendix 539

Scientific Notation 539

Answers A-1

Glossary G-1

Index I-1

Preface

FROM THE AUTHORS

Our goal in writing *Basic College Mathematics through Applications* was to create a text that would help students progress and succeed in their college developmental math course. Throughout, we emphasize an applied approach, which has two advantages. First of all, it can help students prepare to meet their future mathematical demands—across disciplines, in subsequent coursework, in everyday life, and on the job. Secondly, this approach can be motivating, convincing students that mathematics is worth learning and more than just a school subject.

We have attempted to make the text readable, with understandable explanations and exercises for honing skills. We have also put together a set of easy-to-grasp features, consistent across sections and chapters.

In an effort to address many of the issues raised by national professional organizations, including AMA-TYC, NCTM, and NADE, we have been careful to stress connections to other disciplines; to incorporate the appropriate use of technology; to integrate quantitative reasoning skills; to include problem sets that facilitate student writing, critical thinking, and collaborative activities; and to emphasize real world data in examples and exercises. We have also introduced algebra early in the text to show an algebraic solution to a broad range of problems in successive chapters.

Above all, we have tried to develop a flexible text that can meet the needs of students in both traditional and redesigned developmental courses.

This text is part of the *through Applications* series that includes the following:

WHAT'S NEW IN THE FIFTH EDITION?

Say Why Exercises   New fill-in-the-blank problems, located at the beginning of each chapter review, providing practice in reasoning and communicating mathematical ideas (see page 243).

Updated Content   Adjusted content reflecting changing real-world needs. For instance, updates extend the place value concept from billions to trillions and the discussion of units to include the prefixes "mega-," "giga-," and "micro-," which are increasingly common in technology and medicine (see page 446).

Updated and Expanded Section Exercise Sets   Additional practice in mastering skills (see pages 359–361).

Chapter Openers   Extended real-world applications at the beginning of each chapter to motivate student interest and demonstrate how mathematics is used (see page 275).

Lengthening of Cumulative Review Exercise Sets   Twice as many review exercises in response to user demand (see page 247).

Greater Emphasis on Learning Objectives   End-of-section exercises closely aligned with the learning objectives in order to encourage and facilitate review (see pages 3 and 9–11).

More Examples and Exercises Based on Real Data   Additional and more varied applied problems that are useful, realistic, and authentic (see page 8).

Parallel Paired Exercises   Odd/even pairs of problems that more closely reflect the same learning objective (see page 298).

Easy-to-Locate Features   Color borders added for back-of-book answer, glossary, and index pages.

Highlighting of Quantitative Literacy Skills   Additional exercises that provide practice in number sense, proportional reasoning, and the interpretation of tables and graphs (see pages 28–30).

Increased Attention to Photos and Graphics   Carefully selected photos to make problems seem more realistic, and relevant graphics to better meet the needs of visual learners (see pages 203 and 283).

Newly Expanded and Robust MyMathLab Coverage!   One of *every* problem type is now assignable in MyMathLab.

Now Two MyMathLab Course Options

1. **Standard MyMathLab** allows you to build *your* course *your* way, offering maximum flexibility and complete control over all aspects of assignment creation. Starting with a clean slate lets you choose the exact quantity and type of problems you want to include for your students. You can also select from prebuilt assignments to give you a starting point.

2. **Ready-to-Go MyMathLab** comes with assignments prebuilt and preassigned, reducing start-up time. You can always edit individual assignments, as needed, through the semester.

KEY FEATURES

Math Study Skills Foldout   A full-color foldout with tips on organization, test preparation, time management, and more (see inside front cover).

Pretests and Posttests   Chapter tests, which are particularly useful in a self-paced, lab, or digital environment (see page 214).

Section Objectives   Clearly stated learning objectives at the beginning of each section to identify topics to be covered (see page 3).

Side-by-Side Example/Practice Format   Distinctive side-by-side format that pairs each example with a corresponding practice exercise and gets students actively involved from the start (see page 175).

Tips   Helpful suggestions and cautions for avoiding mistakes (see page 83).

Journal Entries   Writing assignments in response to probing questions interspersed throughout the text (see page 233).

Calculator Inserts   Optional calculator and computer software instruction to solve section problems (see page 23).

Cultural Notes   Glimpses of how mathematics has evolved across cultures and throughout history (see page 332).

For Extra Help   Boxes at the beginning of every section's exercise set that direct students to helpful resources that will aid in their study of the material (see page 80).

Mathematically Speaking Exercises   Vocabulary exercises in each section to help students understand and use standard mathematical terminology (see page 90).

Mixed Practice Exercises   Problems in synthesizing section material (see page 63).

Application Exercises   End-of-section problems to apply the topic at hand in a wide range of contexts (see pages 106–107).

Mindstretcher Exercises   Nonstandard section problems in critical thinking, mathematical reasoning, pattern recognition, historical connections, writing, and group work to deepen understanding and provide enrichment (see page 108).

Key Concepts and Skills Summary   With a focus on descriptions and examples, the main points of the chapter organized into a practical and comprehensive chart (see pages 145–147).

Chapter Review Exercises   Problems for reviewing chapter content, arranged by section (see pages 243–244).

Chapter Mixed Application Exercises   Practice in applying topics across the chapter (see page 245).

Cumulative Review Exercises   Problems to maintain and build on the mathematical content covered in previous chapters (see pages 271–272).

Scientific Notation Appendix   A brief appendix of particular value to students in the sciences.

U.S. and Metric Unit Tables   Located opposite the inside back cover for quick reference.

Geometric Formulas   A reference on the inside back cover of the text displaying standard formulas for perimeter, circumference, area, and volume.

Coherent Development   Texts with consistent content and style across the developmental math curriculum.

WHAT SUPPLEMENTS ARE AVAILABLE?

For a complete list of the supplements and study aids that accompany *Basic College Mathematics through Applications*, Fifth Edition, see pp. xi.

ACKNOWLEDGMENTS

We are grateful to everyone who has helped to shape this textbook by responding to questionnaires, participating in telephone surveys and focus groups, reviewing the manuscript, and using the text in their classes. We wish to thank Michele Bach, *Kansas City Kansas Community College;* Irma Bakenhus, *San Antonio College;* Mary Lou Baker, *Columbia State Community College;* Palma Benko, *Passaic County Community College;* Tim Bremer, *Prestonburg Community College;* Sylvia Brown, *Mountain Empire Community College;* Jennifer Caldwell, *Mesa Community College;* Edythe Carter, *Amarillo College;* James Cochran, *Kirkwood Community College;* Robert Denitti, *Westmoreland County Community College;* Eunice Everett, *Seminole Community College;* Alan Greenhalgh, *Borough of Manhattan Community College;* Barbara Gardner, *Carroll Community College;* Janet C. Guynn, *Blue Ridge Community College/CUNY;* Kate Horton, *Portland Community College;* Matthew Hudock, *St. Philip's College;* Judith M. Jones, *Valencia Community College–East Campus;* Joanne Kendall, *College of the Mainland;* Yon Kim, *Passaic County Community College;* Dan Kleinfelter, *College of the Desert;* Roberta Lacefield, *Waycross College;* Lider-Manuel Lamar, *Seminole Community College;* Lee H. LaRue, *Paris Junior College;* Theodore Lai, *Hudson County Community College;*

LeAnn L. Lotz-Todd, *Metropolitan Community College–Longview;* Carol Marinas, *Barry College;* Christopher McNally, *Tallahassee Community College;* Dena S. Messer-Herrera, *Rio Salado College;* James Morgan, *Holyoke Community College;* Kathleen Offenholley; *Borough of Manhattan Community College/CUNY;* Ferdinand O. Orock, *Hudson County Community College;* Margaret Patin, *Vernon College;* Barbara Pearl, *Bucks County Community College;* Pat Roux, *Delgado Community College;* Susan Santolucito, *Delgado Community College;* Sara R. Pries, *Sierra Community College;* Andrew Russell, *Queensborough Community College/CUNY;* Joyce Saxon, *Morehead State University;* Radha Shrinivas, *Forest Park Community College;* Larry Smyrski, *Henry Ford Community College;* Marcia Swope, *Santa Fe Community College;* Sharon A. Testone, *Onondaga Community College;* James Van Ark, *University of Detroit Mercy;* Betty Vix Weinberger, *Delgado Community College;* Harvey S. Weiner, *Marymount Manhattan College;* Lisa Winch, *Kalamazoo Valley Community College;* J. W. Wing, *Angelina College;* James C. Woodall, *Salt Lake Community College;* and Michael D. Yarborough, *Cosumnes River College.* In addition, we would like to extend our gratitude to our accuracy checkers and to those who helped us perfect the content in many ways: Janis Cimperman, St. Cloud University; Beverly Fusfield; Denise Heban; Perian Herring, Okaloosa-Walton College; Sharon O'Donnell, Chicago State University; Ann Ostberg; Lenore Parens; and Deana Richmond.

Writing a textbook requires the contributions of many individuals. Special thanks go to Greg Tobin, President, Mathematics and Statistics, Pearson Arts and Sciences, for encouraging and supporting us throughout the entire process. We thank Kari Heen and Katie DePasquale for their patience and tact, Michelle Renda, Rachel Ross, and Maureen O'Connor for keeping us abreast of market trends, Rachel Haskell for attending to the endless details connected with the project, Ron Hampton, Elka Block, Laura Hakala, Trish O'Kane, Tracy Duff, Marta Johnson, and Rachel Youdelman for their support throughout the production process, Barbara Atkinson for the cover design, and the entire Pearson developmental mathematics team for helping to make this text one of which we are very proud.

Geoffrey Akst   Sadie Bragg

Student Supplements

Student's Solutions Manual
By Beverly Fusfield
- Provides detailed solutions to the odd-numbered exercises in each exercise set and solutions to all chapter pretests and post-tests, practice exercises, review exercises, and cumulative review exercises

ISBN-10: 0-321-75712-2   ISBN-13: 978-0-321-75712-8

New Video Resources on DVD with Chapter Test Prep Videos
- Complete set of digitized videos on DVD for students to use at home or on campus
- Includes a full lecture for each section of the text
- Covers examples, practice problems, and exercises from the textbook that are marked with the ⊙ icon
- Optional captioning in English is available
- Step-by-step video solutions for each chapter test
- Chapter Test Prep Videos are also available on YouTube (search by using author name and book title) and in MyMathLab

ISBN-10: 0-321-78632-7   ISBN-13: 978-0-321-78632-6

MyWorkBook with Chapter Summaries
By Denise Heban
- Provides one worksheet for each section of the text, organized by section objective, along with the end-of-chapter summaries from the textbook
- Each worksheet lists the associated objectives from the text, provides fill-in-the-blank vocabulary practice, and exercises for each objective

ISBN 10: 0-321-75977-X   ISBN-13: 978-0-321-75977-1

MathXL Online Course (access code required)

InterAct Math Tutorial Website
www.interactmath.com
- Get practice and tutorial help online
- Provides algorithmically generated practice exercises that correlate directly to the textbook exercises
- Retry an exercise as many times as desired with new values each time for unlimited practice and mastery
- Every exercise is accompanied by an interactive guided solution that gives the student helpful feedback when an incorrect answer is entered
- View the steps of a worked-out sample problem similar to the one that has been worked on

Instructor Supplements

Annotated Instructor's Edition
- Provides answers to all text exercises in color next to the corresponding problems
- Includes teaching tips

ISBN-10: 0-321-63935-9   ISBN-13: 978-0-321-63935-6

Instructor's Solutions Manual (download only)
By Beverly Fusfield
- Provides complete solutions to even-numbered section exercises
- Contains answers to all Mindstretcher problems

ISBN-10: 0-321-75713-0   ISBN-13: 978-0-321-75713-5

Instructor's Resource Manual with Tests and Mini-Lectures (download only)
By Deana Richmond
- Contains three free-response and one multiple-choice test form per chapter, and two final exams
- Includes resources designed to help both new and adjunct faculty with course preparation and classroom management, including sample syllabi, tips for using supplements and technology, and useful external resources
- Offers helpful teaching tips correlated to the sections of the text

ISBN-10: 0-321-63937-5   ISBN-13: 978-0-321-63937-0

PowerPoint Lecture Slides (available online)
- Present key concepts and definitions from the text

TestGen® (available for download from the Instructor's Resource Center)

AVAILABLE FOR STUDENTS AND INSTRUCTORS

MyMathLab® Ready-to-Go Course (access code required)

These new Ready-to-Go courses provide students with all the same great MyMathLab features that you're used to, but make it easier for instructors to get started. Each course includes preassigned homework and quizzes to make creating your course even simpler. Ask your Pearson representative about the details for this particular course or to see a copy of this course.

MathXL—Instant Access—for *Basic College Mathematics through Applications*

MathXL® is the homework and assessment engine that runs MyMathLab. (MyMathLab is MathXL plus a learning management system.) With MathXL, instructors can

- Create, edit, and assign online homework and tests using algorithmically generated exercises correlated at the objective level to the textbook.
- Create and assign their own online exercises and import TestGen tests for added flexibility.
- Maintain records of all student work tracked in MathXL's online gradebook.

With MathXL, students can

- Take chapter tests in MathXL and receive personalized study plans and/or personalized homework assignments based on their test results.
- Use the study plan and/or the homework to link directly to tutorial exercises for the objectives they need to study.
- Access supplemental animations and video clips directly from selected exercises.

MathXL is available to qualified adopters. For more information, visit www.mathxl.com or contact your Pearson representative.

Index of Applications

Agriculture
Acreage used to grow corn, 295
Bees pollinating crop plants, 248
Bushels of wheat, 459
Farmland in Kansas, 80
Lawn surrounding a garden, 134
Milk needed to produce cream, 319
Number of farms, 200
Recipe for cattle feed, 300
Storing wheat in a silo, 507
Value of leading farm commodities, 379

Astronomy/Aerospace
Astronaut's weight, 401
Brightness of a star, 144, 327
Comets, 335–336
Crater on the Moon, 487
Diameter of planets, 53, 375
Diameter of the Moon, 53
Distance from the Sun to planets, 11, 151, 190, 209
Earth rotating about its axis, 169
Earth's atmosphere, 102
Halley's Comet, 77
Hubble Space Telescope, 451
Iron-nickel meteorite, 448
Light-years, 11
Milky Way galaxy, 56
Missing shuttlecraft, 506
Moons, 214
Orbiting satellite, 458
Revolutions of Mercury around the Sun, 71
Satellites orbiting Earth, 212, 487
Space shuttle Endeavor, 153
Speed of Earth, 186
Surface temperature on planets, 330
Volume of Earth and Jupiter, 506
Weight on the Moon, 245

Automotive
Compression ratio of a sports car, 272
Flexible-fuel vehicles, 300
Fuel-efficient vehicles, 254, 396
Gas mileage, 41, 53, 203, 254, 269
Gasohol vs. gasoline, 144
Hybrid car, 28
Maximum load on a bridge, 435
Oil change recommendation, 91
Passenger cars, 452
Reformulated gasoline, 194
Roof cargo carrier clearance, 181
Speed limit, 231, 371, 451
Stopping distance, 59
Traffic fines, 459
U.S. licensed drivers, 394

Biology
Air sacs in human lungs, 11
Amount of food a sea otter eats, 152
Average gestation for mammals, 457
Bacteria, 170
Bird species, 12
Bones in a human skeleton, 8, 107
Cells in the human body, 63
Cricket chirping, 419
Dinosaur egg, 77
Effects of cold on human skin, 144
Endangered species, 20, 246, 303
Heaviest organ in the body, 204
Human teeth, 151
Hummingbirds, 169
Insect species, 11, 30
Legs on a millipede, 78
Length of a centipede, 458
Length of a dinosaur, 457
Microscopes, 204, 497
Number of fish in a lake, 268
Rat running through a maze, 394
Relationship between bone length and height, 191, 317, 421
Skeleton age, 180
Sound waves of an elephant call, 186
South American frog venom, 209
Spiders, 182
Tallest land animal, 268
Tyrannosaurus rex, 439
Weight of a trout, 460
Weights of a great white shark and whales, 70, 458
Wingspan of a prehistoric bird, 452

Business
Advertising, 273, 492
Automobile dealer, 427
Cargo handled in U.S. ports, 393
Commercials, 94
Company's bottom line, 339
Company's income, 318, 344, 361, 379, 428
Company's loss, 330, 408
Company's net profit, 78
Company's total revenue, 389
Computer store, 272
Daily manufacturing costs, 408
Dairy equipment company, 452
Day-care center, 272
Defective machine parts, 288
Drilling for oil, 348
Factory's output, 287
First commercial telephone exchange, 311
Increased number of hotel beds, 302
Loss ratio of an insurance company, 260
Magazine circulation, 317
Mail-order catalog, 377
Manager ordering pens, 71
Marketing, 426
Microsoft's total revenue, 158
Net sales, 70
Newspaper circulation, 366
Office space, 63, 293
Operating expenses of a library, 272
Original value of a condo, 241
Potato chip factory, 250
Producing flyers, 37
Production, 311
Profit, 177, 217, 300, 318
Property management company, 299
Quarterly revenues, 210, 374
Real estate agent's fees, 317
Redecorating a restaurant, 65
Restaurant's electricity bill, 212
Sales, 310
Selling a home, 71
Selling price vs. assessed value of a house, 232
Soda machine reliability, 393
Steel mill, 299
Suing a business partner, 180
Supermarket selling fruit, 245
Treasurer of a company, 5
U.S. corporations with largest revenues, 156
Value of a copier, 362
Warehouse inventory, 300

Chemistry
Acid, 158, 264, 276
Air, 283
Alcohol and water solution, 241, 300
Atomic weight, 170, 185
Boiling point and freezing point of water, 28
Boiling point, 330, 342
Carbon dioxide molecules, 268
Chemical process and reaction, 339, 456
Copper changing from a liquid to a gas, 12
Density, 272, 507
Endothermic reaction, 246
Gold mixed with other metals, 252
Lead in mechanical pencils, 170
Melting point, 231, 342, 351
Metal alloy, 152, 268
Mixing solutions, 452
Nitrogen gas, 363
pH scale, 158, 387
Rankin temperature scale, 425
Salt content of seawater, 289
Synthetic chemical elements, 20
Valence in a chemical compound, 321
Weight of a compound, 209, 211
Weight of a diamond, 152
Weight of water, 153, 190, 227

INDEX OF APPLICATIONS

Construction

Access ramp construction, 522
Acoustic tiles on a ceiling, 71
Architects rendering designs, 268
Architectural drawing of a
    planned community, 272
Area of a room, 143
Board foot of lumber, 537
Building a family room addition, 301
Building a patio, 209
Building custom-designed swimming pools, 190
Building model railroads, 268
Building stairs, 518
Cabin sinking, 137
Carpenter constructing steps, 209
Combining sand and gravel, 250
Constructing a roof, 522
Construction job schedule, 117
Developer selling land, 99
Digging a tunnel, 177
Drainage pipes around a building complex, 483
Fence posts, 486
Fencing a garden, 71, 478, 480
Flatiron Building in New York City, 221
Foundation of a house, 463
Great Pyramid of Khufu, 11, 398
Hammering a nail, 127
Height of buildings, 77, 78, 451, 513
Housing starts, 363
Installing granite countertop, 143
Installing shelves for DVDs, 70
Ladder, 521, 534
Length of a fence, 17
Length of a side of a square tile, 451
Length of a side of the Pentagon, 236
Lot survey, 221
Model kitchen, 535
Molding length, 29
Paint coverage, 156
Polyurethane applied to a gym floor, 494
Refinishing a basement, 156
Remodeling a bathroom, 53
Support wires, 513
Tallest telecommunication towers, 229
Total length of a building's walls, 535
Wallpaper, 121
Wood molding, 486
Yard space, 497

Consumer

Air conditioning, 534
Auto repair charges, 426
Bargain matinee price at a movie
    theater, 214
Better buy, 255, 257, 258, 271, 273
Bills, 171, 375, 408
Bottled water consumption, 245
Buying products, 181, 190, 239
Car rental costs, 408
Cell phone subscribers, 388, 417
Charges for children's yoga class, 427

Consumer confidence index, 170
Cost of a health club membership, 41
Cost of a marriage license, 302–303
Cost of a product, 80, 143, 152, 240, 480, 486,
    492, 494
Dental bills, 151, 230, 247
Digital photo charges, 71
Discount, 180, 305, 311, 312, 401
Electric company charges, 212
Food expenses, 209, 245
Foods consumed in the
    United States, 198
Gasoline prices, 372
Insurance premiums, 190
Labor Day sale, 427
Leasing a car, 71, 417
Leasing an apartment, 440
Long-distance phone charges, 158, 240,
    408, 427
Lunch bill, 218
Money spent on housing, 143
Monthly cable service, 406
Mortgage, 191, 221
Net income and monthly car payment, 218
Online media rental service, 240
Original price, 71
Parking charges, 414
Pizza parlor charges, 414
Respondents planning to make
    a purchase, 380
Sale price, 152, 224, 305, 311, 312,
    317, 338
Selling price, 498
Shipping fee, 227
Shopping, 71, 212
Tipping, 311
U.S. consumer price index, 387
Unit price, 254–255, 257, 258, 274
Value of a painting, 312
Water usage, 456

Economics

Coal reserves, 317
Country's economic conditions, 300, 318
Current exchange rate, 167, 171
Depreciation, 296, 417, 421
Dow Jones Industrial Average, 170, 538
Imports and exports, 29
Inflation, 317
New York Stock Exchange, 452
Property tax on a building, 211, 259, 311
Real estate property value, 351
Sales tax rate, 132, 171, 288, 300, 304, 311,
    312, 318, 319, 420
Stock, 153, 204, 208, 260, 303, 345, 354,
    357, 361, 362, 408, 428, 459
Tax credit for green space, 419
Taxes, 210, 268, 304, 385
U.S. public debt, 11
Value of a house, 232
Value of currency, 171, 268

Education

Acceptance rate to a college, 297
ACT college entrance exam, 317
Admission rate, 272
Arithmetic and Algebra Placement Test, 386
Campaign to build a new technology
    complex, 180
Campus map, 534
Chemistry majors, 152
Classes closed at registration, 217
College admission exam scores, 170
College credits, 2
College schedule hours, 371
College scholarship fund, 5
College tuition, 42, 71, 267, 300, 319
College-wide fund-raising campaign, 144
Community college applications, 245
Community college enrollment, 276
Cost per credit hour, 53, 230
Course average, 395
Dean's List, 171
Enrollments in public and private colleges,
    79, 398
Financial aid, 152, 293, 426
First algebra textbook, 230
Flesch Reading Ease Formula, 421
Grade in a math course, 152
Grade point average, 365, 369, 374, 396
Hours a college class meets, 215
Largest libraries, 394
Losing points for incorrect answers, 361, 404
Males vs. females at a college, 259
Math books in history, 361
Math exam, 299, 396
Math test scores, 64, 68
Medical school, 273
Missed school days, 366
Number of degrees in the United States, 13, 378
Nursing program, 94
Oldest institutions of higher learning, 227
Passing grades, 82
Postsecondary teachers, 8
Preschool budget for craft kits, 37
SAT and family income, 387
Schedule of math classes, 377
School attendance, 218
Sections of math, 68
Student fee, 204
Student government election, 128, 259
Student typing a report, 117
Students taking a math course, 132
Student-to-faculty ratio, 262, 265
Studying, 106, 217
Test scores, 284, 369, 374, 375, 381, 390
White boards in a community college
    classroom, 300

Energy

Annual oil production, 248
Compact fluorescent lightbulb, 316
Electrical usage, 170, 190

Electricity generated worldwide, 127
Energy efficiency rating of an air conditioner, 165
Nuclear power, 287
Offshore wind farm, 153
Power consumption, 218

Entertainment

Animating a cartoon, 247
Auction, 318
Broadway shows, 230, 319
Brooklyn Museum attendance, 241
Carnegie Hall, 29
Classic horror films, 456
Contestant on *Jeopardy*, 360
Dating service, 212
Disc jockey, 181, 401
Editing a silent film, 272
Elephants at the National Zoo, 401
Ferris wheel, 486
Film length, 155
Graduation dinner, 408
Grammy Lifetime Achievement Award, 152
Guests at a party, 389
Highest-grossing films, 8
Horse race, 115
IMAX movie *The Polar Express*, 431
Length of a double feature, 436
Monster truck rally, 416
Most downloaded authors, 229
Movie screens in the United States, 70
Movie sequel *Highlander II*, 281
Movies, 115, 177
Music sales, 397
Platinum albums, 259
Play at a local theater, 401
Playing time of a DVD, 456
Production of *Romeo and Juliet*, 64
Radio stations, 102, 320, 477
Raffle tickets, 68–69
Regular sources of local news, 287
Rock concert tickets, 236
Roller coasters, 11, 259
Six Flags Great Adventure
        amusement park, 53
Television show ratings, 181, 185
Tickets to a play, 239
Weekend box office receipts, 370
Westminster Dog Show, 320
Zoo, 393

Environment

Air pressure at sea level, 170
Annual precipitation for Phoenix, 345
Barometric pressure, 274
Beetles destroying a forest, 77
Bermuda Triangle, 476
Depth of lakes, 59, 335
Depth of trenches, 330
Distance across a river or lake, 510, 538
Drought, 180, 351
Elevation, 327, 338, 344

Evergreen trees, 440
Fog, 107, 493
Height of a tree, 265, 273, 510
Heights of mountains, 23, 230, 440
Hurricanes, 245, 457, 538
Insecticide, 267, 538
Largest cold snap in U.S. history, 28
Lead emissions in the United States, 171
Length of the Panama Canal, 172
Lightning, 420
Named storms, 156
Nile River, 12
Nuclear waste, 269
Oil spill, 29, 288, 362, 534
Pesticide, 456
Precipitation, 383
Rainfall, 167, 203, 365
Recycled or composted trash, 431
Recycling, 70
Sea level at Kodiak Island, 350
Shrubs surviving the winter, 217
Solar wind streams off the Sun, 63
Solid municipal waste, 317
Temperature below which plants freeze, 327
Temperature, 209, 245, 322, 344, 351, 356, 357,
        361, 362, 363, 382–383, 418
Toxic emissions, 171
Tropical rainforest, 28
U.S. coastline, 397
U.S. residents producing garbage, 248
Water consumption, 180
Water level of the Mississippi River, 344
Weather sensor, 431

Finance

Annual income, 99–100
Assets of largest banks in the United States, 77
ATMs, 322, 366
Bank account balance, 217, 224, 306, 351
Certificate of deposit, 312
Charity donations, 231
Checking account balance, 80, 245, 330, 360, 408
Credit cards, 29, 287, 296, 338, 360
Deposits, 28, 177
Down payment, 143, 295, 426
Family's budget, 91, 416
Fixed interest rate, 317
Grandchildren's inheritance, 374
Half cent, 170
Income spent on housing, 300
Installment plan, 2, 41, 71
Interest compounded annually, 307, 312, 318,
        538
Interest on an account, 171, 276, 305, 311, 317,
        319, 418, 421
Investments, 180, 241, 287
Loan balance, 69
Money left, 229
Monthly car payment, 360
Mortgage on a condo, 41
Mortgage rates, 363
Paying back a loan, 245, 311

Paying off a camcorder, 426
Prime interest rate, 374
Quarters and dimes, 151
Return on Investment (ROI), 259
Rule of 72, 418–419
Salary put into a 401(k) plan, 292
Spending money, 239
Withdrawal, 221

Geology

Cliff erosion, 356
Coral reefs, 354
Earthquakes, 171, 381–382, 458
Glacier, 272
Growth of a stalactite, 203
Largest giant sequoia, 11
Pond evaporation, 144
Ring of Fire, 279
Thickness of Earth's core, 440
Volcanoes, 274
World's land surface covered with ice, 194

Geometry

Angle measurement, 221, 416, 421, 476
Area of a circular region, 190, 419, 493, 497
Area of a rectangular region, 2, 36, 41, 79, 134,
        153, 190, 222, 232, 274, 497, 534, 535
Area of a roll of aluminum foil, 534
Area of a semicircle, 498
Area of a square region, 497
Area of a trapezoid, 497
Area of a walkway, 497
Area of cities or states, 42, 63, 77, 214, 227,
        287, 368, 417
Area of oceans, 53
Area of the base of a pyramid, 78
Circumference of a circular-shaped object,
        481–482, 487
Complementary angles, 230, 467
Diameter of a circular-shaped object, 472, 475, 476
Dimensions of a planter, 477
Dimensions of a rectangular region, 440, 476, 521
Dimensions of the Titanic, 128
Fencing a piece of land, 478, 480
Land area, 11, 127, 170, 172, 212
Length of a pool, 118
Length of the side of a parallelogram, 476
Length of the side of a square, 240
Length of the side of a trapezoid, 118
Perimeter of a figure, 221, 482
Perimeter of a rectangular region, 17, 82, 426, 486
Perimeter of a triangle, 113
Radius of a circular-shaped object, 472, 475
Sides of a polygon, 417
Supplementary angles, 230, 467
Surface area of a cube, 420
Volume of a cake, 503
Volume of a cylindrical-shaped object, 501,
        502, 506
Volume of a medicine capsule, 503
Volume of a rectangular solid, 502, 506

Volume of a sphere-shaped object, 501, 502, 506
Width of a rectangle, 416

Government

Abraham Lincoln, 439
Ages of American presidents, 68, 108,
        381–382, 392
Connecticut Compromise, 249
Countries with largest military expenditure, 64
Democrats and Republicans, 259
Elections, 67–68, 85
Electoral votes, 71
Federal deficit, 344, 354
Federal government income resources, 318
Filibustering, 81
Foreign-aid spending bill, 94
Grand jury, 152, 171
Mayor's approval rating, 317
Number of votes for Nixon, 78
Political parties, 388
Political polls, 275
Presidential election, 288, 389, 476
Presidents born in Indiana, 155
Proposed recovery plan during a recession, 245
Public debt of the United States, 281
Punishment in an oil spill case, 156
Rwanda's legislature, 279
Senate seat, 89
Social Security, 288, 388
State Dining Room in the White House, 476
The Pentagon, 236
U.S. congressional seats held by Florida, 427
U.S. House of Representatives, 89, 374
United States Congress, 209
United States Postal Service, 375
United States Supreme Court, 370–371
Voting age population, 143
Withdrawing troops, 320
World Wars, 28

Health/Life Sciences

Aerobics classes, 89
Anemia, 182
Ascorbic acid to cure tuberculosis, 451
Average weight of a human brain, 452
Avoiding the flu, 396
Babies born each month, 396
Birth weight, 452
Blood tests, 157, 171
Blood volume, 283
Body mass index, 419
Bone density test, 330
Burning calories, 53
Caffeine, 214
Calories, 190, 240, 259
Cancer patients, 366
Carbohydrates, 82, 269
Cholesterol, 456
Cost of generic vs. brand name drugs, 182
Daily reference value for fiber, 456
Decongestant pill, 163

Donated blood, 457
Dosage of medicine for a child, 59, 421
Drinking fluid before surgery, 452
Drip rate for an IV medication, 71
Emergency response times, 365
Emergency room visits, 143
Fast-food calories, 80
Female doctors, 320
Health care expenditures, 395
Health insurance, 276, 302
Heart muscle contractions, 40
Heart rates, 267, 376, 401
Injection, 170
Intensive care unit, 259
Intravenous fluid, 267
Length of the small and large intestine, 446
Life expectancy, 230, 237
Life spans, 365
Measles cases, 30, 391
Medicated shampoo, 431
Medicine dosage, 110, 144, 170, 221, 311,
        330, 350, 363, 404, 428, 451
Nerve cells in the human brain, 11
Nursing home residents, 311
Organ transplants, 395
Patient's pulse, 273
Patient's temperature, 65
Physical and respiratory therapists, 106
Polio cases in the United States, 316
Pressure on a hip joint, 153
Protein, 267, 269, 287
Recommended daily amount of calcium, 27
Recommended dietary allowances, 107, 297, 446
Smoking, 288
Sodium, 175, 451, 456
Tai Chi classes, 89
Taking medication, 71, 85, 190, 268
Temperature, 174, 245, 354
Testing a new drug, 128
Thimerosal, 457
Vitamins, 40, 158, 182, 447, 451, 452
Vocabulary of a human child and a chimp, 388
Waist to Hip Ratio (WHR), 252
Weight, 69, 239, 317, 339
Weight loss, 138, 154, 204, 229, 351, 362

Labor

Celebrity earnings, 28
CEO's compensation, 262
Commission, 30, 304, 311, 318, 385
Days off, 91
Employees and vacation time, 317
Employees responding to a survey, 132
Employment for major U.S. industries, 386
Full-time workers, 398
Gender of employees, 301
Gross income, 53, 153, 300
Hours worked, 154
Job openings, 398
Jobs available to those with a
        college education, 401
Layoffs, 67, 231, 338

Minimum wage, 372
Part-time job, 78, 155
Pay per year, 53
Profit sharing, 237
Projected employment change, 21
Ratio of officers to enlisted personnel, 428
Salary/Income, 64, 80, 175, 190, 245, 253, 262,
        272, 274, 284, 297, 374, 538
U.S. military personnel on active duty, 248
Unemployment rate, 6, 40, 153, 276, 380
Unions, 151, 288, 292, 339
Work stoppages, 64

Miscellaneous

Age of Ethiopia vs. the United States, 344
Age, 2, 28
American Kennel Club registrations, 459
Amount of cereal in a box, 154
Brannock device, 418
Buddha, 361
Burning candle, 144
Buying goldfish for a tank, 153
Capacity of an oil barrel, 448
Child's shoe size, 128
Children with an imaginary companion, 287
Chou dynasty, 360
Cleopatra, 338
Clothesline pulley, 486
Crocus flowers needed to produce saffron, 264
Cutting pizza, 97, 135
Days in a month, 365
Distance Lewis and Clark traveled, 154
Dog's run, 537
Dripping faucet, 267
Elevators, 28, 330, 344, 374
Emergency training, 236–237
Heel pressure, 213
Height of a column, 512
Height of a puppet's image, 512
Height of the Statue of Liberty, 12
Heights, 457
Identity fraud, 397, 538
Landscaper buying flowers, 78
Left handed, 317
Longest reigning monarchs, 259
Mayan calendar, 408
Mona Lisa, 437
National Register of Historic Places, 538
Nobel Prize, 106, 297, 397
Pages in a book, 91
Paper invented in China, 342
Photography, 137, 268
Picnic area, 521
Planting bulbs, 274
Pythagoras's death, 322
Recipe, 106, 246, 269, 440
Record for holding breath under water, 439
Refugee camp, 318
Rescuers searching for survivors, 463
Rhubarb, 435
Robots, 390
Rolling dice, 107

Roman's step, 211
Shutter speed, 151
Soda can, 452
Soil needed to fill a flower box, 535
Spreadsheet, 400, 417
Storm damage to houses, 203
The Fields Medal, 91
Thickness of garbage bags, 165
Three-dimensional paintings, 513
Trim for costumes, 156
Waiting time at the passport office, 387
Water in an aquarium, 200
Weight of various items, 128, 204, 406, 431, 436, 442, 448, 456, 506, 535
Wifi hotspots in the United States, 11
Wreck of an Egyptian ship, 40
Yards of silk to make a tie, 138

Physics

Density of an object, 426
Dropped object, 63
Elevation of an object, 351
Equivalent energy of a mass, 420
Friction, 170
Length of a pendulum, 451
Length of a spring, 420
Newton's second law of motion, 427
Object thrown upward, 361
Oil flowing through a pipe, 268
Pedal sprocket and gears on a bicycle, 268
Properties of atomic particles, 338
Rate of flow of water, 259
Speed of an object, 427
Speed of light, 50
Speed of sound, 50, 190, 425

Sports

Athlete's fluid intake, 456
Attendance at Fenway Park, 153
Barefoot water skiing, 429
Baseball, 30, 128, 204, 236, 253, 363, 398, 420, 425, 518
Basketball, 64, 107, 204, 221, 300, 351
Bowler's score, 245
Champion swimmer, 208
Figure skating, 457
Fishing competition, 440
Football, 41, 78, 301, 327, 339, 356
Golf, 299, 361
Gymnast's scores, 181
Hiking, 113, 121–122, 476
Ice hockey, 331
Indianapolis 500 auto race, 170
Ironman triathlon, 155, 240
Kentucky Derby, 127, 437
Longest field goal, 439
Los Angeles Lakers, 107
Masters tournament, 2
New York City Marathon, 175
Olympic Games, 151, 171, 439, 451, 456
Participants in high school athletic programs, 383
Pole vaulting record, 439
Racquetball, 535
Rugby and lacrosse teams, 91
Runner's time, 174
Scuba diving, 361, 521
Seating capacity of the Rose Bowl Stadium, 12
Shooting pool, 534
Softball team's record, 203
Tennis, 78, 152, 274, 318
The Triple Crown, 211
Tour de France, 79
Weights of players, 108, 396
Wins and losses, 310, 351
Winter Olympic medal counts, 28
World Cup soccer tournament, 91
World Series, 82, 365, 368

Statistics/Demographics

American pet-owning households, 384
Americans age 65 and older, 151, 382–383
Cat and dog owners, 318
Census, 91
Deaths in New York City, 29
Fatalities, 59, 390
First quintuplets to survive beyond infancy, 439
Flood of tourists, 302
Immigrants entering the United States, 70
Largest continents in the world, 80
Most heavily populated countries, 13
Online survey of students sending text messages, 94
Overseas visitors from various countries, 20
People per square mile, 53
Population density, 241
Population of a city, 312, 331, 356
Population of Brazil, 50
Population of China, 50
Population of the United States, 8, 27, 70, 190, 320
Population projections, 50
Probability of winning the lottery, 171
Summer population of Ruidoso, 240
Surveys, 287, 288, 300, 395, 416
Tallest woman, 439
Time spent on daily household activities, 170
Top two languages used online, 23
U.S. population by gender, 300
U.S. tourists visiting other countries, 107
Urban population, 301
Vacationing in Australia, 399
World population, 56, 246
World's largest oceans, 198

Technology

Aspect ratio of an image, 250
Camcorder battery voltage, 170
Cartridge yield of a computer printer, 259
Computer hard drive capacity, 457
Computer memory, 458
Computer network technician, 221
Download/upload speed of a computer, 240, 268
DVD collection, 70
E-mail users, 384
Facebook, 429
High-definition flash memory camcorder, 401
IBM shipping the first hard drive, 457
Internet users, 29, 212, 272, 300
iPod sales, 77
LCD television, 41, 463
Powering a television through recycling, 70
Printing photos, 2
Radio frequencies, 320
Random access memory (RAM), 447
Salvage value of a computer, 356
Spam e-mail, 287
Twitter, 320
Value of a printer, 408
Wireless internet users, 386
Word processing, 181
YouTube, 1

Transportation

Airline overselling a flight, 317
Airline passengers, 241
Air-traffic control tower, 497
Altitude of a plane, 356
Around-the-world flight, 12
Bicycle wheels, 486
Bus travel, 254
Business and economy class seats, 416
Commuting, 301, 317, 483
Cruising altitude of a passenger jet, 458
Deep submergence vehicle, 348
Deep-diving research vessel, 204
Distance a ship is from shore, 513
Distance between airplanes, 344, 537
Distance between cities, 41, 79, 250, 264–265, 268, 386, 431, 460, 486, 534
Distance driven, 29
Distance from a starting point, 70
Distance, 110–111, 153, 175, 221, 274
Domestic flights in the U.S., 393
Dupont Circle in Washington, DC, 537
Express bus, 153
First class vs. coach seats, 272
Flight miles, 70
Flight time, 132
Frequent flier miles, 318
Handicap parking, 319
Largest yachts, 154
Mach speed, 264
Nonstop flight, 440
Passenger departures, 378
Pirates terrorizing shipping lanes, 428
Plane's speed, 153
Top U.S. airlines, 241
Total length of a trip, 483
Trip to an island, 144
Truck driver's mileage, 41
Visibility at JFK airport, 107
Weights of British ships, 70
Wingspan of a plane, 153

Photo Credits

p. 1: Yakov Lapinsky; p. 11(tl): Gerry Ellis/Digital Vision/Getty Images; p. 11(tr): Gary Buss/Taxi/Getty Images; p. 11(b): Al Behrman/AP Images; p. 12(tl): GWImages/Shutterstock; p. 12(bl): Steve Herrmann/Shutterstock; p. 12(br): Karin Hildebrand Lau/Shutterstock; p. 20: Keren Su/Photodisc/Getty Images; p. 29(r): Jack Smith/AP Images; p. 29(l): Angus Oborn/Dorling Kindersley, Ltd.; p. 41: Jochen Sand/Digital Vision/Getty Images; p. 63, 77, 212, 487: NASA; p. 70(l): Stephen Frink/Digital Vision/Getty Images; p. 70(r): Library of Congress Prints and Photographs Division [LC-USZC4-13287]; p. 71: AP Images; p. 78: Richard Nowitz/National Geographic/Getty Images; p. 81: Archives du 7e Art/Columbia Pictures/DR/The Image Works; p. 107(t): Mark J. Terrill/AP Images; 107(b): Claudiofichera/Shutterstock; p. 152(t), 274(l), 288: PhotoLink/Photodisc/Getty Images; p. 152(bl): Album/Newscom; p. 152(br): Tim Lama/National Geographic/Getty Images; p. 153: Ramon Berk/Shutterstock; p. 157: Laurence Gough/Shutterstock; p. 167: Ryan McVay/Photodisc/Getty Images; p. 169(l): InterNetwork Media/Digital Vision/Getty Images; p. 169(r): iDesign/Shutterstock; p. 170: Library of Congress Prints and Photographs Division [DIG-ggbain-11279]; p. 171: InterNetwork Media/Photodisc/Getty Images; p. 186: Tom Brakefield/Photodisc/Getty Images; p. 203(l): Jeffrey M. Frank/Shutterstock; p. 203(r): Petr Mašek/Shutterstock; p. 209: Rolf Nussbaumer Photography/Alamy; p. 213: Tatiana Morozova/Shutterstock; p. 222: Marek Szumlas/Shutterstock; p. 230(l): Darwinsm81/Dreamstime; p. 230(r): Stacy Gold/National Geographic/Getty Images; p. 236: Frontpage/Shutterstock; p. 240(l), 268, 451: Stockbyte/Getty Images; p. 240(r): Jake Schoellkopf/AP Images; p. 245(l): Jack Hollingsworth/Photodisc/Getty Images; p. 245(r): NOAA; p. 247: Sipa/AP Images; p. 248: Purestock/Getty Images; p. 249: Robert Harding Picture Library, Ltd./Alamy; p. 255: Mark McClare/Shutterstock; p. 267(l): Don Farrall/Photodisc/Getty Images; p. 267(r): Jose Luis Pelaez, Inc./Blend Images/Getty Images; p. 272(l): Andersen Ross/Getty Images; p. 272(r): AF Archive/Alamy; p. 274(r): J. Helgason/Shutterstock; p. 275: Tom Pennington/MCT/Newscom; p. 279: Jason Straziuso/AP Images; p. 283: Ocean/Corbis; p. 289: Dorling Kindersley, Ltd.; p. 295: Dewitt/Shutterstock; p. 299(l): Dallas Events Inc/Shutterstock; p. 299(r): Photodisc/Getty Images; p. 303: Steve Reed/Shutterstock; p. 311: Yuri Arcurs/Shutterstock; p. 312: Mypokcik/Shutterstock; p. 316(l): Jose Gil/Shutterstock; p. 316(r): Tom Reed/AP Images; p. 318: DAJ/Getty Images; p. 321: Reflekta/Shutterstock; p. 327: Bellafotos/Dreamstime; p. 332: DDCoral/Shutterstock; p. 348: Rod Catanach/Newscom; p. 350: Alvaro Pantoja/Shutterstock; p. 356: Charles Smith/Corbis; p. 360(l): ABC/Everett Collection; p. 360(r): ChinaFotoPress/Newscom; p. 364: RubberBall/Alamy; p. 367: The Print Collector/Alamy; p. 400: Auremar/Shutterstock; p. 416: Michael Stokes/Shutterstock; p. 419: Kerry Vanessa McQuaid/Shutterstock; p. 420: Martin Fischer/Shutterstock; p. 422: *Madame X (Madame Pierre Gautreau)* (1883–1884), John Singer Sargent. Oil on canvas, 82 1/8 × 43 1/4 in. (208.6 × 109.9 cm). Arthur Hoppock Hearn Fund, 1916 (16.53). The Metropolitan Museum of Art/Art Resource, New York; p. 429: Maurie Hill/Dreamstime; p. 430: Detlev Van Ravensway/Science Photo Library/Photo Researchers, Inc.; p. 437(l): *Portrait of Lisa Gherardini* ("*Mona Lisa*") (1503–1506), Leonardo da Vinci. Oil on poplar wood, 77 × 53 cm. Collection of the Louvre Museum; Purchased by François I in 1518 [Inv. 779]. Photograph by Stuart Dee/Photographer's Choice/Getty Images; p. 437(r): Horst Schafer/AP Images; p. 439: Library of Congress Prints and Photographs Division [LC-DIG-ppmsca-19926]; p. 440: Interfoto/Alamy; p. 456: Dane Penland, Smithsonian Institution/AP Images; p. 457: Testing/Shutterstock; p. 461: Juice Images/Alamy; p. 463: Ragne Kabanova/Shutterstock; p. 506: Jim DeLillo/iStockphoto; p. 513: Harris Shiffman/ShutterstockEctemque iur aut idestem accatur? Ent verferum repe venimperum quas vendam que omnis ulparia aboribus accullu ptatur si volente volorem re, consequ asinctotae doluptamet quo omniet as int, officatest, voloresciasi omnihic te doluptat.

Uptatur magnimus apid minctam, quo coribus inihici demporepe volorepudam quuntem porehenitat asit venestiis pore num era eati od magnis maxim et, comnihilia site sini cus et voluptas modit di te susam am etur? Qui cuptatium que nobisquia aditi de quiduci delescid modis restium quiam volluptatiam la a dolor magnam que nobit aborestibus rem quostiu rionsectota nullab iliti blabor sequas dis dis reptatis verenimos et ea ditati velicie nitatur sequi omnit provide rorest aliquae nit idel essint maxim volupta

CHAPTER 1

1.1 Introduction to Whole Numbers

1.2 Adding and Subtracting Whole Numbers

1.3 Multiplying Whole Numbers

1.4 Dividing Whole Numbers

1.5 Exponents, Order of Operations, and Averages

1.6 More on Solving Word Problems

Whole Numbers

Whole Numbers and YouTube

YouTube is a website where users can upload and view videos. These include movie clips, TV clips, music videos, and amateur content. This site made it feasible for anyone with an Internet connection to publish a video that could be seen by a worldwide audience within a few minutes.

In February 2005, the company was set up in a garage by several work colleagues. The first video posted on YouTube was *Me at the Zoo*, in which founder Jawed Karim is seen at the San Diego Zoo.

The usage of the site grew at an astonishing rate. By July 2006, more than 65,000 new videos were being uploaded every day, with about 10,000,000 visitors and 100,000,000 video views per day. Barely a year after its founding, the company was bought by Google for approximately $1,650,000,000.

YouTube has made sharing online video such an important part of Internet culture that it's been said "if it's not on YouTube, it's like it never happened."

(*Sources:* telegraph.co.uk, comscore.com, wikipedia.org, and cleancutmedia.com)

1. Insert commas as needed in the number 2 0 5 0 0 7. Then write the number in words.

2. Write the number one million, two hundred thirty-five thousand in standard form.

3. What place does the digit 8 occupy in 805,674?

4. Round 8,143 to the nearest hundred.

5. Add: $38 + 903 + 7{,}285$

6. Subtract 286 from 5,000.

7. Subtract: $734 - 549$

8. Find the product of 809 and 36.

9. Find the quotient: $27\overline{)7{,}020}$

10. Divide: $13{,}558 \div 44$

11. Write $2 \cdot 2 \cdot 2$, using exponents.

12. Evaluate: 6^2

Simplify.

13. $26 - 7 \cdot 3$

14. $3 + 2^3 \cdot (8 - 3)$

Solve and check.

15. The mathematician Benjamin Banneker was born in 1731 and died in 1806. About how old was he when he died? (*Source: The New Encyclopedia Britannica*)

16. At a certain college, students pay $105 for each college credit. If a student takes 9 credits and pays with a $1,000 voucher, how much change will he receive?

17. Phil Mickelson had scores of 67, 71, 67, and 67 for his four rounds at the 2010 Masters Tournament. What was his average score for a round of golf?

18. The Epson PictureMate Show Compact Photo Printer can print a 4-inch by 6-inch photo in 37 seconds, and the Epson Artisan 810 All-in-One Printer can print the same size photo in 10 seconds. How much longer would it take the Epson PictureMate Show to print twelve 4-inch by 6-inch photos? (*Source:* epson.com)

19. An insurance company offers an installment plan for paying auto insurance premiums. For a $540 policy, the plan requires a down payment of $81. The balance is paid in nine equal installments of $55, which includes a service charge. How much money would be saved by paying for this policy without using the installment plan?

20. Which of the rooms pictured has the largest area? (feet = ft)

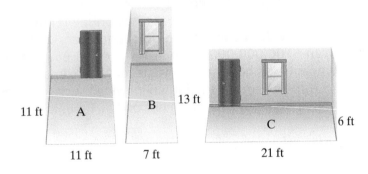

11 ft   A   11 ft   B   7 ft   13 ft   C   21 ft   6 ft

• Check your answers on page A-1.

1.1 Introduction to Whole Numbers

What the Whole Numbers Are and Why They Are Important

We use whole numbers for counting, whether it is the number of *e*'s on this page, the number of stars in the sky, or the number of runs, hits, and errors in a baseball game.

The whole numbers are 0, 1, 2, 3, 4, 5, 6, 7, 8, 9, 10, 11, 12, 13, ... An important property of whole numbers is that there is always a next whole number. This property means that they go on without end, as the three dots above indicate.

Every whole number is either *even* or *odd*. The even whole numbers are 0, 2, 4, 6, 8, 10, 12, ... The odd whole numbers are 1, 3, 5, 7, 9, 11, 13, ...

We can represent the whole numbers on a number line. Similar to a ruler, the number line starts with 0 and extends without end to the right, as the arrow indicates.

Reading and Writing Whole Numbers

Generally speaking, we *read* whole numbers in words, but we use the **digits** 0, 1, 2, 3, 4, 5, 6, 7, 8, and 9 to *write* them. For instance, we read the whole number *fifty-one* but write it *51*, which we call **standard form**.

Each of the digits in a whole number in standard form has a **place value**. Our place value system is very important because it underlies both the way we write and the way we compute with numbers.

The following chart shows the place values in whole numbers up to 15 digits long. For instance, in the number 1,234,056 the digit 2 occupies the hundred thousands place. Study the place values in the chart now.

TRILLIONS			BILLIONS			MILLIONS			THOUSANDS			ONES			
Hundred trillions	Ten trillions	Trillions	Hundred billions	Ten billions	Billions	Hundred millions	Ten millions	Millions	Hundred thousands	Ten thousands	Thousands	Hundreds	Tens	Ones	← Period / ← Place value
								1	2	3	4	0	5	6	
			8	1	6	8	9	3	1	0	4	7			

TIP We read whole numbers from left to right, but it is easier in the place value chart to learn the names of the places *from right to left*.

When we write a large whole number in standard form, we insert *commas* to separate its digits into groups of three, called **periods**. For instance, the number 8,168,931,047 has four periods: *ones, thousands, millions*, and *billions*.

EXAMPLE 1

In each number, identify the place that the digit 7 occupies.

a. 207   **b.** 7,654,000   **c.** 5,700,000,001

Solution

a. The ones place

b. The millions place

c. The hundred millions place

PRACTICE 1

What place does the digit 8 occupy in each number?

a. 278,056

b. 803,746

c. 3,080,700,059

The following rule provides a shortcut for *reading a whole number*:

To Read a Whole Number

Working from left to right,

• read the number in each period and then

• name the period in place of the comma.

For instance, 1,234,056 is read "one million, two hundred thirty-four thousand, fifty-six." Note that the ones period is not read.

EXAMPLE 2

How do you read the number 422,000,085?

Solution   Beginning at the left in the millions period, we read this number as "four hundred twenty-two million, eighty-five." Note that because there are all zeros in the thousands period, we do not read "thousands."

PRACTICE 2

Write 8,000,376,052 in words.

EXAMPLE 3

The display on a calculator shows the answer 3578002105. Insert commas in this answer and then read it.

Solution   The number with commas is 3,578,002,105. It is read "three billion, five hundred seventy-eight million, two thousand, one hundred five."

PRACTICE 3

A company is worth $7372050. After inserting commas, read this amount.

Until now, we have discussed how to *read* whole numbers in standard form. Now, let's turn to the question of how they are *written* in standard form. We simply reverse the process just described. For instance, the number eight billion, one hundred sixty-eight million, nine hundred thirty-one thousand, forty-seven in standard form is 8,168,931,047. Here, we use the 0 as a **placeholder** in the hundreds place because there are no hundreds.

To Write a Whole Number

Working from left to right,

* write the number named in each period and

* replace each period name with a comma.

When writing large whole numbers in standard form, we must remember that the number of commas is always one less than the number of periods. For instance, the number one million, two hundred thirty-four thousand, fifty-six—1,234,056—has three periods and two commas. Similarly, the number 8,168,931,047 has four periods and three commas.

EXAMPLE 4

Write the number eight billion, seven in standard form.

Solution   This number involves billions, so there are four periods—billions, millions, thousands, and ones—and three commas. Writing the number named in each period and replacing each period name with a comma, we get 8,000,000,007. Note that we write three 0's when no number is named in a period.

PRACTICE 4

Use digits and commas to write the amount ninety-five million, three dollars.

EXAMPLE 5

The treasurer of a company writes a check in the amount of four hundred thousand seven hundred dollars. Using digits, how would she write this amount on the check?

Solution   This quantity is written with one comma, because its largest period is thousands. So the treasurer writes $400,700, as shown on the check below.

PRACTICE 5

A rich alumna donates three hundred seventy-five thousand dollars to her college's scholarship fund.

Using digits, how would she write this amount on the check?

When writing checks, we write the amount in both digits and words. Why do we do this?

Writing Whole Numbers in Expanded Form

We have just described how to write whole numbers in standard form. Now, let's turn to how we write these numbers in **expanded form**.

Let's consider the whole number 4,025 and examine the place value of its digits.

$$4{,}025 = 4 \text{ thousands} + 0 \text{ hundreds} + 2 \text{ tens} + 5 \text{ ones}$$

This last expression is called the expanded form of the number, and it can be written as follows

$$4{,}000 + 0 + 20 + 5, \quad \text{or} \quad 4{,}000 + 20 + 5$$

The expanded form of a number spells out its value in terms of place value, helping us understand what the number really means. For instance, think of the numbers 92 and 29. By representing them in *expanded* form, can you explain why they differ in value even though their *standard* form consists of the same digits?

EXAMPLE 6

Write in expanded form:

a. 906   **b.** 3,203,000

Solution

a. The 6 is in the ones place, the 0 is in the tens place, and the 9 is in the hundreds place.

ONES		
Hundreds	Tens	Ones
9	0	6

So 906 is 9 hundreds + 0 tens + 6 ones = 900 + 0 + 6, or 900 + 6 in expanded form.

b. Using the place value chart, we see that
$$3{,}203{,}000 = 3 \text{ millions} + 2 \text{ hundred thousands} + 3 \text{ thousands}$$
$$= 3{,}000{,}000 + 200{,}000 + 3{,}000.$$

PRACTICE 6

Express in expanded form:

a. 27,013

b. 1,270,093

Rounding Whole Numbers

Most people equate mathematics with precision, but some problems require sacrificing precision for simplicity. In this case, we use the technique called **rounding** to approximate the exact answer with a number that ends in a given number of zeros. Rounded numbers have special advantages: They seem clearer to us than other numbers, and they make computation easier—especially when we are trying to compute in our heads.

Of these two headlines, which do you prefer? Why?

Study the following chart to see the connection between place value and rounding.

Rounding to the nearest	Means that the rounded number ends in at least
10	One 0
100	Two 0's
1,000	Three 0's
10,000	Four 0's
100,000	Five 0's
1,000,000	Six 0's

Note in the chart that the place value tells us how many 0's the rounded number must have at the end. Having more 0's than indicated is possible. Can you think of an example? When rounding, we use an underlined digit to indicate the place to which we are rounding. Now, let's consider the following rule for rounding whole numbers:

To Round a Whole Number

- Underline the place to which you are rounding.

- The digit to the right of the underlined digit is called the *critical digit*. Look at the critical digit—if it is 5 or more, add 1 to the underlined digit; if it is less than 5, leave the underlined digit unchanged.

- Replace all the digits to the right of the underlined digit with zeros.

EXAMPLE 7

Round 79,630 to

a. the nearest thousand

b. the nearest hundred

Solution

a. $79{,}630 = 79{,}630$ ← Underline the digit in the thousands place.

$= 79{,}630$ ← The critical digit 6 is greater than 5; add 1 to the underlined digit.

$\approx 80{,}000$ ← Change the digits to the right of the underlined digit to 0's.

This symbol means "is approximately equal to."

Note that adding 1 to the underlined digit gave us 10. As a result we regroup, that is, write 0, carry 1 to the next column, and change the 7 to 8.

b. First, we underline the 6 because that digit occupies the hundreds place: 79,630. The critical digit is 3: 79,630. Since 3 is less than 5, we leave the underlined digit unchanged. Then, we replace all digits to the right with 0's, getting 79,600. We write $79{,}630 \approx 79{,}600$, meaning that 79,630 when rounded to the nearest hundred is 79,600.

PRACTICE 7

Round 51,760 to

a. the nearest thousand

b. the nearest ten thousand

For Example 7a, consider this number line.

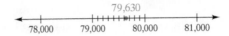

The number line shows that 79,630 lies between 79,000 and 80,000 and that it is closer to 80,000, as the rule indicates.

EXAMPLE 8

In an anatomy and physiology class, a student learned that the adult human skeleton contains 206 bones. How many bones is this to the nearest hundred bones?

Solution   We first write 2̲06. The critical digit 0 is less than 5, so we do *not* add 1 to the underlined digit. However, we do change both the digits to the right of the 2 to 0's. So 2̲06 ≈ 200, and there are approximately 200 bones in the human body.

PRACTICE 8

Based on current population data, the U.S. Bureau of the Census projects that the U.S. resident population will be 419,845,000 in the year 2050. What is the projected population to the nearest million?

EXAMPLE 9

The following table lists five of the highest-grossing films of all time and the amount of money they took in.

Film	Year	World Total (in U.S. dollars)
Titanic	1997	$1,835,300,000
The Lord of the Rings: The Return of the King	2003	$1,129,219,252
Pirates of the Caribbean: Dead Man's Chest	2006	$1,060,332,628
The Dark Knight	2008	$1,001,921,825
Avatar	2009	$2,690,408,054

(*Source:* imdb.com)

a. Write in words the amount of money taken in by the film with the largest world total.

b. Round to the nearest ten million dollars the world total for *Titanic*.

Solution

a. *Avatar* has the largest world total. This total is read "two billion, six hundred ninety million, four hundred eight thousand, fifty-four dollars."

b. The world total for *Titanic* is $1,835,300,000. To round, we underline the digit in the ten millions place: 1,8̲35,300,000. Since the critical digit is 5, we add 1 to the underlined digit, and change the digits to the right to 0's. So the rounded total is $1,840,000,000.

PRACTICE 9

This chart gives the number of U.S. postsecondary teachers in the year 2008 as well as the projected number of postsecondary teachers for the year 2018.

Year	Number of Postsecondary Teachers
2008	1,699,200
2018	1,956,100

(*Source:* bls.gov)

a. Write in words the number of postsecondary teachers in the year 2008.

b. What is the number of projected postsecondary teachers in the year 2018 rounded to the nearest ten thousand?

Mathematically Speaking

Fill in each blank with the most appropriate term or phrase from the given list.

calculated	rounded	periods	odd
even	digits	whole numbers	standard form
placeholder	place value	expanded form	

1. The _____ are 0, 1, 2, 3, 4, 5, ...

2. The numbers 0, 2, 4, 6, 8, 10, . . . are _____.

3. The numbers 1, 3, 5, 7, 9, . . . are _____.

4. The whole numbers are written with the _____ 0, 1, 2, 3, 4, 5, 6, 7, 8, and 9.

5. The number thirty-seven, when written as 37, is said to be in _____.

6. In the number 528, the _____ of the 5 is hundreds.

7. In the number 206, the 0 is used as a _____ in the tens place.

8. Commas separate the digits in a large whole number into groups of three called _____.

9. When the number 973 is written as 9 hundreds + 7 tens + 3 ones, it is said to be in _____.

10. The number 545 _____ to the nearest hundred is 500.

Ⓐ *Underline the digit that occupies the given place.*

11. 4,867   Thousands place

12. 9,752   Thousands place

13. 316   Tens place

14. 728   Tens place

15. 28,461,013   Millions place

16. 73,762,800   Millions place

Identify the place occupied by the underlined digit.

17. 6̲91,400

18. 72̲,109

19. 7,3̲80

20. 35̲1

21. 8̲,450,000,000

22. 3̲5,832,775

Insert commas as needed, and then write the number in words.

23. 4 8 7 5 0 0

24. 5 2 8 0 5 0

25. 2 3 5 0 0 0 0

26. 1 3 5 0 1 3 2

27. 9 7 5 1 3 5 0 0 0

28. 4 2 1 0 0 0 1 3 2

29. 2 0 0 0 0 0 0 3 5 2

30. 4 1 0 0 0 0 0 0 7

31. 1 0 0 0 0 0 0 0 0 0

32. 3 7 9 0 5 2 0 0 0

Write each number in standard form.

33. Ten thousand, one hundred twenty

34. Twelve thousand, two hundred thirty

35. One hundred fifty thousand, eight hundred fifty-six

36. Two hundred forty thousand, seven hundred seventy-two

37. Six million, fifty-five

38. Two million, one hundred twenty-two

39. Fifty million, six hundred thousand, one hundred ninety-five

40. Thirty million, five hundred thousand, four hundred eighty-four

41. Four hundred thousand, seventy-two

42. Three hundred thousand, sixty-one

B *Write each number in expanded form.*

43. 3

44. 6,300

45. 858

46. 9,000,000

47. 2,500,004

48. 7,251,380

C *Round to the indicated place.*

49. 671 to the nearest ten

50. 838 to the nearest ten

51. 7,103 to the nearest hundred

52. 8,204 to the nearest hundred

53. 28,241 to the nearest ten thousand

54. 32,323 to the nearest ten thousand

55. 705,418 to its largest place

56. 806,329 to the largest place

57. 31,972 to its largest place

58. 52,891 to the largest place

Round each number as indicated.

59.

To the nearest	135,842	2,816,533
Hundred		
Thousand		
Ten thousand		
Hundred thousand		

60.

To the nearest	972,055	3,189,602
Thousand		
Ten thousand		
Hundred thousand		
Million		

Mixed Practice

Solve.

61. Write 12,051 in expanded form.

62. Identify the place occupied by the underlined digit in 2̲6,543,009.

63. Underline the digit that occupies the ten thousands place in 40,059.

64. Write five hundred forty-two thousand, sixty-seven in standard form.

65. Insert commas as needed, and then write 1 0 5 6 1 0 0 in words.

66. Round 26,255 to the nearest thousand.

Applications

Ⓓ *Write each whole number in words.*

67. Biologists have classified more than 900,000 species of insects. (*Source:* Smithsonian Institution)

68. In a recent year, there were 71,988 WiFi hotspots in the United States. (*Source:* jiwire.com).

69. The land area of the Dominican Republic, located in the West Indies, is 48,381 square kilometers. (*Source*: infoplease.com)

70. Mercury is the closest planet to the Sun, a distance of approximately 36,000,000 miles.

71. Each pair of human lungs contains some 300,000,000 tiny air sacs. (*Source:* Sylvia S. Mader, *Inquiry Into Life*)

72. The Pyramid of Khufu in Egypt has a base of approximately 2,315,000 blocks. (*Source: The New Encyclopedia Britannica*)

Write each whole number in standard form.

73. Some one hundred billion nerve cells are part of the human brain.

74. Son of Beast, a roller coaster at Paramount's Kings Island in Ohio, has a track length of seven thousand thirty-two feet. (*Source:* American Coasters Network)

75. One of the largest giant sequoias in the United States is three thousand, two hundred eighty-eight inches tall. (*Source:* U.S. National Park Service)

76. The total land area of the United States is nine million, six hundred thirty-one thousand, four hundred eighteen square kilometers. (*Source: The World Factbook,* 2006)

77. In 1990, the U.S. public debt (in dollars) was three trillion, two hundred thirty-three billion, three hundred million. (*Source: The World Almanac 2010*)

78. The light-year is a unit of length used to measure distances to stars and other distances on an astronomical scale. A light-year is equal to about five trillion, eight hundred seventy-eight billion, six hundred thirty million miles. (*Source:* wikipedia.org)

Round to the indicated place.

79. The Statue of Liberty is 152 feet high. What is its height to the nearest 10 feet?

80. The Nile, with a length of 4,180 miles, is the longest river in the world. Find this length to the nearest thousand miles.

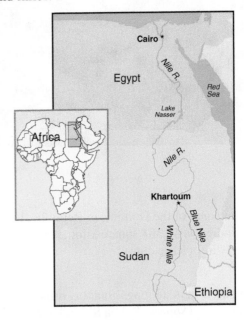

81. In 1949, Air Force Captain James Gallagher led the first team to make an around-the-world flight. The team flew 23,452 miles. What is this distance to the nearest ten thousand miles? (*Source:* Taylor and Mondey, *Milestones of Flight*)

82. The element copper changes from a liquid to a gas at the temperature 2,567 degrees Celsius (°C). Find this temperature to the nearest hundred degrees Celsius.

83. The South American country of Colombia is home to 1,897 bird species—more than any other country. How many species is this to the nearest hundred? (*Source: Avibase—the World Bird Database,* avibase.bsc-eoc.org)

84. The Rose Bowl stadium has a seating capacity of 92,542. Round this number to the nearest ten thousand. (*Source:* Rose Bowl Operating Company)

85. This chart displays the area of seven most heavily populated countries in the world.

Country	Area (in square miles)
China	3,600,930
India	1,147,950
United States	3,537,421
Indonesia	705,189
Brazil	3,265,061
Pakistan	300,664
Bangladesh	51,703

(*Source:* census.gov)

a. Write in words the area of China.

b. Round, to the nearest thousand, the area of Pakistan.

86. This chart displays the number of degrees awarded in the United States during a recent year.

Degree	Number Awarded
Associate	750,164
Bachelor's	1,563,069
Master's	625,023
Doctorate	63,712
Professional	91,309

(*Source:* nces.ed.gov)

a. Write in words the number of bachelor's degrees awarded.

b. Round, to the nearest hundred thousand, the number of associate degrees awarded.

• Check your answers on page A-1.

MINDStretchers

Mathematical Reasoning

1. I am thinking of a certain whole number. My number, rounded to the nearest hundred, is 700. When it is rounded to the nearest ten, it is 750. What numbers could I be thinking of?

Writing

2. How does the number 10 play a special role in the way that we write whole numbers? Would it be possible to have the number 2 play this role? Explain.

Groupwork

3. Here are three ways of writing the number seven: 7   VII   卅 ||

Working with a partner, express each of the numbers 1, 2, . . . , 9 in these three ways.

1.2 Adding and Subtracting Whole Numbers

The Meaning and Properties of Addition and Subtraction

Addition is perhaps the most fundamental of all operations. One way to think about this operation is as *combining sets*. For example, suppose that we have two distinct sets of pens, with 5 pens in one set and 3 in the other. If we put the two sets together, we get a single set that has 8 pens.

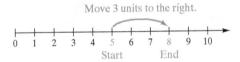

So we can say that 3 added to 5 is 8, or here, 5 pens plus 3 pens equals 8 pens. Numbers being added are called *addends*. The result is called the *sum*, or *total*.

In the above example, note that we are adding quantities of the same thing, or *like quantities*.

Another good way to think about the addition of whole numbers is as *moving to the right on a number line*. In this way, we start at the point on the line corresponding to the first number, 5. Then to add 3, we move 3 units to the right, ending on the point that corresponds to the answer, 8.

Move 3 units to the right.

```
|---|---|---|---|---|---|---|---|---|---|--->
0   1   2   3   4   5   6   7   8   9   10
                  Start       End
```

Now, let's look at subtraction. One way to look at this operation is as *taking away*. For instance, when we subtract 5 pens from 8 pens, we take 5 pens away from 8 pens, leaving 3 pens.

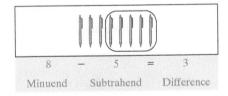

In a subtraction problem, the number from which we subtract is called the *minuend*, the number being subtracted is called the *subtrahend*, and the result is called the *difference*. In other words, the difference between two numbers is the first number take away the second number.

As in the preceding example, we can only subtract *like quantities*: we cannot subtract 5 pens from 8 scissors.

We can also think of subtraction as the *opposite of addition*.

$$8 - 5 = 3 \quad \text{because} \quad 5 + 3 = 8$$
Subtraction   Related addition

Note in this example that, if we add the 5 pens to the 3 pens, we get 8 pens.

Addition and subtraction problems can be written either horizontally or vertically.

$$5 + 3 = 8 \qquad 8 - 5 = 3$$
Horizontal

$$\begin{array}{r} 5 \\ +3 \\ \hline 8 \end{array} \qquad \begin{array}{r} 8 \\ -5 \\ \hline 3 \end{array}$$
Vertical

Either format gives the correct answer. But it is generally easier to figure out the sum and difference of large numbers if the problems are written vertically.

Now, let's briefly consider several special properties of addition that we use frequently. Examples appear to the right of each property.

The Identity Property of Addition

The sum of a number and zero is the original number.

$$3 + 0 = 3$$
$$0 + 5 = 5$$

The Commutative Property of Addition

Changing the order in which two numbers are added does not affect their sum.

$$3 + 2 = 2 + 3$$
$$\downarrow \qquad \downarrow$$
$$5 \qquad 5$$

The Associative Property of Addition

When adding three numbers, regrouping addends gives the same sum. Note that the parentheses tell us which numbers to add first.

We add inside the parentheses first

$$(4 + 7) + 2 = 4 + (7 + 2)$$
$$\downarrow \qquad\qquad\qquad \downarrow$$
$$11 \; + 2 = 4 + \; 9$$
$$\downarrow \qquad \downarrow$$
$$13 \qquad 13$$

Adding Whole Numbers

We add whole numbers by arranging the numbers vertically, keeping the digits with the same place value in the same column. Then, we add the digits in each column.

Consider the sum $32 + 65$. In the vertical format at the right, the sum of the digits in each column is 9 or less. The sum is 97. When the sum of the digits in a column is greater than 9, we must **regroup (carry)** because only a single digit can occupy a single place. Example 1 illustrates this process.

$$\begin{array}{r} 32 \\ +65 \\ \hline 97 \end{array}$$

EXAMPLE 1

Add 47 and 28.

Solution   First, we write the addends in expanded form. Then, we add down the ones column.

1 ten

$$47 = 4 \text{ tens} + 7 \text{ ones} = 4 \text{ tens} + 7 \text{ ones}$$
$$+28 = 2 \text{ tens} + 8 \text{ ones} = 2 \text{ tens} + 8 \text{ ones}$$
$$\overline{\hphantom{47 = }15 \text{ ones}} \qquad \overline{\hphantom{4 \text{ tens} + }5 \text{ ones}}$$

By regrouping, we express 15 ones as 1 ten + 5 ones. Then we carry the 1 ten to the tens place.

Next, we add down the tens column.

1 ten

$$4 \text{ tens} + 7 \text{ ones}$$
$$\underline{2 \text{ tens} + 8 \text{ ones}}$$
$$7 \text{ tens} + 5 \text{ ones} = 75$$

PRACTICE 1

Add: $178 + 207$

The following rule tells how to add whole numbers without using expanded form:

To Add Whole Numbers

- Write the addends vertically, lining up the place values.
- Add the digits in the ones column, writing the rightmost digit of the sum on the bottom. If the sum has two digits, carry the left digit to the top of the next column on the left.
- Add the digits in the tens column, as in the preceding step.
- Repeat this process until you reach the last column on the left, writing the entire sum of that column on the bottom.

EXAMPLE 2

Add: $9,824 + 356 + 2,976$

Solution We write the problem vertically, with the addends lined up on the right.

$$
\begin{array}{r}
\overset{1}{9,824} \\
356 \\
+2,976 \\
\hline
6
\end{array}
$$

The sum of the ones digits is 16 ones. We write the 6 and carry the 1 to the tens column.

$$
\begin{array}{r}
\overset{1\;1}{9,824} \\
356 \\
+2,976 \\
\hline
56
\end{array}
$$

The sum of the tens digits is 15 tens. We write the 5 and carry the 1 to the hundreds column.

$$
\begin{array}{r}
\overset{2\;1\;1}{9,824} \\
356 \\
+2,976 \\
\hline
156
\end{array}
$$

The sum of the hundreds digits is 21 hundreds. We write the 1 and carry the 2 to the thousands column.

$$
\begin{array}{r}
\overset{2\;1\;1}{9,824} \\
356 \\
+2,976 \\
\hline
13,156
\end{array}
$$

The sum of the digits in the thousands column is 13, which we write completely—no need to regroup here.

The sum is 13,156.

PRACTICE 2

Find the total: $838 + 96 + 9,502$

In Example 3, let's apply the operation of addition to finding the geometric perimeter of a figure. The **perimeter** is the distance around a figure, which we can find by adding the lengths of its sides.

EXAMPLE 3

What is the perimeter of the region marked off for the construction of a swimming pool and an adjacent pool cabana?

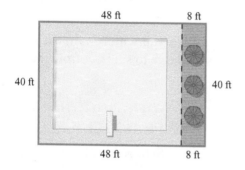

Solution   This figure consists of two rectangles placed side by side. We note that the opposite sides of each rectangle are equal in length.

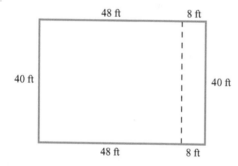

To compute the figure's perimeter, we need to add the lengths of all its sides.

$$
\begin{array}{r}
40 \\
48 \\
8 \\
40 \\
8 \\
+\ 48 \\
\hline
192
\end{array}
$$

The figure's perimeter is 192 feet.

PRACTICE 3

How long a fence is needed to enclose the piece of land sketched?

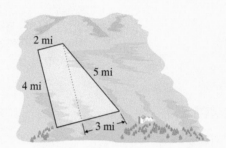

Subtracting Whole Numbers

Consider the subtraction problem 59 − 36, written vertically at the right. We write the whole numbers underneath one another, lined up on the right, so each column contains digits with the same place value. Subtracting the digits within each column, the bottom digit from the top, the result is a difference of 23.

$$
\begin{array}{r}
59 \\
-36 \\
\hline
23
\end{array}
$$

Keep in mind two useful properties of subtraction.

- When we subtract a number from itself, the result is 0: $6 - 6 = 0$
- When we subtract 0 from a number, the result is the original number:

$$25 - 0 = 25$$

TIP   When writing a subtraction problem vertically, be sure that
- the minuend—the number from which we are subtracting—goes on the top and that
- the subtrahend—the number being taken away—goes on the bottom.

Now, we consider subtraction problems in which we must regroup (*borrow*). In these problems a digit on the bottom is too large to subtract from the corresponding digit on top.

EXAMPLE 4

Subtract: $329 - 87$

Solution   We first write these numbers vertically in expanded form.

$$
\begin{array}{r}
329 = \quad 3 \text{ hundreds} + 2 \text{ tens} + 9 \text{ ones} \\
- 87 = - \quad\quad\quad\quad\quad 8 \text{ tens} + 7 \text{ ones} \\
\hline
\end{array}
$$

We then subtract the digits in the ones column: 7 ones from 9 ones gives 2 ones.

$$
\begin{array}{r}
3 \text{ hundreds} + 2 \text{ tens} + 9 \text{ ones} \\
- \quad\quad\quad\quad\quad 8 \text{ tens} + 7 \text{ ones} \\
\hline
2 \text{ ones}
\end{array}
$$

$$10 \text{ tens} + 2 \text{ tens} = 12 \text{ tens}$$

We next go to the tens column. We cannot take 8 tens from 2 tens. But we can *borrow* 1 hundred from the 3 hundreds, leaving 2 in the hundreds place. We *exchange* this hundred for 10 tens (1 hundred = 10 tens). Then combining the 10 tens with the 2 tens gives 12 tens.

$$
\begin{array}{r}
\overset{2}{3} \text{ hundreds} + \overset{1}{2} \text{ tens} + 9 \text{ ones} \\
- \quad\quad\quad\quad\quad 8 \text{ tens} + 7 \text{ ones} \\
\hline
2 \text{ ones}
\end{array}
$$

We next take 8 from 12 in the tens column, giving 4 tens. Finally, we bring down the 2 hundreds. The difference is 242 in standard form.

$$
\begin{array}{r}
\overset{2}{3} \text{ hundreds} + \overset{1}{2} \text{ tens} + 9 \text{ ones} \\
- \quad\quad\quad\quad\quad 8 \text{ tens} + 7 \text{ ones} \\
\hline
2 \text{ hundreds} + 4 \text{ tens} + 2 \text{ ones} = 242
\end{array}
$$

PRACTICE 4

Subtract: $748 - 97$

Although we can always rewrite whole numbers in expanded form so as to subtract them, the following rule provides a shortcut:

To Subtract Whole Numbers

- On top, write the number *from which* we are subtracting. On the bottom, write the number that is being taken *away*, lining up the place values. Subtract in each column separately.

- Start with the ones column.
  a. If the digit on top is *larger* than or *equal* to the digit on the bottom, subtract and write the difference below the bottom digit.
  b. If the digit on top is *smaller* than the digit on the bottom, borrow from the digit to the left on top. Then subtract and write the difference below the bottom digit.

- Repeat this process until the last column on the left is finished.

Recall that for every subtraction problem there is a related addition problem. So we can use addition to check subtraction, as in the following example.

EXAMPLE 5

Find the difference between 500 and 293.

Solution   We rewrite the problem vertically.

$$\begin{array}{r} 500 \\ -293 \end{array}$$

We cannot subtract 3 ones from 0 ones, and we cannot borrow from 0 tens. So we borrow from the 5 hundreds.

$$\begin{array}{r} {\scriptstyle 4\ 1} \longleftarrow 5 \text{ hundreds} = 4 \text{ hundreds} + 10 \text{ tens} \\ 5 0 0 \\ -2 9 3 \end{array}$$

We now borrow from the tens column.

$$\begin{array}{r} {\scriptstyle 9} \longleftarrow 10 \text{ tens} = 9 \text{ tens} + 10 \text{ ones} \\ {\scriptstyle 4\ 10\ 1} \\ 5\ \emptyset\ 0 \\ -2\ 9\ 3 \\ \hline 2\ 0\ 7 \end{array}$$

Check   We check the difference by adding it to the subtrahend. The sum turns out to be the original minuend, so our answer is correct.

$$\begin{array}{r} 207 \\ +293 \\ \hline 500 \end{array}$$

PRACTICE 5

Subtract 3,253 from 8,000.

EXAMPLE 6

There are a total of 118 chemical elements. Ninety-four of these occur naturally on Earth and the rest are synthetic. How many chemical elements are synthetic? (*Source:* wikipedia.org)

Solution   The total number of chemical elements equals the number of natural chemical elements plus the number of synthetic chemical elements.

Natural Chemical Elements (94)	Synthetic Chemical Elements (?)

All Chemical Elements (118)

To compute the number of synthetic chemical elements, we subtract the number of natural chemical elements from the total number of chemical elements.

Total number of chemical elements	118
Number of natural chemical elements	− 94
Number of synthetic chemical elements	24

So 24 chemical elements are synthetic.

PRACTICE 6

Of the 1,324 endangered and threatened species (plants and animals) in the United States, 574 are animal species. How many plant species are endangered and threatened? (*Source:* ecos.fws.gov)

EXAMPLE 7

The following graph shows the number of overseas visitors from various countries who came to the United States during a recent year.

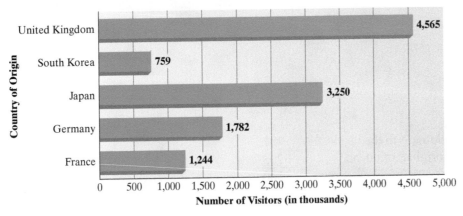

(*Source:* tinet.ita.doc.gov)

a. From which of these countries did the greatest number of visitors come?

b. How many visitors came from either the United Kingdom or Germany?

c. Was the number of German visitors greater or less than the total number of visitors who came from either South Korea or France?

Solution

a. More visitors came to the United States from the United Kingdom than from any other country.

b. To find how many visitors came to the United States from either the United Kingdom or Germany, we add the number of visitors from each country:

$$
\begin{array}{rr}
\text{United Kingdom} \rightarrow & 4,565,000 \\
\text{Germany} \rightarrow & +1,782,000 \\
\hline
\text{Sum} \rightarrow & 6,347,000
\end{array}
$$

So 6,347,000 visitors came to the United States from either the United Kingdom or Germany.

c. The number of German visitors was 1,782,000. The total number of visitors who came from either South Korea or France is the sum of the number of visitors from each country:

$$
\begin{array}{rr}
\text{South Korea} \rightarrow & 759,000 \\
\text{France} \rightarrow & +1,244,000 \\
\hline
\text{Sum} \rightarrow & 2,003,000
\end{array}
$$

Since 2,003,000 is greater than 1,782,000, the number of German visitors was less than the total number of visitors who came from either South Korea or France.

PRACTICE 7

The following chart shows the projected employment change in the United States from 2008 to 2018 for some of the fastest-growing occupations.

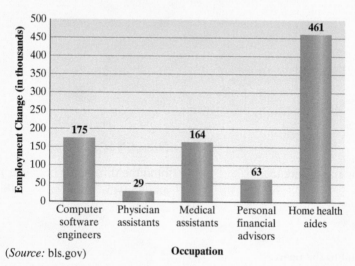

(*Source:* bls.gov)

a. How much greater is the projected employment growth for home health aides than that for computer software engineers?

b. What is the combined increase in employment projected for physician assistants and medical assistants?

c. Is the combined change in employment projected for computer software engineers and personal financial advisors greater or less than the projected change for home health aides?

Estimating Sums and Differences

Because everyone occasionally makes a mistake, we need to know how to check an answer so that we can correct it if it is wrong.

One method of checking addition and subtraction is by *estimation*. In this approach, we first compute and then estimate the answer. Then, we compare the estimate and our "exact answer" to see if they are close. If they are, we can be confident that our answer is reasonable. If they are not close, we should redo the computation.

We can get different estimates for an answer, depending on how we round. For addition, one good way involves rounding each addend to the largest place value, as shown in Example 8. Similarly, for subtraction, we can round the minuend and subtrahend to the largest place value, as Example 9 illustrates.

EXAMPLE 8

Compute the sum of $1{,}923 + 898 + 754 + 2{,}873$. Check by estimation.

Solution

$$
\begin{array}{r}
1{,}923 \\
898 \\
754 \\
+2{,}873 \\
\hline
6{,}448 \leftarrow \text{Exact sum}
\end{array}
$$

Check We round each addend to the largest place value.

$$
\begin{array}{rcr}
1{,}923 & \approx & 2{,}000 \\
898 & \approx & 900 \\
754 & \approx & 800 \\
+2{,}873 & \approx & +3{,}000 \\
\hline
& & 6{,}700 \leftarrow \text{Estimated sum}
\end{array}
$$

Our exact answer (6,448) is reasonably close to the estimate, so we are done.

PRACTICE 8

Add: $3{,}945 + 849 + 4{,}001 + 682$.
Check by estimating the sum.

EXAMPLE 9

Subtract 1,994 from 8,253. Check by estimating the difference.

Solution

$$
\begin{array}{r}
8{,}253 \\
-1{,}994 \\
\hline
6{,}259 \leftarrow \text{Exact difference}
\end{array}
$$

Check We round the minuend and subtrahend to the nearest thousand.

$$
\begin{array}{rcr}
8{,}253 & \approx & 8{,}000 \\
-1{,}994 & \approx & -2{,}000 \\
\hline
& & 6{,}000 \leftarrow \text{Estimated difference}
\end{array}
$$

Our exact answer (6,259) and the estimated difference (6,000) are fairly close.

With practice, we can mentally estimate and check differences and sums quickly and easily.

PRACTICE 9

Find the difference between 17,836 and 15,045. Then estimate this difference to check.

We have already seen how estimation helps us to check an exact answer that is computed. But sometimes an approximate answer is good enough.

EXAMPLE 10

The top two languages used online are English and Chinese, with 478,582,273 and 383,212,617 Internet users, respectively. Estimate how many more English users there are than Chinese. (*Source:* internetworldstats.com)

Solution

$$
\begin{array}{r}
\text{English users} \rightarrow 478,582,273 \approx 500,000,000 \\
\text{Chinese users} \rightarrow 383,212,617 \approx \underline{-400,000,000} \\
100,000,000
\end{array}
$$

So there are about 100,000,000 more English users than there are Chinese users.

PRACTICE 10

Mount Everest is the highest mountain in the world, with an altitude of 29,028 feet above sea level. By contrast, Mauna Kea in Hawaii is considered to be the world's tallest mountain when its height is measured from the nearby ocean floor. Mauna Kea has an altitude of only 13,796 feet above sea level. Estimate the difference in altitude above sea level of the two peaks. (*Source:* geology.com)

Adding and Subtracting Whole Numbers on a Calculator

Calculators are handy and powerful tools for carrying out complex computations. But it is easy to press a wrong key, so be sure to estimate the answer and compare this estimate to the displayed answer to see if it is reasonable.

EXAMPLE 11

On a calculator, compute the sum of 3,125 and 9,391.

Solution

Press	Display
3125 $+$ 9391 $\boxed{\text{ENTER}}$	$3125 + 9391$ $12516.$

To check this answer, we mentally round the addends and then add.

$$
\begin{array}{r}
3125 \approx 3,000 \\
9391 \approx \underline{9,000} \\
12,000
\end{array}
$$

This estimate is reasonably close to our answer 12,516.

PRACTICE 11

Use a calculator to add:
39,822 + 9,710

Pressing the clear key cancels the number in the display. Press this key after completing a computation to be sure that no number remains to affect the next problem. Note that calculator models vary as to how they work, so it may be necessary to consult the manual for a particular model.

EXAMPLE 12

Calculate: $39 + 48 + 277$

Solution

Press	Display
39 ⊞ 48 ⊞ 277 ENTER	$39 + 48 + 277$ $364.$

A reasonable estimate is the sum of 40, 50, and 300, or 390—close to our calculated answer 364.

PRACTICE 12

Find the sum on a calculator:
$23,801 + 7,116 + 982$

When using a calculator to subtract,

- enter the numbers in the correct order—first enter the number **from which** we are subtracting and then the number **being** subtracted; and

- do not confuse the *negative sign key* $\boxed{(-)}$ that some calculators have with the *subtraction key* $\boxed{-}$.

EXAMPLE 13

Subtract on a calculator: $3,000 - 973$

Solution

Press	Display
3000 ⊟ 973 ENTER	$3000 - 973$ $2027.$

A good estimate is $3,000 - 1,000$, or 2,000, which is close to 2,027.

PRACTICE 13

Use a calculator to find the difference between 5,280 feet and 2,781 feet.

Mathematically Speaking

Fill in each blank with the most appropriate term or phrase from the given list.

subtrahend	addends	left	estimates
commutative	right	identity property	associative property
property of	difference	of addition	of addition
addition	minuend	sum	

1. The operation of addition can be thought of as moving to the _____ on a number line.

2. The _____ states that the sum of a number and zero is the original number.

3. The result of addition is called the _____.

4. The _____ states that changing the order in which two numbers are added does not affect the sum.

5. The _____ states that when adding three numbers, regrouping addends gives the same sum.

6. In an addition problem, the numbers being added are called _____.

7. In a subtraction problem, the number being subtracted is called the _____.

8. The result of subtraction is called the _____.

A *Add and check by estimation.*

9. $\begin{array}{r} 100{,}250 \\ +\ 77{,}528 \\ \hline \end{array}$

10. $\begin{array}{r} 200{,}325 \\ +\ 67{,}629 \\ \hline \end{array}$

11. $\begin{array}{r} 8{,}132 \\ +6{,}578 \\ \hline \end{array}$

12. $\begin{array}{r} 6{,}725 \\ +5{,}386 \\ \hline \end{array}$

13. $\begin{array}{r} 7{,}481 \\ 702 \\ +5{,}819 \\ \hline \end{array}$

14. $\begin{array}{r} 8{,}721 \\ 306 \\ +6{,}627 \\ \hline \end{array}$

15. $\begin{array}{r} 49{,}002 \\ 1{,}999 \\ +5{,}187 \\ \hline \end{array}$

16. $\begin{array}{r} 55{,}998 \\ 2{,}988 \\ +3{,}126 \\ \hline \end{array}$

17. $1{,}903 + 5{,}075$

18. $7{,}406 + 2{,}381$

19. $800 + 20 + 4{,}000$

20. $3{,}000 + 800 + 60$

21. $31 + 93 + 277 + 12$

22. $418 + 47 + 365 + 95$

23. $3{,}911 + 2{,}947 + 8{,}007$

24. $5{,}374 + 4{,}055 + 2{,}073$

25. $6{,}482 \text{ meters} + 9{,}027 \text{ meters}$

26. $17{,}812 \text{ miles} + 4{,}283 \text{ miles}$

27. $35 \text{ hours} + 47 \text{ hours}$

28. $25 \text{ square feet} + 96 \text{ square feet}$

29. $\$92{,}258 + \$7{,}447 + \$5{,}126$

30. $\$55{,}709 + \$2{,}822 + \$30{,}819$

31. $\$1{,}863 + \$1{,}089 + \$9{,}772$

32. $\$5{,}009 + \$7{,}993 + \$1{,}026$

33. $8{,}300 \text{ tons} + 22{,}900 \text{ tons}$

34. $7{,}400 \text{ tons} + 32{,}600 \text{ tons}$

35. $\begin{array}{r} 3{,}088{,}281 \\ 5{,}658{,}137 \\ +4{,}550{,}239 \\ \hline \end{array}$

36. $\begin{array}{r} 2{,}008{,}490 \\ 8{,}948{,}227 \\ +11{,}956{,}174 \\ \hline \end{array}$

37. $\begin{array}{r} 638{,}719 \\ 40{,}003 \\ +984{,}035 \\ \hline \end{array}$

38. $\begin{array}{r} 938{,}722 \\ 25{,}411 \\ +517{,}827 \\ \hline \end{array}$

In each addition table, fill in the empty spaces. Check that the sum in the shaded empty space is the same working both downward and across.

39.

+	400	200	1,200	300	Total
300					
800					
Total					

40.

+	4,000	300	3,000	2,000	Total
100					
900					
Total					

41.

+	389	172	1,155	324	Total
255					
799					
Total					

42.

+	3,749	279	2,880	1,998	Total
134					
896					
Total					

*In each group of three sums, one is **wrong**. Use estimation to identify which sum is incorrect.*

43. a.
$$\begin{array}{r} 814 \\ 9,106 \\ +2,811 \\ \hline 15,731 \end{array}$$
b.
$$\begin{array}{r} 30,812 \\ 47,045 \\ +\ 9,338 \\ \hline 87,195 \end{array}$$
c.
$$\begin{array}{r} 183,066 \\ 78,911 \\ +\ 96,527 \\ \hline 358,504 \end{array}$$

44. a.
$$\begin{array}{r} 1,035 \\ 5,210 \\ +7,992 \\ \hline 14,237 \end{array}$$
b.
$$\begin{array}{r} 5,801 \\ 3,882 \\ +12,644 \\ \hline 32,327 \end{array}$$
c.
$$\begin{array}{r} 801,716 \\ 78,001 \\ +5,009,635 \\ \hline 5,889,352 \end{array}$$

45. a.
$$\begin{array}{r} \$711,488 \\ 102,663 \\ +\ 95,003 \\ \hline \$809,154 \end{array}$$
b.
$$\begin{array}{r} \$62,933 \\ 51,858 \\ +\ 49,612 \\ \hline \$164,403 \end{array}$$
c.
$$\begin{array}{r} \$106,729 \\ 99,821 \\ +\ 103,277 \\ \hline \$309,827 \end{array}$$

46. a.
$$\begin{array}{r} \$9,512,622 \\ 8,038,517 \\ +\ 2,615,334 \\ \hline \$20,166,473 \end{array}$$
b.
$$\begin{array}{r} \$4,277,020 \\ 915,611 \\ +\ 3,688,402 \\ \hline \$8,881,033 \end{array}$$
c.
$$\begin{array}{r} \$200,312 \\ 102,683 \\ +\ 504,113 \\ \hline \$707,108 \end{array}$$

Subtract and check.

47.
$$\begin{array}{r} 379 \\ -162 \\ \hline \end{array}$$
48.
$$\begin{array}{r} 362 \\ -120 \\ \hline \end{array}$$
49.
$$\begin{array}{r} 200 \\ -110 \\ \hline \end{array}$$
50.
$$\begin{array}{r} 210 \\ -100 \\ \hline \end{array}$$

51.
$$\begin{array}{r} 401 \\ -\ 39 \\ \hline \end{array}$$
52.
$$\begin{array}{r} 728 \\ -\ 99 \\ \hline \end{array}$$
53.
$$\begin{array}{r} 70,000 \\ -\ 1,759 \\ \hline \end{array}$$
54.
$$\begin{array}{r} 80,000 \\ -\ 1,691 \\ \hline \end{array}$$

55.
$$\begin{array}{r} 5,062 \\ -2,777 \\ \hline \end{array}$$
56.
$$\begin{array}{r} 3,005 \\ -1,666 \\ \hline \end{array}$$
57.
$$\begin{array}{r} 72,000 \\ -19,001 \\ \hline \end{array}$$
58.
$$\begin{array}{r} 64,000 \\ -21,005 \\ \hline \end{array}$$

59.
$$\begin{array}{r} 3,000 \\ -\ 57 \\ \hline \end{array}$$
60.
$$\begin{array}{r} 7,000 \\ -\ 32 \\ \hline \end{array}$$
61.
$$\begin{array}{r} 261,406 \\ -\ 57,941 \\ \hline \end{array}$$
62.
$$\begin{array}{r} 729,888 \\ -\ 92,889 \\ \hline \end{array}$$

Find the difference and check.

63. $550 - 182$

64. $962 - 448$

65. $6,000 - 1,004$

66. $8,000 - 2,007$

67. $3,570 - 2,588$

68. $4,620 - 1,756$

69. 5,000 miles $-$ 3,005 miles

70. 4,000 miles $-$ 1,008 miles

71. $800 - 131$

72. $622 - 137$

73. $4,812 - $1,203

74. $5,923 - $2,304

75. 500 books $-$ 227 books

76. 537 pens $-$ 196 pens

77. 527 meters $-$ 318 meters

78. 642 meters $-$ 214 meters

79.
$$\begin{array}{r} 30,000,000 \\ -27,999,000 \\ \hline \end{array}$$

80.
$$\begin{array}{r} 40,000,000 \\ -18,988,000 \\ \hline \end{array}$$

81.
$$\begin{array}{r} 13,402,331 \\ -12,588,902 \\ \hline \end{array}$$

82.
$$\begin{array}{r} 14,500,007 \\ -13,972,008 \\ \hline \end{array}$$

In each group of three differences, one is **wrong.** *Use estimation to identify which difference is incorrect.*

83. a.
$$\begin{array}{r} 817,770 \\ -502,966 \\ \hline 314,804 \end{array}$$

b.
$$\begin{array}{r} 11,172,055 \\ -\ 7,892,106 \\ \hline 3,279,949 \end{array}$$

c.
$$\begin{array}{r} 71,384,612 \\ -32,016,594 \\ \hline 29,368,018 \end{array}$$

84. a.
$$\begin{array}{r} 67,812 \\ -12,180 \\ \hline 55,632 \end{array}$$

b.
$$\begin{array}{r} 3,997,401 \\ -1,125,166 \\ \hline 1,872,235 \end{array}$$

c.
$$\begin{array}{r} 316,134 \\ -89,164 \\ \hline 226,970 \end{array}$$

85. a.
$$\begin{array}{r} \$381,882 \\ -\ 173,552 \\ \hline \$108,330 \end{array}$$

b.
$$\begin{array}{r} \$479,116 \\ -\ 102,663 \\ \hline \$376,453 \end{array}$$

c.
$$\begin{array}{r} \$200,072,639 \\ -\ 150,038,270 \\ \hline \$50,034,369 \end{array}$$

86. a.
$$\begin{array}{r} \$3,810,662 \\ -\ 299,137 \\ \hline \$3,511,525 \end{array}$$

b.
$$\begin{array}{r} \$4,718,287 \\ -\ 1,002,875 \\ \hline \$5,721,162 \end{array}$$

c.
$$\begin{array}{r} \$381,975 \\ -\ 117,263 \\ \hline \$264,712 \end{array}$$

Mixed Practice

Perform the indicated operation.

87.
$$\begin{array}{r} 7,415 \\ -\ 350 \\ \hline \end{array}$$

88.
$$\begin{array}{r} 90,316 \\ 10,882 \\ +\ 5,281 \\ \hline \end{array}$$

89. $281 + 758 + 104 + 533$

90. $5,233 + $481 + $82

91. $8,286 - 3,100$

92. 410,700 miles $-$ 280,900 miles

Applications

B *Solve and check.*

93. In 1900, the population of the United States was approximately 76,000,000. During the next 100 years, the population grew by about 205,000,000 people. What was the population in 2000? (*Source:* U.S. Bureau of the Census)

94. It is recommended that an adult over 50 consume 1,200 milligrams of calcium each day. Will an adult who has 645 milligrams of calcium at breakfast and 455 milligrams at lunch meet the recommended daily amount? (*Source:* niams.nih.gov)

95. Of the 6,000,000 square miles of tropical rainforest that existed on Earth before deforestation, 2,600,000 square miles remain. How many square miles of rainforest still exist? (*Source:* nature.org)

96. The Great Blue Norther of 1911 was the largest cold snap in U.S. history. On the day of the Norther, the temperature in Oklahoma City dropped from a record high of 83°F to a record low of 17°F in a 24-hour period. By how much did the temperature drop that day? (*Source:* National Weather Service)

97. The chart shows the 2010 Winter Olympic medal counts of selected countries.

Country	Gold	Silver	Bronze
Austria	4	6	6
Canada	14	7	5
Germany	10	13	7
Norway	9	8	6
United States	9	15	13

(*Source:* nbcolympics.com)

a. Calculate the total number of medals won by each country.

b. Which country won the most medals?

98. Consider the deposit slip shown.

Maya Maxine

DATE *April 2, 2011*

Deposits may not be available for immediate withdrawal

Sign here for cash received (if required)

REGENCY BANK

CASH | 857.
CHECKS | 390.
| 2,406.
| 72.

TOTAL $

⑆00258291⑆: 56024036⑈ 02

a. Estimate how much money is being deposited.

b. Fill in the exact total.

99. Blues singer Bessie Smith was born in 1894 and died in 1937. About how old was she when she died? (*Source: Encyclopedia of World Biography*)

100. The United States entered the First World War in 1917 and the Second World War in 1941. Approximately how many years apart were these two events?

101. A sign in an elevator reads: MAXIMUM CAPACITY: 1,000 POUNDS. The passengers in the elevator weigh 187 pounds, 147 pounds, 213 pounds, 162 pounds, 103 pounds, and 151 pounds. Will the elevator be overloaded?

102. According to a magazine article on the recent annual income of celebrities, the rapper 50 Cent earned $150,000,000 whereas the talk-show host Oprah Winfrey earned $125,000,000 more. If J.K. Rowling, the author of the *Harry Potter* series, earned the equivalent of $300,000,000, who earned more—Rowling or Winfrey? (*Source: Forbes*)

103. The thermometer at the right shows the boiling point and the freezing point of water in degrees Fahrenheit (°F). What is the difference between these two temperatures?

104. The following ad for a hybrid car was listed in a local newspaper. How much below the MSRP (manufacturer's suggested retail price) is the selling price?

AUTO PLAZA
Low Price Guarantee
SAVE
MSRP
$26,150
Now on sale for **$23,796**

105. Some friends drive from town A to town B, to town C, to town D, and then back to A, as shown below. How far did they drive in all?

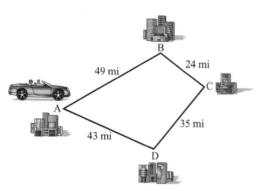

106. What is the length of the molding along the perimeter of the room pictured (yards = yd)?

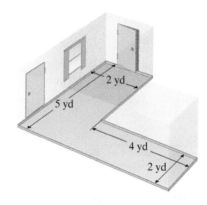

107. In a particular month, 163,038,000 home and work Internet users visited a site or launched an application owned by Google whereas 143,635,000 used a Microsoft-owned site or application. How many more users did Google have than Microsoft? (*Source:* nielsen.com)

108. In a recent year, the United States imported $21,615,426 in fish products from Japan. In the same year, the United States exported $19,579,138 in fish products to Japan. What is the difference between these two trade amounts? (*Source:* st.nmfs.noaa.gov)

109. The following table lists the number of deaths in New York City for a particular week.

Age Group	Number of Deaths
65 and over	1,049
45–64	303
25–44	67
1–24	21
Less than 1	14

(*Source:* cdc.gov)

How many deaths were there in New York City during that week?

110. An oil tanker broke apart at sea. It spilled 150,000 gallons (gal) of crude oil the first day, 400,000 gal the second day, and 1,000,000 gal the third day. How much oil was spilled in all?

111. The large auditorium at Carnegie Hall in New York City has been the site of many great concerts since the hall opened in 1891. The auditorium has five sections with the following seating capacity: Parquet—1,021, First Tier Boxes—264, Second Tier Boxes—238, Dress Circle—444, and Balcony—837. (*Source:* carnegiehall.org)

  a. Is the total seating capacity of the auditorium more or less than 3,000?

  b. For some concerts, 128 stage seats are also placed in the auditorium. What is the total seating capacity for these concerts?

112. A student has a credit card with a credit line of $3,000. On this card, there is a balance due of $1,369.

  a. If the student uses this credit card to purchase an iPad computer for $499, how much credit is still available on the card?

  b. If, instead of purchasing the computer, the student wishes to pay a tuition bill of $1,575, will there be enough credit available to pay the bill?

113. The following graph gives estimates of the number of species for various kinds of insects.

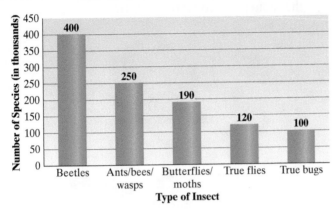

(*Source: Top Ten of Everything 2010*)

   a. How many more beetle species are there than true-fly species?

   b. Find the total number of species for all the insect types shown.

   c. How many fewer beetle species are there than species of the other insect types shown?

114. The following graph shows the number of cases of measles for selected years in the United States as reported by the Centers for Disease Control (CDC).

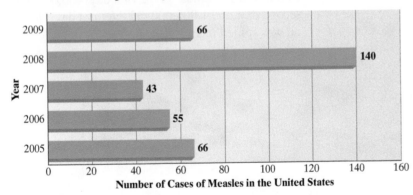

(*Source:* wonder.cdc.gov)

   a. How many more cases of measles were reported in 2009 than in 2007?

   b. What is the total number of cases reported for the years 2005–2009?

   c. How many fewer cases were reported in 2008 than the other years combined?

115. A salesman for a car dealership works on commission. The following table gives his sales commission for each of the first six months of the year.

Month	Sales Commission
January	$5,416
February	$3,791
March	$5,072
April	$3,959
May	$6,283
June	$4,055

What is his total commission for the first half of the year?

116. At its first eight games this season, a professional base-ball team had the following paid attendance:

Game	Attendance
1	11,862
2	18,722
3	14,072
4	9,713
5	25,913
6	28,699
7	19,302
8	18,780

What was the combined attendance for these games?

       ● Check your answers on page A-1.

MIND*Stretchers*

Writing

1. There are many different ways of putting numerical expressions into words.

   a. For example, $3 + 2$ can be expressed as

   > the sum of 3 and 2, 2 more than 3, or 3 increased by 2

   What are some other ways of reading this expression?

   b. For example, $5 - 2$ can be expressed as

   > the difference between 5 and 2, 5 take away 2, or 5 decreased by 2

   Write two other ways.

Critical Thinking

2. In a **magic square**, the sum of every row, column, and diagonal is the same number. Using the given information, complete the square at the right, which contains the whole numbers from 1 to 16. (*Hint:* The sum of every row, column, and diagonal is 34.)

16	3	2	
	10	11	
	6	7	

Groupwork

3. Two methods for borrowing in a subtraction problem are illustrated as follows. In method (a)—the method that we have already discussed—we borrow by taking 1 from the top, and in method (b) by adding 1 to the bottom.

   a.
   $$\begin{array}{r} \overset{7}{8}\,\overset{1}{5}\;9 \\ -3\;7\;6 \\ \hline 4\;8\;3 \end{array}$$

   b.
   $$\begin{array}{r} 8\;\overset{1}{5}\;9 \\ -\overset{4}{3}\;7\;6 \\ \hline 4\;8\;3 \end{array}$$

   Note that we get the same answer with both methods. Working with a partner, discuss the advantages of each method.

1.3   Multiplying Whole Numbers

The Meaning and Properties of Multiplication

A To multiply whole numbers

B To solve applied problems involving the multiplication of whole numbers

What does it mean to multiply whole numbers? A good answer to this question is *repeated addition.*

For instance, suppose that you buy 4 packages of pens and each package contains 3 pens. How many pens are there altogether?

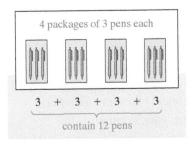

That is, $4 \times 3 = 3 + 3 + 3 + 3 = 12$. Generally, *multiplication means adding the same number repeatedly.*

We can also picture multiplication in terms of a rectangular figure, like this one, that represents 4×3.

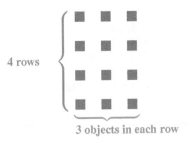

In a multiplication problem, the numbers being multiplied are called *factors*. The result is the *product*.

There are several ways to write a multiplication problem.

		Factor		Factor		Product
$\times$	the times sign	4	$\times$	3	$=$	12
$\cdot$	a multiplication dot	4	$\cdot$	3	$=$	12
( )( )	parentheses		(4)(3)		$=$	12

Like addition and subtraction, multiplication problems can be written either horizontally or vertically.

$$8 \times 5 = 40$$
Horizontal

$$\begin{array}{r} 8 \\ \times\ 5 \\ \hline 40 \end{array}$$
Vertical

The operation of multiplication has several important properties that we use frequently.

The Identity Property of Multiplication

The product of any number and 1 is that number.

$$1 \times 12 = 12$$
$$5 \times 1 = 5$$

The Multiplication Property of 0

The product of any number and 0 is 0.

$$49 \times 0 = 0$$
$$0 \times 8 = 0$$

The Commutative Property of Multiplication

Changing the order in which two numbers are multiplied does not affect their product.

$$2 \times 9 = 9 \times 2$$
$$\downarrow \qquad \downarrow$$
$$18 \quad = \quad 18$$

The Associative Property of Multiplication

When multiplying three numbers, regrouping the factors gives the same product.

We multiply inside the parentheses first.

$$(3 \times 4) \times 5 = 3 \times (4 \times 5)$$
$$12 \quad \times 5 = 3 \times \quad 20$$
$$60 \quad = \quad 60$$

The next—and last—property of multiplication also involves addition.

The Distributive Property

Multiplying a factor by the sum of two numbers gives the same result as multiplying the factor by each of the two numbers and then adding.

$$2 \times (5 + 3) = (2 \times 5) + (2 \times 3)$$
$$2 \times \quad 8 \quad = \quad 10 \quad + \quad 6$$
$$16 \qquad\qquad = \qquad\qquad 16$$

$$2 \times 8 = 16$$

$$2 \times 5 = 10 \qquad 2 \times 3 = 6$$

Before going on to the next section, study these properties of multiplication.

Multiplying Whole Numbers

Now, let's consider problems in which we multiply any whole number by a single-digit whole number.

Note that, to multiply whole numbers with reasonable speed, you must commit to memory the products of all single-digit whole numbers.

EXAMPLE 1

Multiply: 98 · 4

Solution We recall that the dot means multiplication. We first write the problem vertically.

We recall that the 9 in 98 means 9 tens.

So the product of 98 and 4 is 392.

$$
\begin{array}{r}
\overset{3}{9}\,8 \\
\times\ \ 4 \\
\hline
2
\end{array}
$$
← The product of 4 and 8 ones is 32 ones. We write the 2 and carry the 3 to the tens column.

$$
\begin{array}{r}
\overset{3}{9}\,8 \\
\times\ \ 4 \\
\hline
3\,9\,2
\end{array}
$$
← The product of 4 and 9 tens is 36 tens. We add the 3 tens to the 36 tens to get 39 tens.

PRACTICE 1

Find the product of 76 and 8.

EXAMPLE 2

Calculate: (806)(7)

Solution We recall that parentheses side-by-side mean to multiply. We write this problem vertically.

$$
\begin{array}{r}
\overset{4}{8}\,0\,6 \\
\times\ \ \ \ 7 \\
\hline
5,\,6\,4\,2
\end{array}
$$

— Here, 7 × 0 tens = 0 tens. Add the 4 tens to the 0 tens to get 4 tens.

The product of 806 and 7 is 5,642.

PRACTICE 2

Find the product: (705)(6)

Now, let's look at multiplying any two whole numbers.
Consider multiplying 32 by 48. We can write 32 × 48 as follows.

$$32 \times 48 = 32 \times (40 + 8)$$

We then use the distributive property to get the answer.

$$32 \times (40 + 8) = (32 \times 40) + (32 \times 8)$$
$$= 1,280 + 256$$
$$= 1,536$$

Generally, we solve this problem vertically.

Shortcut

$$
\begin{array}{r}
\overset{1}{3}\,2 \\
\times\ \ 4\,8 \\
\hline
2\,5\,6 \\
1\,2\,8\,0 \\
\hline
1,\,5\,3\,6
\end{array}
$$

← Partial product (8 × 32)
← Partial product (40 × 32)
← Add the partial products.

$$
\begin{array}{r}
3\,2 \\
\times\ \ 4\,8 \\
\hline
2\,5\,6 \\
1\,2\,8 \\
\hline
1,\,5\,3\,6
\end{array}
$$

← (8 × 32)
← (4 × 32)

If we use just the tens digit 4, we must write the product 128 leftward, starting at the tens column.

Example 2 suggests the following rule for multiplying whole numbers:

To Multiply Whole Numbers

- Multiply the top factor by the ones digit in the bottom factor, and write down this product.
- Multiply the top factor by the tens digit in the bottom factor, and write this product leftward, beginning with the tens column.
- Repeat this process until all the digits in the bottom factor are used.
- Add the partial products, writing down this sum.

EXAMPLE 3

Multiply: 300×50

Solution

$$
\begin{array}{r}
300 \\
\times\ 50 \\
\hline
000 \leftarrow 0 \times 300 = 0 \\
15\ 00 \leftarrow 5 \times 300 = 1{,}500 \\
\hline
15{,}000
\end{array}
$$

In Example 3, note that the number of zeros in the product equals the total number of zeros in the factors. This result suggests a shortcut for multiplying factors that end in zeros.

$$
\begin{array}{r}
300 \leftarrow \text{2 zeros} \\
\times\quad 50 \leftarrow \text{1 zero} \\
\hline
15{,}000 \leftarrow 2 + 1 = \text{3 zeros}
\end{array}
$$

PRACTICE 3

Find the product of 1,200 and 400.

TIP When multiplying two whole numbers that end in zeros, multiply the nonzero parts of the factors and then attach the total number of zeros to the product.

EXAMPLE 4

Simplify: $739 \cdot 305$

Solution

$$
\begin{array}{r}
739 \\
\times\ 305 \\
\hline
3\ 695 \leftarrow 5 \times 739 \\
0\ 00 \leftarrow 0 \times 739 = 0 \\
221\ 7\quad \leftarrow 3 \times 739 \\
\hline
225{,}395
\end{array}
$$

We don't have to write the row 000. Here is a shortcut.

$$
\begin{array}{r}
739 \\
\times\ 305 \\
\hline
3\ 695 \\
221\ 70 \quad \\
\hline
225{,}395
\end{array}
$$
$\leftarrow$ This one 0 represents the product of the tens digit 0 and 739. This 0 lines up the products correctly.

PRACTICE 4

Find the product of 987 and 208.

Now, let's apply the operation of multiplication to geometric area. Area means the number of square units that a figure contains.

In the rectangle at the right, each small square represents 1 square inch (sq in.). Finding the rectangle's area means finding the number of sq-in. units that it contains. A good strategy here is to find the number of units in each row and then multiply that number by the number of rows.

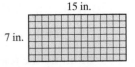

7 in.

There are two ways to find that there are 15 squares in a row—either by directly counting the squares or by noting that the length of the figure is 15 in. Similarly, we find that the figure contains 7 rows. Therefore the area of the figure is 15 × 7, or 105 sq in.

In general, we can compute the *area of a rectangle* by finding the product of its length and its width.

EXAMPLE 5

Calculate the area of the home office shown in the diagram.

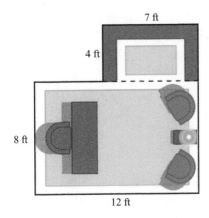

7 ft

4 ft

8 ft

12 ft

Solution The dashed line separates the office into two connected rectangles. The top rectangle measures 7 feet by 4 feet, and so its area is 7 × 4, or 28 square feet. The bottom rectangle measures 12 feet by 8 feet, and its area is 12 × 8, or 96 square feet. The entire area of the office is the sum of two smaller areas: 28 + 96, or 124 square feet. So the area of the home office is 124 square feet.

PRACTICE 5

Find the area of the room pictured.

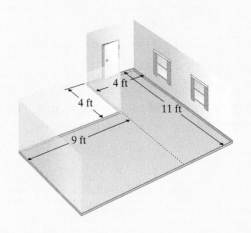

4 ft

4 ft

11 ft

9 ft

Estimating Products

As mentioned before, estimation is a valuable technique for checking an exact answer. When checking a product by estimation, round each factor to its largest place.

EXAMPLE 6

Multiply 328 by 179. Check the answer by estimation.

Solution

$$
\begin{array}{r}
328 \\
\times\ 179 \\
\hline
2\ 952 \\
22\ 96 \\
32\ 8 \\
\hline
58{,}712 \leftarrow \text{Exact product}
\end{array}
$$

PRACTICE 6

Find the product of 455 and 248. Use estimation to check your answer.

Check

$$328 \approx 300 \leftarrow \text{The largest place is hundreds.}$$
$$\underline{\times\ 179} \approx \underline{\times\ 200} \leftarrow \text{The largest place is hundreds.}$$
$$58{,}712 \qquad 60{,}000 \leftarrow \text{Estimated product}$$

Our exact product (58,712) and the estimated product (60,000) are fairly close.

When solving some multiplication problems, we are willing to settle for—or even prefer—an approximate answer.

EXAMPLE 7

The director of a preschool budgeted $900 to purchase supplies for an upcoming art project. She found handprint keepsake craft kits online for $12 each for the 56 children in the preschool. By estimating, decide if the director set aside enough money to purchase craft kits for all the children.

Solution The total cost of the craft kits is the product of $12 and 56. To estimate this product, we first round each factor to its largest place value so that every digit after the first digit is 0.

$$12 \approx 10 \leftarrow \text{The largest place is tens.}$$
$$\underline{\times\ 56} \approx 60 \leftarrow \text{The largest place is tens·}$$

Then, we multiply the rounded factors.

$$10 \times 60 = 600$$

Since the craft kits will cost about $600 and $900 is greater than $600, we conclude that the director set aside enough money for the craft kits.

PRACTICE 7

Producing flyers for your college's registration requires 25,000 sheets of paper. If the college buys 38 reams of paper and there are 500 sheets in a ream, estimate to decide if there is enough paper to produce the flyers.

Multiplying Whole Numbers on a Calculator

Now, let's use a calculator to find a product. When you are using a calculator to multiply large whole numbers, the answer may be too big to fit in the display. When this occurs the answer may be displayed in scientific notation (see the Appendix).

EXAMPLE 8

Use a calculator to multiply: $3,192 \times 41$

Solution

Press	Display
3192 $\times$ 41 ENTER	3192 * 41
	130872.

A reasonable estimate for this product is $3,000 \times 40$, or 120,000, which supports our answer, 130,872.

PRACTICE 8

Find the product: $2,811 \times 365$

EXAMPLE 9

Calculate: $61 \cdot 24 \cdot 19$

Solution

Press	Display
61 $\times$ 24 $\times$ 19 ENTER	61 * 24 * 19
	27816.

A good estimate is $60 \cdot 20 \cdot 20$, or 24,000—in the ballpark of 27,816.

PRACTICE 9

Multiply: $2,133 \cdot 18 \cdot 9$

Mathematically Speaking

Fill in each blank with the most appropriate term or phrase from the given list.

associative property of multiplication	identity property of multiplication	multiplication property of 0	sum product	subtraction addition
distributive property	perimeter	area		

1. The result of multiplying two factors is called their _____.

2. The _____ is illustrated by $3 \times (7 + 2) = (3 \times 7) + (3 \times 2)$.

3. The _____ states that the product of any number and 1 is that number.

4. The _____ states that the product of any number and 0 is 0.

5. The multiplication of whole numbers can be thought of as repeated _____.

6. The _____ of a figure is the number of square units that it contains.

A *Compute.*

7. 4×100

8. 5×100

9. 710×200

10. 270×500

11. $8,500 \times 20$

12. $6,800 \times 30$

13. $10,000 \times 700$

14. $10,000 \times 800$

Multiply and check by estimation.

15. $\begin{array}{r} 6,350 \\ \times \quad 2 \\ \hline \end{array}$

16. $\begin{array}{r} 8,864 \\ \times \quad 7 \\ \hline \end{array}$

17. $\begin{array}{r} 209 \\ \times \quad 2 \\ \hline \end{array}$

18. $\begin{array}{r} 703 \\ \times \quad 9 \\ \hline \end{array}$

19. $\begin{array}{r} 812,000 \\ \times \quad 4 \\ \hline \end{array}$

20. $\begin{array}{r} 19,250 \\ \times \quad 8 \\ \hline \end{array}$

21. $\begin{array}{r} 882 \\ \times \quad 74 \\ \hline \end{array}$

22. $\begin{array}{r} 881 \\ \times \quad 28 \\ \hline \end{array}$

23. $43 \cdot 19$

24. $85 \cdot 72$

25. $709 \cdot 48$

26. $602 \cdot 34$

27. $\begin{array}{r} 273 \\ \times \quad 11 \\ \hline \end{array}$

28. $\begin{array}{r} 607 \\ \times \quad 65 \\ \hline \end{array}$

29. $\begin{array}{r} 301 \\ \times \quad 12 \\ \hline \end{array}$

30. $\begin{array}{r} 513 \\ \times \quad 34 \\ \hline \end{array}$

31. $\begin{array}{r} 3,001 \\ \times \quad 19 \\ \hline \end{array}$

32. $\begin{array}{r} 4,005 \\ \times \quad 72 \\ \hline \end{array}$

33. $\begin{array}{r} 5,072 \\ \times \quad 48 \\ \hline \end{array}$

34. $\begin{array}{r} 8,801 \\ \times \quad 25 \\ \hline \end{array}$

35. $\begin{array}{r} 5,003 \\ \times \quad 40 \\ \hline \end{array}$

36. $\begin{array}{r} 2,881 \\ \times \quad 70 \\ \hline \end{array}$

Find the product and check by estimation.

37. $(372)(403)$

38. $(699)(101)$

39. $8,500 \times 17$

40. $7,200 \times 27$

41. 406×305

42. 702×509

43. $46 \cdot 8 \cdot 9$

44. $13 \cdot 11 \cdot 5$

45. $81 \times 2 \times 13$

46. $3 \times 15 \times 88$

47. $(10)(10)(400)$

48. $(20)(80)(30)$

49. $57 \times 81 \times 5$

50. $73 \times 4 \times 33$

51.   8,972
          $\times \ \ 365$

52.   7,552
          $\times \ \ 841$

53.   18,650
          $\times \ 2,949$

54.   21,320
          $\times \ 7,159$

In each group of three products, one is wrong. Use estimation to identify which product is incorrect.

55. a. $802 \times 755 = 605,510$ **b.** $39 \times 4,722 = 184,158$ **c.** $77 \times 6,005 = 46,385$

56. a. $618 \times 555 = 342,990$ **b.** $86,331 \times 21 = 18,129,511$ **c.** $380 \times 772 = 293,360$

57. a. $9 \times 37,118 = 334,062$ **b.** $82 \times 961 = 7,882$ **c.** $13 \times 986 = 12,818$

58. a. $3,002 \times 9 = 2,718$ **b.** $58 \times 891 = 51,678$ **c.** $106 \times 68 = 7,208$

Mixed Practice

Multiply and check by estimation.

59. $48 \cdot 5 \cdot 12$

60. $89 \times 10,000$

61.   9,605
          $\times \ \ 24$

62. $(809)(201)$

63. $357,000 \times 3$

64. $301 \cdot 34$

65. $(50)(60)(100)$

66. 495×21

Applications

B *Solve. Then check by estimation.*

67. Underwater explorers in the eastern Mediterranean Sea found the wreck of an Egyptian ship that had sunk 33 centuries earlier. How long ago in years did the ship sink? (*Hint:* 1 century $=$ 100 years)

68. Each day, an athlete in training takes two capsules. If each capsule contains 1,600 international units (IU) of vitamin A, how much vitamin A does he take daily?

69. The walls of a human heart are made of muscles that contract about 100,000 times a day. (*Source: American Heart Association's Your Heart: An Owner's Manual*)

a. How many contractions are there in 30 days?

b. How many more contractions are there in 40 days than in 30 days?

70. It is estimated that the United States needs to produce about 125,000 new jobs a month to maintain the present unemployment rate. (*Source:* theatlantic.com)

a. How many new jobs altogether would have to be created in a year for the present unemployment rate to remain constant?

b. If 800,000 new jobs are created in a year, how short of the goal is this?

71. The 2010 Honda Civic Hybrid gets about 45 miles per gallon of gasoline. If the fuel tank holds about 12 gallons of gasoline, can a person drive from San Francisco to Los Angeles, a distance of 276 miles, without refilling the car's fuel tank? (*Source:* automobiles.honda .com)

72. A Canadian football field is 330 ft long and 195 ft wide. By contrast, a football field in the National Football League measures 360 ft by 160 ft. Which field has a larger area? (*Source:* wikipedia.org)

73. Find the area of the countertop shown in the diagram.

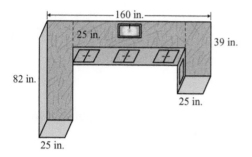

74. Calculate the area of the deck shown in the diagram.

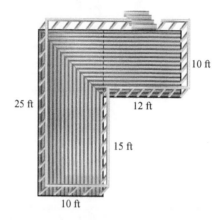

75. On the following map, 1 inch corresponds to 250 miles in the real world. How many miles actually separate towns A and B?

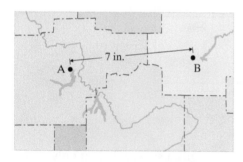

76. Angles are measured in either degrees (°) or radians (rad). A radian is about 57°. Express in degrees the measure of the angle shown.

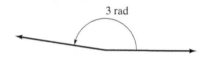

77. It costs $130 to join a local health club and $26 for each month of the membership. How much does a 1-year membership cost?

78. A customer bought an LCD television on the installment plan offered by an electronics store. If the total cost of the television is $1,689 and the customer pays $145 each month, how much does she have left to pay off after 8 months of payments?

79. During a 5-day week, a truck driver daily drove 42 miles an hour for 7 hours.

    a. How far did she drive in one day?
    b. How far did she drive during the week?

80. A young couple took out a mortgage on a condo. They paid $790 per month for 15 years.

    a. How much did they pay annually toward the mortgage?
    b. How much did it cost them to pay off the mortgage altogether?

81. The state of Colorado is approximately rectangular in shape, as shown. If the area of Kansas is about 82,000 sq mi, which state is larger? (*Source: The Columbia Gazeteer of the World*)

388 mi

275 mi

Colorado

82. Tuition at a state college for full-time in-state residents is approximately $1,750 per semester. In a fall semester, there were 30,963 of these students. How much revenue did the full-time in-state resident students generate?

• Check your answers on page A-1.

MINDStretchers

Writing

1. Study the following diagram. Explain how it justifies the Distributive Property.

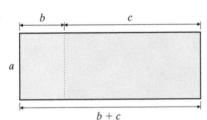

Mathematical Reasoning

2. Consider the six digits 1, 3, 5, 7, 8, and 9. Fill in the blanks with these digits, using each digit only once, so as to form the largest possible product.

$$\underline{}\ \underline{}\ \underline{}\ \times\ \underline{}\ \underline{}\ \underline{}$$

Historical

3. Centuries ago in India and Persia, the **lattice method** of multiplication was popular. The following example, in which we multiply 57 by 43, illustrates this method. Explain how it works.

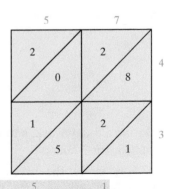

Cultural Note

1	2	3	4	5	6	7	8	9	0	
										Twelfth century
										A.D. 1197
										A.D. 1275
										c. A.D. 1294
										c. A.D. 1303
										c. A.D. 1360
										c. A.D. 1442

The way the ten digits are written has evolved over time. Early Hindu symbols found in a cave in India date from more than two thousand years ago. About twelve hundred years ago, an Indian manuscript on arithmetic, which had been translated into Arabic, was carried by merchants to Europe where it was later translated into Latin.

This table shows European examples of digit notation from the twelfth to the fifteenth century, when the printing press led to today's standardized notation. Through international trade, these symbols became known throughout the world.

Source: David Eugene Smith and Jekuthiel Ginsburg, *Numbers and Numerals, A Story Book for Young and Old* (New York: Bureau of Publications, Teachers College, Columbia University, 1937)

1.4   Dividing Whole Numbers

The Meaning and Properties of Division

What does it mean to divide? One good answer is to think of division as *breaking up a set of objects* into a given number of equal smaller sets.

    For instance, suppose that we want to split a set of 15 objects, say pens, evenly among 3 boxes.

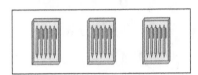

    From the diagram we see that each box ends up with 5 pens. We therefore say that 15 divided by 3 is 5, which we can write as follows:

$$\text{Divisor}\;\;3\overline{)15}\;\;\begin{matrix}5 & \text{Quotient}\\ & \text{Dividend}\end{matrix}$$

    In a division problem, the number that is being used to divide another number is called the *divisor*. The number being divided is the *dividend*. The result is the *quotient*.

    We can also think of division as the *opposite* (*inverse*) of multiplication. Consider the following pair of problems that illustrate this point.

$$\underset{\text{Division}}{3\overline{)15}}\;^{5}\quad\text{because}\quad\underset{\text{Related multiplication}}{5\times 3=15}$$

The following relationship connects multiplication and division.

$$\boxed{\text{Quotient} \times \text{Divisor} = \text{Dividend}}$$

Note that this relationship allows us to check our answer to a division problem by multiplying.

    There are several common ways to write a division problem.

$$3\overline{)15}\;^{5},\quad \frac{15}{3}=5,\quad\text{or}\quad 15\div 3=5$$

Usually, we use the first of these to compute the answer. However, no matter which way we write this problem, 3 is the divisor, 15 is the dividend, and 5 is the quotient.

> **TIP**   When reading a division problem, we say that we are dividing either the divisor *into* the dividend or the dividend *by* the divisor. For instance, $3\overline{)15}$ is read either "3 divided into 15" or "15 divided by 3."

When calculating a quotient, we frequently use the following properties of division.

	Division	**Related Multiplication**
• Any whole number (except 0) divided by itself is 1.	$6\overline{)6}$ (quotient 1)	$1 \times 6 = 6$
• Any whole number divided by 1 is the number itself.	$1\overline{)12}$ (quotient 12)	$12 \times 1 = 12$
• Zero divided by any whole number (other than 0) is 0.	$8\overline{)0}$ (quotient 0)	$0 \times 8 = 0$
• Division by 0 is not permitted.	$0\overline{)5}$ (quotient ?)	$? \times 0 = 5$ There is no number that when multiplied by 0 equals 5.

Dividing Whole Numbers

Multiplication is the opposite of division. So in the simple division problem $3\overline{)15}$, we know that the answer is 5 because we have memorized that $5 \cdot 3$ is 15. But what should we do when the dividend is a larger number?

Consider the following problem: Divide 9 into 5,112 and check the answer.

• We start with the greatest place (thousands) in the dividend. We consider the dividend to be 5 thousands and think $9\overline{)5}$. Since $9 \cdot 1 = 9$ and 9 is larger than 5, there are no thousands in the quotient.

$$0 \longleftarrow \text{Thousands}$$
$$9\overline{)5,112}$$

• So we go to the hundreds place in the dividend. We consider the dividend to be 51 hundreds and think $9\overline{)51}$. Since $9 \cdot 5 = 45$, we position the 5 in the hundreds place of the quotient.

$$5 \longleftarrow \text{Hundreds}$$
$$9\overline{)5,112}$$
$$\underline{-4,500} \longleftarrow 500 \cdot 9 = 4500$$
$$612 \longleftarrow \text{Difference}$$

• Next, we move to the tens place of the difference, 612. We consider the new dividend to be 61 tens and think $9\overline{)61}$. Since $9 \cdot 6 = 54$, we position the 6 in the tens place of the quotient.

$$\text{Tens}$$
$$56$$
$$9\overline{)5,112}$$
$$\underline{-4,500}$$
$$612$$
$$\underline{-540} \longleftarrow 60 \cdot 9 = 540$$
$$72 \longleftarrow \text{Difference}$$

• Finally, we go to the ones place of the difference, 72. We consider the new dividend to be 72 ones. So we think $9\overline{)72}$. Since $9 \cdot 8 = 72$, we position the 8 in the ones place of the quotient.

So 568 is our answer.

$$\text{Ones}$$
$$568$$
$$9\overline{)5,112}$$
$$\underline{-4,500}$$
$$612$$
$$\underline{-540}$$
$$72$$
$$\underline{-72} \longleftarrow 8 \cdot 9 = 72$$
$$0 \longleftarrow \text{Difference}$$

Instead of writing 0's as placeholders, we can use the following shortcut.

$$
\begin{array}{r}
568 \\
9\overline{)5,112} \\
-45 \\
\hline
61 \\
-54 \\
\hline
72 \\
-72 \\
\hline
0
\end{array}
$$

← These arrows help us to keep track of which digit we have brought down.

Check   568
$$
\begin{array}{r}
\times\ \ 9 \\
\hline
5,112
\end{array}
$$
← The product equals the dividend, so our answer is correct.

Note that each time we subtract in a division problem, the difference is less than the divisor. Why must that be true?

EXAMPLE 1

Divide and check: $4,263 \div 7$

Solution

┌─ Think $7\overline{)42}$.

$$
\begin{array}{r}
609 \\
7\overline{)4,263} \\
-42 \\
\hline
06 \\
-0 \\
\hline
63 \\
-63 \\
\hline
0
\end{array}
$$

← $6 \times 7 = 42$. Subtract.

← Think $7\overline{)6}$. There are zero 7's in 6.

← $0 \times 7 = 0$. Subtract.

← Think $7\overline{)63}$.

← $9 \times 7 = 63$. Subtract.

Check   609
$$
\begin{array}{r}
\times\ \ 7 \\
\hline
4,263
\end{array}
$$

The product agrees with our dividend. Note the 0 in the quotient. Can you explain why the 0 is needed?

PRACTICE 1

Compute $9\overline{)7,263}$ and then check your answer.

TIP In writing your answer to a division problem, position the first digit of the quotient over the *rightmost digit* of the number into which you are dividing (the 6 over the 2 in Example 1).

$$
\begin{array}{c}
609 \\
\downarrow\downarrow\downarrow \\
7\overline{)4,\mathbf{2}63}
\end{array}
$$

EXAMPLE 2

Compute $\dfrac{2,709}{9}$. Then check your answer.

Solution
$$
\begin{array}{r}
301 \\
9\overline{)2,709} \\
-27 \\
\hline
00 \\
-0 \\
\hline
09 \\
-9 \\
\hline
0
\end{array}
$$

Check   301
$$
\begin{array}{r}
\times\ \ 9 \\
\hline
2,709
\end{array}
$$

PRACTICE 2

Carry out the following division and check your answer.

$$8\overline{)56,016}$$

In Examples 1 and 2, note that the remainder is 0; that is, the divisor goes evenly into the dividend. However, in some division problems, that is not the case. Consider, for instance, the problem of dividing 16 pens *equally* among 3 boxes.

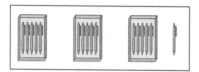

From the diagram, we see that each box contains 5 pens *but* that 1 pen—the *remainder*—is left over.

$$\begin{array}{r} 5 \leftarrow \text{Number of pens in each box} \\ \text{Number of boxes} \rightarrow 3\overline{)16} \leftarrow \text{Total number of pens} \\ -15 \leftarrow \text{Total number of pens in the boxes} \\ \hline 1 \leftarrow \text{Number of pens remaining} \end{array}$$

We write the answer to this problem as 5 R1 (read "5 Remainder 1"). Note that $(3 \times 5) + 1 = 16$. The following relationship is always true.

> (Quotient $\times$ Divisor) + Remainder = Dividend

When a division problem results in a remainder as well as a quotient, we use this relationship for checking.

EXAMPLE 3

Find the quotient of 55,811 and 6. Then check.

Solution

$$\begin{array}{r} 9,301 \text{ R5} \\ 6\overline{)55,811} \\ -54 \\ \hline 1\,8 \\ -1\,8 \\ \hline 01 \\ -0 \\ \hline 11 \\ -6 \\ \hline 5 \end{array}$$

Our answer is therefore 9,301 R5.

(Quotient $\times$ Divisor) + Remainder = Dividend

Check $(9,301 \times 6) + 5 =$
$$55,806 + 5 = 55,811$$

Since this matches the dividend, our answer checks.

PRACTICE 3

Compute $8\overline{)42,329}$ and check.

Now, let's consider division problems in which a divisor has more than one digit. Notice that such problems involve rounding.

EXAMPLE 4

Compute $\dfrac{2,574}{34}$ and check.

Solution   In order to estimate the first digit of the quotient, we round 34 to 30 and 257 to 260.

$$
\begin{array}{r}
8 \\
34\overline{)2,574} \\
-2\,72
\end{array}
$$

← Think $260 \div 30$, or $26 \div 3$. The quotient 8 goes over the 7 because we are dividing 34 into 257.

← $8 \times 34 = 272$. Try to subtract.

Because 272 is too large, we reduce our estimate in the quotient by 1 and try 7.

$$
\begin{array}{r}
76 \\
34\overline{)2,574} \\
-2\,38 \\
\hline
194 \\
-204
\end{array}
$$

← $7 \times 34 = 238$. Subtract.

← Think $190 \div 30$ or $19 \div 3$.

← $6 \times 34 = 204$. Try to subtract.

Because 204 is too large, we reduce our estimate in the quotient by 1 and try 5.

$$
\begin{array}{r}
75 \text{ R}24 \\
34\overline{)2,574} \\
-2\,38 \\
\hline
194 \\
-170 \\
\hline
24
\end{array}
$$

So our answer is 75 R24.

Check $(75 \times 34) + 24 = 2,574$

Since 2,574 is the dividend, our answer checks.

Divide 23 into 1,818. Then check.

EXAMPLE 5

Divide $26\overline{)1,849}$ and then check.

Solution   First, we round 26 to 30 and 184 to 180. Think $180 \div 30 = 6$.

$$
\begin{array}{r}
6 \\
26\overline{)1,849} \\
-1\,56 \\
\hline
28
\end{array}
$$

This difference is larger than the divisor, so we increase the 6 in the quotient by 1.

$$
\begin{array}{r}
71 \\
26\overline{)1,849} \\
-182 \\
\hline
29 \\
-26 \\
\hline
3
\end{array}
$$

Our answer is therefore 71 R3.

Check $(71 \times 26) + 3 = 1,849$

Compute and check: $15\overline{)1,420}$

TIP   If the divisor has more than one digit, estimate each digit in the quotient by rounding and then dividing. If the product is too large or too small, adjust it up or down by 1 and then try again.

EXAMPLE 6

Find the quotient of 13,559 and 44. Then check.

Solution

$$
\begin{array}{r}
308 \text{ R7} \\
44\overline{)13,559} \\
-13\ 2\ \ \ \\
\hline
35\ \ \ \ \\
-0\ \ \ \\
\hline
359\ \\
-352\ \\
\hline
7
\end{array}
$$

← This number is smaller than the divisor, so the next digit in the quotient is 0.

Check $(308 \times 44) + 7 = 13,559$

PRACTICE 6

Divide 16,999 by 28. Then check your answer.

EXAMPLE 7

Divide and check: $6,000 \div 20$

Solution   We set up the problem as before.

$$
\begin{array}{r}
300 \\
20\overline{)6,000} \\
-60\ \ \ \\
\hline
00\ \ \\
-00\ \ \\
\hline
00\ \\
-00\ \\
\hline
0
\end{array}
$$

Check
$$
\begin{array}{r}
300 \\
\times\ 20 \\
\hline
6,000
\end{array}
$$

Because the divisor and dividend both end in zero, a quicker way to do Example 7 is by dropping zeros.

$20\overline{)6,000}$ ← Drop one 0 from both the divisor and the dividend.

$$
\begin{array}{r}
300 \\
2\overline{)600}
\end{array}
$$ ← Then divide.

PRACTICE 7

Compute $40\overline{)8,000}$ and then check.

TIP   Dropping the same number of zeros at the right end of both the divisor and the dividend does not change the quotient.

Estimating Quotients

As for other operations, estimating is an important skill for division. Checking a quotient by estimation is faster than checking it by multiplication, although less exact. And in some division problems, we need only an approximate answer.

How do we estimate a quotient? A good way is to round the divisor to its greatest place. The new divisor then contains only one nonzero digit and so is relatively easy to divide by mentally. Then, we round the dividend to the place of our choice. Finally, we compute the estimated quotient by calculating its first digit and then attaching the appropriate number of zeros.

EXAMPLE 8

Calculate $\dfrac{7{,}004}{34}$ and then check by estimation.

Solution

$$
\begin{array}{r}
206 \leftarrow \text{Exact quotient} \\
34\overline{)7{,}004} \\
-68 \\
\hline
204 \\
-204 \\
\hline
\end{array}
$$

Check $34\overline{)7{,}004}$ Round 34 to 30 and round 7,004 to 7,000.

$\downarrow$ $\downarrow$

$30\overline{)7{,}000}$ Think $70 \div 30$ or $7 \div 3$.

$$
\begin{array}{r}
200 \leftarrow \text{Estimated quotient} \\
30\overline{)7{,}000}
\end{array}
$$

Note that, to the right of the 2 in the estimated quotient, we added a 0 over each of the digits in the dividend. Our answer (206) is close to our estimate (200), and so our answer is reasonable.

EXAMPLE 9

Sound travels at about 340 meters per second, whereas light travels at 299,792,458 meters per second. Estimate how many times as fast as the speed of sound is the speed of light.

Solution   To estimate a quotient, we first round the divisor and the dividend to their largest place value.

$340\overline{)299{,}792{,}458}$

$\downarrow$ $\downarrow$

$300\overline{)300{,}000{,}000}$ Round 340 to 300 and 299,792,458 to 300,000,000.

Then, we divide.

$$
\begin{array}{r}
1{,}000{,}000 \\
300\overline{)300{,}000{,}000}
\end{array}
$$

So the speed of light is about 1,000,000 times faster than the speed of sound.

PRACTICE 8

Compute $100{,}568 \div 104$ and use estimation to check.

PRACTICE 9

Based on population projections, China will have a population of 1,394,638,699 in the year 2025. In that same year, Brazil will have a population of 231,886,946. Estimate how many times the population of Brazil will the population of China be in 2025. (*Source:* sasweb.ssd. census.gov)

Dividing Whole Numbers on a Calculator

When using a calculator to divide, we must enter the numbers in the correct order to get the correct answer. We first enter the number into *which we are dividing (the dividend) and then the number* by *which we are dividing (the divisor).*

EXAMPLE 10

Use a calculator to divide $18\overline{)11{,}718}$.

Solution

Press	Display
11718 $\div$ 18 [ENTER]	$11718 / 18$
	$651.$

A reasonable estimate is $10{,}000 \div 20$, or 500, which is fairly close to 651.

PRACTICE 10

Find the following quotient with a calculator:

$$\frac{47{,}034}{78}$$

Mathematically Speaking

Fill in each blank with the most appropriate term or phrase from the given list.

subtraction	divided	divisor	multiplication
quotient	product	increased	

1. When dividing, the dividend is divided by the _____.

2. The result of dividing is called the _____.

3. The opposite operation of division is _____.

4. Any whole number _____ by 1 is equal to the number itself.

A *Divide and check.*

5. $5\overline{)2{,}000}$

6. $5\overline{)6{,}000}$

7. $5\overline{)12{,}800}$

8. $8\overline{)12{,}504}$

9. $9\overline{)2{,}709}$

10. $2\overline{)5{,}780}$

11. $7\overline{)21{,}021}$

12. $5\overline{)27{,}450}$

13. $3\overline{)24{,}132}$

14. $2\overline{)30{,}534}$

15. $9\overline{)4{,}500}$

16. $3\overline{)4{,}512}$

Find the quotient and check.

17. $300 \div 10$

18. $400 \div 20$

19. $700 \div 50$

20. $6{,}000 \div 20$

21. $\dfrac{8{,}400}{200}$

22. $\dfrac{7{,}500}{300}$

23. $\dfrac{16{,}000}{40}$

24. $\dfrac{48{,}000}{20}$

25. $6{,}996 \div 44$

26. $9{,}660 \div 92$

27. $80{,}295 \div 15$

28. $31{,}031 \div 13$

29. $39{,}078 \div 39$

30. $49{,}497 \div 21$

31. $249{,}984 \div 36$

32. $499{,}992 \div 24$

33. $52\overline{)52{,}052}$

34. $24\overline{)48{,}072}$

35. $12\overline{)36{,}600}$

36. $36\overline{)25{,}560}$

37. $25\overline{)22{,}675}$

38. $15\overline{)30{,}480}$

39. $49\overline{)58{,}849}$

40. $19\overline{)38{,}570}$

41. $6{,}512 \div 10$

42. $8{,}922 \div 25$

43. $304 \div 27$

44. $206 \div 45$

45. $\dfrac{10{,}175}{87}$

46. $\dfrac{21{,}109}{25}$

47. $\dfrac{63{,}002}{90}$

48. $\dfrac{12{,}509}{61}$

49. $47\overline{)34{,}000}$

50. $66\overline{)99{,}980}$

51. $14\overline{)6{,}000}$

52. $32\overline{)3{,}007}$

53. $65\overline{)65{,}660}$

54. $39\overline{)30{,}009}$

55. $42\overline{)39{,}000}$

56. $97\overline{)13{,}502}$

57. $537\overline{)387{,}177}$

58. $265\overline{)197{,}160}$

59. $638\overline{)98{,}890}$

60. $152\overline{)34{,}048}$

In each group of three quotients, one is wrong. Use estimation to identify which quotient is incorrect.

61. **a.** $18{,}473 \div 91 = 203$ **b.** $43{,}364 \div 74 = 586$ **c.** $14{,}562 \div 18 = 8{,}009$

62. **a.** $43{,}710 \div 93 = 47$ **b.** $71{,}048 \div 107 = 664$ **c.** $11{,}501 \div 31 = 371$

63. **a.** $455{,}260 \div 65 = 704$ **b.** $11{,}457 \div 57 = 201$ **c.** $10{,}044 \div 93 = 108$

64. **a.** $178{,}267 \div 89 = 2{,}003$ **b.** $350{,}007 \div 21 = 1{,}667$ **c.** $37{,}185 \div 37 = 1{,}005$

Mixed Practice

Divide and check.

65. 38,095 ÷ 42

66. $\dfrac{63,147}{21}$

67. 6)12,000

68. 4,907 ÷ 7

69. $\dfrac{48,000}{20}$

70. 36)249,986

71. $\dfrac{3,330}{9}$

72. 4,090 ÷ 91

Applications

B *Solve and check.*

73. A part-time student is taking 9 credit-hours this semester at a local community college. If her tuition bill is $1,215, how much does each credit-hour cost?

74. A car used 15 gallons of gas on a 300-mile trip. How many miles per gallon (mpg) of gas did the car get?

75. The area of the Pacific Ocean is about 64 million square miles, and the area of the Atlantic Ocean is approximately 32 million square miles. The Pacific is how many times as large as the Atlantic? (*Source: The New Encyclopedia Britannica*)

76. The diameter of Earth is about 8,000 miles, whereas the diameter of the Moon is about 2,000 miles. How many times the Moon's diameter is Earth's? (*Source: The New Encyclopedia Britannica*)

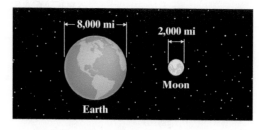

77. In the year 2030, Ohio is projected to have a population of about 12,300,000 people. If Ohio has a total land area of about 41,000 square miles, how many people per square mile will there be in 2030? (*Source:* Ohio Department of Development)

78. A certified medical assistant has an annual salary of $26,472. What is her gross monthly income?

79. A 150-pound person can burn about 360 calories in 1 hour doing yoga. How many calories are burned in 1 minute? (*Source:* American Cancer Society)

80. Ryan Howard signed a 5-year, $125,000,000 contract extension with the Philadelphia Phillies in 2010. On average, what is his pay per year from the contract extension? (*Source:* sportsillustrated.com)

81. A homeowner is remodeling a bathroom with dimensions 96 inches and 114 inches. For the floor, she has selected tiles that measure 6 inches by 6 inches.
   a. How many tiles must she purchase?
   b. The tiles come in boxes of 12. How many boxes of tiles must she purchase?
   c. If each box of tiles costs $18, how much will she spend on the tiles for the floor?

82. The group admission rate for 15 or more people at Six Flags Great Adventure amusement park is $30 per person. A student group hosted a field trip to the park and charged $47 per ticket, covering both the cost of admission to the park and the bus transportation. (*Source:* Six Flags Great Adventure, 2010)
   a. If the total amount the group collected for tickets was $1,739, how many students went on the field trip?
   b. Calculate the total cost of admissions for the students on the field trip.
   c. What was the cost of the bus transportation?

• Check your answers on page A-2.

MINDStretchers

Writing

1. Use the problem $10 \div 2 = 5$ to help explain why division can be thought of as repeated subtraction.

Mathematical Reasoning

2. Consider the following pair of problems.

   a. $2\overline{)7}$ **b.** $4\overline{)13}$

   Are the answers the same? Explain.

Groupwork

3. In the following division problem, A, B, and C each stand for a different digit. Working with a partner, identify all the digits. (*Hint:* There are two answers.)

$$
\begin{array}{r}
\text{ABA} \\
\text{AB}\overline{)\text{CACAB}} \\
-\text{CAB} \\
\hline
\text{CA} \\
-\text{B} \\
\hline
\text{CAB} \\
-\text{CAB} \\
\hline
\end{array}
$$

Exponents

There are many mathematical situations in which we multiply a number by itself repeatedly. Writing such expressions in **exponential form** provides a shorthand method for representing this repeated multiplication of the same factor.

For instance, we can write $5 \cdot 5 \cdot 5 \cdot 5$ in exponential form as

$$5^4 \longleftarrow \text{Exponent}$$
$$\text{Base}$$

This expression is read "5 to the fourth *power*" or simply "5 to the fourth."

OBJECTIVES

A To evaluate expressions involving exponents

B To evaluate expressions using the rule for order of operations

C To compute averages

D To solve applied problems involving exponents, order of operations, or averages

> **DEFINITION**
>
> An **exponent** (or **power**) is a number that indicates how many times another number (called the **base**) is used as a factor.

We read the power 2 or the power 3 in a special way. For instance, 5^2 is usually read "5 *squared*" rather than "5 to the second power." Similarly, we usually read 5^3 as "5 *cubed*" instead of "5 to the third power."

Let's look at a number written in exponential form—namely, 2^4. To evaluate this expression, we multiply 4 factors of 2.

$$
\begin{aligned}
2^4 &= 2 \cdot 2 \cdot 2 \cdot 2 \\
&= 4 \cdot 2 \cdot 2 \\
&= 8 \cdot 2 \\
&= 16
\end{aligned}
$$

In short, $2^4 = 16$. Do you see the difference between 2^4 and $2 \cdot 4$?

Sometimes we prefer to shorten expressions by writing them in exponential form. For instance, we can write $3 \cdot 3 \cdot 4 \cdot 4 \cdot 4$ in terms of powers of 3 and 4.

$$\underbrace{3 \cdot 3}_{\substack{\text{2 factors} \\ \text{of 3}}} \cdot \underbrace{4 \cdot 4 \cdot 4}_{\substack{\text{3 factors} \\ \text{of 4}}} = 3^2 \cdot 4^3$$

EXAMPLE 1

Rewrite

$$6 \cdot 6 \cdot 6 \cdot 10 \cdot 10 \cdot 10 \cdot 10$$

in exponential form.

Solution

$$\underbrace{6 \cdot 6 \cdot 6}_{\text{3 factors of 6}} \cdot \underbrace{10 \cdot 10 \cdot 10 \cdot 10}_{\text{4 factors of 10}} = 6^3 \cdot 10^4$$

PRACTICE 1

Write

$$5 \cdot 5 \cdot 5 \cdot 5 \cdot 5 \cdot 2 \cdot 2$$

in terms of powers.

EXAMPLE 2

Compute:

a. 1^5

b. 22^2

Solution

a. $1^5 = \underbrace{1 \cdot 1 \cdot 1 \cdot 1 \cdot 1}$
   $\quad = \quad 1$

Note that 1 raised to any power is 1.

b. $22^2 = 22 \cdot 22$
   $\quad\;\; = 484$

After considering this example, can you explain the difference between squaring and doubling a number?

PRACTICE 2

Calculate:

a. 1^8

b. 11^3

EXAMPLE 3

Write $4^3 \cdot 5^3$ in standard form.

Solution

$$4^3 \cdot 5^3 = (4 \cdot 4 \cdot 4) \cdot (5 \cdot 5 \cdot 5)$$
$$= 64 \cdot 125$$
$$= 8,000$$

From this example, do you see the difference between cubing and tripling a number?

PRACTICE 3

Express $7^2 \cdot 2^4$ in standard form.

It is especially easy to compute *powers of 10*.

$$10^2 = 10 \cdot 10 = 100, \qquad 10^3 = 10 \cdot 10 \cdot 10 = 1{,}000$$
$$\underbrace{\qquad}_{2\text{ zeros}} \qquad\qquad\qquad \underbrace{\qquad}_{3\text{ zeros}}$$

$$10^4 = 10 \cdot 10 \cdot 10 \cdot 10 = 10{,}000$$
$$\underbrace{\qquad}_{4\text{ zeros}}$$

and so on.

Note the pattern.

EXAMPLE 4

The Milky Way, the galaxy to which the Sun and Earth belong, contains about 100 billion stars. Express this number in terms of a power of 10. (*Source: The New York Times Almanac 2010*)

Solution

$$\underbrace{100{,}000{,}000{,}000}_{11\text{ zeros}} = 10^{11}$$

So the Milky Way contains about 10^{11} stars.

PRACTICE 4

In 1804, the world population reached the milestone of one billion. Represent this number as a power of 10. (*Source: U.S. Census Bureau*)

Order of Operations

Some mathematical expressions involve more than one mathematical operation. For instance, consider $5 + 3 \cdot 2$. This expression seems to have two different values, depending on the order in which we perform the given operations.

Adding first	**Multiplying first**
$5 + 3 \cdot 2$	$5 + 3 \cdot 2$
$= \quad 8 \quad \cdot 2$	$= 5 + \quad 6$
$= \quad 16$	$= \quad 11$

How are we to know which operation to carry out first? By consensus we agree to follow the rule called the **order of operations** so that everyone always gets the same value for an answer.

Order of Operations Rule

To evaluate mathematical expressions, carry out the operations *in the following order*.

1. First, perform the operations within any grouping symbols, such as parentheses ( ) or brackets [ ].

2. Then, raise any number to its power ■■.

3. Next, perform all multiplications and divisions as they appear from left to right.

4. Finally, do all additions and subtractions as they appear from left to right.

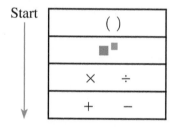

Applying this rule to the preceding example gives us the following result.

$$5 + \underbrace{3 \cdot 2}_{} \quad \text{Multiply first.}$$
$$= \underbrace{5 + 6}_{} \quad \text{Then add.}$$
$$= \quad 11$$

So 11 is the correct answer.

Let's consider more examples that depend on the order of operations rule.

EXAMPLE 5

Simplify: $18 - 7 \cdot 2$

Solution Applying the rule, we multiply first, and then subtract.

$$18 - \underbrace{7 \cdot 2}_{} =$$
$$18 - 14 = 4$$

PRACTICE 5

Evaluate: $2 \cdot 8 + 4 \cdot 3$

EXAMPLE 6

Find the value of $3 + 2 \cdot (8 + 3^2)$.

Solution

$$3 + 2 \cdot (8 + 3^2) = 3 + 2 \cdot (8 + 9)$$ First, perform the operations in parentheses: square the 3.

$$= 3 + 2 \cdot 17$$ Then, add 8 and 9.

$$= 3 + 34$$ Next, multiply 2 by 17.

$$= 37$$ Finally, add 3 and 34.

PRACTICE 6

Simplify: $(4 + 1)^2 \times 6 - 4$

TIP   When a division problem is written in the format $\dfrac{\square}{\square}$, parentheses are understood to be around both the dividend and the divisor. For instance,

$$\frac{10 - 2}{3 + 1} \text{ means } \frac{(10 - 2)}{(3 + 1)}.$$

EXAMPLE 7

Evaluate: $6 \cdot 2^3 - \dfrac{21 - 11}{2}$

Solution $6 \cdot 2^3 - \dfrac{21 - 11}{2} = 6 \cdot 2^3 - \dfrac{10}{2}$ First, simplify the dividend by subtracting.

$$= 6 \cdot 8 - \frac{10}{2}$$ Then, cube.

$$= 48 - 5$$ Next, multiply and divide.

$$= 43$$ Finally, subtract.

PRACTICE 7

Simplify: $10 + \dfrac{24}{12 - 8} - 3 \times 4$

Some arithmetic expressions contain not only parentheses but also brackets. When simplifying expressions containing these grouping symbols, first perform the operations within the innermost grouping symbols and then continue to work outward.

EXAMPLE 8

Simplify: $5 \cdot [4(10 - 3^2) - 2]$

Solution

$$5 \cdot [4(10 - 3^2) - 2] = 5 \cdot [4(10 - 9) - 2]$$ Perform the operation in parentheses: square the 3.

$$= 5 \cdot [4 \cdot 1 - 2]$$ Subtract 9 from 10.

$$= 5 \cdot [4 - 2]$$ Multiply.

$$= 5 \cdot 2$$ Subtract.

$$= 10$$ Multiply.

PRACTICE 8

Evaluate: $[4 + 3(2^3 - 5)] \cdot 10$

EXAMPLE 9

Young's Rule is a rule of thumb for calculating the dose of medicine recommended for a child of a given age. According to this rule, the dose of acetaminophen in milligrams (mg) for a child who is eight years old can be calculated using the expression.

$$\frac{8 \times 500}{8 + 12}$$

What is the recommended dose?

Solution

$$\frac{8 \times 500}{8 + 12} = \frac{4,000}{20} \qquad \text{First, simplify the dividend and the divisor.}$$

$$= 200 \qquad \text{Then, divide.}$$

So the recommended dose is 200 milligrams.

PRACTICE 9

The minimum distance (in feet) that it takes a car to stop if it is traveling on a particular road surface at a speed of 30 miles per hour is given by the expression.

$$\frac{10 \times 30^2}{30 \times 5}$$

What is this minimum stopping distance?

Averages

We use an **average** to represent a set of numbers. Averages allow us to compare two or more sets. (For example, do the men or the women in your class spend more time studying?) Averages also allow us to compare an individual with a set. (For example, is the amount of time you spend studying above or below the class average?) The following definition shows how to compute an average.

DEFINITION

The **average** (or **mean**) of a set of numbers is the sum of those numbers divided by however many numbers are in the set.

EXAMPLE 10

What is the average of 100, 94, and 100?

Solution   The average equals the sum of these three numbers divided by 3.

$$\frac{100 + 94 + 100}{3} = \frac{294}{3} = 98$$

PRACTICE 10

Find the average of $30, $0, and $90.

EXAMPLE 11

The following map shows the five Great Lakes. The maximum depth of each of these lakes is given in the table. (*Source:* U.S. Environmental Protection Agency)

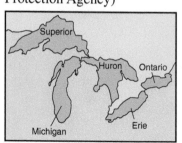

Lake	Maximum Depth (in meters)
Erie	64
Huron	229
Michigan	282
Ontario	244
Superior	406

PRACTICE 11

The table shown gives the number of at-home fatalities due to tornadoes in the United States each year from 2006 through 2009. (*Source:* spc.noaa.gov)

Year	Number of At-Home Fatalities
2006	58
2007	68
2008	99
2009	19

EXAMPLE 11 (continued)

a. What is the average maximum depth of the Great Lakes?

b. Which of the Great Lakes is deeper than the average?

Solution

a. $\dfrac{\text{The sum of the depths}}{\text{The number of lakes}} = \dfrac{64 + 229 + 282 + 244 + 406}{5}$

$$= \frac{1{,}225}{5}$$

$$= 245$$

So the average maximum depth is 245 meters.

b. Lake Michigan and Lake Superior are deeper than the average.

a. What was the average annual number of at-home fatalities for these years?

b. In which years was the number of fatalities below the average?

Powers and Order of Operations on a Calculator

Let's use a calculator to carry out computations that involve either powers or the order of operations rule.

EXAMPLE 12

Calculate 23^3.

Solution

Press	Display
23 [^] 3 [ENTER]	23^3
	12167.

PRACTICE 12

Use a calculator to compute 375^2.

EXAMPLE 13

Combine: $2 + 3 \times 4$

Solution

Press	Display
2 [+] 3 [×] 4 [ENTER]	2 + 3 * 4
	14.

Note that some calculators do not follow the order of operations rule. When using this kind of calculator, enter the operations in the order specified by the order of operations rule to get the correct answer.

PRACTICE 13

On a calculator, compute $135 - 44 \div 11$.

Mathematically Speaking

Fill in each blank with the most appropriate term or phrase from the given list.

product	sum	adding	listing
subtracting	grouping	power	base

1. An exponent indicates how many times the _____ is used as a factor.

2. Parentheses and brackets are examples of _____ symbols.

3. An average of numbers on a list is found by _____ the numbers and then dividing by how many numbers there are on the list.

4. In evaluating an expression involving both a sum and a product, the _____ is evaluated first.

Complete each table by squaring the numbers given.

5.

n	0	2	4	6	8	10	12
n^2							

6.

n	1	3	5	7	9	11	13
n^2							

A *Complete each table by cubing the numbers given.*

7.

n	0	2	4	6	8
n^3					

8.

n	1	3	5	7	9
n^3					

Express each number as a power of 10.

9. $100 = 10^{\square}$

10. $1,000 = 10^{\square}$

11. $10,000 = 10^{\square}$

12. $100,000 = 10^{\square}$

13. $1,000,000 = 10^{\square}$

14. $10,000,000 = 10^{\square}$

Write each number in terms of powers.

15. $2 \cdot 2 \cdot 3 \cdot 3 = 2^{\square} \cdot 3^{\square}$

16. $2 \cdot 2 \cdot 5 \cdot 2 \cdot 5 = 2^{\square} \cdot 5^{\square}$

17. $5 \cdot 4 \cdot 4 \cdot 4 = 4^{\square} \cdot 5^{\square}$

18. $6 \cdot 7 \cdot 6 \cdot 7 \cdot 6 \cdot 7 = 6^{\square} \cdot 7^{\square}$

Write each number in standard form.

19. $6^2 \cdot 5^2$

20. $10^3 \cdot 9^2$

21. $2^5 \cdot 7^2$

22. $3^4 \cdot 4^3$

B *Evaluate.*

23. $8 + 5 \cdot 2$

24. $9 + 10 \cdot 2$

25. $8 - 12 \div 3$

26. $12 - 6 \div 2$

27. $18 \div 2 + 4$

28. $30 \div 3 + 6$

29. $6 \cdot 3 - 16 \div 4$

30. $7 \cdot 3 - 12 \div 4$

31. $10 + 5^2$

32. $9 + 2^3$

33. $(10 + 5)^2$

34. $(9 + 2)^3$

35. 10×5^2

36. 12×2^2

37. $(12 \div 2)^2$

38. $(10 \div 5)^2$

39. $15 \div (6 - 3)$

40. $24 \div (4 + 2)$

41. $2^6 - 6^2$

42. $3^5 - 5^3$

43. $8 + 5 - 3 - 2 \times 2$

44. $7 - 1 + 2 + 3 \cdot 2$

45. $(10 - 1)(10 + 1)$

46. $(8 - 1)(8 + 1)$

47. $10^2 - 1$

48. $8^2 - 1$

49. $\left(\dfrac{8 + 2}{7 - 2}\right)^2$

50. $\left(\dfrac{9 - 1}{3 + 5}\right)^3$

51. $\dfrac{5^3 - 2^3}{3}$

52. $\dfrac{3^2 + 5^2}{2}$

53. $4 + 12(10 - 3^2)$

54. $3 + 10(20 - 2^3)$

55. $10 \cdot 3^2 + \dfrac{10 - 4}{2}$

56. $\dfrac{3^3 + 1^3 + 2^3}{4}$

57. $(21 \div 7) + [(9 - 5) \cdot 2]^2$

58. $(30 \div 3) + [(7 - 4) \cdot 3]^2$

59. $[9 + 2(3^2 - 8)] + 7$

60. $15 + [3(8 - 2^2) - 6]$

61. $[2 \cdot (3 + 4)^2 - 3 \cdot (7 - 2)^2]^2$

62. $[3 \cdot (2 + 1)^2 - 2 \cdot (5 - 4)^2]^2$

 63. $32 + 9 \cdot 215 \div 5$

64. $84 \cdot 27 + 32 \cdot 27^2 \div 2$

65. $48(48 - 31)(48 - 24)(48 - 41)$

66. $137^2 - 4(36)(22)$

In each exercise, the three squares stand for the numbers 4, 6, and 8 in some order.
Fill in the squares to make true statements.

67. $\square \cdot 3 + \square \cdot 5 + \square \cdot 7 = 98$

68. $\square + 10 \times \square - \dfrac{\square}{2} = 42$

69. $(\square)(3 + \square) - 2 \cdot \square = 44$

70. $\square \cdot 3 + \square \cdot 5 + \square \cdot 7 = 82$

71. $\square + 10 \times \square - \square \div 2 = 45$

72. $\dfrac{48}{\square} - \dfrac{\square}{2} + (3 + \square)^2 = 127$

Insert parentheses, if needed, to make the expression on the left equal to the number on the right.

73. $5 + 2 \cdot 4^2 = 112$

74. $5 + 2 \cdot 4^2 = 69$

75. $5 + 2 \cdot 4^2 = 169$

76. $5 + 2 \cdot 4^2 = 37$

77. $8 - 4 \div 2^2 = 1$

78. $8 - 4 \div 2^2 = 7$

Find the area of each shaded region.

79.

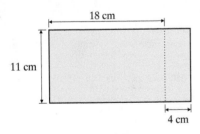

80.

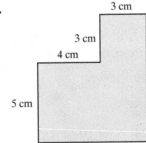

81.

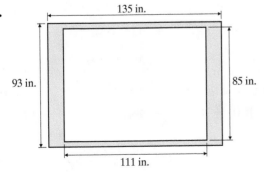

82.

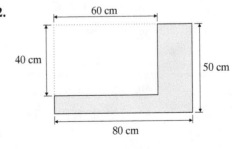

Complete each table.

83.

Input	Output
0	$21 + 3 \times 0 =$
1	$21 + 3 \times 1 =$
2	$21 + 3 \times 2 =$

84.

Input	Output
0	$14 - 5 \times 0 =$
1	$14 - 5 \times 1 =$
2	$14 - 5 \times 2 =$

C *Find the average of each set of numbers.*

85. 20 and 30

86. 10 and 50

87. 30, 60, and 30

88. 17, 17, and 26

89. 10, 0, 3, and 3

90. 5, 7, 7, and 17

91. 3,527 miles, 1,788 miles, and 1,921 miles

92. 3,432 miles, 1,822 miles, and 1,436 miles

93. Six 10's and four 5's

94. Sixteen 5's and four 0's

Mixed Practice

Solve.

95. Express 100,000,000 as a power of 10.

96. Find the area of the shaded region.

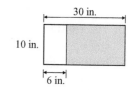

30 in.
10 in.
6 in.

97. Square 17.

98. Rewrite in terms of powers of 2 and 7:
$2 \cdot 2 \cdot 2 \cdot 7 \cdot 7 = 2 \cdot 7$

99. Simplify: $50 - 2(10 - 3^2)$.

100. Cube 10.

101. Find the average of 10, 10, and 4.

102. Evaluate: 6×4^2

Applications

D *Solve and check.*

103. A 40-story office building has 25,000 square feet of space to rent. What is the average rental space on a floor?

104. The total area of the 50 states in the United States is about 3,700,000 square miles. If the state of Georgia's area is about 60,000 square miles, is its size above the average of all the states? Explain. (*Source: The New Encyclopedia Britannica*)

105. In a branch of mathematics called number theory, the numbers 3, 4, and 5 are called a *Pythagorean triple* because $3^2 + 4^2 = 5^2$ (that is, $9 + 16 = 25$). Show that 5, 12, and 13 are a Pythagorean triple.

106. If an object is dropped off a cliff, after 10 seconds it will have fallen $\dfrac{32 \cdot 10^2}{2}$ feet, ignoring air resistance. Express this distance in standard form, without exponents.

107. The solar wind streams off the Sun at speeds of about 1,000,000 miles per hour. Express this number as a power of 10. (*Source:* NASA)

108. It has been estimated that there are 100,000,000,000,000 cells in the adult human body. Represent this number as a power of 10. (*Source:* ehd.org)

109. The following table shows a lab assistant's salary in various years.

Year	1	2	3
Salary	$19,400	$21,400	$23,700

a. Find the average salary for the three years.

b. How much greater was her average salary for the last two years than for all three years?

111. In the last four home games, a college basketball team had scores of 68, 79, 57, and 72.

a. What was the average score for these games?

b. The average score for the last four away games was 64. On average, did the team score more at home or away? Explain.

113. The following table gives the work stoppages for stoppages involving 1,000 or more workers in the United States in selected years.

Year	Total Number of Workers Involved	Total Number of Days Idle
2005	100,000	1,736,000
2006	70,000	2,688,000
2007	189,000	1,265,000
2008	72,000	1,954,000

(*Source:* U.S. Bureau of Labor Statistics)

a. Find the average number of workers per year involved in the work stoppages for the given four years, rounded to the nearest thousand.

b. Find the average annual number of days idle for the years 2006 through 2008. Was the number of days idle in 2008 above or below this average?

110. The following grade book shows a student's math test scores.

Test 1	Test 2	Test 3	Test 4
85	63	98	82

a. What is the average of his math scores?

b. If he were to get a 92 on the next math test, by how much would his average score increase?

112. A small theater company's production of *Romeo and Juliet* had 10 performances over two weekends. The attendance for each performance during the second weekend was 171, 297, 183, 347, and 232.

a. What was the average attendance for the performances during the second weekend?

b. If the average attendance at a performance during the first weekend was 272, was the average greater in the first or second weekend? Explain.

114. The chart below shows the countries that, in a recent year, had the largest military expenditures.

Country	Spending Level (in billions of U.S. dollars)	Per Capita Spending Level (in U.S. dollars)
United States	529	1,756
United Kingdom	59	990
France	53	875
China	50	37
Japan	44	341
Germany	37	447
Russia	35	244

(*Source:* infoplease.com)

a. Find the average military spending level for the five countries with the largest military spending levels.

b. What is the average per capita spending level for the seven countries shown?

115. Owners of a restaurant agreed to invest in redecorating the restaurant if the average number of customers per month for the coming 12 months is more than 500. The monthly tallies of customers for the restaurant during this period turned out to be: 372, 618, 502, 411, 638, 465, 572, 377, 521, 488, 458, and 602. Will the restaurant be redecorated?

116. The hospital chart shown is a record of a patient's temperature for two days.

Time	Temp. (°F)	Time	Temp. (°F)
6 A.M.	98	6 A.M.	101
10 A.M.	100	10 A.M.	102
2 P.M.	98	2 P.M.	101
6 P.M.	100	6 P.M.	102
10 P.M.	98	10 P.M.	100
2 A.M.	100	2 A.M.	100

What was her average temperature for this period of time?

• Check your answers on page A-2.

MINDStretchers

Writing

1. Evaluate the expressions in parts (a) and (b).
   a. $7^2 + 4^2$ ___
   b. $(7 + 4)^2$ ____
   c. Are the answers to parts (a) and (b) the same? ___ If not, explain why not.

Mathematical Reasoning

2. The square of any whole number (called a **perfect square**) can be represented as a geometric square, as follows:

4

9

Try to represent the numbers 16, 25, 5, and 8 the same way.

                16   25   5   8

Critical Thinking

3. Find the average of the whole numbers from 1 through 999.

1.6 More on Solving Word Problems

What Word Problems Are and Why They Are Important

A To solve applied problems involving the addition, subtraction, multiplication, or division of whole numbers using various problem-solving strategies

In this section, we consider some general tips to help solve word problems.

Word problems can deal with any subject—from shopping to physics and geography to business. Each problem is a brief story that describes a particular situation and ends with a question. Our job, after reading and thinking about the problem, is to answer that question by using the given information.

Although there is no magic formula for solving word problems, you should keep the following problem-solving steps in mind.

To Solve Word Problems

- Read the problem carefully.

- Choose a strategy (such as drawing a picture, breaking up the question, substituting simpler numbers, or making a table).

- Decide which basic operation(s) are relevant and then translate the words into mathematical symbols.

- Perform the operations.

- Check the solution to see if the answer is reasonable. If it is not, start again by rereading the problem.

Reading the Problem

In a math problem, each word counts. So it is important to read the problem slowly and carefully, and not to scan it as if it were a magazine or newspaper article.

When reading a problem, we need to understand the problem's key points: *What information is given* and *what question is posed*. Once these points are clear, jot them down so as to help keep them in mind.

After taking notes, decide on a plan of action that will lead to the answer. For many problems, just thinking back to the meaning of the four basic operations will be helpful.

Operation	Meaning
+	Combining
−	Taking away
×	Adding repeatedly
÷	Splitting up

Many word problems contain *clue words* that suggest performing particular operations. If we spot a clue word in a problem, we should consider whether the operation indicated in the table on the opposite page will lead us to a solution.

+	−	×	÷
• add	• subtract	• multiply	• divide
• sum	• difference	• product	• quotient
• total	• take away	• times	• over
• plus	• minus	• double	• split up
• more	• less	• twice	• fit into
• increase	• decrease	• triple	• per
• gain	• loss	• of	• goes into

However, be on guard—a clue word can be misleading. For instance, in the problem *What number increased by 2 is 6?*, we solve by subtracting, not adding.

Consider the following "translations" of these clues.

The patient's fever increased by 5°.	+ 5
The number of unemployed people tripled.	× 3
The length of the bedroom is 8 feet less than the kitchen's.	− 8
The company's earnings were split among the four partners.	÷ 4

Choosing a Strategy

If no method of solution comes to mind after reading a problem, there are a number of problem-solving strategies that may help. Here we discuss four of these strategies: drawing a picture, breaking up the question, substituting simpler numbers, and making a table.

Drawing a Picture

Sketching even a rough representation of a problem—say, a diagram or a map—can provide insight into its solution, if the sketch accurately reflects the given information.

EXAMPLE 1

In an election, everyone voted for one of three candidates. The winner received 188,000 votes, and the second-place candidate got 177,000 votes. If 380,000 people voted in the election, how many people voted for the third candidate?

Solution   To help us understand the given information, let's draw a diagram to represent the situation.

Candidate

1	2	3
188,000	177,000	

—————— 380,000 ——————

We see from this diagram that to find the answer we need to do two things.

PRACTICE 1

A company slashed its workforce by laying off 1,150 employees during one month and laying off 2,235 employees during another month. Afterward, 7,285 employees remained. How many employees worked for the company before the layoffs began?

EXAMPLE 1 (continued)

- First, we need to add 188,000 to 177,000.

$$\begin{array}{r} 188{,}000 \\ +177{,}000 \\ \hline 365{,}000 \end{array}$$

- Then, we need to subtract this sum from 380,000.

$$\begin{array}{r} 380{,}000 \\ -365{,}000 \\ \hline 15{,}000 \end{array}$$

A good way to check our answer here is by adding.

$$188{,}000 + 177{,}000 + 15{,}000 = 380{,}000$$

Our answer checks, so 15,000 people voted for the third candidate.

Breaking Up the Question

Another effective problem-solving strategy is to break up the given question into a chain of simpler questions.

EXAMPLE 2

A student took a math test consisting of 20 questions, answering 3 questions wrong. How many more questions did she get right than wrong?

Solution   Say that we do not know how to answer this question directly. Try to split it into several easier questions that lead to a solution.

- How many questions did the student get *right*? $20 - 3 = 17$
- How many questions did she get *wrong*?   3
- How many *more* questions did she get right than wrong? $17 - 3 = 14$

So the student had 14 more questions right than wrong.

This answer seems reasonable, because it must be less than 17, the number of questions that the student answered correctly.

PRACTICE 2

Teddy and Franklin Roosevelt were both U.S. presidents. Teddy was born in 1858 and died in 1919. Franklin was born in 1882 and died in 1945. How much longer did Franklin live than Teddy? (*Source:* Foner and Garraty, *The Reader's Companion to American History*)

Substituting Simpler Numbers

A word problem involving large numbers often seems difficult just because of the numbers. A good problem-solving strategy here is to consider first the identical problem but with simpler numbers. Solve the revised problem and then return to the original problem.

EXAMPLE 3

Raffle tickets cost $4 each. How many tickets must be sold for the raffle to break even if the prizes total $4,736?

Solution   Suppose that we are not sure which operation to perform to solve this problem. Let's try substituting a simpler amount (say, $8) for the break-even amount of $4,736 and see if we can solve the resulting problem.

PRACTICE 3

A college has 47 sections of Math 110. If 33 students are enrolled in each section, how many students are taking Math 110?

The question would then become: How many $4 tickets must be sold to make back $8? Because it is a "fit-in" question, we must *divide* the $8 by the $4. Going back to the original problem, we see that we must divide $4,736 by 4.

$$\$4,736 \div 4 = 1,184 \text{ tickets}$$

Is this answer reasonable? We can check either by estimating ($5,000 \div 4 = 1,250$, which is close to our answer) or by multiplying ($1,184 \times 4 = 4,736$, which also checks).

Making a Table

Finally, let's consider a strategy for solving word problems that involve many numbers. Organizing these numbers into a table often leads to a solution.

EXAMPLE 4

A borrower promises to pay back $50 per month until a $1,000 loan is settled. What is the remaining loan balance at the end of 5 months?

Solution   We can solve by organizing the information in a table.

After Month	Remaining Balance
1	$1,000 - 50 = 950$
2	$950 - 50 = 900$
3	$900 - 50 = 850$
4	$850 - 50 = 800$
5	$800 - 50 = 750$

From the table, we see that the remaining balance after 5 months is $750.

We can also solve this problem by breaking up the question into simpler questions.

- How much money did the borrower pay after 5 months? $5 \cdot 50 = \$250$

- How much money did the borrower still owe after 5 months? $1,000 - 250 = \$750$

Again, the remaining balance after 5 months is $750.

PRACTICE 4

An athlete weighs 210 pounds and decides to go on a diet. If he loses 2 pounds a week while on the diet, how much will he weigh after 15 weeks?

Applications

A *Choose a strategy. Solve and check.*

1. In retailing, the difference between the gross sales and customer returns and allowances is called the net sales. If a store's gross sales were $2,538 and customer returns and allowances amounted to $388, what was the store's net sales?

2. The population of the United States in 1800 was 5,308,483. Ten years later, the population had grown to 7,239,881. During this period of time, did the country's population double? Justify your answer. (*Source: The Time Almanac 2000*)

3. A delivery van travels 27 miles west, 31 miles east, 45 miles west, and 14 miles east. How far is the van from its starting point?

4. Recycling one aluminum can saves enough energy to run a television for three hours. The average American watches 3,048 hours of television a year. For a year, how many aluminum cans would it take to power a television for the average American? (*Sources:* recycling-revolution.com and tvb.org)

5. A blue whale weighs about 300,000 pounds, and a great white shark weighs about 4,000 pounds. How many times the weight of a great white shark is the weight of a blue whale? (*Source:* wikipedia.com)

6. Two major naval disasters of the twentieth century involved the sinking of British ships—the *Titanic* and the *Lusitania*. The *Titanic,* which weighed about 93,000,000 pounds, was the most luxurious liner of its time; it struck an iceberg on its maiden voyage in 1912. The *Lusitania,* which weighed about 63,000,000 pounds, was sunk by a German submarine in 1915. How much heavier was the *Titanic* than the *Lusitania?* (*Source: The Oxford Companion to Ships and the Sea*)

7. A sales representative flew from Los Angeles to Miami (2,339 miles), then to New York (1,092 miles), and finally back to LA (2,451 miles). How many total miles did he fly?

8. A movie fan installed shelves for his collection of 400 DVDs. If 36 DVDs fit on each shelf, how many shelves did he need to house his entire collection?

9. Immigrants from all over the world came to the United States between 1931 and 1940 in the following numbers: 348,289 (Europe), 15,872 (Asia), 160,037 (Americas, outside the United States), 1,750 (Africa), and 2,231 (Australia/New Zealand). What was the total number of immigrants? (*Source:* George Thomas Kurian, *Datepedia of the United States*)

10. In 2008, there were 38,834 movie screens in the United States. A year later, there were 39,233 movie screens. What was the increase in the number of movie screens from 2008 to 2009? (*Source:* natoonline.org)

11. For each 4 × 6 print of a digital photo, a lab usually charges 10¢. During a promotion, the first twenty prints of each order are free. How much does the lab charge for fifty 4 × 6 prints during the promotion?

12. Because of a noisy neighbor, a young man decided to put acoustical tiles on the living room ceiling, which measures 21 feet by 18 feet. The tiles are square, with a side length of 1 foot. If the tiles cost $3 apiece, what is the total cost to cover the ceiling?

13. After a house was on the market for 4 months, the sellers reduced the asking price by $14,000. After 6 months, they reduced the asking price a second and final time. If the original asking price had been $229,000 and the final asking price was $198,000, by how much did the sellers reduce the price the final time?

14. A nurse sets the drip rate for an IV medication at 25 drops each minute. How many drops does a patient receive in 2 hours?

15. A car dealer offered to lease a car for $1,500 down and $189 per month. If a customer accepted a lease contract of 2 years, how much did the customer have to pay over the lease period?

16. A doctor instructed a patient to take 100 milligrams of a medication daily for 4 weeks. The local pharmacy dispensed 120 tablets, each containing 25 milligrams of the medication. After taking the tablets for 4 weeks, how many remained?

17. The part-time tuition rates per credit-hour at a community college were $95 for in-state residents and $257 for out-of-state residents. To take 9 credit-hours, how much more than an in-state resident does an out-of-state resident pay?

18. A scarf placed on sale is marked down by $16. At the register, the customer receives an additional discount of $6. If the final sale price of the scarf was $18, what was the original price?

19. An office manager needs to order 1,000 pens from an office supply catalog. If the catalog sells pens by the gross (that is, in sets of 144) and 7 gross were ordered, how many extra pens did the manager order?

20. At a sale, a shopper decides to buy three shirts costing $39 apiece and two pairs of shoes at $62 per pair. If he has $300 with him, is that enough money to pay for these items? Explain.

21. Dwight Eisenhower beat Adlai Stevenson in the 1952 and 1956 presidential elections. In 1952, Eisenhower received 442 electoral votes and Stevenson 89. In 1956, Eisenhower got 457 electoral votes and Stevenson 73. Which election was closer? By how many electoral votes? (*Source: World Almanac*)

22. A garden is rectangular in shape—26 feet in length and 14 feet in width. If fencing costs $13 a foot, how much will it cost to enclose the garden with this fencing?

23. A couple agrees to pay the seller of the house of their dreams $165,000. They put down $23,448 and promise to pay the balance in 144 equal installments. How much money will each installment be?

24. Earth revolves around the Sun in 365 days, but the planet Mercury does so in only 88 days. Compared to Earth, how many more complete revolutions will Mercury make in 1,000 days?

• Check your answers on page A-2.

Key Concepts and Skills

Concept/Skill	Description	Example
[1.1] **Place value**	<table><tr><td>**Thousands**</td><td>**Ones**</td></tr><tr><td>Hundreds Tens Ones</td><td>Hundreds Tens Ones</td></tr></table>	846,120 ↑ 4 is in the ten thousands place.
[1.1] **To read a whole number**	Working from left to right, • read the number in each period, and then • name the period in place of the comma.	71,400 is read "seventy-one thousand, four hundred".
[1.1] **To write a whole number**	Working from left to right, • write the number named in each period, and • replace each period name with a comma.	"Five thousand, twelve" is written 5,012.
[1.1] **To round a whole number**	• Underline the place to which you are rounding. • The digit to the right of the underlined digit is called the *critical digit*. Look at the critical digit—if it is 5 or more, add 1 to the underlined digit; if it is less than 5, leave the underlined digit unchanged. • Replace all the digits to the right of the underlined digit with zeros.	$386 \approx 390$ $4,817 \approx 4,800$
[1.2] **Addend, sum**	In an addition problem, the numbers being added are called *addends*. The result is called their *sum*.	$6 \quad + \quad 4 \quad = \quad 10$ ↑ ↑ ↑ Addend Addend Sum
[1.2] **The identity property of addition**	The sum of a number and zero is the original number.	$4 + 0 = 4$ $0 + 7 = 7$
[1.2] **The commutative property of addition**	Changing the order in which two numbers are added does not affect their sum.	$7 + 8 = 8 + 7$
[1.2] **The associative property of addition**	When adding three numbers, regrouping addends gives the same sum.	$(5 + 4) + 1 = 5 + (4 + 1)$
[1.2] **To add whole numbers**	• Write the addends vertically, lining up the place values. • Add the digits in the ones column, writing the right-most digit of the sum on the bottom. If the sum has two digits, carry the left digit to the top of the next column on the left. • Add the digits in the tens column as in the preceding step. • Repeat this process until you reach the last column on the left, writing the entire sum of that column on the bottom.	$\begin{array}{r} {}^{1}{}^{1\,1} \\ 7,385 \\ 92,551 \\ + 2,007 \\ \hline 101,943 \end{array}$
[1.2] **Minuend, subtrahend, difference**	In a subtraction problem, the number that is being subtracted from is called the *minuend*. The number that is being subtracted is called the *subtrahend*. The answer is called the *difference*.	Difference ↓ $10 \quad - \quad 6 = 4$ ↑ ↑ Minuend Subtrahend

Concept/Skill	Description	Example

[1.2] **To subtract whole numbers**	• On top, write the number *from which* we are subtracting. On the bottom, write the number that is being *taken away,* lining up the place values. Subtract in each column separately.
	• Start with the ones column.
	  a. If the digit on top is *larger* than or *equal* to the digit on the bottom, subtract and write the difference below.
	  b. If the digit on top is *smaller* than the digit on the bottom, borrow from the digit to the left on top. Then subtract and write the difference below the bottom digit.
	• Repeat this process until the last column on the left is finished, subtracting and writing its difference below.
		$\begin{array}{r} {}^{8}\ {}^{1}4\ 1 \\ 7,9\ 5\ 2 \\ -1,8\ 8\ 3 \\ \hline 6,0\ 6\ 9 \end{array}$

[1.3] **Factor, product**	In a multiplication problem, the numbers being multiplied are called *factors*. The result is called their *product.*	Factor Product $4 \times 5 = 20$
[1.3] **The identity property of multiplication**	The product of any number and 1 is that number.	$1 \times 6 = 6$ $7 \times 1 = 7$
[1.3] **The multiplication property of 0**	The product of any number and 0 is 0.	$51 \times 0 = 0$
[1.3] **The commutative property of multiplication**	Changing the order in which two numbers are multiplied does not affect their product.	$3 \times 2 = 2 \times 3$
[1.3] **The associative property of multiplication**	When multiplying three numbers, regrouping the factors gives the same product.	$(4 \times 5) \times 6 = 4 \times (5 \times 6)$
[1.3] **The distributive property**	Multiplying a factor by the sum of two numbers gives the same result as multiplying the factor by each of the two numbers and then adding.	$2 \times (4 + 3)$ $= (2 \times 4) + (2 \times 3)$
[1.3] **To multiply whole numbers**	• Multiply the top factor by the ones digit in the bottom factor and write this product. • Multiply the top factor by the tens digit in the bottom factor and write this product leftward, beginning with the tens column. • Repeat this process until all the digits in the bottom factor are used. • Add the partial products, writing this sum.	$\begin{array}{r} 693 \\ \times\ \ 71 \\ \hline 693 \\ 48\,51\ \ \\ \hline 49,203 \end{array}$
[1.4] **Divisor, dividend, quotient**	In a division problem, the number that is being used to divide another number is called the *divisor.* The number into which it is being divided is called the *dividend.* The result is called the *quotient.*	Quotient $\begin{array}{r} 3 \\ 4\overline{)12} \end{array}$ Divisor —⌐ ⌐— Dividend

continued

Concept/Skill	Description	Example
[1.4] **To divide whole numbers**	• Divide 17 into 39, which gives 2. Multiply the 17 by 2 and subtract the result (34) from 39. Beside the difference (5), bring down the next digit (3) of the dividend. • Repeat this process, dividing the divisor (17) into 53. • At the end, there is a remainder of 2. Write it beside the quotient on top.	$$\begin{array}{r} 23\ R2 \\ 17\overline{)393} \\ \underline{34} \\ 53 \\ \underline{51} \\ 2 \end{array}$$
[1.5] **Exponent (or power), base**	An *exponent* (or *power*) is a number that indicates how many times another number (called the *base*) is used as a factor.	┌─Exponent ↓ $5^3 = 5 \times 5 \times 5$ ↑ Base
[1.5] **Order of operations rule**	To evaluate mathematical expressions, carry out the operations *in the following order.* **1.** First, perform the operations within any grouping symbols, such as parentheses ( ) or brackets [ ]. **2.** Then, raise any number to its power ■■. **3.** Next, perform all multiplications and divisions as they appear from left to right. **4.** Finally, do all additions and subtractions as they appear from left to right. | ( ) | | ■■ | | × ÷ | | + − |	$$\begin{aligned} 8 + 5 \cdot (3+1)^2 &= 8 + 5 \cdot 4^2 \\ &= 8 + 5 \cdot 16 \\ &= 8 + 80 \\ &= 88 \end{aligned}$$
[1.5] **Average (or mean)**	The *average* (or *mean*) of a set of numbers is the sum of those numbers divided by however many numbers are in the set.	The average of 3, 4, 10, and 3 is 5 because $$\frac{3+4+10+3}{4} = \frac{20}{4} = 5$$
[1.6] **To solve word problems**	• Read the problem carefully. • Choose a strategy (such as drawing a picture, breaking up the question, substituting simpler numbers, or making a table). • Decide which basic operation(s) are relevant and then translate the words into mathematical symbols. • Perform the operations. • Check the solution to see if the answer is reasonable. If it is not, start again by rereading the problem.	

Say Why

Fill in each blank.

1. The place values of 4 in 410 and of 6 in 7,699 _____ the same because _____ are/are not _____.

2. 5,605 rounded to the nearest thousand _____ 5,000 is/is not because _____.

3. The perimeter of a four-sided figure for which all sides have length 5 _____ 25 because _____ is/is not _____.

4. The product of 8 and 7 _____ 15 because is/is not _____.

5. The area of a rectangle with length 10 and width 7 _____ 70 because _____ is/is not _____.

6. In the expression 9^2, 9 _____ the exponent because is/is not _____.

7. $2(3 + 5)$ _____ equal to $2 \cdot 3 + 2 \cdot 5$ because is/is not _____.

8. The quotient of 10 and 5 is _____ 2 because is/is not _____.

9. The average of 7, 11, and 0 _____ $\dfrac{7 + 11 + 0}{2}$ is/is not because _____.

10. In evaluating the expression $9 + 3 \cdot 4$, we multiply _____ adding because _____ before/after _____.

[1.1] *In each whole number, identify the place that the digit 3 occupies.*

11. 23

12. 30,802

13. 385,000,000

14. 30,000,000,000

Write each number in words.

15. 497

16. 2,050

17. 3,000,007

18. 85,000,000,000

Write each number in standard form.

19. Two hundred fifty-one

20. Nine thousand, two

21. Fourteen million, twenty-five

22. Three billion, three thousand

Express each number in expanded form.

23. 2,500,000

24. 42,707

Round each number to the place indicated.

25. 571 to the nearest hundred

26. 938 to the nearest thousand

27. 384,056 to the nearest ten thousand

28. 68,332 to its largest place

[1.2] *Find the sum and check.*

29.
$$\begin{array}{r} 102 \\ 4,251 \\ + \ 5,133 \\ \hline \end{array}$$

30.
$$\begin{array}{r} 53,569 \\ 10,000 \\ + \ 2,123 \\ \hline \end{array}$$

31.
$$\begin{array}{r} 48,758 \\ 37,226 \\ + \ 87,559 \\ \hline \end{array}$$

32.
$$\begin{array}{r} 95,000 \\ 25,895 \\ + \ 30,000 \\ \hline \end{array}$$

Add and check.

33. $972{,}558 + 87{,}055 + 36{,}488 + 861{,}724$

34. $\$138{,}865 + \$729 + \$8{,}002 + \$75{,}471$

Find the difference and check.

35.
$$\begin{array}{r} 876 \\ - \ 431 \\ \hline \end{array}$$

36.
$$\begin{array}{r} 56,000 \\ - \ 45,984 \\ \hline \end{array}$$

37.
$$\begin{array}{r} 98,118 \\ - \ 87,009 \\ \hline \end{array}$$

38.
$$\begin{array}{r} 7,100 \\ - \ 1,590 \\ \hline \end{array}$$

39. $60{,}000{,}000 - 48{,}957{,}777$

40. $\$5{,}000{,}000 - \$2{,}937{,}148$

41. From 67,502 subtract 56,496.

42. Subtract 89,724 from 92,713.

[1.3] *Find the product and check.*

43.
$$\begin{array}{r} 72 \\ \times \ 6 \\ \hline \end{array}$$

44.
$$\begin{array}{r} 400 \\ \times \ 3 \\ \hline \end{array}$$

45.
$$\begin{array}{r} 2,923 \\ \times \ 51 \\ \hline \end{array}$$

46.
$$\begin{array}{r} 6,000 \\ \times \ 2,000 \\ \hline \end{array}$$

47.
$$\begin{array}{r} 14,921 \\ \times \ 32 \\ \hline \end{array}$$

48.
$$\begin{array}{r} 8,152 \\ \times \ 125 \\ \hline \end{array}$$

Multiply and check.

49. $2{,}751 \cdot 508$

50. $(681)(498)(555)$

[1.4] *Divide and check.*

51. $\dfrac{975}{25}$

52. $21\overline{)6{,}450}$

53. $13\overline{)491}$

54. $7{,}488 \div 11$

Find the quotient and check.

55. $8\overline{)205{,}000}$

56. $347\overline{)332{,}079}$

[1.5] *Compute.*

57. 7^3

58. 1^{10}

59. $2^3 \cdot 3^2$

60. $3 \cdot 10^5$

61. $20 - 3 \times 5$

62. $(9 + 4)^2$

63. $10 - \dfrac{6 + 4}{2}$

64. $3 + (5 - 1)^2$

65. $5 + [4^2 - 3(2 + 1)]$

66. $17 + [2(3^2 - 6) - 5]$

67. $98(50 - 1)(50 - 2)(50 - 3)$

68. $\dfrac{28^3 + 29^3 + 37^3 - 10}{(7 - 1)^2}$

Rewrite each expression, using exponents.

69. $7 \cdot 7 \cdot 5 \cdot 5 = 7^{\blacksquare} \cdot 5^{\blacksquare}$

70. $5 \cdot 2 \cdot 5 \cdot 2 \cdot 5 = 2^{\blacksquare} \cdot 5^{\blacksquare}$

Find the average.

71. 34 and 44

72. 20, 0, and 1

73. 5, 8, and 5

74. 4, 6, 3, and 7

Mixed Applications

Solve and check.

75. Beetles about the size of a pinhead destroyed 2,400,000 acres of forest. Express this number in words.

76. Scientists in Utah found a dinosaur egg one hundred fifty million years old. Write this number in standard form.

77. The following graph shows the consolidated assets of the six largest banks in the United States.

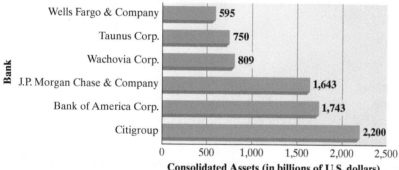

(*Source:* infoplease.com)

Find combined assets of Citigroup and Wachovia.

78. Halley's Comet is expected to visit Earth next in 2061. If the comet has a 76-year orbit, in what year did it last visit Earth? (*Source:* science.nasa.gov)

79. What is the land area of Texas to the nearest hundred thousand square miles? (*Source: Time Almanac 2010*)

80. Apple Computer sold 31,855,000 iPods in the first two quarters of its 2010 fiscal year. How many iPods is this to the nearest million? (*Source:* wikipedia.org)

81. The Empire State Building is 1,250 feet high, and the Statue of Liberty is 152 feet in height. What is the minimum number of Statues of Liberty that would have to be stacked to be taller than the Empire State Building?

82. Both a singles tennis court and a football field are rectangular in shape. A tennis court measures 78 feet by 27 feet, whereas a football field measures 360 feet by 160 feet. About how many times the area of a tennis court is that of a football field?

83. The tallest building in the United States is Chicago's Willis Tower, which is 1,450 ft high. By contrast, the Dubai Tower, the tallest building in the world, is 1,267 ft higher. Find the height of the Dubai Tower.

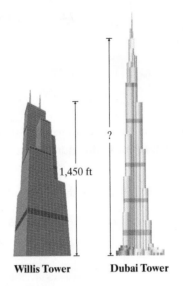

Willis Tower   Dubai Tower

84. A landscaper needs 550 flower plants for a landscaping project. If a local garden center sells flats containing 24 plants, how many flats should the landscaper buy?

85. In a part-time job, a graduate student earned $15,964 a year. How much money did she earn per week? (*Hint:* 1 year equals 52 weeks.)

86. Compute a company's net profit by completing the following business *skeletal profit and loss statement*.

Net sales	$430,000
− Cost of merchandise sold	− 175,000
Gross margin	$
− Operating expenses	− 135,000
Net profit	$

87. In Giza, Egypt, the pyramid of Khufu has a base that measures 230 meters by 230 meters, whereas the pyramid of Khafre has a base that measures 215 meters by 215 meters. In area, how much larger than the base of the pyramid of Khafre is that of Khufu? (*Source:* pbs.org)

88. A millipede—a small insect with 68 body segments—has 4 legs per segment. How many legs does a millipede have?

89. Richard Nixon ran for the U.S. presidency three times. According to the table below, which was greater —the increase from 1960 to 1972 in the number of votes he got or the increase from 1968 to 1972? (*Source: The New York Times Almanac 2010*)

Year	Number of Votes for Nixon
1960	34,106,671
1968	31,785,148
1972	47,170,179

90. On a business trip, a sales representative flew from Chicago to Los Angeles to Boston. The chart below shows the air distances in miles between these cities.

Air Distance	Chicago	Los Angeles	Boston
Chicago	—	1,745	1,042
Los Angeles	1,745	—	2,596
Boston	1,042	2,596	—

If the sales rep earned a frequent flier point for each mile flown, how many points did he earn?

91. The Tour de France is a 20-stage bicycle race held in France annually. The chart shows the distances for the first 10 stages of the 2010 Tour de France. (*Source:* Le Tour de France)

Stage	Distance (in kilometers)
1	223
2	201
3	216
4	154
5	188
6	228
7	166
8	189
9	205
10	179

a. What was the total distance covered in the first 10 stages?

b. The entire race covered a distance of 3,632 kilometers. How many kilometers were covered in the last 10 stages?

92. The projected enrollment for public colleges in the United States from 2014 through 2018 is given in the table.

Year	Projected Enrollment
2014	14,758,000
2015	14,874,000
2016	14,981,000
2017	15,116,000
2018	15,241,000

(*Source:* census.gov)

a. What is the projected average enrollment in the years 2014 through 2018?

b. If a projected enrollment of 15,366,000 for the year 2019 was included, how would the average annual enrollment change?

93. Find the area of the figure.

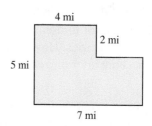

94. Find the perimeter of the figure.

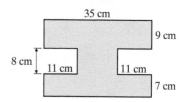

● Check your answers on page A-2.

To see if you have already mastered the topics in this chapter, take this test.

1. Write two hundred twenty-five thousand, sixty-seven in standard form.

2. Underline the digit that occupies the ten thousands place in 1,768,405.

3. Write 1,205,007 in words.

4. Round 196,593 to the nearest hundred thousand.

5. Find the sum of 398 and 1,496.

6. Subtract 398 from 1,005.

7. Subtract: $2,000 - 1,853$

8. Multiply: 328×907

9. Compute: $\dfrac{23,923}{47}$

10. Find the quotient: $59\overline{)36,717}$

11. Evaluate: 5^4

12. Write $5 \cdot 5 \cdot 4 \cdot 4 \cdot 4$ using exponents.

Simplify.

13. $4 \cdot 9 + 3 \cdot 4^2$

14. $29 - 3^3 \cdot (10 - 9)$

Solve and check.

15. The two largest continents in the world are Asia and Africa. To the nearest hundred thousand square miles, Asia's area is 17,200,000 and Africa's is 11,600,000. How much larger is Asia than Africa? (*Source: National Geographic Atlas of the World*)

16. In the year 2009, the state of Kansas had about 65,500 farms with an average size of 705 acres. How many acres of land in Kansas were devoted to farming? (*Source:* nossausda.gov)

17. A part-time student had $1,679 in his checking account. He wrote a $625 check for tuition, a $546 check for rent, and a $39 check for groceries. How much money remained in the account after these checks cleared?

18. A part-time taxi driver worked 4 days last week and made the following amounts of money: Monday $95, Tuesday $110, Wednesday $132, and Friday $155. How much money on the average did he make per work day?

19. A homeowner wishes to carpet the hallway shown below. If the cost of carpeting is about $10 per square foot, approximately how much will the carpeting cost?

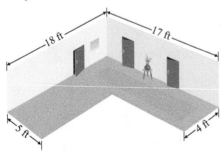

20. Many fast food chains display the caloric intake and the number of grams of fat associated with the chain's dishes.

Food	Calories	Grams of Fat
Original-recipe chicken whole wing	150	9
Original-recipe chicken breast	380	19
Original-recipe drumstick	140	8
Original-recipe thigh	360	25

How many more grams of fat are there in 2 original-recipe thighs than in 3 original-recipe drumsticks? (*Source: Washington Post*)

• Check your answers on page A-2.

Jimmy Stewart made the practice of filibustering famous in the Hollywood film *Mr. Smith Goes to Washington.*

CHAPTER 2

2.1 **Factors and Prime Numbers**

2.2 **Introduction to Fractions**

2.3 **Adding and Subtracting Fractions**

2.4 **Multiplying and Dividing Fractions**

Fractions

Fractions and Filibustering

The rules of the United States Senate allow one or more members to *filibuster*, that is, to talk for as long as they wish and on any topic they choose. So a single member can in effect block the vote on a proposal.

The use of the filibuster to obstruct legislative action in the Senate has a long history going back to the early years of Congress. Unlimited debate was condoned on the grounds that any senator should have the right to address any issue for as long as necessary. However, in the course of time, the *cloture* procedure was developed to end a filibuster. In 1917, the Senate adopted the rule that invoking cloture requires a $\frac{2}{3}$ vote of the current 100 senators. This new rule was first put to the test in 1919, when a motion of cloture was passed ending a filibuster against the Treaty of Versailles. As a result, the state of war between Germany and the Allied Powers was over. In 1975, the Senate changed the rule, reducing the number of votes needed to stop a filibuster from $\frac{2}{3}$ to $\frac{3}{5}$ of the senators.

(*Sources:* senate.gov and wikipedia.org)

To see if you have already mastered the topics in this chapter, take this test.

1. Find all the factors of 20.

2. Express 72 as the product of prime factors.

3. What fraction does the shaded part of the diagram represent?

4. Write $20\frac{1}{3}$ as an improper fraction.

5. Express $\frac{31}{30}$ as a mixed number.

6. Write $\frac{9}{12}$ in simplest form.

7. What is the least common multiple of 10 and 4?

8. Which is greater, $\frac{1}{8}$ or $\frac{1}{9}$?

Add.

9. $\frac{1}{2} + \frac{7}{10}$

10. $7\frac{1}{3} + 5\frac{1}{2}$

Subtract.

11. $8\frac{1}{4} - 6$

12. $12\frac{1}{2} - 7\frac{7}{8}$

Multiply.

13. $2\frac{1}{3} \times 1\frac{1}{2}$

14. $\frac{5}{8} \times 96$

15. Divide: $3\frac{1}{3} \div 5$

16. Calculate: $2 + 1\frac{1}{3} \div \frac{4}{5}$

Solve. Write your answer in simplest form.

17. The St. Louis Cardinals, a National League baseball team, won 10 World Series. If 105 World Series have been played, what fraction of these series has this team won? (*Source:* wikipedia.org)

18. In a biology class, three-fourths of the students received a passing grade. If there are 24 students in the class, how many students received failing grades?

19. Find the perimeter of Central Park using the map below.

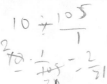

20. According to the nutrition information given, one serving of Total® Cereal contains 23 grams of carbohydrates. If one serving is $\frac{3}{4}$ cup, what amount of carbohydrates is contained in $2\frac{1}{4}$ cups of Total Cereal? (*Source:* General Mills)

(*Source:* centralpark.nyc.org)

• Check your answers on page A-2.

82

2.1 Factors and Prime Numbers

What Factors Mean and Why They Are Important

Recall that in a multiplication problem, the whole numbers that we are multiplying are called **factors** of the product. For instance, 2 is said to be a factor of 8 because $2 \cdot 4 = 8$. Likewise, 4 is a factor of 8.

Another way of expressing the same idea is in terms of division: We say that 8 is **divisible** by 2, meaning that there is a remainder 0 when we divide 8 by 2.

$$\frac{8}{2} = 4 \ R0$$

Note that: 1, 2, 4, and 8 are all factors of 8.

Although we factor whole numbers, a major application of factoring involves working with fractions, as we demonstrate in the next section.

A To find the factors of a whole number

B To identify prime and composite numbers

C To find the prime factorization of a whole number

D To find the least common multiple of two or more numbers

E To solve applied problems using factoring or the least common multiple

Finding Factors

To identify the factors of a whole number, we divide the whole number by the numbers 1, 2, 3, 4, 5, 6, and so on, looking for remainders of 0.

EXAMPLE 1

Find all the factors of 6.

Solution   Starting with 1, we divide each whole number into 6.

$\underset{\text{A factor}}{\frac{6}{1} = 6\,R0}$ $\underset{\text{A factor}}{\frac{6}{2} = 3\,R0}$ $\underset{\text{A factor}}{\frac{6}{3} = 2\,R0}$ $\underset{\text{Not a factor}}{\frac{6}{4} = 1\,R2}$ $\underset{\text{Not a factor}}{\frac{6}{5} = 1\,R1}$ $\underset{\text{A factor}}{\frac{6}{6} = 1\,R0}$

In finding the factors of 6, we do not need to divide 6 by the numbers 7 or greater. The reason is that no number larger than 6 could divide evenly into 6, that is, divide into 6 with no remainder.

So the factors of 6 are 1, 2, 3, and 6. Note that

- 1 is a factor of 6 and
- 6 is a factor of 6.

PRACTICE 1

What are the factors of 7?

TIP   For any whole number, both *the number itself* and *1* are always factors. Therefore, all whole numbers (except 1) have at least two factors.

When checking to see if one number is a factor of another, it is generally faster to use the following **divisibility tests** than to divide.

The number is divisible by	if
2	the ones digit is 0, 2, 4, 6, or 8, that is, if the number is even.
3	the sum of the digits is divisible by 3.
4	the number named by the last two digits is divisible by 4.
5	the ones digit is either 0 or 5.
6	the number is even and the sum of the digits is divisible by 3.
9	the sum of the digits is divisible by 9.
10	the ones digit is 0.

EXAMPLE 2

What are the factors of 45?

Solution   Let's see if 45 is divisible by 1, 2, 3, and so on, using the divisibility tests wherever they apply.

Is 45 divisible by	Answer
1?	Yes, because 1 is a factor of any number; $\frac{45}{1} = 45$, so 45 is also a factor.
2?	No, because the ones digit is not even.
3?	Yes, because the sum of the digits, $4 + 5 = 9$, is divisible by 3; $\frac{45}{3} = 15$, so 15 is also a factor.
4?	No, because 4 will not divide into 45 evenly.
5?	Yes, because the ones digit is 5; $\frac{45}{5} = 9$, so 9 is also a factor.
6?	No, because 45 is not even.
7?	No, because $45 \div 7$ has remainder 3.
8?	No, because $45 \div 8$ has remainder 5.
9?	We already know that 9 is a factor.
10?	No, because the ones digit is not 0.

The factors of 45 are, therefore, 1, 3, 5, 9, 15, and 45.

Note that we really didn't have to check to see if 9 was a factor—we learned that it was when we checked for divisibility by 5. Also, because the factors were beginning to repeat with 9, there was no need to check numbers greater than 9.

PRACTICE 2

Find all the factors of 75.

EXAMPLE 3

Identify all the factors of 60.

Solution   Let's check to see if 60 is divisible by 1, 2, 3, 4, and so on.

Is 60 divisible by	Answer
1?	Yes, because 1 is a factor of all numbers; $\frac{60}{1} = 60$, so 60 is also a factor.
2?	Yes, because the ones digit is even; $\frac{60}{2} = 30$, so 30 is also a factor.
3?	Yes, because the sum of the digits, $6 + 0 = 6$, is divisible by 3; $\frac{60}{3} = 20$, so 20 is also a factor.
4?	Yes, because 4 will divide into 60 evenly; $\frac{60}{4} = 15$, so 15 is also a factor.
5?	Yes, because the ones digit is 0; $\frac{60}{5} = 12$, so 12 is also a factor.
6?	Yes, because the number is even, and the sum of the digits is divisible by 3; $\frac{60}{6} = 10$, so 10 is also a factor.
7?	No, because $60 \div 7$ has remainder 4.
8?	No, because $60 \div 8$ has remainder 4.
9?	No, because the sum of the digits, $6 + 0 = 6$, is not divisible by 9.
10?	We already know that 10 is a factor.

The factors of 60 are, therefore, 1, 2, 3, 4, 5, 6, 10, 12, 15, 20, 30, and 60.

EXAMPLE 4

A presidential election takes place in the United States every year that is a multiple of 4. Was there a presidential election in 1866? Explain.

Solution   The question is: Does 4 divide into 1866 evenly? Using the divisibility test for 4, we check whether 66 is a multiple of 4.

$$\frac{66}{4} = 16 \text{ R2}$$

Because $\frac{66}{4}$ has remainder 2, 4 is not a factor of 1866. So there was no presidential election in 1866.

PRACTICE 3

What are the factors of 90?

PRACTICE 4

The doctor instructs a patient to take a pill every 3 hours. If the patient took a pill at 8:00 this morning, should she take one tomorrow at the same time? Explain.

Identifying Prime and Composite Numbers

Now, let's discuss the difference between prime numbers and composite numbers.

> **DEFINITIONS**
> A **prime number** is a whole number that has exactly two different factors: itself and 1.
> A **composite number** is a whole number that has more than two factors.

Note that the numbers 0 and 1 are neither prime nor composite. But every whole number greater than 1 is either prime or composite, depending on its factors.

For instance, 5 is prime because its only factors are 1 and 5. But 8 is composite because it has more than two factors (it has four factors: 1, 2, 4, and 8).

Let's practice distinguishing between primes and composites.

EXAMPLE 5

Indicate whether each number is prime or composite.

a. 2   **b.** 78   **c.** 51   **d.** 19   **e.** 31

Solution

a. The only factors of 2 are 1 and 2. Therefore, 2 is prime.

b. Because 78 is even, it is divisible by 2. Having 2 as an "extra" factor—in addition to 1 and 78—means that 78 is composite. Do you see why all even numbers, except for 2, are composite?

c. Using the divisibility test for 3, we see that 51 is divisible by 3, because the sum of the digits 5 and 1, or 6, is divisible by 3. Because 51 has more than two factors, it is composite.

d. The only factors of 19 are itself and 1. Therefore, 19 is prime.

e. Because 31 has no factors other than itself and 1, it is prime.

PRACTICE 5

Decide whether each number is prime or composite.

a. 3   **b.** 57   **c.** 29

d. 34   **e.** 17

Finding the Prime Factorization of a Number

Every composite number can be written as the product of prime factors. This product is called its **prime factorization.** For instance, the prime factorization of 12 is $2 \cdot 2 \cdot 3$.

> **DEFINITION**
> The **prime factorization** of a whole number is the number written as the product of its prime factors.

Being able to find the prime factorization of a number is an important skill to have for working with fractions, as we show later in this chapter. A good way to find the prime factorization of a number is by making a **factor tree**, as illustrated in Example 6.

EXAMPLE 6

Write the prime factorization of 72.

Solution   We start building a
factor tree for 72 by dividing
72 by the smallest prime, 2.
Because 72 is 2 · 36, we write
both 2 and 36 underneath the
72. Then, we circle the 2 because
it is prime.

Next, we divide 36 by 2,
writing both 2 and 18, and
circling 2 because it is prime.

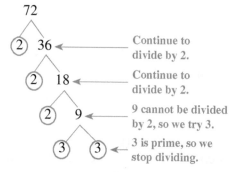

Below the 18, we write 2 and 9, again circling the 2. Because 9 is not
divisible by 2, we divide it by the next smallest prime, 3. We stop this
process because all the factors in the bottom row are prime. The prime
factorization of 72 is the product of the circled factors.

$$72 = 2 \times 2 \times 2 \times 3 \times 3$$

We can also write this prime factorization as $2^3 \times 3^2$.

PRACTICE 6

Write the prime factorization of 56,
using exponents.

EXAMPLE 7

Express 80 as the product of prime factors.

Solution   The factor tree method for 80 is as shown.

80 ←——————— Divide by 2.

② 40 ←——————— Divide by 2.

② 20 ←——————— Divide by 2.

② 10 ←——————— Divide by 2.

② ⑤ ←——— Both 2 and 5 are primes, so we stop
dividing.

The prime factorization of 80 is $2 \times 2 \times 2 \times 2 \times 5$, or $2^4 \times 5$.

PRACTICE 7

What is the prime factorization of
75?

Finding the Least Common Multiple

The *multiples* of a number are the products of that number and the whole numbers. For
instance, some multiples of 5 are the following:

$$\underset{0 \times 5}{0} \qquad \underset{1 \times 5}{5} \qquad \underset{2 \times 5}{10} \qquad \underset{3 \times 5}{15}$$

A number that is a multiple of two or more numbers is called a *common multiple* of these numbers. To find the common multiples of 6 and 8, we first list the multiples of 6 and the multiples of 8 separately.

- The multiples of 6 are 0, 6, 12, 18, 24, 30, 36, 42, 48, 54, 60, ...

- The multiples of 8 are 0, 8, 16, 24, 32, 40, 48, 56, 64, ...

So the common multiples of 6 and 8 are 0, 24, 48, ... Of the nonzero common multiples, the *least* common multiple of 6 and 8 is 24.

DEFINITION

The **least common multiple (LCM)** of two or more whole numbers is the smallest nonzero whole number that is a multiple of each number.

A shortcut for finding the LCM—often faster than listing multiples—involves prime factorization.

To Compute the Least Common Multiple (LCM)

- Find the prime factorization of each number.

- Identify the prime factors that appear in each factorization.

- Multiply these prime factors, using each factor the greatest number of times that it occurs in any of the factorizations.

EXAMPLE 8

Find the LCM of 8 and 12.

Solution   We first find the prime factorization of each number.

$$8 = 2 \times 2 \times 2 = 2^3 \qquad 12 = 2 \times 2 \times 3 = 2^2 \times 3$$

The factor 2 appears *three times* in the factorization of 8 and *twice* in the factorization of 12, so it must be included three times in forming the least common multiple. Also, the factor 3 appears once in the prime factorization of 12.

The highest power of 2

$$\text{LCM} = 2^3 \times 3 = 8 \times 3 = 24$$

As always, it is a good idea to check that our answer makes sense. We do so by verifying that 8 and 12 really are factors of 24.

PRACTICE 8

What is the LCM of 9 and 6?

EXAMPLE 9

Find the LCM of 5 and 9.

Solution   First, we write each number as the product of primes.

$$5 = 5 \qquad 9 = 3 \times 3 = 3^2$$

To find the LCM, we multiply the highest power of each prime.

$$LCM = 3^2 \times 5 = 9 \times 5 = 45$$

So the LCM of 5 and 9 is 45. Note that 45 is also the product of 5 and 9.

PRACTICE 9

Find the LCM for 3 and 22.

TIP   If two or more numbers have no common factor (other than 1), the LCM is their product. If one number is a multiple of another number, then their LCM is the larger of the two numbers.

Now, let's find the LCM of three numbers.

EXAMPLE 10

Find the LCM of 3, 5, and 6.

Solution   First, we find the prime factorizations of these three numbers.

$$3 = 3 \qquad 5 = 5 \qquad 6 = 2 \times 3$$

The LCM is therefore the product $2 \times 3 \times 5$, which is 30. Note that 30 is a multiple of 3, 5, and 6, which supports our answer.

PRACTICE 10

Find the LCM of 2, 3, and 4.

EXAMPLE 11

A gym that is open every day of the week offers aerobics classes every third day and Tai Chi classes every fourth day. A student took both classes this morning. In how many days will the gym offer both classes on the same day?

Solution   To answer this question, we ask: What is the LCM of 3 and 4? As usual, we begin by finding prime factorizations.

$$3 = 3 \qquad 4 = 2 \times 2 = 2^2$$

To find the LCM, we multiply 3 by 2^2.

$$LCM = 2^2 \times 3 = 12$$

So both classes will be offered again on the same day in 12 days.

PRACTICE 11

Suppose that a Senate seat and a House of Representatives seat were both filled this year. If the Senate seat is filled every 6 years and the House seat every 2 years, in how many years will both seats be up for election?

Mathematically Speaking

Fill in each blank with the most appropriate term or phrase from the given list.

division	least common multiple	composite	factor tree
divisibility	prime	remainders	common multiple
prime factorization	factors	multiples	

1. 1, 2, 3, 5, 6, 10, 15, and 30 are _____ of 30.

2. A(n) _____ number is a whole number that has more than two factors.

3. A(n) _____ number has exactly two different factors: itself and 1.

4. The _____ of two or more numbers is the smallest nonzero number that is a multiple of each number.

5. A number written as the product of its prime factors is called its _____.

6. The _____ test for 10 is to check if the ones digit is 0.

Ⓐ *List all the factors of each number.*

7. 21	8. 10	9. 17	10. 9
11. 12	12. 15	13. 31	14. 47
15. 36	16. 35	17. 29	18. 73
19. 100	20. 98	21. 28	22. 48

Ⓑ *Indicate whether each number is prime or composite. If it is composite, identify a factor other than the number itself and 1.*

23. 13	24. 7	25. 16	26. 24	27. 49
28. 75	29. 11	30. 31	31. 81	32. 45

Ⓒ *Write the prime factorization of each number.*

33. 8	34. 10	35. 49	36. 14	37. 24
38. 18	39. 50	40. 40	41. 77	42. 63
43. 51	44. 57	45. 25	46. 49	47. 32
48. 64	49. 21	50. 22	51. 104	52. 105
53. 121	54. 169	55. 142	56. 62	57. 100
58. 200	59. 125	60. 90	61. 135	62. 400

Ⓓ *Find the LCM in each case.*

63. 3 and 15	64. 9 and 12	65. 8 and 10	66. 4 and 6
67. 9 and 30	68. 20 and 21	69. 10 and 11	70. 15 and 60
71. 18 and 24	72. 30 and 150	73. 40 and 180	74. 100 and 90

75. 12, 5, and 50   **76.** 2, 8, and 10   **77.** 4, 7, and 12   **78.** 2, 3, and 5

79. 3, 5, and 7   **80.** 6, 8, and 12   ⊙ **81.** 5, 15, and 20   **82.** 8, 24, and 56

Mixed Practice

Solve.

83. Write the prime factorization of 75.

84. Is 63 prime or composite? If it is composite, identify a factor other than the number itself and 1.

85. List all the factors of 72.

86. Find the LCM of 5, 10, and 12.

Applications

Ⓔ *Solve.*

87. The federal government conducts a census every year that is a multiple of 10. Explain whether there will be a census in
   a. 2015.
   b. 2020.

88. Because of production considerations, the number of pages in a book that you are writing must be a multiple of 4. Can the book be
   a. 196 pages long?
   b. 198 pages long?

89. In 2006, the men's World Cup soccer tournament was held in Munich, Germany. If the tournament is held every 4 years, will there be a tournament in 2036? (*Source:* FIFA World Cup; Soccer Hall of Fame)

90. A car manufacturer recommends changing the oil every 3,000 miles. Would an oil change be recommended at 21,000 miles? Explain.

91. There are 15 players on a rugby team and 10 players on a men's lacrosse team. What is the smallest number of male students in a college that can be split evenly into either rugby or lacrosse teams? (*Source:* wikipedia.org)

92. The Fields Medal, the highest scientific award for mathematicians, is awarded every 4 years. The Dantzig Prize, an achievement award in the field of mathematical programming, is awarded every 3 years. If both were given in 2006, in what year will both be given again? (*Sources:* mathunion.org and siam.org.)

93. Two friends work in a hospital. One gets a day off every 5 days, and the other every 6 days. If they were both off today, in how many days will they again both be off?

94. A family must budget for life insurance premiums every 6 months, car insurance premiums every 3 months, and payments for a home security system every 4 months. If all these bills were due this month, in how many months will they again all fall due?

• Check your answers on page A-3.

MINDStretchers

Historical

1. The eighteenth-century mathematician Christian Goldbach made several famous conjectures (guesses) about prime numbers. One of these conjectures states: Every odd number greater than 7 can be expressed as the sum of three odd prime numbers. For instance, 11 can be expressed as $3 + 3 + 5$. Write the following odd numbers as the sum of three odd primes.

   a. $57 = \blacksquare + \blacksquare + \blacksquare$

   b. $81 = \blacksquare + \blacksquare + \blacksquare$

Mathematical Reasoning

2. What is the smallest whole number divisible by every whole number from 1 to 10?

Critical Thinking

3. Choose a three-digit number, say, 715. Find three prime numbers so that, when 715 is multiplied by the product of the three prime numbers, the product of all four numbers is 715,715.

2.2 Introduction to Fractions

OBJECTIVES

A To read or write fractions or mixed numbers

B To write improper fractions as mixed numbers or mixed numbers as improper fractions

C To find equivalent fractions or to write fractions in simplest form

D To compare fractions

E To solve applied problems involving fractions

What Fractions Are and Why They Are Important

A fraction can mean *part of a whole*. Just as a whole number answers the question "How many?", a fraction answers the question "What part of?". Every day we use fractions in this sense. For example, we can speak of *two-thirds* of a class (meaning two of every three students) or *three-fourths* of a dollar (indicating that we have split a dollar into four equal parts and have taken three of these parts).

A fraction can also mean *the quotient of two whole numbers*. In this sense, the fraction $\frac{3}{4}$ tells us what we get when we divide the whole number 3 by the whole number 4.

DEFINITION

A **fraction** is any number that can be written in the form $\frac{a}{b}$, where a and b are whole numbers and b is nonzero.

From this definition, $\frac{1}{2}, \frac{3}{9}, \frac{6}{5}, \frac{8}{2}$, and $\frac{0}{1}$ are all fractions.

When written as $\frac{a}{b}$, a fraction has three components: $\dfrac{\text{Numerator}}{\text{Denominator}} \leftarrow \begin{smallmatrix}\text{Fraction}\\\text{line}\end{smallmatrix}$

- The **denominator** (on the bottom) stands for the number of parts into which the whole is divided.
- The **numerator** (on top) tells us how many parts of the whole the fraction contains.
- The **fraction line** separates the numerator from the denominator and stands for "out of" or "divided by."

Alternatively, a fraction can be represented as either a decimal or a percent. We discuss decimals and percents in Chapters 3 and 6.

Fraction Diagrams and Proper Fractions

Diagrams help us work with fractions. The fraction three-fourths, or $\frac{3}{4}$, is represented by the shaded part in each of the following diagrams:

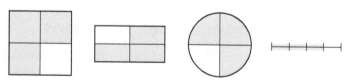

Note that in each diagram the whole has been divided into 4 *equal* parts, with 3 of the parts shaded.

The number $\frac{3}{4}$ is an example of a **proper fraction** because its numerator is smaller than its denominator. Let's consider some other examples of proper fractions.

EXAMPLE 1

In the diagram, what does the shaded portion represent?

Solution   In this diagram, the whole is divided into nine equal parts, so the denominator of the fraction shown is 9. Four of these parts are shaded, so the numerator is 4. The diagram represents the fraction $\frac{4}{9}$.

EXAMPLE 2

A college accepted 147 out of 341 applicants for admission into the nursing program. What fraction of the applicants were accepted into this program?

Solution   Since there was a total of 341 applicants, the denominator of our fraction is 341. Because 147 of the applicants were accepted, 147 is the numerator. So the college accepted $\frac{147}{341}$ of the applicants into the nursing program.

EXAMPLE 3

The U.S. Senate approved a foreign-aid spending bill by a vote of 83 to 17. What fraction of the senators voted against the bill?

Solution   First, we find the total number of senators. Because 83 senators voted for the bill and 17 voted against it, the total number of senators is $83 + 17$, or 100.

So $\frac{17}{100}$ of the senators voted against the bill.

PRACTICE 1

The diagram illustrates what fraction?

PRACTICE 2

During a 30-minute television program, 7 minutes were devoted to commercials. What fraction of the time was for commercials?

PRACTICE 3

A college conducted an online survey of how many students send text messages. Of the 800 students who were surveyed, about 200 did *not* respond. Express the response rate as a fraction.

Mixed Numbers and Improper Fractions

On many jobs, if you work overtime, the rate of pay increases to one-and-a-half times the regular rate. A number such as $1\frac{1}{2}$, with a whole number part and a proper fraction part, is called a mixed number. A mixed number can also be expressed as an improper fraction, that is, a fraction whose numerator is greater than or equal to its denominator. The number $\frac{3}{2}$ is an example of an improper fraction.

Diagrams help us understand that mixed numbers and improper fractions are different forms of the same numbers, as Example 4 illustrates.

EXAMPLE 4

Draw diagrams to show that $2\dfrac{1}{3} = \dfrac{7}{3}$.

Solution   First, represent the mixed number and the improper fraction in diagrams.

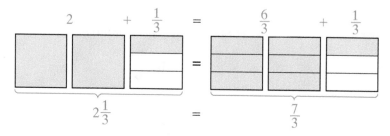

Both diagrams represent $2 + \dfrac{1}{3}$, so the numbers $2\dfrac{1}{3}$ and $\dfrac{7}{3}$ must be equal.

PRACTICE 4

By means of diagrams, explain why $1\dfrac{2}{3} = \dfrac{5}{3}$.

In Example 4, each unit (or square) corresponds to 1 whole, which is also three-thirds. That is why the total number of *thirds* in $2\dfrac{1}{3}$ is $(2 \times 3) + 1$, or 7. The number of *wholes* in $\dfrac{7}{3}$ is 2 wholes, with $\dfrac{1}{3}$ of a whole left over. We can generalize these observations into two rules.

To Change a Mixed Number to an Improper Fraction

- Multiply the denominator of the fraction by the whole-number part of the mixed number.

- Add the numerator of the fraction to this product.

- Write this sum over the denominator to form the improper fraction.

EXAMPLE 5

Write each of the following mixed numbers as an improper fraction.

a. $3\dfrac{2}{9}$ **b.** $12\dfrac{1}{4}$

Solution

a. $3\dfrac{2}{9} = \dfrac{(9 \times 3) + 2}{9}$ Multiply the denominator 9 by the whole number 3, adding the numerator 2. Place over the denominator.

$= \dfrac{27 + 2}{9} = \dfrac{29}{9}$ Simplify the numerator.

b. $12\dfrac{1}{4} = \dfrac{(4 \times 12) + 1}{4}$

$= \dfrac{48 + 1}{4} = \dfrac{49}{4}$

PRACTICE 5

Express each mixed number as an improper fraction.

a. $5\dfrac{1}{3}$ **b.** $20\dfrac{2}{5}$

> ### To Change an Improper Fraction to a Mixed Number
>
> - Divide the numerator by the denominator.
>
> - If there is a remainder, write it over the denominator.

EXAMPLE 6

Write each improper fraction as a mixed or whole number.

a. $\dfrac{11}{2}$ **b.** $\dfrac{20}{20}$ **c.** $\dfrac{42}{5}$

Solution

a. $\dfrac{11}{2} = 2\overline{)11}^{\,5\text{ R1}}$ Divide the numerator by the denominator.

$\dfrac{11}{2} = 5\dfrac{1}{2}$ Write the remainder over the denominator.

In other words, 5 R1 means that in $\dfrac{11}{2}$ there are 5 wholes with $\dfrac{1}{2}$ of a whole left over.

b. $\dfrac{20}{20} = 1$

c. $\dfrac{42}{5} = 8\dfrac{2}{5}$

PRACTICE 6

Express as a whole or mixed number.

a. $\dfrac{4}{2}$ **b.** $\dfrac{50}{9}$ **c.** $\dfrac{8}{3}$

Changing an improper fraction to a mixed number is important when we are dividing whole numbers: It allows us to express any remainder as a fraction. Previously, we would have said that the problems $2\overline{)7}$ and $4\overline{)13}$ both have the answer 3 R1. But by interpreting these problems as improper fractions, we see that their answers are different.

$$\frac{7}{2} = 3\frac{1}{2} \qquad \text{but} \qquad \frac{13}{4} = 3\frac{1}{4}$$

When a number is expressed as a mixed number, we know its size more readily than when it is expressed as an improper fraction. For instance, consider the mixed number $11\dfrac{7}{8}$. We immediately see that it is larger than 11 and smaller than 12 (that is, between 11 and 12). We could not reach this conclusion so easily if we were to examine only $\dfrac{95}{8}$, its improper form. However, there are situations—when we multiply or divide fractions—in which the use of improper fractions is preferable.

Equivalent Fractions

Some fractions that at first glance appear to be different from one another are really the same.

For instance, suppose that we cut a pizza into 8 equal slices, and then eat 4 of the slices. The shaded portion of the diagram at the right represents the amount eaten. Can you explain why in this diagram the fractions $\frac{4}{8}$ and $\frac{1}{2}$ describe the same part of the whole pizza? We say that these fractions are **equivalent**.

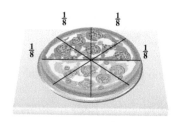

Any fraction has infinitely many equivalent fractions. To see why, let's consider the fraction $\frac{1}{3}$. We can draw different diagrams representing one-third of a whole.

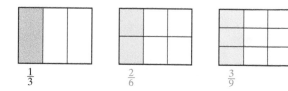

$$\frac{1}{3} \qquad \frac{2}{6} \qquad \frac{3}{9}$$

All the shaded portions of the diagrams are identical, so $\frac{1}{3} = \frac{2}{6} = \frac{3}{9}$.

A faster way to generate fractions equivalent to $\frac{1}{3}$ is to multiply both its numerator and denominator by the *same* whole number. Any whole number except 0 will do.

$$\frac{1}{3} = \frac{1 \cdot 2}{3 \cdot 2} = \frac{2}{6}$$

$$\frac{1}{3} = \frac{1 \cdot 3}{3 \cdot 3} = \frac{3}{9}$$

$$\frac{1}{3} = \frac{1 \cdot 4}{3 \cdot 4} = \frac{4}{12}$$

$$\frac{1}{3} = \frac{1 \cdot 5}{3 \cdot 5} = \frac{5}{15}$$

So $\frac{1}{3} = \frac{2}{6} = \frac{3}{9} = \frac{4}{12} = \frac{5}{15} = \ldots$.

Can you explain how you would generate fractions equivalent to $\frac{3}{5}$?

To Find an Equivalent Fraction

Multiply the numerator and denominator of $\frac{a}{b}$ by the same whole number n,

$$\frac{a}{b} = \frac{a \cdot n}{b \cdot n},$$

where both b and n are nonzero.

An important property of equivalent fractions is that their **cross products** are always equal.

In this case, $1 \cdot 6 = 3 \cdot 2 = 6$

EXAMPLE 7

Find two fractions equivalent to $\frac{1}{7}$.

Solution   Let's multiply the numerator and denominator by 2 and then by 6.

$$\frac{1}{7} = \frac{1 \cdot 2}{7 \cdot 2} = \frac{2}{14} \quad \text{and} \quad \frac{1}{7} = \frac{1 \cdot 6}{7 \cdot 6} = \frac{6}{42}$$

We use cross products to check.

$$\frac{1}{7} \stackrel{?}{=} \frac{2}{14}$$

$$1 \cdot 14 \stackrel{?}{=} 7 \cdot 2$$

$$14 \stackrel{\checkmark}{=} 14$$

So $\frac{1}{7}$ and $\frac{2}{14}$ are equivalent.

$$\frac{1}{7} \stackrel{?}{=} \frac{6}{42}$$

$$1 \cdot 42 \stackrel{?}{=} 7 \cdot 6$$

$$42 \stackrel{\checkmark}{=} 42$$

So $\frac{1}{7}$ and $\frac{6}{42}$ are equivalent.

PRACTICE 7

Identify three fractions equivalent to $\frac{2}{5}$.

EXAMPLE 8

Write $\frac{3}{7}$ as an equivalent fraction whose denominator is 35.

Solution $\frac{3}{7} = \frac{3 \cdot 5}{7 \cdot 5} = \frac{15}{35}$ Multiply the numerator and denominator by 5.

Therefore, $\frac{15}{35}$ is equivalent to $\frac{3}{7}$. To check, we find the cross products: Both $3 \cdot 35$ and $7 \cdot 15$ equal 105.

PRACTICE 8

Express $\frac{5}{8}$ as a fraction whose denominator is 72.

Writing a Fraction in Simplest Form

Previously in this section, we saw that $\frac{4}{8}$ and $\frac{1}{2}$ are equivalent fractions: $\frac{1}{2} = \frac{1 \cdot 4}{2 \cdot 4} = \frac{4}{8}$. We also can start with $\frac{4}{8}$ and find the equivalent fraction $\frac{1}{2}$ by dividing its numerator and denominator by the common factor 4:

$$\frac{4}{8} = \frac{\overset{1}{\cancel{4}}}{\underset{2}{\cancel{8}}} = \frac{1}{2}$$

Note that in the fraction $\frac{1}{2}$, the only common factor of the numerator and denominator is 1. A fraction is said to be **simplified** or **written in lowest terms** when the only common factor of its numerator and denominator is 1. The simplified form of a fraction is the equivalent fraction with the smallest numerator and denominator.

A good way to simplify a fraction is to first express both the numerator and denominator as the product of their prime factors. We can then divide out or cancel all common factors as the following example illustrates:

EXAMPLE 9

Simplify $\frac{9}{15}$.

Solution   To express this fraction in simplest form, we write both the numerator and denominator as the product of primes.

$$\frac{9}{15} = \frac{\overset{1}{\cancel{3}} \cdot 3}{\underset{1}{\cancel{3}} \cdot 5} = \frac{3}{5}$$

Note that the only common factor of 3 and 5 is 1. To be sure that we have not made an error, let's check whether the cross products are equal: $9 \cdot 5 = 3 \cdot 15 = 45$.

PRACTICE 9

Write $\frac{14}{21}$ in lowest terms.

EXAMPLE 10

Write $\frac{42}{28}$ in lowest terms.

Solution $\frac{42}{28} = \frac{2 \cdot 3 \cdot 7}{2 \cdot 2 \cdot 7}$ Express the numerator and denominator as the product of primes.

$= \frac{\overset{1}{\cancel{2}} \cdot 3 \cdot \overset{1}{\cancel{7}}}{\underset{1}{\cancel{2}} \cdot 2 \cdot \underset{1}{\cancel{7}}}$ Divide out the common factors, noting that 1 remains.

$= \frac{3}{2}$ Multiply the remaining factors.

PRACTICE 10

Simplify $\frac{42}{18}$.

EXAMPLE 11

A couple's annual income is $75,000. If they pay $9,000 for rent and $3,000 for food per year, rent and food account for what fraction of their income? Simplify the answer.

Solution   First, we must find the part of the income that is paid for rent and food per year.

$$\$9,000 + \$3,000 = \$12,000$$
$$\quad\downarrow\qquad\quad\downarrow\qquad\qquad\downarrow$$
$$\text{Rent}\qquad\text{Food}\qquad\text{Part}$$

PRACTICE 11

An acre is a unit of area approximately equal to 4,800 square yards. A developer is selling parcels of land of 50 yards by 30 yards. What fraction of an acre is each parcel? Simplify the answer.

EXAMPLE 11 (continued)

The part is $12,000 and the whole is $75,000, so the fraction is $\dfrac{12,000}{75,000}$.
We can simplify this fraction by cancelling common factors:

$$\frac{12,000}{75,000} = \frac{12,\cancel{000}}{75,\cancel{000}} = \frac{12}{75} \qquad \begin{array}{l}\text{Note that canceling a 0 is}\\ \text{the same as dividing by 10.}\end{array}$$

$$= \frac{3 \cdot 4}{3 \cdot 25} = \frac{\overset{1}{\cancel{3}} \cdot 4}{\underset{1}{\cancel{3}} \cdot 25} = \frac{4}{25}$$

Therefore, $\dfrac{4}{25}$ of the couple's income goes for rent and food.

Comparing Fractions

Some situations require us to *compare* fractions, that is, to rank them in order of size.

For instance, suppose that $\dfrac{5}{8}$ of one airline's flights arrive on time, in contrast to $\dfrac{3}{5}$ of another airline's flights. To decide which airline has a better record for on-time arrivals, we need to compare the fractions.

Or to take another example, suppose that the drinking water in your home, according to a lab report, has 2 parts per million (ppm) of lead. Is the water safe to drink if the federal limit on lead in drinking water is 15 parts per billion (ppb)? Again, we need to compare fractions.

One way to handle such problems is to draw diagrams corresponding to the fractions in question. The larger fraction corresponds to the larger shaded region.

For instance, the diagrams to the right show that $\dfrac{3}{4}$ is greater than $\dfrac{1}{4}$. The symbol $>$ stands for "greater than."

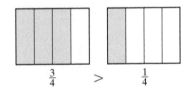

$$\frac{3}{4} \quad > \quad \frac{1}{4}$$

Both $\dfrac{3}{4}$ and $\dfrac{1}{4}$ have the same denominator, so we can rank them simply by comparing their numerators.

$$\frac{3}{4} > \frac{1}{4} \quad \text{because} \quad 3 > 1$$

For **like fractions**, the fraction with the larger numerator is the larger fraction.

DEFINITIONS
Like fractions are fractions with the same denominator.
Unlike fractions are fractions with different denominators.

To Compare Fractions

- If the fractions are like, compare their numerators.
- If the fractions are unlike, write them as equivalent fractions with the same denominator, and then compare their numerators.

EXAMPLE 12

Compare $\dfrac{7}{15}$ and $\dfrac{4}{9}$.

Solution   These fractions are unlike because they have different denominators. Therefore, we need to express them as equivalent fractions having the same denominator. But what should that denominator be?

One common denominator that we can use is the *product of the denominators*: $15 \cdot 9 = 135$.

$$\frac{7}{15} = \frac{7 \cdot 9}{15 \cdot 9} = \frac{63}{135} \qquad \text{135 = 15 · 9, so the new numerator is 7 · 9 or 63.}$$

$$\frac{4}{9} = \frac{4 \cdot 15}{9 \cdot 15} = \frac{60}{135} \qquad \text{135 = 9 · 15, so the new numerator is 4 · 15 or 60.}$$

Next, we compare the numerators of the like fractions that we just found.

Because $63 > 60$, $\dfrac{63}{135} > \dfrac{60}{135}$. Therefore, $\dfrac{7}{15} > \dfrac{4}{9}$.

Another common denominator that we can use is the least common multiple of the denominators.

$$15 = 3 \times 5 \qquad 9 = 3 \times 3 = 3^2$$

The LCM is $3^2 \times 5 = 9 \times 5 = 45$. We then compute the equivalent fractions.

$$\frac{7}{15} = \frac{7 \cdot 3}{15 \cdot 3} = \frac{21}{45} \qquad \text{Multiply the numerator and denominator by 3.}$$

$$\frac{4}{9} = \frac{4 \cdot 5}{9 \cdot 5} = \frac{20}{45} \qquad \text{Multiply the numerator and denominator by 5.}$$

Because $\dfrac{21}{45} > \dfrac{20}{45}$, we know that $\dfrac{7}{15} > \dfrac{4}{9}$.

PRACTICE 12

Which is larger, $\dfrac{13}{24}$ or $\dfrac{11}{16}$?

Note that in Example 12 we computed the LCM of the two denominators. This type of computation is used frequently in working with fractions.

DEFINITION

For two or more fractions, their **least common denominator** (LCD) is the least common multiple of their denominators.

In Example 13, pay particular attention to how we use the LCD.

EXAMPLE 13

Order from smallest to largest: $\dfrac{3}{4}$, $\dfrac{7}{10}$, and $\dfrac{29}{40}$

Solution   Because these fractions are unlike, we need to find equivalent fractions with a common denominator. Let's use their LCD as that denominator.

$$4 = 2 \times 2 = 2^2$$
$$10 = 2 \times 5$$
$$40 = 2 \times 2 \times 2 \times 5 = 2^3 \times 5$$

The LCD = $2^3 \times 5 = 8 \times 5 = 40$. Check: 4 and 10 are both factors of 40.

We write each fraction with a denominator of 40.

$$\frac{3}{4} = \frac{3 \cdot 10}{4 \cdot 10} = \frac{30}{40} \qquad \frac{7}{10} = \frac{7 \cdot 4}{10 \cdot 4} = \frac{28}{40} \qquad \frac{29}{40} = \frac{29}{40}$$

Then, we order the fractions from smallest to largest. (The symbol < stands for "less than.")

$$\frac{28}{40} < \frac{29}{40} < \frac{30}{40} \qquad \text{or} \qquad \frac{7}{10} < \frac{29}{40} < \frac{3}{4}$$

PRACTICE 13

Arrange $\dfrac{9}{10}$, $\dfrac{23}{30}$, and $\dfrac{8}{15}$ from smallest to largest.

EXAMPLE 14

About $\dfrac{39}{50}$ of Earth's atmosphere is made up of nitrogen, and $\dfrac{21}{100}$ is made up of oxygen. Does nitrogen or oxygen make up more of Earth's atmosphere? (*Source: The New York Times Almanac, 2010*)

Solution   We need to compare $\dfrac{39}{50}$ with $\dfrac{21}{100}$. The LCD is 100.

$$\frac{39}{50} = \frac{78}{100}$$
$$\frac{21}{100} = \frac{21}{100}$$

Since $\dfrac{78}{100} > \dfrac{21}{100}$, $\dfrac{39}{50} > \dfrac{21}{100}$. Therefore, nitrogen makes up more of Earth's atmosphere than oxygen does.

PRACTICE 14

In a recent year, about $\dfrac{3}{20}$ of the commercial radio stations in the United States had an adult contemporary format and $\dfrac{1}{5}$ had a country format. In that year, were there more adult contemporary stations or country stations? (*Source: musicbizacademy.com*)

Mathematically Speaking

Fill in each blank with the most appropriate term or phrase from the given list.

improper fraction	proper fraction	like fractions
greatest common factor	simplify	mixed
convert	least common denominator	composite
equivalent		

1. A fraction whose numerator is smaller than its denominator is called a(n) _____.

2. The improper fraction $\frac{5}{2}$ can be expressed as a(n) _____ number.

3. The fractions $\frac{6}{8}$ and $\frac{3}{4}$ are _____.

4. Divide the numerator and denominator of a fraction by the same whole number in order to _____ it.

5. Fractions with the same denominator are said to be _____.

6. The _____ of two or more fractions is the least common multiple of their denominators.

A *Identify a fraction or mixed number represented by the shaded portion of each figure.*

7.

8.

9.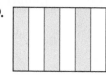

10.

11.

12.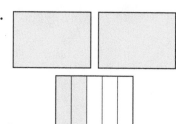

13.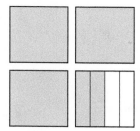

14.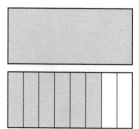

Draw a diagram to represent each fraction or mixed number.

15. $\frac{5}{7}$

16. $\frac{6}{11}$

17. $\frac{2}{9}$

18. $\dfrac{4}{10}$

19. $\dfrac{6}{6}$

20. $\dfrac{11}{11}$

21. $\dfrac{6}{5}$

22. $\dfrac{8}{3}$

23. $2\dfrac{1}{2}$

24. $4\dfrac{1}{5}$

25. $2\dfrac{1}{3}$

26. $3\dfrac{4}{9}$

B *Indicate whether each number is a proper fraction, an improper fraction, or a mixed number.*

27. $\dfrac{2}{5}$

28. $\dfrac{7}{12}$

29. $\dfrac{10}{9}$

30. $\dfrac{11}{10}$

31. $16\dfrac{2}{3}$

32. $12\dfrac{1}{2}$

33. $\dfrac{5}{5}$

34. $\dfrac{4}{4}$

35. $\dfrac{4}{9}$

36. $\dfrac{5}{6}$

37. $66\dfrac{2}{3}$

38. $10\dfrac{3}{4}$

Write each number as an improper fraction.

39. $2\dfrac{3}{5}$

40. $1\dfrac{1}{3}$

41. $6\dfrac{1}{9}$

42. $10\dfrac{2}{3}$

43. $11\dfrac{2}{5}$

44. $12\dfrac{3}{4}$

45. 5

46. 8

47. $7\dfrac{3}{8}$

48. $6\dfrac{5}{6}$

49. $9\dfrac{7}{9}$

50. $10\dfrac{1}{2}$

51. $13\dfrac{1}{2}$

52. $20\dfrac{1}{8}$

53. $19\dfrac{3}{5}$

54. $11\dfrac{5}{7}$

55. 14

56. 10

57. $4\dfrac{10}{11}$

58. $2\dfrac{7}{13}$

59. $8\dfrac{3}{14}$

60. $4\dfrac{1}{6}$

61. $8\dfrac{2}{25}$

62. $14\dfrac{1}{10}$

Express each fraction as a mixed or whole number.

63. $\dfrac{4}{3}$

64. $\dfrac{6}{5}$

65. $\dfrac{10}{9}$

66. $\dfrac{12}{5}$

67. $\dfrac{9}{3}$

68. $\dfrac{12}{12}$

69. $\dfrac{15}{15}$

70. $\dfrac{100}{100}$

71. $\dfrac{99}{5}$

72. $\dfrac{31}{2}$

73. $\dfrac{82}{9}$

74. $\dfrac{62}{3}$

75. $\dfrac{45}{45}$

76. $\dfrac{40}{3}$

77. $\dfrac{74}{9}$

78. $\dfrac{41}{8}$

79. $\dfrac{27}{2}$ **80.** $\dfrac{58}{11}$ **81.** $\dfrac{100}{9}$ **82.** $\dfrac{38}{3}$

83. $\dfrac{27}{1}$ **84.** $\dfrac{72}{9}$ **85.** $\dfrac{56}{7}$ **86.** $\dfrac{19}{1}$

C *Find two fractions equivalent to each fraction.*

87. $\dfrac{1}{8}$ **88.** $\dfrac{3}{10}$ **89.** $\dfrac{2}{11}$ **90.** $\dfrac{1}{10}$

91. $\dfrac{3}{4}$ **92.** $\dfrac{5}{6}$ **93.** $\dfrac{1}{9}$ **94.** $\dfrac{3}{5}$

Write an equivalent fraction with the given denominator.

95. $\dfrac{3}{4} = \dfrac{}{12}$ **96.** $\dfrac{2}{9} = \dfrac{}{18}$ **97.** $\dfrac{5}{8} = \dfrac{}{24}$ **98.** $\dfrac{7}{10} = \dfrac{}{20}$

99. $4 = \dfrac{}{10}$ **100.** $5 = \dfrac{}{15}$ **101.** $\dfrac{3}{5} = \dfrac{}{60}$ **102.** $\dfrac{4}{9} = \dfrac{}{63}$

103. $\dfrac{5}{8} = \dfrac{}{64}$ **104.** $\dfrac{3}{10} = \dfrac{}{40}$ **105.** $3 = \dfrac{}{18}$ **106.** $2 = \dfrac{}{21}$

107. $\dfrac{4}{9} = \dfrac{}{81}$ **108.** $\dfrac{7}{8} = \dfrac{}{24}$ **109.** $\dfrac{6}{7} = \dfrac{}{49}$ **110.** $\dfrac{5}{6} = \dfrac{}{48}$

111. $\dfrac{2}{17} = \dfrac{}{51}$ **112.** $\dfrac{1}{3} = \dfrac{}{90}$ **113.** $\dfrac{7}{12} = \dfrac{}{84}$ **114.** $\dfrac{1}{4} = \dfrac{}{100}$

115. $\dfrac{2}{3} = \dfrac{}{48}$ **116.** $\dfrac{7}{8} = \dfrac{}{56}$ **117.** $\dfrac{3}{10} = \dfrac{}{100}$ **118.** $\dfrac{5}{6} = \dfrac{}{144}$

Simplify, if possible.

119. $\dfrac{6}{9}$ **120.** $\dfrac{9}{12}$ **121.** $\dfrac{10}{10}$ **122.** $\dfrac{21}{21}$

123. $\dfrac{5}{15}$ **124.** $\dfrac{4}{24}$ **125.** $\dfrac{9}{20}$ **126.** $\dfrac{25}{49}$

127. $\dfrac{25}{100}$ **128.** $\dfrac{75}{100}$ **129.** $\dfrac{125}{1,000}$ **130.** $\dfrac{875}{1,000}$

131. $\dfrac{20}{16}$ **132.** $\dfrac{15}{9}$ **133.** $\dfrac{66}{32}$ **134.** $\dfrac{30}{18}$

135. $\dfrac{18}{32}$ **136.** $\dfrac{36}{45}$ **137.** $\dfrac{7}{24}$ **138.** $\dfrac{19}{51}$

139. $\dfrac{27}{9}$ **140.** $\dfrac{36}{144}$ **141.** $\dfrac{12}{84}$ **142.** $\dfrac{21}{36}$

143. $3\dfrac{38}{57}$ **144.** $11\dfrac{51}{102}$ **145.** $2\dfrac{100}{100}$ **146.** $1\dfrac{144}{144}$

D *Between each pair of numbers, insert the appropriate sign: $<, =,$ or $>$.*

147. $\dfrac{7}{20}$ $\dfrac{11}{20}$

148. $\dfrac{5}{10}$ $\dfrac{3}{10}$

149. $\dfrac{1}{8}$ $\dfrac{1}{9}$

150. $\dfrac{5}{6}$ $\dfrac{7}{8}$

151. $\dfrac{2}{3}$ $\dfrac{6}{9}$

152. $\dfrac{9}{12}$ $\dfrac{3}{4}$

153. $2\dfrac{1}{3}$ $2\dfrac{9}{15}$

154. $2\dfrac{3}{7}$ $1\dfrac{1}{2}$

Arrange in increasing order.

155. $\dfrac{1}{2}, \dfrac{1}{3}, \dfrac{1}{4}$

156. $\dfrac{3}{2}, \dfrac{3}{3}, \dfrac{3}{4}$

157. $\dfrac{2}{3}, \dfrac{7}{12}, \dfrac{5}{6}$

158. $\dfrac{3}{4}, \dfrac{5}{6}, \dfrac{7}{8}$

159. $\dfrac{3}{5}, \dfrac{2}{3}, \dfrac{8}{9}$

160. $\dfrac{5}{8}, \dfrac{1}{2}, \dfrac{4}{11}$

Mixed Practice

Solve.

161. Choose the number whose value is between the other two: $\dfrac{7}{10}, \dfrac{8}{9}, \dfrac{5}{6}$.

162. Express $\dfrac{32}{6}$ as a mixed number.

163. Find two fractions equivalent to $\dfrac{2}{9}$.

164. Draw a diagram to represent $\dfrac{9}{10}$.

165. Write an equivalent fraction for $\dfrac{4}{5}$ with denominator 15.

166. Write $2\dfrac{3}{8}$ as an improper fraction.

Applications

E *Solve. Write your answer in simplest form.*

167. During the last 5 days, a student spent 11 hours studying mathematics at home. On the average, how much time is this per day?

168. A recipe for pasta with garlic and oil calls for 6 garlic cloves, peeled and chopped. If the recipe serves 4, how many garlic cloves on the average are in each serving?

169. As of 2009, the Nobel Prize was awarded to 40 women and 762 men. (*Source:* nobelprize.org)
  a. What fraction of the Nobel prize winners were women?
  b. What fraction were men?

170. It is projected that in 2015 there will be 182,000 physical therapists and 94,000 respiratory therapists employed as health care practitioners in the United States. (*Source: U.S. Census Statistical Abstract 2010*)
  a. What fraction of these practitioners will be physical therapists?
  b. What fraction will be respiratory therapists?

171. Of the 206 bones in the human skeleton, 106 are in the hands and feet. What fraction of these bones are *not* in the hands and feet? (*Source:* Henry Gray, *Anatomy of the Human Body*)

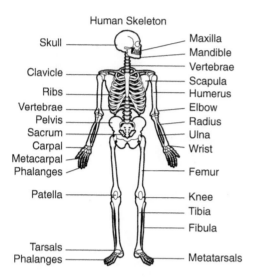

Human Skeleton

Skull — Maxilla
— Mandible
Clavicle — Vertebrae
— Scapula
Ribs — Humerus
Vertebrae — Elbow
Pelvis — Radius
Sacrum — Ulna
Carpal — Wrist
Metacarpal
Phalanges — Femur

Patella — Knee
— Tibia
— Fibula

Tarsals
Phalanges — Metatarsals

172. In a recent year of a National Basketball Association season, the Los Angeles Lakers won 65 of their 82 games led by the team captain, Kobe Bryant. Of the total games played, what fraction did the team *not* win? (*Sources:* Wikipedia.org and *Sports Illustrated Almanac 2010*)

173. A serving of frozen yogurt provides approximately $\frac{1}{10}$ of the recommended dietary allowance (RDA) of calcium, while a serving of plain yogurt provides $\frac{2}{5}$ of the RDA. Which of the two kinds of yogurt provides more calcium? Explain. (*Source:* dietary-supplements.info.nih.gov)

174. In a course on probability and statistics, a student learns that when rolling a pair of dice, the probability of getting a 5 is $\frac{1}{9}$, and the probability of getting a 6 is $\frac{5}{36}$. Does getting a 5 or a 6 have a greater probability? Explain.

175. In a recent year, of 64 million visits to other countries by U.S. tourists, approximately 19 million visits were to Mexico, 13 million were to Canada, and 4 million were to the United Kingdom. (*Source:* U.S. Department of Commerce)
  a. The visits to the United Kingdom were what fraction of these 64 million visits?
  b. What fraction of the visits were to either Mexico or Canada?

176. When fog rolled into the New York City area, visibility was reduced to one-sixteenth mile at JFK Airport, one-eighth mile at LaGuardia Airport, and one-half mile at Newark Airport.
  a. Which of the three airports had the best visibility?

  b. Which of the three airports had the worst visibility?

177. In a recent year, the weights of the first six draft picks for the Pittsburgh Steelers football team are given in the table below.

Player	Pouncey	Worilds	Sanders	Gibson	Scott	Butler
Weight (in pounds)	312	240	180	240	346	185

(*Source:* sports.yahoo.com)

What was their average weight?

178. The following chart gives the age of the first six American presidents at the time of their inauguration.

President	Washington	J. Adams	Jefferson	Madison	Monroe	J. Q. Adams
Age (in years)	57	61	57	57	58	57

What was their average age at inauguration? (*Source: Significant American Presidents of the United States*)

• Check your answers on page A-3.

MIND*Stretchers*

Mathematical Reasoning

1. Identify the fraction that the shaded portion of the figure to the right represents.

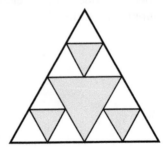

Groupwork

2. Working with a partner, determine how many fractions there are between the numbers 1 and 2.

Critical Thinking

3. Consider the three equivalent fractions shown. Note that the numerators and denominators are made up of the digits 1, 2, 3, 4, 5, 6, 7, 8, and 9—each appearing once.

$$\frac{3}{6} = \frac{7}{14} = \frac{29}{58}$$

a. Verify that these fractions are equivalent by making sure that their cross products are equal.

b. Write another trio of equivalent fractions that use the same nine digits only once.

$$\frac{2}{4} = \frac{-}{-} = \frac{}{-}$$

2.3 Adding and Subtracting Fractions

OBJECTIVES

Ⓐ To add or subtract fractions or mixed numbers

Ⓑ To solve applied problems involving the addition or subtraction of fractions or mixed numbers

In Section 2.2 we examined what fractions mean, how they are written, and how they are compared. In the rest of this chapter, we discuss computations involving fractions, beginning with sums and differences.

Adding and Subtracting Like Fractions

Let's first discuss how to add and subtract like fractions. Suppose that an employee spends $\frac{1}{7}$ of his weekly salary for food and $\frac{2}{7}$ for rent. What part of his salary does he spend for food and rent combined? A diagram can help us understand what is involved. First, we shade one-seventh of the diagram, then another two-sevenths. We see in the diagram that the total shaded area is three-sevenths, $\frac{1}{7} + \frac{2}{7} = \frac{3}{7}$. Note that we added the original numerators to get the numerator of the answer but that *the denominator stayed the same.*

The diagram at the right illustrates the subtraction of like fractions, namely, $\frac{3}{7} - \frac{1}{7}$. If we shade three-sevenths of the diagram and then remove the shading in one-seventh, two-sevenths remain shaded. Therefore, $\frac{3}{7} - \frac{1}{7} = \frac{2}{7}$. Note that we could have gotten this answer simply by subtracting numerators without changing the denominator.

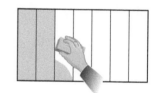

The following rule summarizes how to add or subtract fractions, *provided that they have the same denominator.*

To Add (or Subtract) Like Fractions

- Add (or subtract) the numerators.
- Use the given denominator.
- Write the answer in simplest form.

EXAMPLE 1

Add: $\frac{7}{12} + \frac{2}{12}$

Solution Applying the rule, we get $\dfrac{7}{12} + \dfrac{2}{12} = \dfrac{7 + 2}{12} = \dfrac{9}{12}$

$$= \frac{3 \cdot 3}{4 \cdot 3} = \frac{3 \cdot \overset{1}{\cancel{3}}}{4 \cdot \cancel{3}} = \frac{3}{4}.$$

Add the numerators.

Keep the same denominator.

Simplest form

PRACTICE 1

Find the sum of $\dfrac{7}{15}$ and $\dfrac{3}{15}$.

TIP Be careful *not* to add the denominators when adding fractions.

EXAMPLE 2

Find the sum of $\frac{12}{16}$, $\frac{3}{16}$, and $\frac{9}{16}$.

Solution

Answer as a
mixed number
↓

$$\frac{12}{16} + \frac{3}{16} + \frac{9}{16} = \frac{24}{16} = \frac{3}{2}, \text{ or } 1\frac{1}{2}$$

So the sum of $\frac{12}{16}$, $\frac{3}{16}$, and $\frac{9}{16}$ is $1\frac{1}{2}$.

PRACTICE 2

Add: $\frac{13}{40}$, $\frac{11}{40}$ and $\frac{23}{40}$

EXAMPLE 3

Find the difference between $\frac{11}{7}$ and $\frac{3}{7}$.

Solution

Subtract the numerators.
↓

$$\frac{11}{7} - \frac{3}{7} = \frac{11 - 3}{7} = \frac{8}{7}, \text{ or } 1\frac{1}{7}$$

↑
Keep the same denominator.

PRACTICE 3

Subtract: $\frac{19}{20} - \frac{11}{20}$

⊙ EXAMPLE 4

In the following diagram,
a. how far is it from the Administration Building to the Library via the Science Center?

b. which route from the Administration Building to the Library is shorter—via the Science Center or via the Student Center? By how much?

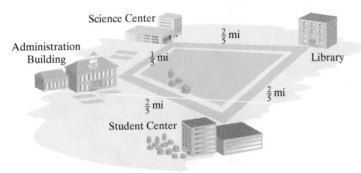

Solution   a. Examining the diagram, we see that

● the distance from the Administration Building to the Science Center is $\frac{1}{5}$ mile, and

● the distance from the Science Center to the Library is $\frac{2}{5}$ mile.

PRACTICE 4

A pediatrician prescribed $\frac{9}{20}$ gram of pain medication for a patient to take every 4 hours.

a. If the dosage were increased by $\frac{3}{20}$ gram, what would the new dosage be?

b. If the original dosage were decreased by $\frac{1}{20}$ gram, find the new dosage.

To find the distance from the Administration Building to the Library via the Science Center, we add.

$$\frac{1}{5} + \frac{2}{5} = \frac{3}{5}$$

So this distance is $\frac{3}{5}$ mile.

b. To find the distance from the Administration Building to the Library via the Student Center, we again add.

$$\frac{2}{5} + \frac{2}{5} = \frac{4}{5}$$

So this distance is $\frac{4}{5}$ mile. Since $\frac{3}{5} < \frac{4}{5}$, the route from the Administration Building to the Library via the Science Center is shorter than the route via the Student Center. Now we find the difference.

$$\frac{4}{5} - \frac{3}{5} = \frac{1}{5}$$

Therefore, the route via the Science Center is $\frac{1}{5}$ mile shorter than the route via the Student Center.

Adding and Subtracting Unlike Fractions

Adding (or subtracting) **unlike fractions** is more complicated than adding (or subtracting) like fractions. An extra step is required: changing the unlike fractions to equivalent like fractions. For instance, suppose that we want to add $\frac{1}{10}$ and $\frac{2}{15}$. Even though we can use any common denominator for these fractions, let's use their *least* common denominator to find equivalent fractions.

$$10 = 2 \cdot 5$$
$$15 = 3 \cdot 5$$
$$\text{LCD} = 2 \cdot 3 \cdot 5 = 30$$

Let's rewrite the fractions vertically as equivalent fractions with the denominator 30.

$$\frac{1}{10} = \frac{1 \cdot 3}{10 \cdot 3} = \frac{3}{30}$$
$$+\frac{2}{15} = \frac{2 \cdot 2}{15 \cdot 2} = +\frac{4}{30}$$

Now, we add the equivalent like fractions.

$$\begin{array}{r} \frac{3}{30} \\ +\frac{4}{30} \\ \hline \frac{7}{30} \end{array}$$

So $\frac{1}{10} + \frac{2}{15} = \frac{7}{30}$.

We can also add and subtract unlike fractions horizontally.

$$\frac{1}{10} + \frac{2}{15} = \frac{3}{30} + \frac{4}{30} = \frac{3+4}{30} = \frac{7}{30}$$

> ### To Add (or Subtract) Unlike Fractions
>
> - Write the fractions as equivalent fractions with the same denominator, usually the LCD.
> - Add (or subtract) the numerators, keeping the same denominator.
> - Write the answer in simplest form.

EXAMPLE 5

Add: $\dfrac{5}{12} + \dfrac{5}{16}$

Solution First, we find the LCD, which is 48. After finding equivalent fractions, we add the numerators, keeping the same denominator.

$$\dfrac{5}{12} = \dfrac{5 \cdot 4}{12 \cdot 4} = \dfrac{20}{48}$$
$$+\dfrac{5}{16} = \dfrac{5 \cdot 3}{16 \cdot 3} = +\dfrac{15}{48}$$
$$\dfrac{35}{48} \leftarrow \text{Already in lowest terms}$$

PRACTICE 5

Add: $\dfrac{11}{12} + \dfrac{3}{4}$

EXAMPLE 6

Subtract $\dfrac{1}{12}$ from $\dfrac{1}{3}$.

Solution Because 3 is a factor of 12, the LCD is 12. Again, let's set up the problem vertically.

$$\dfrac{1}{3} = \dfrac{4}{12}$$
$$-\dfrac{1}{12} = -\dfrac{1}{12} \qquad \text{Subtract the numerators, keeping the same denominator.}$$
$$\dfrac{3}{12} = \dfrac{1}{4} \qquad \text{Write } \dfrac{3}{12} \text{ in lowest terms.}$$

PRACTICE 6

Calculate: $\dfrac{4}{5} - \dfrac{1}{2}$

EXAMPLE 7

Combine: $\dfrac{1}{3} + \dfrac{1}{6} - \dfrac{3}{10}$

Solution First, we find the LCD of all three fractions. The LCD is 30.

$$\dfrac{1}{3} = \dfrac{10}{30}, \qquad \dfrac{1}{6} = \dfrac{5}{30}, \qquad \text{and} \qquad \dfrac{3}{10} = \dfrac{9}{30}.$$

$$\text{So } \dfrac{1}{3} + \dfrac{1}{6} - \dfrac{3}{10} = \dfrac{10}{30} + \dfrac{5}{30} - \dfrac{9}{30} = \dfrac{10 + 5 - 9}{30} = \dfrac{6}{30} = \dfrac{1}{5}.$$

PRACTICE 7

Combine: $\dfrac{1}{3} - \dfrac{2}{9} + \dfrac{7}{8}$

EXAMPLE 8

A forest ranger leaves his lodge, hiking to three fire camps before returning to his lodge, as shown below. How far did he hike?

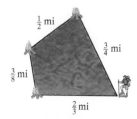

Solution The distance that the ranger hiked is the perimeter of the figure shown, that is, the sum of the lengths of its sides.

$$\text{Perimeter} = \frac{2}{3} + \frac{3}{8} + \frac{1}{2} + \frac{3}{4}$$

$$\frac{2}{3} = \frac{16}{24} \leftarrow \text{LCD}$$

$$\frac{3}{8} = \frac{9}{24}$$

$$\frac{1}{2} = \frac{12}{24}$$

$$+\frac{3}{4} = +\frac{18}{24}$$

$$\frac{55}{24}, \text{ or } 2\frac{7}{24}$$

So the ranger hiked $2\frac{7}{24}$ miles.

PRACTICE 8

Vet's Park Triangle is a neighborhood in Ann Arbor, Michigan, shown below. Find the perimeter. (*Source:* City-data.com)

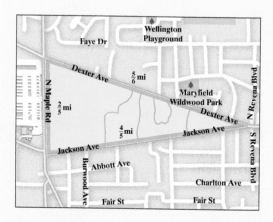

Adding Mixed Numbers

Now, let's consider how to add **mixed numbers**, starting with those that have the same denominator.

Suppose, for instance, that we want to add $1\frac{1}{5}$ and $2\frac{1}{5}$. Let's draw a diagram to represent this sum.

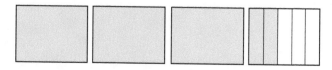

We can rearrange the elements of the diagram by combining the whole numbers and the fractions separately.

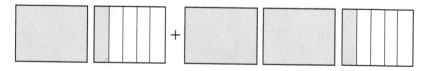

This diagram shows that the sum is $3\frac{2}{5}$.

Note that we can also write and solve this problem vertically.

$$1\frac{1}{5}$$
$$+2\frac{1}{5}$$
$$\overline{}$$
$$3\frac{2}{5} \leftarrow \text{Sum of the fractions}$$
$$\uparrow\text{Sum of the whole numbers}$$

EXAMPLE 9

Add: $8\frac{5}{9} + 10\frac{1}{9}$

Solution
$$8\frac{5}{9}$$
$$+10\frac{1}{9}$$
$$\overline{}$$
$$18\frac{6}{9} = 18\frac{2}{3}$$

PRACTICE 9

Add: $25\frac{3}{10} + 9\frac{1}{10}$

EXAMPLE 10

Find the sum of $3\frac{3}{5}$, $2\frac{4}{5}$, and 6.

Solution Add the fractions, and then add the whole numbers.
$$3\frac{3}{5}$$
$$2\frac{4}{5}$$
$$+6$$
$$\overline{}$$
$$11\frac{7}{5} = 12\frac{2}{5} \quad \text{Since } \frac{7}{5} = 1\frac{2}{5}, \text{ we get } 11\frac{7}{5} = 11 + 1\frac{2}{5} = 12\frac{2}{5}.$$

So the sum is $12\frac{2}{5}$.

PRACTICE 10

Find the sum of $2\frac{5}{16}$, $1\frac{3}{16}$, and 4.

EXAMPLE 11

Two movies are shown back-to-back on TV without commercial interruption. The first runs $1\frac{3}{4}$ hours, and the second $2\frac{1}{4}$ hours. How long will it take to watch both movies?

Solution

We need to add $1\frac{3}{4}$ and $2\frac{1}{4}$.

$$1\frac{3}{4}$$
$$+2\frac{1}{4}$$
$$\overline{3\frac{4}{4}} = 3 + 1 = 4$$

Therefore, it will take 4 hours to watch the two movies.

PRACTICE 11

In a horse race, the winner beat the second-place horse by $1\frac{1}{2}$ lengths, and the second-place horse finished $2\frac{1}{2}$ lengths ahead of the third-place horse. By how many lengths did the third-place horse lose?

We have previously shown that when we add fractions with different denominators, we must first change the unlike fractions to equivalent like fractions. The same applies to adding mixed numbers that have different denominators.

To Add Mixed Numbers

- Write the fractions as equivalent fractions with the same denominator, usually the LCD.
- Add the fractions.
- Add the whole numbers.
- Write the answer in simplest form.

EXAMPLE 12

Find the sum of $3\frac{1}{5}$ and $7\frac{2}{3}$.

Solution The LCD is 15. Add the fractions, and then add the whole numbers.

$$3\frac{1}{5} = 3\frac{3}{15}$$
$$+7\frac{2}{3} = +7\frac{10}{15}$$
$$\overline{10\frac{13}{15}}$$

The sum of $3\frac{1}{5}$ and $7\frac{2}{3}$ is $10\frac{13}{15}$.

PRACTICE 12

Add $4\frac{1}{8}$ to $3\frac{1}{2}$.

EXAMPLE 13

Find the sum of $1\frac{2}{3}$, $8\frac{1}{4}$, and $3\frac{4}{5}$.

Solution Set up the problem vertically and use the LCD, which is 60. Add the fractions, and then add the whole numbers.

$$1\frac{2}{3} = 1\frac{40}{60}$$

$$8\frac{1}{4} = 8\frac{15}{60}$$

$$+3\frac{4}{5} = +3\frac{48}{60}$$

$$12\frac{103}{60} = 12 + 1\frac{43}{60} = 13\frac{43}{60}$$

PRACTICE 13

What is the sum of $5\frac{5}{8}$, $3\frac{1}{6}$, and $2\frac{5}{12}$?

Subtracting Mixed Numbers

Now, let's discuss how to subtract mixed numbers, beginning with those that have the same denominator.

For instance, suppose that we want to subtract $2\frac{1}{5}$ from $3\frac{2}{5}$. We draw a diagram to represent $3\frac{2}{5}$.

If we remove the shading from $2\frac{1}{5}$, then $1\frac{1}{5}$ remains shaded.

So the difference is $1\frac{1}{5}$.

We can also write and solve this problem vertically.

$$3\frac{2}{5}$$

$$-2\frac{1}{5}$$

$$1\frac{1}{5} \leftarrow \text{Difference of the fractions}$$

↑5 └── Difference of the whole numbers

EXAMPLE 14

Subtract: $4\dfrac{5}{6} - 2\dfrac{1}{6}$

Solution We set up the problem vertically. Subtract the fractions, and then subtract the whole numbers.

$$4\dfrac{5}{6}$$
$$-2\dfrac{1}{6}$$
$$\overline{\quad 2\dfrac{4}{6} = 2\dfrac{2}{3}}$$

Therefore, the difference is $2\dfrac{2}{3}$.

PRACTICE 14

Subtract $5\dfrac{3}{10}$ from $9\dfrac{7}{10}$.

EXAMPLE 15

A construction job was scheduled to last $5\dfrac{3}{4}$ days, but was finished in $4\dfrac{1}{4}$ days. How many days ahead of schedule was the job?

Solution

This question asks us to subtract $4\dfrac{1}{4}$ from $5\dfrac{3}{4}$.

$$5\dfrac{3}{4}$$
$$-4\dfrac{1}{4}$$
$$\overline{\quad 1\dfrac{2}{4} = 1\dfrac{1}{2}}$$

So the job was $1\dfrac{1}{2}$ days ahead of schedule.

PRACTICE 15

A student is typing a report using a word processing program. To make room for the binding, the left margin is set at $2\dfrac{7}{10}$ inches and the right margin at $1\dfrac{3}{10}$ inches. The left margin is how much greater than the right margin?

When subtracting mixed numbers with different denominators, we begin by finding the least common denominator.

EXAMPLE 16

Subtract $2\dfrac{7}{100}$ from $5\dfrac{9}{10}$.

Solution   As usual, we use the LCD (which is 100) to find equivalent fractions. Then we subtract the equivalent mixed numbers with the same denominator. Again, let's set up the problem vertically. Subtract the fractions, and then subtract the whole numbers.

$$
\begin{array}{rcl}
5\dfrac{9}{10} & = & 5\dfrac{90}{100} \\[2ex]
-2\dfrac{7}{100} & = & -2\dfrac{7}{100} \\[2ex]
& & \overline{3\dfrac{83}{100}}
\end{array}
$$

The answer is $3\dfrac{83}{100}$.

PRACTICE 16

Calculate: $8\dfrac{2}{3} - 4\dfrac{1}{12}$

EXAMPLE 17

Find the length of the pool shown below.

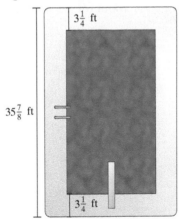

Solution   The total length of the pool and the walkway is $35\dfrac{7}{8}$ feet. To find the length of the pool, we first add $3\dfrac{1}{4}$ feet and $3\dfrac{1}{4}$ feet. Then we subtract this sum from $35\dfrac{7}{8}$ feet.

$$
\begin{array}{c}
3\dfrac{1}{4} \\[2ex]
+3\dfrac{1}{4} \\[1ex]
\hline
6\dfrac{2}{4} = 6\dfrac{1}{2}
\end{array}
\qquad\qquad
\begin{array}{rcl}
35\dfrac{7}{8} & = & 35\dfrac{7}{8} \\[2ex]
-6\dfrac{1}{2} & = & -6\dfrac{4}{8} \\[1ex]
\hline
& & 29\dfrac{3}{8}
\end{array}
$$

So the length of the pool is $29\dfrac{3}{8}$ feet. We can check this answer by adding $3\dfrac{1}{4}$, $29\dfrac{3}{8}$, and $3\dfrac{1}{4}$, getting $35\dfrac{7}{8}$.

PRACTICE 17

The outline of the state of Nevada is roughly in the shape of a *trapezoid*. The diagram shows the lengths of the borders that Nevada shares with each neighboring state. What is the total length of Nevada's border? (*Source:* econ.umn.edu)

Recall from our discussion of subtracting whole numbers that, in problems in which a digit in the subtrahend is larger than the corresponding digit in the minuend, we need to regroup.

$$\begin{array}{r} \overset{2\ 1}{\cancel{3}\ 2\ 9} \\ -\ \ 8\ 7 \\ \hline 2\ 4\ 2 \end{array}$$

A similar situation can arise when we are subtracting mixed numbers. If the fraction on the bottom is larger than the fraction on top, we *regroup*, or *borrow from* the whole number on top.

EXAMPLE 18	PRACTICE 18
Subtract: $6 - 1\dfrac{1}{3}$	Subtract: $9 - 7\dfrac{5}{7}$

Solution   Let's rewrite the problem vertically.

$$\begin{array}{r} 6 \\ -1\dfrac{1}{3} \\ \hline \end{array}$$ There is no fraction on top from which to subtract $\dfrac{1}{3}$.

$$\begin{array}{r} 5\dfrac{3}{3} \\ -1\dfrac{1}{3} \\ \hline \end{array}$$ Regrouping, we express 6 as $5 + 1$, or $5 + \dfrac{3}{3}$, or $5\dfrac{3}{3}$.

$$\begin{array}{r} 5\dfrac{3}{3} \\ -1\dfrac{1}{3} \\ \hline 4\dfrac{2}{3} \end{array}$$ Now subtract.

So $6 - 1\dfrac{1}{3} = 4\dfrac{2}{3}$.

As in any subtraction problem, we can check our answer by addition.

$$4\dfrac{2}{3} + 1\dfrac{1}{3} = 5\dfrac{3}{3} = 6$$

In Example 18, the answer is $4\dfrac{2}{3}$. Would we get the same answer if we compute $6\dfrac{1}{3} - 1$?

We have already discussed subtracting mixed numbers without regrouping as well as subtracting a mixed number from a whole number. Now, let's consider the general rule for subtracting mixed numbers.

To Subtract Mixed Numbers

- Write the fractions as equivalent fractions with the same denominator, usually the LCD.
- Regroup, or borrow from the whole number on top if the fraction on the bottom is larger than the fraction on top.
- Subtract the fractions.
- Subtract the whole numbers.
- Write the answer in simplest form.

EXAMPLE 19

Compute: $13\frac{2}{9} - 7\frac{8}{9}$

Solution   First, we write the problem vertically.

$$13\frac{2}{9}$$

$$-7\frac{8}{9}$$

Because $\frac{8}{9}$ is larger than $\frac{2}{9}$, we need to regroup as follows:

$$13\frac{2}{9} = 12 + 1 + \frac{2}{9} = 12 + \frac{9}{9} + \frac{2}{9} = 12\frac{11}{9}$$

$$12\frac{11}{9}$$

$$-7\frac{8}{9}$$

Finally, we subtract, and then write the answer in simplest form.

$$13\frac{2}{9} = 12\frac{11}{9}$$

$$-7\frac{8}{9} = -7\frac{8}{9}$$

$$5\frac{3}{9}, \text{ or } 5\frac{1}{3}$$

PRACTICE 19

Find the difference between $15\frac{1}{12}$ and $9\frac{11}{12}$.

EXAMPLE 20

Find the difference between $10\frac{1}{4}$ and $1\frac{5}{12}$.

Solution First, we write the equivalent fractions, using the LCD.

$$10\frac{1}{4} = 10\frac{3}{12}$$
$$-1\frac{5}{12} = -1\frac{5}{12}$$

Then, we subtract.

$$10\frac{3}{12} = 9\frac{15}{12} \quad \text{We regroup: } 10\frac{3}{12} = 9 + \frac{12}{12} + \frac{3}{12} = 9\frac{15}{12}$$
$$-1\frac{5}{12} = -1\frac{5}{12}$$
$$8\frac{10}{12} = 8\frac{5}{6}$$

PRACTICE 20

Find the difference between $16\frac{1}{10}$ and $3\frac{3}{5}$.

EXAMPLE 21

In Oregon's Columbia River Gorge, a hiker walks along the Eagle Creek Trail, headed for Punchbowl Falls $2\frac{1}{10}$ miles away. After reaching Metlako Falls, does he have more or less than $\frac{1}{2}$ mile left to go? (*Source:* USDA Forest Service)

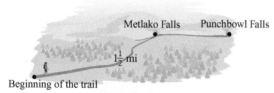

Eagle Creek Trail

Solution First, we must find the difference between the length of the trail from its begining to Punchbowl Falls, namely, $2\frac{1}{10}$ miles, and the distance already hiked, $1\frac{1}{2}$ miles.

$$2\frac{1}{10} = 2\frac{1}{10} = 1\frac{11}{10}$$
$$-1\frac{1}{2} = -1\frac{5}{10} = -1\frac{5}{10}$$
$$\frac{6}{10} = \frac{3}{5}$$

PRACTICE 21

A homeowner purchased the American single roll of wallpaper that is shown below and used $2\frac{7}{8}$ yards of the roll to paper a door panel. Is there enough paper left on the roll for a job that requires 2 yards of paper?

EXAMPLE 21 (continued)

So the distance left to hike is $\frac{3}{5}$ mile. Finally, we compare $\frac{3}{5}$ mile and $\frac{1}{2}$ mile.

$$\frac{3}{5} = \frac{6}{10} \qquad \frac{1}{2} = \frac{5}{10}$$

Because $6 > 5$, $\frac{6}{10} > \frac{5}{10}$. Therefore, $\frac{3}{5} > \frac{1}{2}$, and the hiker has more

than $\frac{1}{2}$ mile left to go from Metlako Falls to Punchbowl Falls.

Another Method of Adding and Subtracting Mixed Numbers

Recall that any mixed number can be rewritten as an improper fraction. So when adding or subtracting mixed numbers, we can first express them as improper fractions. In a subtraction problem, this method has an advantage over the method previously discussed; namely, we never have to regroup. However, expressing mixed numbers as improper fractions may have the disadvantage of involving unnecessarily large numbers, as the following examples show.

EXAMPLE 22

Add: $14\frac{1}{6} + 8\frac{2}{3}$

Solution   We begin by writing each mixed number as an improper fraction.

$$14\frac{1}{6} + 8\frac{2}{3} = \frac{85}{6} + \frac{26}{3} \qquad \text{Express } 14\frac{1}{6} \text{ and } 8\frac{2}{3} \text{ as improper fractions.}$$

$$= \frac{85}{6} + \frac{52}{6} \qquad \text{Write the fractions to be added as equivalent fractions.}$$

$$= \frac{137}{6} \qquad \text{Add the like fractions.}$$

$$= 22\frac{5}{6} \qquad \text{Express the improper fraction as a mixed number.}$$

PRACTICE 22

Find the sum: $7\frac{4}{5} + 2\frac{3}{4}$

Can you show that this method gives the same sum that we would have gotten if we had not expressed the mixed numbers as improper fractions? Explain.

EXAMPLE 23

Find the difference: $8\dfrac{5}{6} - 4\dfrac{9}{10}$

Solution $8\dfrac{5}{6} - 4\dfrac{9}{10} = \dfrac{53}{6} - \dfrac{49}{10}$ Write as improper fractions.

$$= \dfrac{265}{30} - \dfrac{147}{30}$$ Write as equivalent fractions.

$$= \dfrac{118}{30}$$ Subtract the like fractions.

$$= 3\dfrac{28}{30}$$ Express as a mixed number.

$$= 3\dfrac{14}{15}$$ Simplify.

Check that this answer is the same as we would have gotten without changing the mixed numbers to improper fractions.

PRACTICE 23

Subtract: $13\dfrac{1}{4} - 11\dfrac{7}{8}$

Estimating Sums and Differences of Mixed Numbers

When adding or subtracting mixed numbers, we can check by *estimating*, determining whether our estimate and our answer are close. Note that when we round mixed numbers, we round to the nearest whole number.

Checking a Sum by Estimating

$1\dfrac{1}{5} \rightarrow \quad 1$ Because $\dfrac{1}{5} < \dfrac{1}{2}$, round *down* to the whole number 1.

$+2\dfrac{3}{5} \rightarrow +3$ Because $\dfrac{3}{5} > \dfrac{1}{2}$, round *up* to the whole number 3.

$\overline{3\dfrac{4}{5} \quad\;\; \overline{4}}$ Our answer, $3\dfrac{4}{5}$, is close to 4, the sum of the rounded addends (1 and 3).

Checking a Difference by Estimating

$3\dfrac{2}{5} \rightarrow \quad 3$ Because $\dfrac{2}{5} < \dfrac{1}{2}$, round *down* to 3.

$-1\dfrac{1}{5} \rightarrow -1$ Round *down* to 1.

$\overline{2\dfrac{1}{5} \quad\;\; \overline{2}}$ Our answer, $2\dfrac{1}{5}$, is close to 2, the difference of the rounded numbers (3 and 1).

EXAMPLE 24

Combine and check: $5\frac{1}{3} - \left(2\frac{4}{5} + 1\frac{1}{10}\right)$

Solution Following the order of operations rule, we begin by adding the two mixed numbers in parentheses.

$$2\frac{4}{5} = 2\frac{8}{10}$$
$$+1\frac{1}{10} = +1\frac{1}{10}$$
$$\overline{\quad\quad\quad\quad 3\frac{9}{10}}$$

Next, we subtract this sum from $5\frac{1}{3}$.

$$5\frac{1}{3} = 5\frac{10}{30} = 4\frac{40}{30}$$
$$-3\frac{9}{10} = -3\frac{27}{30} = -3\frac{27}{30}$$
$$\overline{\quad\quad\quad\quad\quad\quad\quad\quad 1\frac{13}{30}}$$

So $5\frac{1}{3} - \left(2\frac{4}{5} + 1\frac{1}{10}\right) = 1\frac{13}{30}$.

Now, let's check this answer by estimating:

$$5\frac{1}{3} - \left(2\frac{4}{5} + 1\frac{1}{10}\right)$$
$$\downarrow \quad\quad\quad \downarrow \quad\quad \downarrow$$
$$5 - (3 + 1) = 5 - 4 = 1$$

The estimate, 1, is close to our answer, $1\frac{13}{30}$.

PRACTICE 24

Calculate and check:

$$8\frac{1}{4} - \left(3\frac{2}{5} - 1\frac{9}{10}\right)$$

Mathematically Speaking

Fill in each blank with the most appropriate term or phrase from the given list.

denominators	regroup	equivalent
add	numerators	improper

1. To add like fractions, add the _____.

2. To subtract unlike fractions, rewrite them as _____ fractions with the same denominator.

3. When subtracting $2\frac{4}{5}$ from 7, _____ by writing 7 as $6\frac{5}{5}$.

4. Fractions with equal numerators and _____ are equivalent to 1.

A *Add and simplify.*

5. $\frac{5}{8} + \frac{5}{8}$

6. $\frac{7}{10} + \frac{9}{10}$

7. $\frac{11}{12} + \frac{7}{12}$

8. $\frac{71}{100} + \frac{79}{100}$

9. $\frac{1}{5} + \frac{1}{5} + \frac{2}{5}$

10. $\frac{1}{7} + \frac{3}{7} + \frac{2}{7}$

11. $\frac{3}{20} + \frac{1}{20} + \frac{8}{20}$

12. $\frac{1}{10} + \frac{3}{10} + \frac{1}{10}$

13. $\frac{2}{3} + \frac{1}{2}$

14. $\frac{1}{4} + \frac{2}{5}$

15. $\frac{1}{2} + \frac{3}{8}$

16. $\frac{1}{6} + \frac{2}{3}$

17. $\frac{7}{10} + \frac{7}{100}$

18. $\frac{5}{6} + \frac{1}{12}$

19. $\frac{4}{5} + \frac{1}{8}$

20. $\frac{3}{4} + \frac{3}{7}$

21. $\frac{4}{9} + \frac{5}{6}$

22. $\frac{9}{10} + \frac{4}{5}$

23. $\frac{87}{100} + \frac{3}{10}$

24. $\frac{7}{20} + \frac{3}{4}$

25. $\frac{1}{3} + \frac{1}{4} + \frac{1}{6}$

26. $\frac{1}{5} + \frac{1}{6} + \frac{1}{3}$

27. $\frac{3}{8} + \frac{1}{10} + \frac{3}{16}$

28. $\frac{3}{10} + \frac{1}{3} + \frac{1}{9}$

29. $\frac{2}{9} + \frac{5}{8} + \frac{1}{4}$

30. $\frac{1}{2} + \frac{1}{3} + \frac{1}{4}$

31. $\frac{7}{8} + \frac{1}{5} + \frac{1}{4}$

32. $\frac{1}{10} + \frac{2}{5} + \frac{5}{6}$

Add and simplify. Then check by estimating.

33. $1 + 2\frac{1}{3}$

34. $4\frac{1}{5} + 2$

35. $8\frac{1}{10} + 7\frac{3}{10}$

36. $6\frac{1}{12} + 4\frac{1}{12}$

37. $7\frac{3}{10} + 6\frac{9}{10}$

38. $8\frac{2}{3} + 6\frac{2}{3}$

39. $5\frac{1}{6} + 9\frac{5}{6}$

40. $2\frac{3}{10} + 7\frac{9}{10}$

41. $5\frac{1}{4} + 5\frac{1}{6}$

42. $17\frac{3}{8} + 20\frac{1}{5}$

43. $3\frac{1}{3} + \frac{2}{5}$

44. $4\frac{7}{10} + \frac{7}{20}$

45. $8\frac{1}{5} + 5\frac{2}{3}$

46. $4\frac{1}{9} + 20\frac{7}{10}$

47. $\frac{2}{3} + 6\frac{1}{8}$

48. $\frac{1}{6} + 3\frac{2}{5}$

49. $9\frac{2}{3} + 10\frac{7}{12}$

50. $20\frac{3}{5} + 4\frac{1}{2}$

51. $6\frac{1}{10} + 3\frac{93}{100}$

52. $4\frac{8}{9} + 5\frac{1}{3}$

53. $4\dfrac{1}{2} + 6\dfrac{7}{8}$

54. $10\dfrac{5}{6} + 8\dfrac{1}{4}$

55. $30\dfrac{21}{100} + 5\dfrac{17}{20}$

56. $8\dfrac{3}{10} + 2\dfrac{321}{1,000}$

57. $80\dfrac{1}{3} + \dfrac{3}{4} + 10\dfrac{1}{2}$

58. $\dfrac{1}{3} + 25\dfrac{7}{24} + 100\dfrac{1}{2}$

59. $2\dfrac{1}{3} + 2 + 2\dfrac{1}{6}$

60. $4\dfrac{1}{8} + 4\dfrac{3}{16} + \dfrac{5}{4}$

61. $6\dfrac{7}{8} + 2\dfrac{3}{4} + 1\dfrac{1}{5}$

62. $1\dfrac{2}{3} + 5\dfrac{5}{6} + 3\dfrac{1}{4}$

63. $2\dfrac{1}{2} + 5\dfrac{1}{4} + 3\dfrac{5}{8}$

64. $4\dfrac{2}{3} + 2\dfrac{11}{36} + 1\dfrac{1}{2}$

Subtract and simplify.

65. $\dfrac{4}{5} - \dfrac{3}{5}$

66. $\dfrac{7}{9} - \dfrac{5}{9}$

67. $\dfrac{7}{10} - \dfrac{3}{10}$

68. $\dfrac{11}{12} - \dfrac{5}{12}$

69. $\dfrac{23}{100} - \dfrac{7}{100}$

70. $\dfrac{3}{2} - \dfrac{1}{2}$

71. $\dfrac{3}{4} - \dfrac{1}{4}$

72. $\dfrac{7}{9} - \dfrac{4}{9}$

73. $\dfrac{12}{5} - \dfrac{2}{5}$

74. $\dfrac{1}{8} - \dfrac{1}{8}$

75. $\dfrac{3}{4} - \dfrac{2}{3}$

76. $\dfrac{2}{5} - \dfrac{1}{6}$

77. $\dfrac{4}{9} - \dfrac{1}{6}$

78. $\dfrac{9}{10} - \dfrac{3}{100}$

79. $\dfrac{4}{5} - \dfrac{3}{4}$

80. $\dfrac{5}{6} - \dfrac{1}{8}$

81. $\dfrac{4}{7} - \dfrac{1}{2}$

82. $\dfrac{2}{5} - \dfrac{2}{9}$

83. $\dfrac{4}{9} - \dfrac{3}{8}$

84. $\dfrac{11}{12} - \dfrac{1}{3}$

85. $\dfrac{3}{4} - \dfrac{1}{2}$

86. $\dfrac{5}{6} - \dfrac{2}{3}$

Subtract and simplify. Then, check either by adding or by estimating.

87. $5\dfrac{3}{7} - 1\dfrac{1}{7}$

88. $6\dfrac{2}{3} - 1\dfrac{1}{3}$

89. $3\dfrac{7}{8} - 2\dfrac{1}{8}$

90. $10\dfrac{5}{6} - 2\dfrac{5}{6}$

91. $20\dfrac{1}{2} - \dfrac{1}{2}$

92. $7\dfrac{3}{4} - \dfrac{1}{4}$

93. $8\dfrac{1}{10} - 4$

94. $2\dfrac{1}{3} - 2$

95. $6 - 2\dfrac{2}{3}$

96. $4 - 1\dfrac{1}{5}$

97. $8 - 4\dfrac{7}{10}$

98. $2 - 1\dfrac{1}{2}$

99. $10 - 3\dfrac{2}{3}$

100. $5 - 4\dfrac{9}{10}$

101. $6 - \dfrac{1}{2}$

102. $9 - \dfrac{3}{4}$

103. $7\dfrac{1}{4} - 2\dfrac{3}{4}$

104. $5\dfrac{1}{10} - 2\dfrac{3}{10}$

105. $6\dfrac{1}{8} - 2\dfrac{7}{8}$

106. $3\dfrac{1}{5} - 1\dfrac{4}{5}$

107. $12\dfrac{2}{5} - \dfrac{3}{5}$

108. $3\dfrac{7}{10} - \dfrac{9}{10}$

109. $8\dfrac{1}{3} - 1\dfrac{2}{3}$

110. $2\dfrac{1}{5} - \dfrac{4}{5}$

111. $13\dfrac{1}{2} - 5\dfrac{2}{3}$

112. $7\dfrac{1}{10} - 2\dfrac{1}{7}$

113. $9\dfrac{3}{8} - 5\dfrac{5}{6}$

114. $2\dfrac{1}{10} - 1\dfrac{27}{100}$

115. $20\dfrac{2}{9} - 4\dfrac{5}{6}$

116. $9\dfrac{13}{100} - 6\dfrac{7}{10}$

117. $3\dfrac{4}{5} - \dfrac{5}{6}$

118. $1\dfrac{2}{8} - \dfrac{2}{6}$

119. $1\dfrac{3}{4} - 1\dfrac{1}{2}$

120. $2\dfrac{1}{2} - 1\dfrac{3}{4}$

121. $10\dfrac{1}{12} - 4\dfrac{2}{3}$

122. $7\dfrac{1}{4} - 1\dfrac{5}{16}$

123. $22\dfrac{7}{8} - 8\dfrac{9}{10}$

124. $9\dfrac{1}{10} - 3\dfrac{1}{2}$

125. $3\dfrac{1}{8} - 2\dfrac{3}{4}$

126. $3\dfrac{1}{4} - 2\dfrac{5}{16}$

Combine and simplify.

127. $\dfrac{5}{8} + \dfrac{9}{10} - \dfrac{1}{4}$

128. $\dfrac{2}{3} - \dfrac{1}{5} + \dfrac{1}{2}$

129. $12\dfrac{1}{6} + 5\dfrac{9}{10} - 1\dfrac{3}{10}$

130. $7\dfrac{1}{3} - 2\dfrac{4}{5} - 1\dfrac{1}{3}$

131. $15\dfrac{1}{2} - 3\dfrac{4}{5} - 6\dfrac{1}{2}$

132. $4\dfrac{1}{10} + 2\dfrac{9}{10} - 3\dfrac{3}{4}$

133. $20\dfrac{1}{10} - \left(\dfrac{1}{20} + 1\dfrac{1}{2}\right)$

134. $19\dfrac{1}{6} - \left(8\dfrac{9}{10} - \dfrac{1}{5}\right)$

Mixed Practice

Perform the indicated operations and simplify.

135. Subtract $1\dfrac{7}{8}$ from 6.

136. Add: $6\dfrac{1}{10} + 3\dfrac{7}{15}$

137. Calculate: $12\dfrac{2}{3} - \left(8\dfrac{5}{6} - 4\dfrac{1}{2}\right)$

138. Find the sum of $\dfrac{3}{8}, \dfrac{1}{2},$ and $\dfrac{1}{3}$.

139. Find the difference between $4\dfrac{3}{5}$ and $1\dfrac{2}{3}$.

140. Subtract: $\dfrac{9}{10} - \dfrac{1}{4}$

Applications

B *Solve. Write the answer in simplest form.*

141. A $\dfrac{7}{8}$-inch nail was hammered through a $\dfrac{3}{4}$-inch door. How far did it extend from the door?

142. A building occupies $\dfrac{1}{4}$ acre on a $\dfrac{7}{8}$-acre plot of land. What is the area of the land not occupied by the building?

143. The Kentucky Derby, Belmont Stakes, and the Preakness Stakes are three prestigious horse races that comprise the Triple Crown. (*Source:* http://infoplease.com)

   a. Horses run $1\dfrac{3}{16}$ mile in the Preakness Stakes. If the Preakness Stakes is $\dfrac{5}{16}$ mile shorter than the Belmont Stakes, how far do horses run in the Belmont Stakes?

   b. Horses run $1\dfrac{1}{4}$ miles in the Kentucky Derby. How much farther do horses run in the Belmont Stakes than in the Kentucky Derby?

144. In the year 2030, the total amount of electricity generated worldwide is projected to be approximately 32 trillion kilowatt-hours. Of this amount, $\dfrac{1}{32}$ is expected to be generated by liquid fuels, $\dfrac{1}{8}$ by nuclear power, and $\dfrac{7}{16}$ by coal. (*Source:* eia.doe.gov)

   a. According to these projections, the combined amount of electricity generated by liquid fuels and nuclear power will be what fraction of the total world electricity?

   b. As a fraction of the electricity generated worldwide, the amount of electricity generated by coal will be how much greater than the combined amount generated by liquid fuel and nuclear power?

145. The first game of a baseball doubleheader lasted $2\frac{1}{4}$ hours. The second game began after a $\frac{1}{4}$-hour break and lasted $2\frac{1}{2}$ hours. How long did the doubleheader take to play?

146. Three student candidates competed in a student government election. The winner got $\frac{5}{8}$ of the votes, and the second-place candidate got $\frac{1}{4}$ of the votes. If the rest of the votes went to the third candidate, what fraction of the votes did that student get?

147. In 1912, the Titanic, the largest passenger ship in the world, sank on its maiden voyage. The steamship had a length of $882\frac{3}{4}$ feet. Its width at the widest point was $92\frac{1}{2}$ feet. How much greater was its length than its width? (*Source:* titanic-titanic.com)

148. A shopper purchased two boxes of chocolates: one box containing a sugar-free assortment weighs $20\frac{5}{8}$ ounces, and the other box, containing milk toffee sticks, weighs $10\frac{1}{2}$ ounces. Find the total weight of the boxes. (*Source:* Russellstover.com)

149. In testing a new drug, doctors found that $\frac{1}{2}$ of the patients given the drug improved, $\frac{2}{5}$ showed no change in their condition, and the remainder got worse. What fraction got worse?

150. The size of a child's shoe is related to the length of his or her foot. The following table shows the relationship between shoe size and foot length for a variety of sizes.

Size	Foot Length (in inches)	Size	Foot Length (in inches)
4	$5\frac{3}{4}$	8	$6\frac{3}{4}$
5	6	9	7
6	$6\frac{1}{4}$	10	$7\frac{1}{4}$
7	$6\frac{1}{2}$	11	$7\frac{1}{2}$

(*Source:* kidbean.com/sizecharts.html)

Is the difference in foot length greater when comparing sizes 4 and 7 or when comparing sizes 7 and 10?

151. Suppose that four packages are placed on a scale, as shown. If the scale balances, how heavy is the small package on the right?

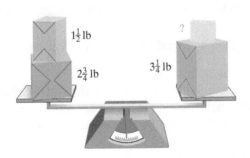

152. If the scale pictured balances, how heavy is the small package on the left?

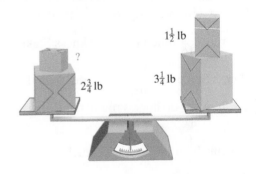

• Check your answers on page A-3.

MINDStretchers

Groupwork

1. Working with a partner, complete the following magic square in which each row, column, and diagonal adds up to the same number.

$1\frac{1}{4}$		
	1	
$\frac{11}{12}$		$\frac{3}{4}$

Mathematical Reasoning

2. A fraction with 1 as the numerator is called a **unit fraction**. For example, $\frac{1}{7}$ is a unit fraction. Write $\frac{3}{7}$ as the sum of three unit fractions, using no unit fraction more than once.

$$\frac{3}{7} = \frac{1}{\blacksquare} + \frac{1}{\blacksquare} + \frac{1}{\blacksquare}$$

Writing

3. Consider the following two ways of subtracting $2\frac{4}{5}$ from $4\frac{1}{5}$.

Method 1

$$4\frac{1}{5} = 3 + \frac{5}{5} + \frac{1}{5} = \quad 3\frac{6}{5}$$
$$-2\frac{4}{5} \qquad\qquad\quad = -2\frac{4}{5}$$
$$\qquad\qquad\qquad\qquad\qquad 1\frac{2}{5}$$

Method 2

$$4\frac{1}{5} \rightarrow 4 + \frac{1}{5} + \frac{1}{5} = \quad 4\frac{2}{5}$$
$$-2\frac{4}{5} \rightarrow 2 + \frac{4}{5} + \frac{1}{5} = -3$$
$$\qquad\qquad\qquad\qquad\qquad\quad 1\frac{2}{5}$$

a. Explain the difference between the two methods.

b. Explain which method you prefer.

c. Explain why you prefer that method.

2.4 Multiplying and Dividing Fractions

This section begins with a discussion of multiplying fractions. We then move on to multiplying mixed numbers and conclude with dividing fractions and mixed numbers.

Multiplying Fractions

Many situations require us to multiply fractions. For instance, suppose that a mixture in a chemistry class calls for $\frac{4}{5}$ gram of sodium chloride. If we make only $\frac{2}{3}$ of that mixture, we need

$$\frac{2}{3} \text{ of } \frac{4}{5}$$
$$\downarrow$$
$$\frac{2}{3} \times \frac{4}{5}$$

that is, $\frac{2}{3} \times \frac{4}{5}$ gram of sodium chloride.

To illustrate how to find this product, we diagram these two fractions.

$\frac{4}{5}$

$\frac{2}{3}$

In the following diagram, we are taking $\frac{2}{3}$ of the $\frac{4}{5}$.

Note that we divided the whole into 15 parts and that our product, containing 8 of the 15 small squares, represents the double-shaded region. The answer is, therefore, $\frac{8}{15}$ of the original whole, which we can compute as follows:

$$\frac{2}{3} \times \frac{4}{5} = \frac{8}{15}$$

The numerator and denominator of the answer are the products of the original numerators and denominators.

To Multiply Fractions

- Multiply the numerators.
- Multiply the denominators.
- Write the answer in simplest form.

EXAMPLE 1

Multiply: $\dfrac{7}{8} \cdot \dfrac{9}{10}$

Solution

Multiply the numerators.

$$\dfrac{7}{8} \cdot \dfrac{9}{10} = \dfrac{7 \cdot 9}{8 \cdot 10} = \dfrac{63}{80}$$

Multiply the denominators.

PRACTICE 1

Find the product of $\dfrac{3}{4}$ and $\dfrac{5}{7}$.

EXAMPLE 2

Calculate: $\left(\dfrac{4}{5}\right)^2$

Solution

$$\left(\dfrac{4}{5}\right)^2 = \dfrac{4}{5} \cdot \dfrac{4}{5} = \dfrac{4 \cdot 4}{5 \cdot 5} = \dfrac{16}{25}$$

PRACTICE 2

Square $\dfrac{9}{10}$.

EXAMPLE 3

What is $\dfrac{3}{8}$ of 10?

Solution Finding $\dfrac{3}{8}$ of 10 means multiplying $\dfrac{3}{8}$ by 10.

$$\dfrac{3}{8} \times 10 = \dfrac{3}{8} \times \dfrac{10}{1} = \dfrac{3 \times 10}{8 \times 1} = \dfrac{30}{8} = \dfrac{15}{4}, \text{ or } 3\dfrac{3}{4}$$

PRACTICE 3

What is $\dfrac{2}{3}$ of 30?

In Example 3, we multiplied the two fractions first, and then simplified the answer. It is preferable, however, to reverse these steps: Simplify first, and then multiply. By first simplifying, sometimes referred to as *canceling*, we divide *any* numerator and *any* denominator by a common factor. Canceling before multiplying allows us to work with smaller numbers and still gives us the same answer.

EXAMPLE 4

Find the product of $\dfrac{4}{9}$ and $\dfrac{5}{8}$.

Solution

$$\dfrac{4}{9} \times \dfrac{5}{8} = \dfrac{\overset{1}{\cancel{4}}}{9} \times \dfrac{5}{\underset{2}{\cancel{8}}}$$ Divide the numerator 4 and the denominator 8 by 4.

$$= \dfrac{1 \times 5}{9 \times 2}$$ Multiply the resulting fractions.

$$= \dfrac{5}{18}$$

PRACTICE 4

Multiply: $\dfrac{7}{10} \cdot \dfrac{5}{11}$

EXAMPLE 5

Multiply: $\dfrac{9}{8} \times \dfrac{6}{5} \times \dfrac{7}{9}$

Solution We simplify and then multiply.

$$\dfrac{9}{8} \times \dfrac{6}{5} \times \dfrac{7}{9} = \dfrac{\overset{1}{\cancel{9}}}{\underset{4}{\cancel{8}}} \times \dfrac{\overset{3}{\cancel{6}}}{5} \times \dfrac{7}{\underset{1}{\cancel{9}}}$$

Divide the numerator 9 and the denominator 9 by 9.
Divide the numerator 6 and the denominator 8 by 2.

$$= \dfrac{21}{20}, \text{ or } 1\dfrac{1}{20}$$

PRACTICE 5

Multiply: $\dfrac{7}{27} \cdot \dfrac{9}{4} \cdot \dfrac{8}{21}$

EXAMPLE 6

At a college, $\dfrac{3}{5}$ of the students take a math course. Of these students, $\dfrac{1}{6}$ take elementary algebra. What fraction of the students in the college take elementary algebra?

Solution We must find $\dfrac{1}{6}$ of $\dfrac{3}{5}$.

$$\dfrac{1}{6} \times \dfrac{3}{5} = \dfrac{1}{\underset{2}{\cancel{6}}} \times \dfrac{\overset{1}{\cancel{3}}}{5} = \dfrac{1 \times 1}{2 \times 5} = \dfrac{1}{10}$$

One-tenth of the students in the college take elementary algebra.

PRACTICE 6

A flight from New York to Los Angeles took 7 hours. With the help of the jet stream, the return trip took $\dfrac{3}{4}$ the time. How long did the trip from Los Angeles to New York take?

EXAMPLE 7

Of the 639 employees at a company, $\dfrac{4}{9}$ responded to a voluntary survey distributed by the human resources department. How many employees did not respond to the survey?

Solution Apply the strategy of breaking the problem into two parts.

- First, find $\dfrac{4}{9}$ of 639.

- Then, subtract the result from 639.

In short, we can solve this problem by computing $639 - \left(\dfrac{4}{9} \times 639 \right)$.

$$639 - \left(\dfrac{4}{9} \times 639 \right) = 639 - \left(\dfrac{4}{\underset{1}{\cancel{9}}} \times \dfrac{\overset{71}{\cancel{639}}}{1} \right) = 639 - 284 = 355$$

So 355 employees did not respond to the survey.

PRACTICE 7

The state sales tax on a car in Wisconsin is $\dfrac{1}{20}$ of the price of the car. What is the total amount a consumer would pay for a $19,780 car? (*Source:* revenue.wi.gov)

Multiplying Mixed Numbers

Some situations require us to multiply mixed numbers. For instance, suppose that your regular hourly wage is $\$7\frac{1}{2}$ and that you make time-and-a-half for working overtime. To find your overtime hourly wage, you need to multiply $1\frac{1}{2}$ by $7\frac{1}{2}$. The key here is to first rewrite each mixed number as an improper fraction.

$$1\frac{1}{2} \times 7\frac{1}{2} = \frac{3}{2} \times \frac{15}{2} = \frac{45}{4}, \text{ or } 11\frac{1}{4}$$

So you make $\$11\frac{1}{4}$ per hour overtime.

To Multiply Mixed Numbers

- Write the mixed numbers as improper fractions.
- Multiply the fractions.
- Write the answer in simplest form.

EXAMPLE 8

Multiply $2\frac{1}{5}$ by $1\frac{1}{4}$.

Solution
$$2\frac{1}{5} \times 1\frac{1}{4} = \frac{11}{5} \times \frac{5}{4} \qquad \text{Write each mixed number as an improper fraction.}$$

$$= \frac{11 \times \overset{1}{\cancel{5}}}{\underset{1}{\cancel{5}} \times 4} \qquad \text{Simplify and multiply.}$$

$$= \frac{11}{4}, \text{ or } 2\frac{3}{4}$$

PRACTICE 8

Find the product of $3\frac{3}{4}$ and $2\frac{1}{10}$.

EXAMPLE 9

Multiply: $\left(4\frac{3}{8}\right)\left(4\right)\left(2\frac{2}{5}\right)$

Solution
$$\left(4\frac{3}{8}\right)\left(4\right)\left(2\frac{2}{5}\right) = \left(\frac{35}{8}\right)\left(\frac{4}{1}\right)\left(\frac{12}{5}\right)$$

$$= \left(\frac{\overset{7}{\cancel{35}}}{\underset{2}{\cancel{8}}}\right)\left(\frac{\overset{1}{\cancel{4}}}{1}\right)\left(\frac{\overset{6}{\cancel{12}}}{\underset{1}{\cancel{5}}}\right) = 42$$

Note in this problem that, although there are several ways to simplify, the answer always comes out the same.

PRACTICE 9

Multiply: $\left(1\frac{3}{4}\right)\left(5\frac{1}{3}\right)\left(3\right)$

EXAMPLE 10

A lawn surrounding a garden is to be installed, as depicted in the following drawing.

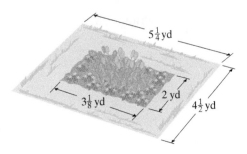

How many square yards of turf will we need to cover the lawn?

Solution Let's break this problem into three steps. First, we find the area of the rectangle with dimensions $5\frac{1}{4}$ yards and $4\frac{1}{2}$ yards. Then, we find the area of the small rectangle whose length and width are $3\frac{1}{8}$ yards and 2 yards, respectively.

$$5\frac{1}{4} \times 4\frac{1}{2} = \frac{21}{4} \times \frac{9}{2}$$

$$= \frac{189}{8}, \text{ or } 23\frac{5}{8} \qquad \text{The area of the large rectangle is } 23\frac{5}{8} \text{ square yards.}$$

$$3\frac{1}{8} \times 2 = \frac{25}{8} \times \frac{2}{1}$$

$$= \frac{25}{4}, \text{ or } 6\frac{1}{4} \qquad \text{The area of the small rectangle is } 6\frac{1}{4} \text{ square yards.}$$

Finally, we subtract the area of the small rectangle from the area of the large rectangle.

$$23\frac{5}{8} = 23\frac{5}{8}$$
$$-6\frac{1}{4} = -6\frac{2}{8}$$
$$\overline{\phantom{-6\frac{1}{4} =}\ 17\frac{3}{8}}$$

The area of the lawn is, therefore, $17\frac{3}{8}$ square yards. So we will need $17\frac{3}{8}$ square yards of turf for the lawn.

PRACTICE 10

Two student club posters are shown below. How much greater is the area of the legal-size poster than the letter-size poster?

$8\frac{1}{2}$ in. $\times$ 11 in.
Letter-size paper

$8\frac{1}{2}$ in. $\times$ 14 in.
Legal-size paper

EXAMPLE 11

Simplify: $16\frac{1}{4} - 2 \cdot 4\frac{3}{5}$

Solution We use the order of operations rule, multiplying before subtracting.

$$16\frac{1}{4} - 2 \cdot 4\frac{3}{5} = 16\frac{1}{4} - \frac{2}{1} \cdot \frac{23}{5}$$

$$= 16\frac{1}{4} - \frac{46}{5}$$

$$= 16\frac{1}{4} - 9\frac{1}{5}$$

$$= 16\frac{5}{20} - 9\frac{4}{20}$$

$$= 7\frac{1}{20}$$

PRACTICE 11

Calculate: $6 + \left(3\frac{1}{2}\right)^2$

Dividing Fractions

We now turn to quotients, beginning with dividing a fraction by a whole number. Suppose, for instance, that you want to share $\frac{1}{3}$ of a pizza with a friend, that is, to divide the $\frac{1}{3}$ into two equal parts. What part of the whole pizza will each of you receive?

This diagram shows $\frac{1}{3}$ of a pizza.

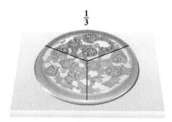

If we split each third into two equal parts, each part is $\frac{1}{6}$ of the pizza.

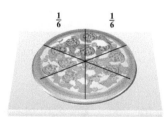

You and your friend will each get $\frac{1}{6}$ of the whole pizza, which you can compute as follows.

$$\frac{1}{3} \div 2 = \frac{1}{6}$$

Note that dividing a number by 2 is the same as taking $\frac{1}{2}$ of it. This equivalence suggests the procedure for dividing fractions shown next.

Divisor

$$\frac{1}{3} \div 2 = \frac{1}{3} \div \frac{2}{1} = \frac{1}{3} \times \frac{1}{2} = \frac{1 \times 1}{3 \times 2} = \frac{1}{6}$$

$\frac{2}{1}$ and $\frac{1}{2}$ are reciprocals.

This procedure involves *inverting*, or finding the *reciprocal* of the divisor. The reciprocal is found by switching the numerator and denominator.

To Divide Fractions

- Change the divisor to its reciprocal, and multiply the resulting fractions.

- Write the answer in simplest form.

EXAMPLE 12

Divide: $\dfrac{4}{5} \div \dfrac{3}{10}$

Solution $\dfrac{4}{5} \div \dfrac{3}{10} = \dfrac{4}{5} \times \dfrac{10}{3}$ Change the divisor to its reciprocal and multiply.

$$= \frac{4}{\overset{}{\underset{1}{5}}} \times \frac{\overset{2}{10}}{3}$$ Divide the numerator 10 and the denominator 5 by 5.

$$= \frac{4 \times 2}{1 \times 3}$$ Multiply the fractions.

$$= \frac{8}{3}$$ Simplify.

$$= 2\frac{2}{3}$$

As in any division problem, we can check our answer by multiplying it by the divisor.

$$\frac{\overset{4}{8}}{\underset{1}{3}} \times \frac{\overset{1}{3}}{\underset{5}{10}} = \frac{4}{5}$$

Because $\dfrac{4}{5}$ is the dividend, we have confirmed our answer.

PRACTICE 12

Divide: $\dfrac{3}{4} \div \dfrac{1}{8}$

TIP In a division problem, the fraction to the right of the division sign is the divisor. Always invert the divisor (the second fraction) and not the dividend (the first fraction).

EXAMPLE 13

What is $\frac{4}{7}$ divided by 20?

Solution $\frac{4}{7} \div 20 = \frac{4}{7} \times \frac{1}{20}$ Invert $\frac{20}{1}$ and multiply.

$$= \frac{\overset{1}{\cancel{4}}}{7} \times \frac{1}{\underset{5}{\cancel{20}}}$$ Divide the numerator 4 and the denominator 20 by 4.

$$= \frac{1 \times 1}{7 \times 5} = \frac{1}{35}$$

PRACTICE 13

Compute the following quotient:

$5 \div \frac{5}{8}$

EXAMPLE 14

To stop the developing process, photographers use a chemical called stop bath. Suppose that a photographer needs $\frac{1}{4}$ bottle of stop bath for each roll of film. If the photographer has $\frac{2}{3}$ bottle of stop bath left, can he develop three rolls of film?

Solution We want to find out how many $\frac{1}{4}$'s there are in $\frac{2}{3}$, that is, to compute $\frac{2}{3} \div \frac{1}{4}$.

$$\frac{2}{3} \div \frac{1}{4} = \frac{2}{3} \times \frac{4}{1} = \frac{8}{3} \quad \text{or} \quad 2\frac{2}{3}$$

Find the reciprocal of the divisor, $\frac{1}{4}$, and then multiply.

So the photographer cannot develop three rolls of film.

PRACTICE 14

A cabin is built on ground that is sinking $\frac{3}{4}$ inch per year. How many years will it take the cabin to sink 2 inches?

Dividing Mixed Numbers

Dividing mixed numbers is similar to dividing fractions, except that there is an additional step.

To Divide Mixed Numbers

- Write the mixed numbers as improper fractions.
- Divide the fractions.
- Write the answer in simplest form.

EXAMPLE 15

Find: $9 \div 2\frac{7}{10}$

Solution $9 \div 2\frac{7}{10} = \frac{9}{1} \div \frac{27}{10}$ Write the whole number and the mixed number as improper fractions.

$$= \frac{\overset{1}{9}}{1} \times \frac{10}{\underset{3}{27}}$$ Invert and multiply.

$$= \frac{10}{3}, \text{ or } 3\frac{1}{3}$$

PRACTICE 15

Divide: $6 \div 3\frac{3}{4}$

EXAMPLE 16

What is $2\frac{1}{2} \div 4\frac{1}{2}$?

Solution $2\frac{1}{2} \div 4\frac{1}{2} = \frac{5}{2} \div \frac{9}{2} = \frac{5}{2} \times \frac{\overset{1}{2}}{9} = \frac{5}{9}$

Invert and multiply.

PRACTICE 16

Divide $2\frac{3}{8}$ by $5\frac{3}{7}$.

EXAMPLE 17

There are $6\frac{3}{4}$ yards of silk in a roll. If it takes $\frac{3}{4}$ yard to make one designer tie, how many ties can be made from the roll?

Solution The question is: How many $\frac{3}{4}$'s fit into $6\frac{3}{4}$? It tells us that we must divide.

$$6\frac{3}{4} \div \frac{3}{4} = \frac{\overset{9}{27}}{\underset{1}{4}} \times \frac{\overset{1}{4}}{\underset{1}{3}} = 9$$

So nine ties can be made from the roll of silk.

PRACTICE 17

According to a newspaper advertisement for a "diet shake," a man lost 33 pounds in $5\frac{1}{2}$ months. How much weight did he lose per month?

Estimating Products and Quotients of Mixed Numbers

As with adding or subtracting mixed numbers, it is important to check our answers when multiplying or dividing. We can check a product or a quotient of mixed numbers by estimating the answer and then confirming that our estimate and answer are reasonably close.

Checking a Product by Estimating

$$2\frac{1}{5} \times 7\frac{2}{3} = \frac{11}{5} \times \frac{23}{3} = \frac{253}{15}, \text{ or } 16\frac{13}{15}$$

Our answer, $16\frac{13}{15}$, is close to 16, the product of the rounded factors.

$$\downarrow \qquad \downarrow$$
$$2 \times \quad 8 = 16$$

Because $16\frac{13}{15}$ is near 16, $16\frac{13}{15}$ is a reasonable answer.

Checking a Quotient by Estimating

$$6\frac{1}{4} \div 2\frac{7}{10} = \frac{25}{4} \div \frac{27}{10} = \frac{25}{\overset{}{4}_{2}} \times \frac{\overset{5}{10}}{27} = \frac{125}{54}, \text{ or } 2\frac{17}{54}$$

Our answer, $2\frac{17}{54}$, is close to 2, the quotient of the rounded dividend and divisor.

$$\downarrow \qquad \downarrow$$
$$6 \div \quad 3 = 2$$

Because 2 is near $2\frac{17}{54}$, $2\frac{17}{54}$ is a reasonable answer.

EXAMPLE 18

Simplify and check: $3\frac{3}{4} \times 5\frac{1}{3} \div 2\frac{7}{9}$

Solution   Following the order of operations rule, we work from left to right, multiplying the first two mixed numbers.

$$3\frac{3}{4} \times 5\frac{1}{3} = \frac{\overset{5}{15}}{\underset{1}{4}} \times \frac{\overset{4}{16}}{\underset{1}{3}} = 20$$

Then, we divide 20 by $2\frac{7}{9}$ to get the answer.

$$20 \div 2\frac{7}{9} = \frac{20}{1} \div \frac{25}{9} = \frac{\overset{4}{20}}{1} \times \frac{9}{\underset{5}{25}} = \frac{36}{5}, \text{ or } 7\frac{1}{5}$$

Now, let's check by estimating.

$$3\frac{3}{4} \times 5\frac{1}{3} \div 2\frac{7}{9}$$
$$\downarrow \qquad \downarrow \qquad \downarrow$$
$$4 \times \quad 5 \div \quad 3 = 20 \div 3 \approx 7$$

The answer, $7\frac{1}{5}$, and the estimate, 7, are reasonably close, confirming the answer.

PRACTICE 18

Compute and check:
$$5\frac{3}{5} \div 2\frac{1}{10} \times 2\frac{1}{4}$$

EXAMPLE 19

Calculate and check: $12 \div 1\frac{2}{3} + 5 \cdot 2\frac{9}{10}$

Solution   According to the order of operations rule, we divide and multiply before adding.

$$12 \div 1\frac{2}{3} + 5 \cdot 2\frac{9}{10} = \frac{12}{1} \div \frac{5}{3} + \frac{5}{1} \cdot \frac{29}{10}$$

$$= \frac{12}{1} \cdot \frac{3}{5} + \frac{5}{1} \cdot \frac{29}{10}$$

$$= \frac{12}{1} \cdot \frac{3}{5} + \frac{\overset{1}{\cancel{5}}}{1} \cdot \frac{29}{\underset{2}{\cancel{10}}}$$

$$= \frac{36}{5} + \frac{29}{2}$$

$$= 7\frac{1}{5} + 14\frac{1}{2}$$

$$= 7\frac{2}{10} + 14\frac{5}{10}$$

$$= 21\frac{7}{10}$$

Now, we estimate the answer in order to check.

$$12 \div 1\frac{2}{3} + 5 \cdot 2\frac{9}{10}$$
$$\downarrow \quad \downarrow \quad \downarrow \quad \downarrow$$
$$12 \div \ 2 + 5 \cdot \ \ 3 \approx 21$$

The estimate and the answer are close, confirming the answer.

PRACTICE 19

Compute and check:

$14\frac{1}{3} \div 2 - 6 \div 2\frac{1}{4}$

Mathematically Speaking

Fill in each blank with the most appropriate term or phrase from the given list.

reverse	proper fraction	multiply
divide	simplify	reciprocal
invert	factor	improper fraction

1. To find the product of the fractions $\frac{1}{7}$ and $\frac{5}{8}$, _____ 1 and 5, and 7 and 8.

2. To multiply mixed numbers, change each mixed number to its equivalent _____.

3. The fraction $\frac{2}{3}$ is said to be the _____ of the fraction $\frac{3}{2}$.

4. To _____ fractions, change the divisor to its reciprocal, and multiply the resulting fractions.

5. To _____ a fraction is to find its reciprocal.

6. When multiplying fractions, we can divide any numerator and any denominator by a common _____.

A *Multiply and simplify.*

7. $\frac{1}{3} \times \frac{2}{5}$

8. $\frac{7}{8} \times \frac{1}{2}$

9. $\left(\frac{5}{8}\right)\left(\frac{2}{3}\right)$

10. $\left(\frac{3}{10}\right)\left(\frac{1}{4}\right)$

11. $\left(\frac{3}{4}\right)^2$

12. $\left(\frac{1}{8}\right)^2$

13. $\frac{4}{5} \times \frac{2}{5}$

14. $\frac{1}{2} \times \frac{3}{2}$

15. $\frac{7}{8} \times \frac{5}{4}$

16. $\frac{20}{3} \times \frac{2}{7}$

17. $\frac{5}{2} \cdot \frac{9}{8}$

18. $\frac{11}{10} \cdot \frac{9}{5}$

19. $\left(\frac{2}{5}\right)\left(\frac{5}{9}\right)$

20. $\left(\frac{4}{5}\right)\left(\frac{1}{4}\right)$

21. $\frac{7}{9} \times \frac{3}{4}$

22. $\frac{4}{5} \times \frac{1}{2}$

23. $\left(\frac{1}{8}\right)\left(\frac{6}{10}\right)$

24. $\left(\frac{4}{6}\right)\left(\frac{3}{8}\right)$

25. $\frac{10}{9} \times \frac{93}{100}$

26. $\frac{12}{5} \times \frac{15}{4}$

27. $\frac{2}{3} \times 20$

28. $\frac{5}{6} \times 5$

29. $\left(\frac{10}{3}\right)(4)$

30. $\left(\frac{5}{3}\right)(7)$

31. $\frac{2}{3} \times 24$

32. $\frac{3}{4} \times 12$

33. $\frac{2}{3} \cdot 6$

34. $100 \cdot \frac{2}{5}$

35. $18 \cdot \frac{2}{9}$

36. $20 \cdot \frac{4}{5}$

37. $\frac{7}{8} \times 10$

38. $\frac{5}{8} \times 12$

39. $\left(\frac{7}{8}\right)\left(1\frac{1}{2}\right)$

40. $\left(4\frac{1}{3}\right)\left(\frac{1}{5}\right)$

41. $\frac{1}{4} \cdot 8\frac{1}{2}$

42. $\frac{1}{3} \cdot 2\frac{1}{5}$

43. $\left(\frac{5}{6}\right)\left(1\frac{1}{9}\right)$

44. $\left(\frac{9}{10}\right)\left(2\frac{1}{7}\right)$

45. $\frac{1}{2} \times 5\frac{1}{3}$

46. $4\frac{1}{2} \times \frac{2}{3}$

47. $\frac{4}{5} \cdot 1\frac{1}{4}$

48. $\frac{3}{8} \cdot 5\frac{1}{3}$

49. $\left(\frac{3}{16}\right)\left(4\frac{2}{3}\right)$

50. $\left(\frac{7}{9}\right)\left(2\frac{1}{4}\right)$

51. $1\frac{1}{7} \times 1\frac{1}{5}$

52. $2\frac{1}{3} \times 1\frac{1}{2}$

53. $\left(2\frac{1}{10}\right)^2$

54. $\left(1\frac{1}{2}\right)^2$

55. $3\frac{9}{10} \cdot 2$

56. $5 \cdot 1\frac{1}{2}$

57. $100 \times 3\frac{3}{4}$

58. $1\frac{5}{6} \times 20$

59. $1\frac{1}{2} \times 5\frac{1}{3}$

60. $5\frac{1}{4} \times 1\frac{1}{9}$

61. $\left(2\frac{1}{2}\right)\left(1\frac{1}{5}\right)$

62. $\left(1\frac{3}{10}\right)\left(2\frac{4}{9}\right)$

63. $12\frac{1}{2} \cdot 3\frac{1}{3}$

64. $5\frac{1}{10} \cdot 1\frac{2}{3}$

65. $66\frac{2}{3} \times 1\frac{7}{10}$

66. $37\frac{1}{2} \times 1\frac{3}{5}$

67. $1\frac{5}{9} \times \frac{3}{8} \times 2$

68. $\frac{1}{8} \times 2\frac{1}{4} \times 6$

69. $\left(\frac{1}{2}\right)^2\left(2\frac{1}{3}\right)$

70. $\left(1\frac{1}{4}\right)^2\left(\frac{1}{5}\right)$

71. $\frac{4}{5} \times \frac{7}{8} \times 1\frac{1}{10}$

72. $8\frac{1}{3} \times \frac{3}{10} \times \frac{5}{6}$

73. $\left(1\frac{1}{2}\right)^3$

74. $\left(2\frac{1}{2}\right)^3$

Divide and simplify.

75. $\frac{3}{5} \div \frac{2}{3}$

76. $\frac{2}{3} \div \frac{3}{5}$

77. $\frac{4}{5} \div \frac{7}{8}$

78. $\frac{7}{8} \div \frac{4}{5}$

79. $\frac{1}{2} \div \frac{1}{7}$

80. $\frac{1}{7} \div \frac{1}{2}$

81. $\frac{5}{9} \div \frac{1}{8}$

82. $\frac{1}{8} \div \frac{5}{9}$

83. $\frac{4}{5} \div \frac{8}{15}$

84. $\frac{3}{10} \div \frac{6}{5}$

85. $\frac{7}{8} \div \frac{3}{8}$

86. $\frac{10}{3} \div \frac{5}{6}$

87. $\frac{9}{10} \div \frac{3}{4}$

88. $\frac{5}{6} \div \frac{1}{3}$

89. $\frac{1}{10} \div \frac{2}{5}$

90. $\frac{3}{4} \div \frac{6}{5}$

91. $\frac{2}{3} \div 7$

92. $\frac{7}{10} \div 10$

93. $\frac{2}{3} \div 6$

94. $\frac{1}{20} \div 2$

95. $8 \div \frac{1}{5}$

96. $8 \div \frac{2}{9}$

97. $7 \div \frac{3}{7}$

98. $10 \div \frac{2}{5}$

99. $4 \div \frac{3}{10}$

100. $10 \div \frac{2}{3}$

101. $1 \div \frac{1}{7}$

102. $3 \div \frac{1}{8}$

103. $2\frac{5}{6} \div \frac{3}{7}$

104. $5\frac{1}{9} \div \frac{2}{3}$

105. $1\frac{1}{3} \div \frac{4}{5}$

106. $7\frac{1}{10} \div \frac{1}{2}$

107. $8\frac{5}{6} \div \frac{9}{10}$

108. $6\frac{1}{2} \div \frac{1}{2}$

109. $20\frac{1}{10} \div \frac{1}{5}$

110. $15\frac{2}{3} \div \frac{5}{6}$

111. $\frac{1}{6} \div 2\frac{1}{7}$

112. $\frac{2}{7} \div 1\frac{1}{3}$

113. $\frac{1}{2} \div 2\frac{3}{5}$

114. $\frac{3}{4} \div 3\frac{1}{9}$

115. $4 \div 1\frac{1}{4}$

116. $7 \div 1\frac{9}{10}$

117. $2\frac{1}{10} \div 20$

118. $5\frac{6}{7} \div 14$

119. $2\frac{1}{2} \div 3\frac{1}{7}$

120. $3\frac{1}{7} \div 2\frac{1}{2}$

121. $8\frac{1}{10} \div 5\frac{3}{4}$

122. $1\frac{7}{10} \div 5\frac{1}{8}$

123. $2\frac{1}{3} \div 4\frac{1}{2}$

124. $8\frac{1}{6} \div 2\frac{1}{2}$

125. $6\frac{3}{8} \div 2\frac{5}{6}$

126. $1\frac{2}{3} \div 1\frac{2}{5}$

Simplify.

127. $\dfrac{1}{2} + \dfrac{2}{3} \times 1\dfrac{1}{3}$

128. $\dfrac{9}{10} + \dfrac{4}{5} \cdot 8$

129. $5 - \dfrac{1}{3} \times \dfrac{2}{5}$

130. $3 \div \dfrac{2}{5} - 2\dfrac{1}{3}$

131. $2\dfrac{3}{4} \times \dfrac{1}{8} + \dfrac{1}{5}$

132. $\dfrac{3}{8} \cdot \dfrac{1}{2} - \dfrac{1}{10}$

133. $4 - \dfrac{2}{9} \div \dfrac{3}{4}$

134. $6 \div 5 \times \dfrac{1}{4}$

135. $3\dfrac{1}{2} \times 6 \div 5$

136. $4 \cdot \dfrac{2}{3} - 1\dfrac{1}{8}$

137. $10 \times \dfrac{1}{8} \times 2\dfrac{1}{2}$

138. $\dfrac{1}{3} \div \dfrac{1}{6} \times \dfrac{2}{3}$

139. $8 \div 1\dfrac{1}{5} + 3 \cdot 1\dfrac{1}{2}$

140. $3\dfrac{1}{8} \div 5 + 4 \div 2\dfrac{1}{2}$

141. $\dfrac{5}{6} \cdot \dfrac{9}{10} - \dfrac{3}{5} \div \dfrac{6}{7}$

142. $\dfrac{6}{11} \div \dfrac{18}{55} - \dfrac{7}{26} \cdot \dfrac{13}{14}$

143. $\left(\dfrac{1}{4}\right)^2 \cdot \left(3 - 1\dfrac{2}{3}\right)^2$

144. $\left(1 - \dfrac{2}{5}\right)^2 \div \left(1\dfrac{1}{2}\right)^2$

145. $\left(1\dfrac{1}{2} \div \dfrac{1}{3}\right)^2 + \left(1 - \dfrac{1}{4}\right)^2$

146. $\left(3\dfrac{1}{2}\right)^2 + 2\left(1\dfrac{1}{2} - 1\dfrac{1}{3}\right)$

Mixed Practice

147. Divide $6\dfrac{1}{8}$ by $2\dfrac{3}{4}$.

148. Compute: $14 - 3 \div \left(\dfrac{4}{5}\right)^2$

149. Find the product of $\dfrac{3}{5}$ and $\dfrac{7}{8}$.

150. Find the quotient of $\dfrac{9}{10}$ and $\dfrac{2}{5}$.

151. Multiply $\dfrac{2}{3}$ by 12.

152. Calculate: $\left(4\dfrac{1}{2}\right)\left(6\dfrac{2}{3}\right)$

Applications

B *Solve. Write the answer in simplest form.*

153. In a local town, $\dfrac{5}{6}$ of the voting-age population is registered to vote. If $\dfrac{7}{10}$ of the registered voters voted in the election for mayor, what fraction of the voting-age population voted?

154. Last year, $\dfrac{1}{8}$ of the emergency room visits at a hospital were injury related. Of these, $\dfrac{2}{5}$ were due to motor vehicle accidents. What fraction of the emergency room visits were due to motor vehicle accidents?

155. A couple would like to add on an extension to their house. One of the construction companies that bid on the job would charge $40,200 with $\dfrac{1}{30}$ down. How much money does the couple need to put down if they choose to use this company?

156. There is a rule of thumb to not spend more than $\dfrac{1}{4}$ of one's income on rent. If someone makes $24,000 a year, what is the most he or she should spend per month on rent according to this rule?

157. A tile store charges $46\dfrac{1}{2}$ per square foot for granite countertops, including installation. Find the cost of buying and installing a granite countertop on the kitchen island shown.

158. Which of these rooms has the larger area?

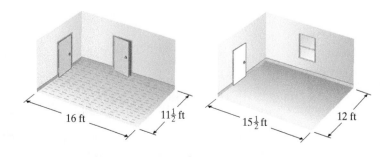

159. Students in an astronomy course learn that a first-magnitude star is $2\frac{1}{2}$ times as bright as a second-magnitude star, which in turn is $2\frac{1}{2}$ times as bright as a third-magnitude star. How many times as bright as a third-magnitude star is a first-magnitude star?

161. Because of evaporation, a pond loses $\frac{1}{4}$ of its remaining water each month of summer. If it is full at the beginning of summer, what fraction of the original amount will the pond contain after three summer months?

163. A trip to a nearby island takes $3\frac{1}{2}$ hours by boat and $\frac{1}{2}$ hour by airplane. How many times as fast as the boat is the plane?

165. A store sells two types of candles. The scented candle is 8 inches tall and burns $\frac{1}{2}$ inch per hour, whereas the unscented candle is 10 inches tall and burns $\frac{1}{3}$ inch per hour.

a. In an hour, which candle will burn more?

b. Which candle will last longer?

160. Some people believe that gasohol is superior to gasoline as an automotive fuel. Gasohol is a mixture of gasoline $\left(\frac{9}{10}\right)$ and ethyl alcohol $\left(\frac{1}{10}\right)$. How much more gasoline than ethyl alcohol is there in $10\frac{1}{2}$ gallons of gasohol?

162. A scientist is investigating the effects of cold on human skin. In one of the scientist's experiments, the temperature starts at 70°F and drops by $\frac{1}{10}$° every 2 minutes. What is the temperature after 6 minutes?

164. Each dose of aspirin weighs $\frac{3}{4}$ grain. If a hospital pharmacist has 9 grains of aspirin on hand, how many doses can he provide?

166. A college-wide fund-raising campaign collected $3 million in $1\frac{1}{2}$ years for student scholarships.

a. What was the average amount collected per year?

b. By how much would this average increase if an additional $1 million were collected?

• Check your answers on page A-3.

MINDStretchers

Writing

1. Every number except 0 has a reciprocal. Explain why 0 does not have a reciprocal.

Groupwork

2. In the following magic square, the *product* of every row, column, and diagonal is 1. Working with a partner, complete the square.

$\frac{2}{3}$		$1\frac{1}{2}$
$\frac{1}{2}$		

Patterns

3. Find the product: $1\frac{1}{2} \cdot 1\frac{1}{3} \cdot 1\frac{1}{4} \cdot \cdots \cdot 1\frac{1}{99} \cdot 1\frac{1}{100}$

Key Concepts and Skills

CONCEPT   SKILL

Concept/Skill	Description	Example
[2.1] **Prime number**	A whole number that has exactly two different factors: itself and 1.	2, 3, 5
[2.1] **Composite number**	A whole number that has more than two factors.	4, 8, 9
[2.1] **Prime factorization of a whole number**	The number written as the product of its prime factors.	$30 = 2 \cdot 3 \cdot 5$
[2.1] **Least common multiple (LCM) of two or more whole numbers**	The smallest nonzero whole number that is a multiple of each number.	The LCM of 30 and 45 is 90.
[2.1] **To compute the least common multiple (LCM)**	• Find the prime factorization of each number. • Identify the prime factors that appear in each factorization. • Multiply these prime factors, using each factor the greatest number of times that it occurs in any of the factorizations.	$20 = 2 \cdot 2 \cdot 5$ $\quad = 2^2 \cdot 5$ $30 = 2 \cdot 3 \cdot 5$ The LCM of 20 and 30 is $2^2 \cdot 3 \cdot 5$, or 60.
[2.2] **Fraction**	Any number that can be written in the form $\frac{a}{b}$, where a and b are whole numbers and b is nonzero.	$\frac{3}{11}, \frac{9}{5}$
[2.2] **Proper fraction**	A fraction whose numerator is smaller than its denominator.	$\frac{2}{7}, \frac{1}{2}$
[2.2] **Mixed number**	A number with a whole-number part and a proper fraction part.	$5\frac{1}{3}, 4\frac{5}{6}$
[2.2] **Improper fraction**	A fraction whose numerator is greater than or equal to its denominator.	$\frac{9}{4}, \frac{5}{5}$
[2.2] **To change a mixed number to an improper fraction**	• Multiply the denominator of the fraction by the whole-number part of the mixed number. • Add the numerator of the fraction to this product. • Write this sum over the denominator to form the improper fraction.	$4\frac{2}{3} = \frac{3 \times 4 + 2}{3}$ $\quad = \frac{14}{3}$
[2.2] **To change an improper fraction to a mixed number**	• Divide the numerator by the denominator. • If there is a remainder, write it over the denominator.	$\frac{14}{3} = 4\frac{2}{3}$
[2.2] **To find an equivalent fraction**	Multiply the numerator and denominator of $\frac{a}{b}$ by the same whole number; that is, $\frac{a}{b} = \frac{a \cdot n}{b \cdot n}$, where both b and n are nonzero.	$\frac{3}{4} = \frac{3 \cdot 2}{4 \cdot 2} = \frac{6}{8}$

continued

145

Concept/Skill	Description	Example
[2.2] **To simplify a fraction**	• First, express both the numerator and denominator as the product of their prime factors. • Then, divide out or cancel all common factors.	$\dfrac{30}{84} = \dfrac{\overset{1}{2} \cdot \overset{1}{3} \cdot 5}{\underset{1}{2} \cdot 2 \cdot \underset{1}{3} \cdot 7} = \dfrac{5}{14}$
[2.2] **Like fractions**	Fractions with the same denominator.	$\dfrac{2}{5}, \dfrac{3}{5}$
[2.2] **Unlike fractions**	Fractions with different denominators.	$\dfrac{3}{5}, \dfrac{3}{10}$
[2.2] **To compare fractions**	• If the fractions are like, compare their numerators. • If the fractions are unlike, write them as equivalent fractions with the same denominator and then compare their numerators.	$\dfrac{6}{8}, \dfrac{7}{8}$ $6 < 7$, so $\dfrac{6}{8} < \dfrac{7}{8}$ $\dfrac{2}{3}, \dfrac{12}{15}$ or $\dfrac{10}{15}, \dfrac{12}{15}$ $12 > 10$, so $\dfrac{12}{15} > \dfrac{2}{3}$
[2.2] **Least common denominator (LCD) of two or more fractions**	The least common multiple of their denominators.	The LCD of $\dfrac{11}{30}$ and $\dfrac{7}{45}$ is 90.
[2.3] **To add (or subtract) like fractions**	• Add (or subtract) the numerators. • Use the given denominator. • Write the answer in simplest form.	$\dfrac{1}{8} + \dfrac{1}{8} = \dfrac{2}{8} = \dfrac{1}{4}$ $\dfrac{3}{8} - \dfrac{1}{8} = \dfrac{2}{8} = \dfrac{1}{4}$
[2.3] **To add (or subtract) unlike fractions**	• Write the fractions as equivalent fractions with the same denominator, usually the LCD. • Add (or subtract) the numerators, keeping the same denominator. • Write the answer in simplest form.	$\dfrac{2}{3} + \dfrac{1}{2} = \dfrac{4}{6} + \dfrac{3}{6}$ $\qquad = \dfrac{7}{6}$, or $1\dfrac{1}{6}$ $\dfrac{5}{12} - \dfrac{1}{6} = \dfrac{5}{12} - \dfrac{2}{12}$ $\qquad = \dfrac{3}{12}$, or $\dfrac{1}{4}$
[2.3] **To add mixed numbers**	• Write the fractions as equivalent fractions with the same denominator, usually the LCD. • Add the fractions. • Add the whole numbers. • Write the answer in simplest form.	$\begin{aligned} 4\tfrac{1}{2} &= 4\tfrac{3}{6} \\ +6\tfrac{2}{3} &= +6\tfrac{4}{6} \\ \hline & 10\tfrac{7}{6} = 11\tfrac{1}{6} \end{aligned}$
[2.3] **To subtract mixed numbers**	• Write the fractions as equivalent fractions with the same denominator, usually the LCD. • Regroup or borrow from the whole number on top if the fraction on the bottom is larger than the fraction on top. • Subtract the fractions. • Subtract the whole numbers. • Write the answer in simplest form.	$\begin{aligned} 4\tfrac{1}{5} &= 3\tfrac{6}{5} \\ -1\tfrac{2}{5} &= -1\tfrac{2}{5} \\ \hline & 2\tfrac{4}{5} \end{aligned}$

Concept/Skill	Description	Example
[2.4] **To multiply fractions**	• Multiply the numerators. • Multiply the denominators. • Write the answer in simplest form.	$\frac{1}{2} \cdot \frac{3}{5} = \frac{3}{10}$
[2.4] **To multiply mixed numbers**	• Write the mixed numbers as improper fractions. • Multiply the fractions. • Write the answer in simplest form.	$2\frac{1}{2} \cdot 1\frac{2}{3} = \frac{5}{2} \cdot \frac{5}{3}$ $= \frac{25}{6}$, or $4\frac{1}{6}$
[2.4] **Reciprocal of $\frac{a}{b}$**	The fraction $\frac{b}{a}$ formed by switching the numerator and denominator.	The reciprocal of $\frac{4}{3}$ is $\frac{3}{4}$.
[2.4] **To divide fractions**	• Change the divisor to its reciprocal, and multiply the resulting fractions. • Write the answer in simplest form.	$\frac{2}{5} \div \frac{3}{7} = \frac{2}{5} \cdot \frac{7}{3}$ $= \frac{14}{15}$
[2.4] **To divide mixed numbers**	• Write the mixed numbers as improper fractions. • Divide the fractions. • Write the answer in simplest form.	$2\frac{1}{2} \div 1\frac{1}{3} =$ $\frac{5}{2} \div \frac{4}{3} =$ $\frac{5}{2} \cdot \frac{3}{4} = \frac{15}{8}$, or $1\frac{7}{8}$

Cultural Note

In societies throughout the world and across the centuries, people have written fractions in strikingly different ways. In ancient Greece, for example, the fraction $\frac{1}{4}$ was written Δ″ where Δ (read "delta") is the fourth letter of the Greek alphabet.

At one time, people wrote the numerator and denominator of fractions in Roman numerals, as shown at the left in a page from a sixteenth-century German book. In today's notation, the last fraction shown on the page is $\frac{200}{460}$.

Source: David Eugene Smith and Jekuthiel Ginsburg, *Numbers and Numerals, a Story Book for Young and Old* (New York: Bureau of Publications, Teachers College, Columbia University, 1937).

Say Why   *Fill in each blank.*

1. Twenty-seven _____ a composite number
   is/is not

   because _____

   _____.

2. The prime factorization of 180 _____ $3^2 \times 4 \times 5$
   is/is not

   because _____

   _____.

3. The expression $\frac{3}{0}$ _____ a fraction because
   is/is not

   _____.

4. The expression $\frac{12}{11}$ _____ an improper fraction
   is/is not

   because _____

   _____.

5. The expression $\frac{16}{48}$ _____ equivalent to $\frac{1}{3}$ because
   is/is not

   _____

   _____.

6. The expressions $\frac{12}{15}$ and $\frac{12}{16}$ _____ unlike
   are/are not

   fractions because _____

   _____.

7. The least common denominator of $\frac{5}{8}$ and $\frac{7}{12}$ _____
   is/is not

   24 because _____

   _____.

8. The reciprocal of $\frac{6}{8}$ _____ $\frac{3}{4}$ because _____
   is/is not

   _____

   _____.

[2.1]   *Find all the factors of each number.*

9. 150
10. 180
11. 57
12. 70

Indicate whether each number is prime or composite.

13. 23
14. 33
15. 87
16. 67

Write the prime factorization of each number, using exponents.

17. 36
18. 75
19. 99
20. 54

Find the LCM.

21. 6 and 14
22. 5 and 10
23. 18, 24, and 36
24. 10, 15, and 20

[2.2]   *Identify the fraction or mixed number represented by the shaded portion of each figure.*

25.
26.
27.
28.

Indicate whether each number is a proper fraction, an improper fraction, or a mixed number.

29. $4\frac{1}{8}$
30. $\frac{5}{6}$
31. $\frac{3}{2}$
32. $\frac{7}{1}$

Write each mixed number as an improper fraction.

33. $7\frac{2}{3}$

34. $1\frac{4}{5}$

35. $9\frac{1}{10}$

36. $8\frac{3}{7}$

Write each fraction as a mixed number or a whole number.

37. $\frac{13}{2}$

38. $\frac{14}{3}$

39. $\frac{11}{4}$

40. $\frac{12}{12}$

Write an equivalent fraction with the given denominator.

41. $7 = \frac{}{12}$

42. $\frac{2}{7} = \frac{}{14}$

43. $\frac{1}{2} = \frac{}{10}$

44. $\frac{9}{10} = \frac{}{30}$

Simplify.

45. $\frac{14}{28}$

46. $\frac{15}{21}$

47. $\frac{30}{45}$

48. $\frac{54}{72}$

49. $5\frac{2}{4}$

50. $8\frac{10}{15}$

51. $6\frac{12}{42}$

52. $8\frac{45}{63}$

Insert the appropriate sign: $<$, $=$, or $>$.

53. $\frac{5}{8} \quad \frac{3}{8}$

54. $\frac{5}{6} \quad \frac{1}{6}$

55. $\frac{2}{3} \quad \frac{4}{5}$

56. $\frac{9}{10} \quad \frac{7}{8}$

57. $\frac{3}{4} \quad \frac{5}{8}$

58. $\frac{7}{10} \quad \frac{5}{9}$

59. $3\frac{1}{5} \quad 1\frac{9}{10}$

60. $5\frac{1}{8} \quad 5\frac{1}{9}$

Arrange in increasing order.

61. $\frac{2}{7}, \frac{3}{8}, \frac{1}{2}$

62. $\frac{1}{5}, \frac{1}{3}, \frac{2}{15}$

63. $\frac{4}{5}, \frac{9}{10}, \frac{3}{4}$

64. $\frac{7}{8}, \frac{7}{9}, \frac{13}{18}$

[2.3] *Add and simplify.*

65. $\frac{2}{5} + \frac{4}{5}$

66. $\frac{7}{20} + \frac{8}{20}$

67. $\frac{5}{8} + \frac{7}{8} + \frac{3}{8}$

68. $\frac{3}{10} + \frac{1}{10} + \frac{2}{10}$

69. $\frac{1}{3} + \frac{2}{5}$

70. $\frac{7}{8} + \frac{5}{6}$

71. $\frac{9}{10} + \frac{1}{2} + \frac{2}{5}$

72. $\frac{3}{8} + \frac{4}{5} + \frac{3}{4}$

73. $2 + 3\frac{7}{8}$

74. $6\frac{1}{4} + 3\frac{1}{4}$

75. $8\frac{7}{10} + 1\frac{9}{10}$

76. $5\frac{5}{6} + 2\frac{1}{6}$

77. $2\frac{1}{3} + 4\frac{1}{3} + 5\frac{2}{3}$

78. $1\frac{3}{10} + \frac{9}{10} + 2\frac{1}{10}$

79. $5\frac{2}{5} + \frac{3}{10}$

80. $9\frac{1}{6} + 8\frac{3}{8}$

81. $10\frac{2}{3} + 12\frac{3}{4}$

82. $20\frac{1}{2} + 25\frac{7}{8}$

83. $10\frac{3}{5} + 7\frac{9}{10} + 2\frac{1}{4}$

84. $20\frac{7}{8} + 30\frac{5}{6} + 4\frac{1}{3}$

Subtract and simplify.

85. $\frac{3}{8} - \frac{1}{8}$

86. $\frac{7}{9} - \frac{1}{9}$

87. $\frac{5}{3} - \frac{2}{3}$

88. $\frac{4}{6} - \frac{4}{6}$

89. $\dfrac{3}{10} - \dfrac{1}{20}$

90. $\dfrac{1}{2} - \dfrac{1}{8}$

91. $\dfrac{3}{5} - \dfrac{1}{4}$

92. $\dfrac{1}{3} - \dfrac{1}{10}$

93. $12\dfrac{1}{2} - 5$

94. $4\dfrac{3}{10} - 2$

95. $8\dfrac{7}{8} - 5\dfrac{1}{8}$

96. $20\dfrac{3}{4} - 2\dfrac{1}{4}$

97. $12 - 5\dfrac{1}{2}$

98. $4 - 2\dfrac{3}{10}$

99. $7 - 4\dfrac{1}{3}$

100. $1 - \dfrac{4}{5}$

101. $6\dfrac{1}{10} - 4\dfrac{3}{10}$

102. $2\dfrac{5}{8} - 1\dfrac{7}{8}$

103. $5\dfrac{1}{4} - 2\dfrac{3}{4}$

104. $7\dfrac{1}{6} - 3\dfrac{5}{6}$

105. $3\dfrac{1}{10} - 2\dfrac{4}{5}$

106. $7\dfrac{1}{2} - 4\dfrac{5}{8}$

107. $5\dfrac{1}{12} - 4\dfrac{1}{2}$

108. $6\dfrac{2}{9} - 2\dfrac{1}{3}$

109. $\dfrac{1}{3} + \dfrac{5}{6} - \dfrac{1}{2}$

110. $7\dfrac{9}{10} - 1\dfrac{1}{5} + 2\dfrac{3}{4}$

[2.4] *Multiply and simplify.*

111. $\dfrac{3}{4} \times \dfrac{1}{4}$

112. $\dfrac{1}{2} \times \dfrac{7}{8}$

113. $\left(\dfrac{5}{6}\right)\left(\dfrac{3}{4}\right)$

114. $\left(\dfrac{2}{3}\right)\left(\dfrac{1}{4}\right)$

115. $\dfrac{2}{3} \cdot 8$

116. $\dfrac{1}{10} \cdot 7$

117. $\left(\dfrac{1}{5}\right)^3$

118. $\left(\dfrac{2}{3}\right)^3$

119. $\dfrac{1}{2} \times \dfrac{2}{3} \times \dfrac{3}{4}$

120. $\dfrac{7}{8} \times \dfrac{2}{5} \times \dfrac{1}{6}$

121. $\dfrac{4}{5} \times 1\dfrac{1}{5}$

122. $\dfrac{2}{3} \times 2\dfrac{1}{3}$

123. $5\dfrac{1}{3} \cdot \dfrac{1}{2}$

124. $\dfrac{1}{10} \cdot 6\dfrac{2}{3}$

125. $1\dfrac{1}{3} \cdot 4\dfrac{1}{2}$

126. $3\dfrac{1}{4} \cdot 5\dfrac{2}{3}$

127. $6\dfrac{3}{4} \times 1\dfrac{1}{4}$

128. $8\dfrac{1}{2} \times 2\dfrac{1}{2}$

129. $\dfrac{7}{8} \times 1\dfrac{1}{5} \times \dfrac{3}{7}$

130. $1\dfrac{3}{8} \times \dfrac{10}{11} \times 1\dfrac{1}{4}$

131. $\left(3\dfrac{1}{3}\right)^3$

132. $\left(1\dfrac{1}{2}\right)^3$

133. $\dfrac{5}{8} + \dfrac{1}{2} \cdot 5$

134. $1\dfrac{9}{10} - \left(\dfrac{2}{3}\right)^2$

135. $4\left(\dfrac{2}{5}\right) + 3\left(\dfrac{1}{6}\right)$

136. $6\left(1\dfrac{1}{2} - \dfrac{3}{10}\right)$

Find the reciprocal.

137. $\dfrac{2}{3}$

138. $1\dfrac{1}{2}$

139. 8

140. $\dfrac{1}{4}$

Divide and simplify.

141. $\dfrac{7}{8} \div 5$

142. $\dfrac{5}{9} \div 9$

143. $\dfrac{2}{3} \div 5$

144. $\dfrac{1}{100} \div 2$

145. $\dfrac{1}{2} \div \dfrac{2}{3}$

146. $\dfrac{2}{3} \div \dfrac{1}{2}$

147. $6 \div \dfrac{1}{5}$

148. $7 \div \dfrac{4}{5}$

149. $\dfrac{7}{8} \div \dfrac{3}{4}$

150. $\dfrac{9}{10} \div \dfrac{1}{2}$

151. $\dfrac{3}{5} \div \dfrac{3}{10}$

152. $\dfrac{2}{3} \div \dfrac{1}{6}$

153. $3\frac{1}{2} \div 2$

154. $2 \div 3\frac{1}{2}$

155. $6\frac{1}{3} \div 4$

156. $4 \div 6\frac{1}{3}$

157. $8\frac{1}{4} \div 1\frac{1}{2}$

158. $3\frac{2}{5} \div 1\frac{1}{3}$

159. $4\frac{1}{2} \div 2\frac{1}{4}$

160. $7\frac{1}{5} \div 2\frac{2}{5}$

161. $\left(5 - \frac{2}{3}\right) \div \frac{4}{9}$

162. $6\frac{1}{2} \div \left(\frac{1}{2} + 4\frac{1}{2}\right)$

163. $7 \div 2\frac{1}{4} + 5 \div \left(1\frac{1}{2}\right)^2$

164. $\left(1\frac{2}{3}\right)^2 \times 2 + 9 \div 4\frac{1}{2}$

Mixed Applications

Solve. Write the answer in simplest form.

165. The Summer Olympic Games are held during each year divisible by 4. Were the Olympic Games held in 1990?

166. What is the smallest amount of money that you can pay in both all quarters and all dimes?

167. Eight of the 32 human teeth are incisors. What fraction of human teeth are incisors? (*Source:* Ilsa Goldsmith, *Human Anatomy for Children*)

168. The planets in the solar system (including the "dwarf planet" Pluto) consist of Earth, two planets closer to the Sun than Earth, and six planets farther from the Sun than Earth. What fraction of the planets in the solar system are closer than Earth to the Sun? (*Source:* Patrick Moore, *Astronomy for the Beginner*)

169. A Filmworks camera has a shutter speed of $\frac{1}{8,000}$ second and a Lensmax camera has a shutter speed of $\frac{1}{6,000}$ second. Which shutter is faster? (*Hint:* The faster shutter has the smaller shutter speed.)

170. In a recent year, among Americans who were 65 years of age or older 15 million were male and 21 million female. What fraction of this population was female? (*Source:* U. S. Census Bureau)

171. An insurance company reimbursed a patient $275 on a dental bill of $700. Did the patient get more or less than $\frac{1}{3}$ of the money paid back? Explain.

172. A union goes on strike if at least $\frac{2}{3}$ of the workers voting support the strike call. If 23 of the 32 voting workers support a strike, should a strike be declared? Explain.

173. A grand jury has 23 jurors. Sixteen jurors are needed for a quorum, and a vote of 12 jurors is needed to indict.

   a. What fraction of the full jury is needed to indict?

   b. Suppose that 16 jurors are present. What fraction of those present is needed to indict?

174. In a tennis match, Lisa Gregory went to the net 12 times, winning the point 7 times. By contrast, Monica Yates won the point 4 of the 6 times that she went to the net.

   a. Which player went to the net more often?

   b. Which player had a better rate of winning points at the net?

175. In a math course, $\frac{3}{5}$ of a student's grade is based on four in-class exams, and $\frac{3}{20}$ of the grade is based on homework. What fraction of a student's grade is based on in-class exams and homework?

176. A metal alloy is made by combining $\frac{1}{4}$ ounce of copper with $\frac{2}{3}$ ounce of tin. Find the alloy's total weight.

177. The weight of a diamond is measured in carats. What is the difference in weight between a $\frac{3}{4}$-carat and a $\frac{1}{2}$-carat diamond?

$\frac{1}{4}$

178. During a sale, the price of a sweater was marked $\frac{1}{4}$ off the original price of $45. Using a coupon, a customer received an additional $\frac{1}{5}$ off the sale price. What fraction of the original price was the final sale price?

179. In a math class, $\frac{3}{8}$ of the students are chemistry majors and $\frac{2}{3}$ of those students are women. If there are 48 students in the math class, how many women are chemistry majors?

180. Three-eighths of the undergraduate students at a two-year college receive financial aid. If the college has 4,296 undergraduate students, how many undergraduate students do not receive financial aid?

181. Of the first 10 artists to receive the Grammy Lifetime Achievement Award, $\frac{4}{5}$ were men. How many of these awardees were women? (*Source: Top 10 of Everything 2010*)

182. A sea otter eats about $\frac{1}{5}$ of its body weight each day. How much will a 35-pound otter eat in a day? (*Source: Karl W. Kenyon, The Sea Otter in the Eastern Pacific Ocean*)

183. An investor bought $1,000 worth of a technology stock. At the beginning of last year, it had increased in value by $\frac{2}{5}$. During the year, the value of the stock declined by $\frac{1}{4}$. What was the value of the stock at the end of last year?

184. In Roseville, 40 of every 1,000 people who want to work are unemployed, in contrast to 8 of every 100 people in Georgetown. How many times as great as the unemployment rate in Roseville is the unemployment rate in Georgetown?

185. A brother and sister want to buy as many goldfish as possible for their new fish tank. A rule of thumb is that the total length of fish (in inches) should be less than the capacity of the tank (in gallons). If they have a 10-gallon tank and goldfish average $\frac{1}{2}$ inch in length, how many fish should they buy?

186. A commuter is driving to the city of Denver 15 miles away. If he has already driven $3\frac{1}{4}$ miles, how far is he from Denver?

187. The wingspread of a Boeing 777-300 jet is $199\frac{11}{12}$ feet, whereas the wingspread of a Boeing 747-400 is $211\frac{5}{12}$ feet. How much longer is the wingspread of a Boeing 747-400 jet? (*Source:* boeing.com)

188. A Chicago family plans to take a vacation traveling by express bus either to Kansas City or to Indianapolis. The trip to Kansas City takes $11\frac{3}{4}$ hours, in contrast to a trip to Indianapolis that takes only $4\frac{1}{3}$ hours. How much longer is the first trip? (*Source:* greyhound.com)

189. An airplane is flying $1\frac{1}{2}$ times the speed of sound. If sound travels at about 1,000 feet per second, at what speed is the plane flying?

190. When standing upright, the pressure per square inch on a person's hip joint is about $2\frac{1}{2}$ times his or her body weight. If the person weighs 200 pounds, what is that pressure? (*Source:* pnas.org)

191. A cubic foot of water weighs approximately $62\frac{1}{2}$ pounds. If a basin contains $4\frac{1}{2}$ cubic feet of water, how much does the water weigh?

192. In 2009, the attendance at Fenway Park in Boston was about $1\frac{1}{4}$ times the attendance ten years earlier. If attendance in 1999 was approximately 2,500,000, what was the attendance in 2009? Round to the nearest hundred thousand. (*Source:* ballparks.com)

193. It took the space shuttle Endeavor $1\frac{1}{2}$ hours to orbit Earth. How many orbits did the Endeavor make in 12 hours? (*Source:* NASA)

194. An offshore wind farm measures $10\frac{1}{4}$ miles by $2\frac{1}{2}$ miles. Find the area of the wind farm.

195. The following chart is a record of the amount of time (in hours) that two employees spent working the past weekend. Complete the chart.

Employee	Saturday	Sunday	Total
L. Chavis	$7\frac{1}{2}$	$4\frac{1}{4}$	
R. Young	$5\frac{3}{4}$	$6\frac{1}{2}$	
Total			

196. Complete the following chart.

Worker	Hours per Day	Days Worked	Total Hours	Wage per Hour	Gross Pay
Maya	5	3		$7	
Noel	$7\frac{1}{4}$	4		$10	
Alisa	$4\frac{1}{2}$	$5\frac{1}{2}$		$9	

197. According to a newspaper advertisement, a man on a diet lost 60 pounds in $5\frac{1}{2}$ months. On the average, how much weight did he lose per month?

198. According to the nutrition label on a box of cereal, one serving is $1\frac{1}{4}$ cups. If the box contains 18 servings of cereal, how many cups of cereal does it contain?

199. The American explorers Lewis and Clark traveled about 8,000 miles in $2\frac{1}{2}$ years, mapping an overland route to the Pacific Ocean. Approximately how many miles did they travel per year? (*Source:* nps.gov)

200. One of the largest yachts in the world is the German-built motor yacht Arctic P. If the yacht's length is $87\frac{2}{3}$ meters and its beam (its width at the widest point) is $14\frac{3}{4}$ meters, how many times its width is its length, to the nearest whole number? (*Source:* superyachts.com)

CHAPTER 2   Posttest

FOR EXTRA HELP

CHAPTER Test Prep VIDEOS

The Chapter Test Prep Videos with test solutions are available on DVD, in MyMathLab, and on YouTube (search "AkstBasicMath" and click on "Channels").

To see if you have mastered the topics in this chapter, take this test.

1. List all the factors of 63.

2. Write 54 as the product of prime factors.

3. What fraction of the diagram is shaded?

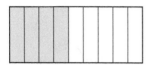

4. Write 12 as an improper fraction.

5. Express $\dfrac{41}{4}$ as a mixed number.

6. Write $\dfrac{875}{1,000}$ in simplest form

7. Which is smaller, $\dfrac{2}{3}$ or $\dfrac{5}{10}$?

8. What is the LCD for $\dfrac{3}{8}$ and $\dfrac{1}{12}$?

Add.

9. $\dfrac{2}{3} + \dfrac{1}{8} + \dfrac{3}{4}$

10. $6\dfrac{7}{8} + 1\dfrac{3}{10}$

Subtract.

11. $6 - 1\dfrac{5}{7}$

12. $10\dfrac{1}{6} - 4\dfrac{2}{5}$

Multiply.

13. $\left(\dfrac{1}{9}\right)^2$

14. $2\dfrac{2}{3} \times 4\dfrac{1}{2}$

15. Divide: $2\dfrac{1}{3} \div 3$

16. Calculate: $14\dfrac{1}{2} - 5 \cdot 1\dfrac{1}{3}$

Solve. Write your answer in simplest form.

17. Four of the 44 men who have served as vice-president of the United States were born in Indiana. What fraction of these men were *not* born in Indiana? (*Source: The New York Times Almanac 2010*)

18. In an Ironman triathlon, an athlete completed the 112-mile bike ride in $5\dfrac{5}{6}$ hours. What was the average number of miles she bicycled each hour?

19. The film *Super Troopers* lasts $1\dfrac{2}{3}$ hours. If the film is half over, how much remains to the running time of the film?

20. A college student has a part-time job, working $5\dfrac{1}{2}$ hours on Monday and $6\dfrac{1}{4}$ hours on Tuesday. If the student makes $8 an hour, how much money did the student make for the two days of work?

• Check your answers on page A-4.

Cumulative Review Exercises

To help you review, solve the following:

1. Write in words: 5,000,315

2. Round 1,876,529 to the nearest hundred thousand.

3. Multiply: $5,814 \times 100$

4. Find the quotient: $89\overline{)80,812}$

5. Evaluate: $24 \div (2 + 4) - 3$

6. Evaluate: $\left(\dfrac{6 - 5}{2 + 3}\right)^2$

7. Write the prime factorization of 84 using exponents.

8. Find the least common multiple of 20 and 24.

9. Write $\dfrac{75}{100}$ in simplest form.

10. Which is larger, $\dfrac{1}{4}$ or $\dfrac{3}{8}$?

11. Add: $\dfrac{5}{8} + \dfrac{5}{6}$

12. Subtract: $8 - 1\dfrac{3}{5}$

13. Find the product: $1\dfrac{1}{2} \cdot 4\dfrac{2}{3}$

14. Divide: $4 \div 2\dfrac{3}{4}$

15. In a recent year, the two U.S. corporations with largest revenues were ExxonMobil and Walmart Stores. How much greater were the ExxonMobil revenues? (*Source: Fortune*)

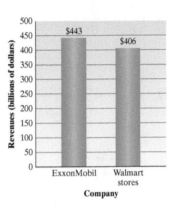

16. A jury decided on punishments in an oil spill case. The jury ordered the captain of the oil barge to pay $5,000 in punitive damages and the oil company to pay $5 billion. The amount that the company had to pay is how many times the amount that the captain had to pay?

17. The following table gives the number of named storms (tropical storms, hurricanes, and subtropical storms) that hit the United States in recent years:

Year	Number of Named Storms
2005	28
2006	10
2007	15
2008	18
2009	9

(*Source:* aoml.noaa.gov)

How far above the five-year average was the number of named storms in 2005?

18. A gallon of paint covers approximately 400 square feet. A room has two walls that are 8 feet high and 13 feet wide, and two walls that are 8 feet high and 15 feet wide. The doors and windows along those walls total 78 square feet. Will one gallon of paint cover the walls? Why or why not?

19. A homeowner wants to refinish his basement over three weekends. He completes $\dfrac{1}{4}$ of the job the first weekend and $\dfrac{5}{12}$ of the job the second weekend. What fraction of the job remains to be completed?

20. In a theater program, a student purchases a 7-inch-long piece of trim for costumes. From this purchase, how many $1\dfrac{3}{4}$-inch-long pieces of trim can be made?

• Check your answers on page A-4.

CHAPTER 3

3.1 **Introduction to Decimals**

3.2 **Adding and Subtracting Decimals**

3.3 **Multiplying Decimals**

3.4 **Dividing Decimals**

Decimals

Decimals and Blood Tests

Blood tests reveal a great deal about a person's health—whether to reduce the cholesterol level to lower the risk of heart disease, or raise the red blood cell count to prevent anemia. And blood tests identify a variety of diseases, for example, AIDS and mononucleosis.

Blood analyses are typically carried out in clinical laboratories. Technicians in these labs operate giant machines that perform thousands of blood tests per hour.

What these blood tests, known as "chemistries," actually do is to analyze blood for a variety of substances, such as creatinine and calcium.

In any blood test, doctors look for abnormal levels of the substance being measured. For instance, the normal range on the creatinine test is typically from 0.7 to 1.5 milligrams (mg) per unit of blood. A high level may mean kidney disease; a low level, muscular dystrophy.

The normal range on the calcium test may be 9.0 to 10.5 mg per unit of blood. A result outside this range is a clue for any of several diseases.

(*Source:* Dixie Farley, "Top 10 Laboratory Tests: Blood Will Tell," *FDA Consumer*, Vol. 23)

To see if you have already mastered the topics in this chapter, take this test.

1. In the number 27.081, what place does the 8 occupy?

2. Write in words: 4.012

3. Round 3.079 to the nearest tenth.

4. Which is largest: 0.00212, 0.0029, or 0.000888?

Perform the indicated operations.

5. $7.02 + 3.5 + 11$

6. $2.37 + 5.0038$

7. $13.79 - 2.1$

8. $9 - 2.7 + 3.51$

9. $8.3 \times 1{,}000$

10. 8.01×2.3

11. $(0.12)^2$

12. $5 + 3 \times 0.7$

13. $6.05 \div 1{,}000$

14. $\dfrac{9.81}{0.3}$

Express as a decimal.

15. $\dfrac{7}{8}$

16. $2\dfrac{5}{6}$, rounded to the nearest hundredth

Solve.

17. In a science course, a student learns that an acid is stronger if it has a lower pH value. Which is stronger, an acid with a pH value of 3.7 or an acid with a pH value of 2.95?

18. The following table shows the quarterly revenues for Microsoft Corporation in a recent fiscal year.

	First	Second	Third	Fourth
Revenue (in billions of dollars)	15.06	16.63	13.65	13.1

What was Microsoft's total revenue for the four quarters? (*Source:* microsoft.com)

19. A serving of iceberg lettuce contains 3.6 milligrams (mg) of vitamin C, whereas romaine lettuce contains 11.9 mg of vitamin C. Romaine lettuce is how many times as rich in vitamin C as iceberg lettuce? Round the answer to the nearest whole number. (*Source: The Concise Encyclopedia of Foods and Nutrition*)

20. A tourist visiting Orlando makes a long-distance telephone call that costs $0.85 for the first 3 minutes and $0.17 for each additional minute. What is the cost of a 20-minute call?

• Check your answers on page A-4.

3.1 Introduction to Decimals

OBJECTIVES

A To read or write decimals

B To find the fraction equivalent to a decimal

C To compare decimals

D To round decimals

E To solve applied problems involving decimals

What Decimals Are and Why They Are Important

Decimal notation is in common use. When we say that the price of a book is $32.75, that the length of a table is 1.8 meters, or that the answer displayed on a calculator is 5.007, we are using decimals.

A number written as a **decimal** has

- a whole-number part, which *precedes* the decimal point, and
- a fractional part, which *follows* the decimal point.

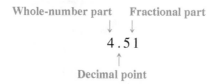

A decimal without a decimal point shown is understood to have one at the right end and is the same as a whole number. For instance, 3 and 3. are the same number.

The fractional part of any decimal has as its denominator a power of 10, such as 10, 100, or 1,000. The use of the word *decimal* reminds us of the importance of the number 10 in this notation, just as decade means 10 years or December meant the 10th month of the year (which it was for the early Romans).

In many problems, we can choose to work with either decimals or fractions. Therefore, we need to know how to work with both if we are to use the easier approach to solve a particular problem.

Decimal Places

Each digit in a decimal has a place value. The place value system for decimals is an extension of the place value system for whole numbers.

The places to the right of the decimal point are called **decimal places**. For instance, the number 64.149 is said to have three decimal places.

For a whole number, place values are powers of 10: $1, 10, 100, \ldots$. By contrast, each place value for the fractional part of a decimal is the reciprocal of a power of 10: $\frac{1}{10}, \frac{1}{100}, \frac{1}{1,000}, \ldots$

The first decimal place after the decimal point is the tenths place. Working to the right, the next decimal places are the hundredths place, the thousandths place, and so on.

The following table shows the place values in the decimals 0.54 and 0.30716.

Ones	.	Tenths	Hundredths	Thousandths	Ten-thousandths	Hundred-thousandths
1	and	$\frac{1}{10}$	$\frac{1}{100}$	$\frac{1}{1,000}$	$\frac{1}{10,000}$	$\frac{1}{100,000}$
0	.	5	4			
0	.	3	0	7	1	6

The next table shows the place values for the decimals 7,204.5 and 513.285.

Thousands	Hundreds	Tens	Ones	.	Tenths	Hundredths	Thousandths
1,000	100	10	1	and	$\frac{1}{10}$	$\frac{1}{100}$	$\frac{1}{1,000}$
7	2	0	4	.	5		
	5	1	3	.	2	8	5

EXAMPLE 1

In each number, identify the place that the digit 3 occupies.

a. 0.134   **b.** 92.388   **c.** 0.600437

Solution

a. The hundredths place

b. The tenths place

c. The hundred-thousandths place

PRACTICE 1

What place does the digit 1 occupy in each number?

a. 566.184

b. 43.57219

c. 0.921

Changing Decimals to Fractions

Knowing the place value system is the key to understanding what decimals mean, how to read them, and how to write them.

- The decimal 0.9, or .9, is another way of writing $(0 \times 1) + \left(9 \times \frac{1}{10}\right)$, or $\frac{9}{10}$. This decimal is read the same as the equivalent fraction: "nine tenths."

- The decimal 0.21 represents 2 tenths + 1 hundredth. This expression simplifies to the following:

$$\left(2 \times \frac{1}{10}\right) + \left(1 \times \frac{1}{100}\right) = \frac{2}{10} + \frac{1}{100} = \frac{20}{100} + \frac{1}{100}, \text{ or } \frac{21}{100}$$

So 0.21 is read "twenty-one hundredths."

- The decimal 0.149 stands for $\frac{149}{1,000}$.

$$\left(1 \times \frac{1}{10}\right) + \left(4 \times \frac{1}{100}\right) + \left(9 \times \frac{1}{1,000}\right) = \frac{1}{10} + \frac{4}{100} + \frac{9}{1,000}$$
$$= \frac{100}{1,000} + \frac{40}{1,000} + \frac{9}{1,000}$$
$$= \frac{149}{1,000}$$

So 0.149 is read "one hundred forty-nine thousandths."

Let's summarize these examples.

Decimal	Equivalent Fraction	Read as
0.9	$\dfrac{9}{10}$	Nine tenths
0.21	$\dfrac{21}{100}$	Twenty-one hundredths
0.149	$\dfrac{149}{1,000}$	One hundred forty-nine thousandths

Note that in each of these decimals, the fractional part is the same as the numerator of the equivalent fraction: $0.149 = \dfrac{149}{1,000}$.

We can use the following rule to rewrite any decimal as a fraction or a mixed number.

To Change a Decimal to the Equivalent Fraction or Mixed Number

- Copy the nonzero whole-number part of the decimal and drop the decimal point.
- Place the fractional part of the decimal in the numerator of the equivalent fraction.
- Make the denominator of the equivalent fraction 1 followed by as many zeros as the decimal has decimal places.
- Simplify the resulting fraction, if possible.

EXAMPLE 2

Express 0.75 in fractional form and simplify.

Solution   The whole-number part of the decimal is 0. We drop the decimal point. The fractional part (75) of the decimal becomes the numerator of the equivalent fraction. Since the decimal has two decimal places, we make the denominator of the equivalent fraction 1 followed by two zeros (100). So we can write 0.75 as $\dfrac{75}{100}$, which simplifies to $\dfrac{3}{4}$.

PRACTICE 2

Write 0.875 as a fraction in lowest terms.

EXAMPLE 3

Express 1.87 as a mixed number.

Solution   This decimal is equivalent to a mixed number whose whole-number part is 1. The fractional part (87) of the decimal is the numerator of the equivalent fraction. The decimal has two decimal places, so the fraction's denominator has two zeros (that is, it is 100).

$$1.87 = 1\frac{87}{100}$$

Do you see that the answer can also be written as $\dfrac{187}{100}$?

PRACTICE 3

The decimal 2.03 is equivalent to what mixed number?

EXAMPLE 4

Find the equivalent fraction of each decimal.

a. 3.2   **b.** 3.200

Solution

a. 3.2 represents $3\frac{2}{10}$, or $3\frac{1}{5}$.

b. 3.200 equals $3\frac{200}{1,000}$, or $3\frac{1}{5}$.

PRACTICE 4

Express each decimal in fractional form.

a. 5.6   **b.** 5.6000

TIP   Adding zeros in the rightmost decimal places does not change a decimal's value. However, generally decimals can be written without these extra zeros.

EXAMPLE 5

Write each decimal as a mixed number.

a. 1.309   **b.** 1.39

Solution

a. $1.309 = 1\frac{309}{1,000}$

b. $1.39 = 1\frac{39}{100}$

PRACTICE 5

What mixed number is equivalent to each decimal?

a. 7.003   **b.** 4.1

Knowing how to change a decimal to its equivalent fraction also helps us read the decimal.

EXAMPLE 6

Express each decimal in words.

a. 0.319   **b.** 2.71   **c.** 0.08

Solution

a. $0.319 = \frac{319}{1,000}$

We read the decimal as "three hundred nineteen thousandths."

b. $2.71 = 2\frac{71}{100}$

The decimal point is read as "and." We read the decimal as "two and seventy-one hundredths."

c. $0.08 = \frac{8}{100}$

We read the decimal as "eight hundredths." Note that we *do not simplify* the equivalent fraction when reading the decimal.

PRACTICE 6

Express each decimal in words.

a. 0.61

b. 4.923

c. 7.05

EXAMPLE 7

Write each number in decimal notation.

a. Seven tenths   **b.** Five and thirty-two thousandths

Solution

a. Since 7 is in the tenths place, the decimal is written as 0.7.

b. The whole number preceding   The last digit of 32 is in
    and is in the ones place. ─┐   the thousandths place.
                                  │   │
                                  ↓   ↓
                        5 . 0 3 2
                              ↑ ↑
    We replace *and* with ───┘ └─── We need a 0 to hold
    the decimal point.   the tenths place.

The answer is 5.032.

PRACTICE 7

Write each number in decimal notation.

a. Forty-three thousandths

b. Ten and twenty-six hundredths

EXAMPLE 8

For hay fever, an allergy sufferer takes a decongestant pill that has a tablet strength of three hundredths of a gram. Write the equivalent decimal.

Solution   "Three hundredths" is written 0.03, with the digit 3 in the hundredths place.

PRACTICE 8

The number pi (usually written π) is approximately three and fourteen hundredths. Write this approximation as a decimal.

Comparing Decimals

Suppose that we want to compare two decimals—say, 0.6 and 0.7. The key is to rethink the problem in terms of fractions.

$$0.6 = \frac{6}{10} \qquad 0.7 = \frac{7}{10}$$

Because $\frac{7}{10} > \frac{6}{10}$, 0.7 > 0.6.

The following procedure provides another way to compare decimals that is faster than converting the decimals to fractions.

To Compare Decimals

*   Rewrite the numbers vertically, lining up the decimal points.

*   Working from left to right, compare the digits that have the same place value. At the first place value where the digits differ, the decimal which has the largest digit with this place value is the largest decimal.

EXAMPLE 9

Which is larger, 0.729 or 0.75?

Solution   First, let's line up the decimal point.

↓
0.729
0.75
↑

We see that both decimals have a 0 in the ones place. We next compare the digits in the tenths place and see that, again, they are the same. Looking to the right in the hundredths place, we see that $5 > 2$. Therefore, $0.75 > 0.729$. Note that the decimal with more digits is not necessarily the larger decimal.

PRACTICE 9

Which is smaller, 0.83 or 0.8297?

EXAMPLE 10

Rank from smallest to largest: 2.17, 2.1, and 0.99

Solution   First, we position the decimals so that the decimal points are aligned.

↓
2.17
2.1
0.99
↑

Working from left to right, we see that in the ones place, the first two decimals have a 2 and the third decimal has a 0, so the third decimal is the smallest of the three. To decide which of the first two decimals is smaller, we compare the digits in the tenths place. Since both of these decimals have a 1 in the tenths place, we proceed to the hundredths place. A 0 is understood to the right of the 1 in 2.1, so we compare 0 and 7.

↓
2.17
2.10
0.99
↑

Since $0 < 7$, we conclude that $2.10 < 2.17$. Therefore, the three decimals from smallest to largest are 0.99, 2.1, and 2.17.

PRACTICE 10

Rewrite in decreasing order: 3.5, 3.51, and 3.496

EXAMPLE 11

Plastic garbage bags come in three thicknesses (or gauges): 0.003 inch, 0.0025 inch, and 0.002 inch. The three gauges are called lightweight, regular weight, and heavyweight. Which is the lightweight gauge?

Solution To find the smallest of the decimals, we first line up the decimal points.

$$\downarrow$$
$$0.003$$
$$0.0025$$
$$0.002$$
$$\uparrow$$

Working from left to right, we see that the three decimals have the same digits until the thousandths place, where $3 > 2$. Therefore, 0.003 must be the heavyweight gauge. To compare 0.0025 and 0.002, we look at the ten-thousandths place. The 5 is greater than the 0 that is understood to be there (0.0020). So 0.0025 inch must be the regular-weight gauge, and 0.002 the lightweight gauge.

PRACTICE 11

The higher the energy efficiency rating (EER) of an air conditioner, the more efficiently it uses electricity. Which of the following air conditioners is least efficient? (*Source:* Consumer Guide)

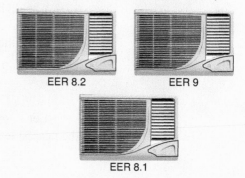

EER 8.2   EER 9

EER 8.1

Rounding Decimals

As with whole numbers, we can round decimals to a given place value. For instance, suppose that we want to round the decimal 1.38 to the nearest tenth. The decimal 1.38 lies between 1.3 and 1.4, so one of these two numbers will be our answer—but which? To decide, let's take a look at a number line.

```
        1.31   1.33   1.35   1.37   1.39
   ←──┼──┼──┼──┼──┼──┼──┼──┼──┼──┼──→
     1.3  1.32  1.34  1.36  1.38  1.4
```

Do you see from this diagram that 1.38 is closer to 1.4 than to 1.3?

$$1.38 \approx 1.4$$

Tenths place

Rounding a decimal to the nearest tenth means that the last digit lies in the tenths place.

The following table shows the relationship between the place to which we are rounding and the number of decimal places in our answer.

Rounding to the Nearest	Means That the Rounded Decimal Has
tenth $\left(\dfrac{1}{10}\right)$	one decimal place.
hundredth $\left(\dfrac{1}{100}\right)$	two decimal places.
thousandth $\left(\dfrac{1}{1,000}\right)$	three decimal places.
ten-thousandth $\left(\dfrac{1}{10,000}\right)$	four decimal places.

Note that the number of decimal places is the same as the number of zeros in the corresponding denominator.

The following rule can be used to round decimals.

To Round a Decimal to a Given Decimal Place

- Underline the digit in the place to which the number is being rounded.

- The digit to the right of the underlined digit is called the *critical digit*. Look at the critical digit—if it is 5 or more, add 1 to the underlined digit; if it is less than 5, leave the underlined digit unchanged.

- Drop all decimal places to the right of the underlined digit.

Let's apply this rule to the problem that we just considered—namely, rounding 1.38 to the nearest tenth.

┌─ Tenths place

1.38   Underline the digit 3, which occupies the tenths place.

1.38 ≈ 1.4   The critical digit, 8, is 5 or more, so add 1 to the 3 and then drop all digits to its right.

Critical digit ─┘

The following examples illustrate this method of rounding.

EXAMPLE 12

Round 94.735 to

a. the nearest tenth.

b. two decimal places.

c. the nearest thousandth.

d. the nearest ten.

e. the nearest whole number.

Solution

a. First, we underline the digit 7 in the tenths place: 94.735. The critical digit, 3, is less than 5, so we do not add 1 to the underlined digit. Dropping all digits to the right of the 7, we get 94.7. Note that our answer has only one decimal place because we are rounding to the nearest tenth.

b. We need to round 94.735 to two decimal places (to the nearest hundredth).

$$94.735 \approx 94.74$$

The critical digit is 5 or more. Add 1 to the underlined digit and drop the decimal place to the right.

c. 94.735 ≈ 94.735 because the critical digit to the right of the 5 is understood to be 0.

PRACTICE 12

Round 748.0772 to

a. the nearest tenth.

b. the nearest hundredth.

c. three decimal places.

d. the nearest whole number.

e. the nearest hundred.

d. We are rounding 94.735 to the nearest ten (*not tenth*), which is a whole-number place.

$$94.735 \approx 90$$

Because $4 < 5$, keep 9 in the tens place, insert 0 in the ones place and drop all decimal places.

e. Rounding to the nearest whole number means rounding to the nearest 1.

$$94.735 \approx 95$$

Because $7 > 5$, change the 4 to 5 and drop all decimal places.

EXAMPLE 13

Round 3.982 to the nearest tenth.

Solution First, we underline the digit 9 in the tenths place and identify the critical digit: 3.9<u>8</u>2. The critical digit, 8, is more than 5, so we add 1 to the 9, get 10, and write down the 0. We add the 1 to 3, getting 4, and drop the 8 and 2.

$$3.\underline{9}82 \approx 4.0$$

Drop

The answer is 4.0. Note that we do not drop the 0 in the tenths place of the answer to indicate that we have rounded to that place.

PRACTICE 13

Round 7.2962 to two decimal places.

EXAMPLE 14

The rate of exchange between currencies varies with time. On a particular day the euro, the currency used in many countries of Western Europe, could have been exchanged for 1.23502 dollars. What was this price to the nearest cent? (*Source:* xe.com)

Solution A cent is one-hundredth of a dollar. Therefore, we need to round 1.23502 to the nearest hundredth.

$$1.23\underline{5}02 \approx 1.24$$

So the price to the nearest cent was $1.24.

PRACTICE 14

Mount Waialeale on the Hawaiian island of Kauai is one of the world's wettest places, with an average annual rainfall of 11.68 meters. What is the amount of rainfall to the nearest tenth of a meter? (*Source:* wikipedia.org)

Mathematically Speaking

Fill in each blank with the most appropriate term or phrase from the given list.

less	greater	increasing	left
decreasing	ten	hundredths	multiple
thousandths	power	right	tenth

1. A decimal place is a place to the _____ of the decimal point.

2. The fractional part of a decimal has as its denominator a _____ of 10.

3. The decimal 0.17 is equivalent to the fraction seventeen _____.

4. The decimal 209.95 rounded to the nearest _____ is 210.0.

5. The decimal 0.371 is _____ than the decimal 0.3499.

6. The decimals 0.48, 0.4, and 0.371 are written in _____ order.

A *Underline the digit that occupies the given place.*

7. 2.78   Tenths place

8. 6.835   Tenths place

9. 9.01   Hundredths place

10. 0.772   Hundredths place

11. 2.00175   Ten-thousandths place

12. 4.00189   Ten-thousandths place

13. 823.001   Thousandths place

14. 829.006   Thousandths place

Identify the place occupied by the underlined digit.

15. 25.7<u>1</u>

16. 3.00<u>2</u>

17. 8.1<u>8</u>3

18. <u>4</u>9.771

19. 1,077.04<u>2</u>

20. 2.8371<u>07</u>

21. $253.<u>7</u>2

22. $7,571.3<u>9</u>

Write each decimal in words.

23. 0.53

24. 0.72

25. 0.305

26. 0.849

27. 0.6

28. 0.3

29. 5.72

30. 3.89

31. 24.002

32. 370.081

Write each number in decimal notation.

33. Eight tenths

34. Six tenths

35. One and forty-one thousandths

36. Eighteen and four thousandths

37. Sixty and one hundredth

38. Ninety-two and seven hundredths

39. Four and one hundred seven thousandths

40. Five and sixty-three thousandths

41. Three and two tenths meters

42. Ninety-eight and six tenths degrees

B *For each decimal, find the equivalent fraction or mixed number, written in lowest terms.*

43. 0.6

44. 0.8

45. 0.39

46. 0.27

47. 1.5

48. 9.8

49. 8.000

50. 6.700

51. 5.012

52. 20.304

C *Between each pair of numbers, insert the appropriate sign, <, =, or >, to make a true statement.*

53. 3.21   2.5

54. 8.66   4.952

55. 0.71   0.8

56. 1.2   1.38

57. 9.123   9.11

58. 0.72   0.7

59. 4   4.000

60. 7.60   7.6

61. 8.125 feet   8.2 feet

62. 2.45 pounds   2.5 pounds

Rearrange each group of numbers from smallest to largest.

63. 7.1, 7, 7.07

64. 0.002, 0.2, 0.02

65. 5.001, 4.9, 5.2

66. 3.85, 3.911, 2

67. 9.6 miles, 9.1 miles, 9.38 miles

68. 2.7 seconds, 2.15 seconds, 2 seconds

D *Round as indicated.*

69. 17.36 to the nearest tenth

70. 8.009 to two decimal places

71. 3.5905 to the nearest thousandth

72. 3.5902 to the nearest thousandth

73. 37.08 to one decimal place

74. 3.08 to one decimal place

75. 0.396 to the nearest hundredth

76. 0.978 to the nearest hundredth

77. 7.0571 to two decimal places

78. 3.038 to one decimal place

79. 8.7 miles to the nearest mile

80. $3.57 to the nearest dollar

Round to the indicated place.

81.

To the Nearest	8.0714	0.9916
Tenth		
Hundredth		
Ten		

82.

To the Nearest	0.8166	72.3591
Tenth		
Hundredth		
Ten		

Mixed Practice

Solve.

83. In the decimal 0.024, underline the digit in the tenths place.

84. What is the equivalent fraction of 3.8?

85. Round 870.062 to the nearest hundredth.

86. Write four and thirty-one thousandths in decimal notation.

87. Write in increasing order: 2.14 meters, 2.4 meters, and 2.04 meters.

88. Write 0.05 in words.

Applications

The following statements involve decimals. Write all decimals in words.

89. It takes the Earth 23.934 hours to rotate once about its axis. (*Source:* NASA)

90. Male Rufous hummingbirds weigh an average of 0.113 ounce. (*Source:* Lanny Chambers, *Facts about Hummingbirds*)

91. Over two years, the average score on a college admissions exam increased from 18.7 to 18.8.

92. A chemistry text gives 55.85 as the atomic mass of iron and 63.55 as the atomic mass of copper.

93. The following table shows the average amount of time spent on selected daily household activities each year by U.S. civilians.

Activity	Average Amount of Time (in number of hours per year)
Housework	211.7
Lawn and garden care	69.4
Food preparation and cleanup	189.8
Caring for household members	193.5
Household management	47.5

(*Source:* bls.gov)

94. The coefficient of friction is a measure of the amount of friction produced when one surface rubs against another. The following table gives these coefficients for various surfaces.

Materials	Coefficient of Friction
Wood on wood	0.3
Steel on steel	0.15
Steel on wood	0.5
A rubber tire on a dry concrete road	0.7
A rubber tire on a wet concrete road	0.5

(*Source: CRC Handbook of Chemistry and Physics*)

95. Bacteria are single-celled organisms that typically measure from 0.00001 inch to 0.00008 inch across.

96. In one month, the consumer confidence index rose from 71.9 points to 80.2 points.

The following statements involve numbers written in words. Write each number in decimal notation.

97. The area of a plot of land is one and two tenths acres.

98. The lead in many mechanical pencils is seven tenths millimeter thick.

99. At the first Indianapolis 500 auto race in 1911, the winning speed was seventy-four and fifty-nine hundredths miles per hour. (*Source:* Jack Fox, *The Indianapolis 500*)

100. In 1796, there was a U.S. coin in circulation, the half cent, worth five thousandths of a dollar.

101. At sea level, the air pressure on each square inch of surface area is fourteen and seven tenths pounds.

102. A doctor prescribed a dosage of one hundred twenty-five thousandths milligram of Prolixin.

103. According to the owner's manual, the voltage produced by a camcorder battery is nine and six tenths volts (V).

104. In preparing an injection, a nurse measured out one and eight tenths milliliters of sterile water.

105. The electrical usage in a tenant's apartment last month amounted to three hundred fifty-two and one tenth kilowatt hours (kWh).

106. In one day, the Dow Jones Industrial Average fell by three and sixty-three hundredths points.

Solve.

107. The following table shows the three medalists in the men's skating short program at the 2010 Winter Olympics in Vancouver, Canada.

Country	Skater	Score
United States	Evan Lysacek	90.3
Japan	Daisuke Takahashi	90.25
Russian Federation	Evgeni Plushenko	90.85

(*Source:* sports.yahoo.com/olympics/vancouver)

Which of these three top skaters earned the highest score for the short program?

109. Last winter, a homeowner's average daily heating bill was for 8.75 units of electricity. This winter, it was for 8.5 units. During which winter was the average higher?

111. The following table shows estimates of the lead emissions in the United States for two given years.

Year	Amount of Lead (in millions of tons)
1985	0.022
2005	0.003

(*Source:* Environmental Protection Agency)

In which year was the amount of lead emissions less?

113. The following table shows the amount of money that a jury awarded a husband and wife who were plaintiffs in a lawsuit.

Plaintiff	Award (in millions of dollars)
Husband	1.875
Wife	1.91

Whose award was less than the $1.9 million that each plaintiff had demanded?

Round to the indicated place.

115. A bank pays interest on all its accounts to the nearest cent. If the interest on an account is $57.0285, how much interest does the bank pay?

117. According to the organizers of a lottery, the probability of winning the lottery is 0.0008. Round this probability to three decimal places.

108. The more powerful an earthquake is, the higher its magnitude is on the Richter scale. Great earthquakes, such as the 1906 San Francisco earthquake, have magnitudes of 8.0 or higher. Is an earthquake with magnitude 7.8 considered to be a great earthquake? (*Source: The New Encyclopedia Britannica*)

110. In order to qualify for the dean's list at a community college, a student's grade point average (GPA) must be 3.5 or above. Did a student with a GPA of 3.475 make the dean's list?

112. As part of her annual checkup, a patient had a blood test. The normal range for a particular substance is 1.1 to 2.3. If she scored 0.95, was her blood in the normal range?

114. The table below shows the amount of toxic emissions released into the air from three factories during the same time in a recent year. Which of the factories released the most toxic emissions?

	Electronics Factory	Food Factory	Chemical Factory
Toxic emissions (in millions of pounds)	1.5	1.4	1.48

116. A city's sales tax rate, expressed as a decimal, is 0.0825. What is this rate to the nearest hundredth?

118. One day last week, a particular foreign currency was worth $0.7574. How much is this currency worth to the nearest tenth of a dollar?

119. In terms of land area, North America is 1.36 times as large as South America. Round this decimal to the nearest tenth. (*Source: National Geographic Atlas of the World*)

120. The length of the Panama Canal is 50.7 miles. Round this length to the nearest mile. (*Source: The New Encyclopedia Britannica*)

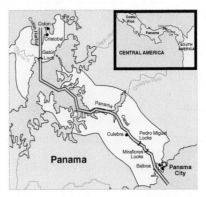

• Check your answers on page A-4.

MIND*Stretchers*

Critical Thinking

1. For each question, either give the answer or explain why there is none.

   a. Find the *smallest* decimal that when rounded to the nearest tenth is 7.5.

   b. Find the *largest* decimal that when rounded to the nearest tenth is 7.5.

Writing

2. The next whole number after 7 is 8. What is the next decimal after 0.7? Explain.

Groupwork

3. Working with a partner, list fifteen numbers between 2.5 and 2.6.

Cultural Note

In 1585, Simon Stevin, a Dutch engineer, published a book entitled *The Art of Tenths* (*La Disme in French*) in which he presented a thorough account of decimals. Stevin sought to teach everyone "with an ease unheard of, all computations necessary between men by integers without fractions."

Stevin did not invent decimals; their history dates back thousands of years to ancient China, medieval Arabia, and Renaissance Europe. However, Stevin's writings popularized decimals and also supported the notion of decimal coinage—as in American currency, where there are 10 dimes to the dollar.

Source: Morris Kline, *Mathematics, a Cultural Approach* (Reading, Massachusetts: Addison-Wesley Publishing Company, 1962), p. 614.

3.2 Adding and Subtracting Decimals

In Section 3.1 we discussed the meaning of decimals and how to compare and round them. Now, we turn our attention to computing with decimals, starting with addition and subtraction.

A To add or subtract decimals

B To solve applied problems involving the addition or subtraction of decimals

Adding Decimals

Adding decimals is similar to adding whole numbers: We add the digits in each place value position, regrouping when necessary. Suppose that we want to find the sum of two decimals: $1.2 + 3.5$. First, we rewrite the problem vertically, lining up the decimal points in the addends. Then, we add as usual, inserting the decimal point below the other decimal points.

$$
\begin{array}{r}
\downarrow \\
1.2 \\
+3.5 \\
\hline
4.7 \\
\uparrow
\end{array}
\qquad \text{This addition is equivalent to} \qquad
\begin{array}{r}
1\dfrac{2}{10} \\
+3\dfrac{5}{10} \\
\hline
4\dfrac{7}{10}
\end{array}
$$

Note that when we added the mixed numbers corresponding to the decimals, we got $4\dfrac{7}{10}$, which is equivalent to 4.7. This example suggests the following rule:

To Add Decimals

- Rewrite the numbers vertically, lining up the decimal points.
- Add.
- Insert a decimal point in the sum below the other decimal points.

EXAMPLE 1

Find the sum: $2.7 + 80.13 + 5.036$

Solution
$$
\begin{array}{r}
2.7 \\
80.13 \\
+5.036 \\
\hline
87.866
\end{array}
$$

Rewrite the addends with decimal points lined up vertically.

Add.

Insert the decimal point in the sum.

PRACTICE 1

Add: $5.12 + 4.967 + 0.3$

EXAMPLE 2

Compute: $2.367 + 5 + 0.143$

Solution Recall that 5 and 5. are equivalent.
$$
\begin{array}{r}
2.367 \\
5. \\
+0.143 \\
\hline
7.510 = 7.51
\end{array}
$$

Line up the decimal points and add.

Insert the decimal point in the sum.

We can drop the extra 0 at the right end.

PRACTICE 2

What is the sum of 7.31, 8, and 23.99?

EXAMPLE 3

A runner's time was 0.06 second longer than the world record of 21.71 seconds. What was the runner's time?

Solution We need to compute the sum of the two numbers. The runner's time was 21.77 seconds.

$$
\begin{array}{r}
0.06 \\
+21.71 \\
\hline
21.77
\end{array}
$$

PRACTICE 3

A child has the flu. This morning, his body temperature was 99.4°F. What was his temperature after it went up by 2.7°?

Subtracting Decimals

Now, let's discuss subtracting decimals. As with addition, subtracting decimals is similar to subtracting whole numbers. To compute the difference between 12.83 and 4.2, we rewrite the problem vertically, lining up the decimal points. Then, we subtract as usual, inserting a decimal point below the other decimal points.

$$
\begin{array}{r}
\downarrow \\
12.83 \\
-4.2 \\
\hline
8.63 \\
\uparrow
\end{array}
$$

is equivalent to

$$
\begin{array}{rcl}
12\dfrac{83}{100} &=& 12\dfrac{83}{100} \\[2mm]
-4\dfrac{2}{10} &=& -4\dfrac{20}{100} \\[2mm]
\hline
&& 8\dfrac{63}{100}, \quad \text{or} \quad 8.63
\end{array}
$$

Again, note that when we subtracted the equivalent mixed numbers, we got the same difference.

As in any subtraction problem, we can check this answer by adding the subtrahend (4.2) to the difference (8.63), confirming that we get the original minuend (12.83). This example suggests the following rule:

$$
\begin{array}{r}
8.63 \\
+4.2 \\
\hline
12.83
\end{array}
$$

To Subtract Decimals

- Rewrite the numbers vertically, lining up the decimal points.
- Subtract, inserting extra zeros in the minuend if necessary for regrouping.
- Insert a decimal point in the difference, below the other decimal points.

EXAMPLE 4

Subtract and check: 5.038 − 2.11

Solution

$$
\begin{array}{r}
\downarrow \\
5.038 \\
-2.11 \\
\hline
2.928 \\
\uparrow
\end{array}
$$

Rewrite the problem with decimal points lined up vertically.

Subtract. Regroup when necessary.

Insert the decimal point in the answer.

Check To verify that our difference is correct, we check by addition.

$$
\begin{array}{r}
2.928 \\
+2.11 \\
\hline
5.038
\end{array}
$$

PRACTICE 4

Find the difference and check:
71.3825 − 25.17

EXAMPLE 5

65 is how much larger than 2.04?

Solution   Recall that 65 and 65. are equivalent.

Insert the zeros needed for regrouping.

$$
\begin{array}{r}
65.\overset{\downarrow}{\overline{0}}0 \\
-2.04 \\
\hline
62.96
\end{array}
$$
Line up the decimal points.
Subtract.

Insert the decimal point in the answer.

Check
$$
\begin{array}{r}
62.96 \\
+\ 2.04 \\
\hline
65.00 = 65
\end{array}
$$

PRACTICE 5

How much greater is $735 than $249.57?

EXAMPLE 6

A Burger King Whopper Jr.® contains 1.02 grams of sodium, whereas a McDonald's Quarter Pounder ® contains 0.73 grams. How much more sodium does the Whopper Jr.® contain?
(*Sources:* nutrition.mcdonalds.com and bk.com)

Solution   We need to find the difference between 1.02 and 0.73.

$$
\begin{array}{r}
1.02 \\
-0.73 \\
\hline
0.29
\end{array}
$$

So a Burger King Whopper Jr.® contains 0.29 grams more sodium.

PRACTICE 6

The New York Marathon has timing mats located every 3.1 miles throughout its 26.2-mile course. A runner passes one of the mats 9.3 miles into the race. How much further does the runner have to go to finish the race? (*Source*: nycmarathon.org)

EXAMPLE 7

Suppose that a part-time employee's salary is $350 a week, less deductions. The following table shows these deductions.

Deduction	Amount
Federal, state, and city taxes	$100.80
Social Security	26.78
Union dues	8.88

What is the employee's take-home pay?

Solution   Let's use the strategy of breaking the question into two simpler questions.

- *How much money is deducted per week?* The weekly deductions ($100.80, $26.78, and $8.88) add up to $136.46.
- *How much of the salary is left after subtracting the total deductions?* The difference between $350 and $136.46 is $213.54, which is the employee's take-home pay.

PRACTICE 7

A sales rep, working in Ohio, wants to drive from Circleville to Columbus. How much shorter is it to drive directly to Columbus instead of going by way of Lancaster? (*Source:* mapquest.com)

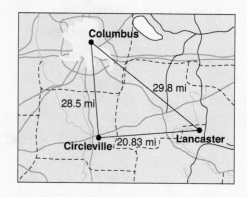

Estimating Sums and Differences

Being able to estimate in your head the sum or difference between two decimals is a useful skill, for either checking or approximating an exact answer. To estimate, simply round the numbers to be added or subtracted and then carry out the operation on the rounded numbers.

EXAMPLE 8

Compute the sum $0.17 + 0.4 + 0.083$. Use estimation to check.

Solution   First, we add. Then, to check, we round the addends—say, to the nearest tenth—and add the rounded numbers.

$$
\begin{array}{rcl}
0.17 & \approx & 0.2 \\
0.4 & \approx & 0.4 \\
+0.083 & \approx & +0.1 \\
\end{array}
$$

Exact sum $\rightarrow 0.653 \qquad 0.7 \leftarrow$ Estimated sum

Our exact sum is close to our estimated sum, and in fact, rounds to it.

PRACTICE 8

Add 0.093, 0.008, and 0.762. Then, check by estimating.

EXAMPLE 9

Subtract $0.713 - 0.082$. Then check by estimating.

Solution   First, we find the exact answer and then round the given numbers to get an estimate.

$$
\begin{array}{rcl}
0.713 & \approx & 0.7 \\
-0.082 & \approx & -0.1 \\
\end{array}
$$

Exact difference $\rightarrow 0.631 \qquad 0.6 \leftarrow$ Estimated difference

Our exact answer, 0.631, is close to 0.6.

PRACTICE 9

Compute: $0.17 - 0.091$. Use estimation to check.

EXAMPLE 10

Combine and check: $0.4 - (0.17 + 0.082)$

Solution   Following the order of operations rule, we begin by adding the two decimals in parentheses.

$$
\begin{array}{r}
0.17 \\
+0.082 \\
\hline
0.252 \\
\end{array}
$$

Next, we subtract this sum from 0.4.

$$
\begin{array}{r}
0.400 \\
-0.252 \\
\hline
0.148 \\
\end{array}
$$

So $0.4 - (0.17 + 0.082) = 0.148$.

Now, let's check this answer by estimating:

$$0.4 - (0.17 + 0.082)$$
$$\downarrow \qquad \downarrow \qquad \downarrow$$
$$0.4 - (0.2 + 0.1) = 0.4 - 0.3 = 0.1$$

The estimate, 0.1, is close to 0.148.

PRACTICE 10

Calculate and check:
$0.813 - (0.29 - 0.0514)$

In the following examples, we estimate a sum or difference to approximate the correct answer, not to check it.

EXAMPLE 11

A movie budgeted at $7.25 million ended up costing $1.655 million more. Estimate the final cost of the movie.

Solution Let's round each number to the nearest million dollars.

$$
\begin{array}{rl}
1.655 \approx & 2 \text{ million} \\
7.25 \approx & +7 \text{ million} \\
\hline
& 9 \text{ million}
\end{array}
$$

Adding the rounded numbers, we see that the movie cost approximately $9 million.

PRACTICE 11

From the deposit ticket shown below, estimate the total amount deposited.

Estimate: _____

EXAMPLE 12

When the underwater tunnel connecting the United Kingdom and France was built, French and British construction workers dug from their respective countries. They met at the point shown on the map.

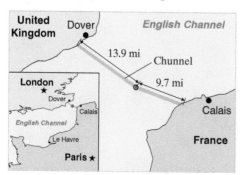

Estimate how much farther the British workers had dug than the French workers. (*Source: The New York Times*)

Solution We can round 13.9 to 14 and 9.7 to 10. The difference between 14 and 10 is 4, so the British workers dug about 4 miles farther than the French workers.

PRACTICE 12

An art collector bought a painting for $2.3 million. A year later, she sold the painting for $4.1 million. Estimate her profit on the sale.

Adding and Subtracting Decimals on a Calculator

When adding or subtracting decimals, press the ☐ key to enter the decimal point. If a sum or difference ends with a 0 in the rightmost decimal place, does your calculator drop the 0? If a sum or difference has no whole-number part, does your calculator insert a 0?

EXAMPLE 13

Compute: $2.7 + 4.1 + 9.2$

Solution

Press	Display
2.7 ⊞ 4.1 ⊞ 9.2 [ENTER]	2.7 + 4.1 + 9.2 16.

We can check this sum by estimating: $3 + 4 + 9 = 16$, which is the same as the answer calculated.

PRACTICE 13

Find the sum: $3.82 + 9.17 + 66.24$

EXAMPLE 14

Find the difference: $83.71 - 83.70002$

Solution

Press	Display
83.71 ⊟ 83.70002 [ENTER]	83.71 - 83.70002 0.00998

We can check this difference by adding:
$0.00998 + 83.70002 = 83.71$.

PRACTICE 14

Compute: $5.00003 - 5.00001$

Mathematically Speaking

Fill in each blank with the most appropriate term or phrase from the given list.

sum	decimal points	difference
any number	rightmost digits	zeros

1. When adding decimals, rewrite the numbers vertically, lining up the _____.

2. Inserting _____ at the right end of a decimal does not change its value.

3. To estimate the _____ of 0.31 and 0.108, add 0.3 and 0.1.

4. To estimate the _____ between 0.31 and 0.108, subtract 0.1 from 0.3.

Ⓐ *Find the sum. Check by estimating.*

5. $3.89 + 5.44$

6. $2.17 + 4.29$

7. $0.6 + 0.3$

8. $0.2 + 0.6$

9. $6.03 + 2.1$

10. $1.4 + 3.96$

11. $13.05 + 8.4$

12. $21.07 + 5.1$

13. $2.67 + 5$

14. $8 + 4.99$

15. $\$74 + \$3.21$

16. $\$8.77 + \$62$

17. $0.49023 + 0.5997$

18. $1.002 + 0.20013$

19. $8.01 + 6.7 + 9.45$

20. $9.73 + 5.99 + 3.688$

21. $34.7 + 5.84 + 3 + 0.882$

22. $75.285 + 2 + 3.871 + 0.5$

23. 7 millimeters + 3.5 millimeters + 9.82 millimeters

24. 10.35 inches + 32 inches + 54.9 inches

25. 4.7 kilograms + 2.98 kilograms + 9.002 kilograms

26. 0.85 second + 1.72 seconds + 3.009 seconds

27. $3.861 + 2.89 + 3.775 + 9.00813 + 3.77182$

28. $\$8.99 + \$3.99 + \$17.83 + \$15 + \$201.75$

Find the difference. Check either by estimating or by adding.

29. $0.8 - 0.1$

30. $0.9 - 0.3$

31. $20.72 - 3.92$

32. $12.98 - 5.73$

33. $23.81 - 5.4$

34. $17.49 - 10.2$

35. $80.2 - 4.57$

36. $97.1 - 3.23$

37. $25.99 - 3.666$

38. $32.99 - 7.555$

39. $0.27 - 0.1$

40. $0.29 - 0.2$

41. $1.032 - 0.9178$

42. $0.01 - 0.0001$

43. $13.2 - 7$

44. $9.6 - 4$

45. $20 - 4.63$

46. $8 - 2.55$

47. $10 - 4.1$

48. $13 - 7.2$

49. $8 - 1.79$

50. $9 - 4.63$

51. 3.2 pounds − 1.35 pounds

52. 23.5 seconds − 2.8 seconds

53. $103.7°F - 98.8°F$

54. 32.5 grams − 19.27 grams

Compute.

55. $35.2 - 2.86 + 9.07 - 1.658$

56. $10 - 2.38 + 4.92 - 6.02$

57. 30 milligrams $-$ 0.5 milligram $-$ 1.6 milligrams

58. $\$20.93 + \$1.07 - \$19.58$

59. $5.21 - (1.03 + 0.975)$

60. $6.953 - (4.09 + 0.008)$

61. $41.075 - 2.87104 - 17.005$

62. $0.00661 + 1.997 - 0.05321$

In each group of three computations, one answer is wrong. Use estimation to identify which answer is incorrect.

63. a.
$$\begin{array}{r} 0.059 \\ 0.00234 \\ +0.036 \\ \hline 0.09734 \end{array}$$
b.
$$\begin{array}{r} 0.1903 \\ 0.074 \\ +0.2051 \\ \hline 0.4694 \end{array}$$
c.
$$\begin{array}{r} 0.00441 \\ 0.06882 \\ +0.0103 \\ \hline 0.8353 \end{array}$$

64. a.
$$\begin{array}{r} \$32.71 \\ 43.09 \\ + \quad 8.27 \\ \hline \$74.07 \end{array}$$
b.
$$\begin{array}{r} \$19.37 \\ 2. \\ + \quad 7.22 \\ \hline \$28.59 \end{array}$$
c.
$$\begin{array}{r} \$139.26 \\ 82.87 \\ + \quad 3.01 \\ \hline \$225.14 \end{array}$$

65. a.
$$\begin{array}{r} 0.35 \\ -0.1007 \\ \hline 0.2493 \end{array}$$
b.
$$\begin{array}{r} 0.072 \\ -0.0056 \\ \hline 0.664 \end{array}$$
c.
$$\begin{array}{r} 0.03 \\ -0.008 \\ \hline 0.022 \end{array}$$

66. a.
$$\begin{array}{r} 8.551 \\ -2.9995 \\ \hline 5.5515 \end{array}$$
b.
$$\begin{array}{r} 78.328 \\ - \quad 5.5 \\ \hline 7.2828 \end{array}$$
c.
$$\begin{array}{r} 65 \\ - \quad 2.778 \\ \hline 62.222 \end{array}$$

Mixed Practice

Solve.

67. Calculate: $4.78 + 13 - 10.009$

68. Find the difference between 90.1 and 12.58.

69. Add: 0.5 pound $+$ 3 pounds $+$ 4.25 pounds

70. Subtract: $\$20 - \$6.95$

71. Compute: $8 - 2.4 + 6.0013$

72. What is the sum of 1.265, 7, and 0.14?

Applications

B *Solve and check.*

73. A paperback book that normally sells for $13 is now on sale for $11.97. What is the discount in dollars and cents?

74. During a drought, the mayor of a city attempted to reduce daily water consumption to 3.1 million gallons. If daily water consumption fell to 1.948 million gallons above that goal, estimate the city's consumption.

75. A skeleton was found at an archaeological dig. Radiocarbon dating—a technique used for estimating age—indicated that the skeleton was 56 centuries old, plus or minus 0.8 centuries. According to this estimate, what is the greatest possible age of the skeleton?

76. A college launched a campaign to collect $3 million to build a new technology complex. If $1.316 million has been collected so far, how much more money, to the nearest million dollars, is needed?

77. As an investment, a couple bought an apartment house for $2.3 million. Two years later, they sold the apartment house for $4 million. What was their profit?

78. A woman sued her business partner and was awarded $1.5 million. On appeal, however, the award was reduced to $0.75 million. By how much was the award reduced?

79. In setting up a page in word processing, the margins of a page are usually expressed in decimal parts of an inch. How long is each typed line on the page?

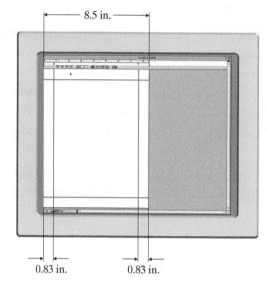

8.5 in.

0.83 in.   0.83 in.

80. In the picture below, how much clearance will there be between the top of the roof cargo carrier and the top of the garage door?

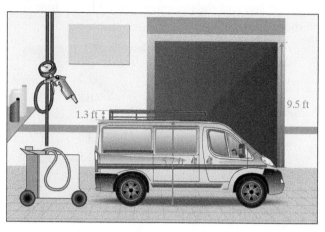

9.5 ft

1.3 ft

81. A radio disc jockey wants to choose among compact disc tracks that last 3.5, 2.8, 2.9, 2.6, and 1.6 minutes. Can he select tracks so as to get between 9.8 and 10 minutes of music? Explain.

82. A shopper plans to buy three items that cost $4.99, $7.99, and $2.99 each. If she has $15 with her, will she have enough money to pay for all three items? Explain.

83. When gymnasts compete, they receive scores in four separate events: vault (VT), uneven bar (UB), balance beam (BB), and floor exercises (FX). The total of these four event scores is called the all-around score (AA). The following chart shows the qualifying scores earned by three gymnasts at the Beijing, China 2008 Summer Olympics.

Gymnast	VT	UB	BB	FX	AA
Nastia Liukin (U.S.)	15.1	15.95	15.975	15.35	
Yang Yilin (China)	15.2	16.65	15.5	15	
Shawn Johnson (U.S.)	16	15.325	15.975	15.425	

(*Source*: wikipedia.org)

a. Calculate the all-around scores for these three competitors.

b. Which competitor had the highest all-around score?

84. The graph shown gives the number of households that watched particular TV programs in a given week, according to the Nielsen Top 20 ratings.

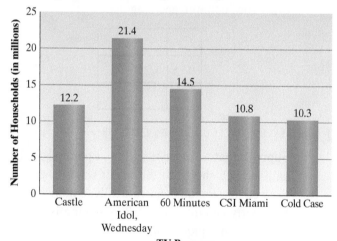

(*Source:* usatoday.com)

a. How many more households watched *American Idol-Wednesday* than *60 Minutes*?

b. Write the names of the five programs in increasing order of viewership.

85. To prevent anemia, a doctor advises his patient to take at least 18 milligrams of iron each day. The following table shows the amount of iron in the food that the patient ate yesterday. Did she get enough iron? If not, how much more does she need?

Food	Iron (in milligrams)
Chicken, breast	1.1
Canned tuna	0.8
Fortified oatmeal	10
Seedless raisins	1.5
Frozen spinach	1.9
Whole wheat bread	0.9

(*Source:* ods.od.nih.gov)

86. When filling a prescription, buying a generic drug rather than a brand-name drug can often save money. The following table shows the prices of various brand-name and generic drugs.

Drug	Brand-Named Price	Generic Price
Fexofenadine	$30	$8.80
Furosemide	$35.35	$17.94
Omeprazole	$48.47	$37.44
Metformin	$186.89	$78.39
Synthroid	$61.56	$38.02

How much money will a shopper save if he buys all five generic drugs rather than the brand-name drugs?

• Check your answers on page A-4.

MINDStretchers

Groupwork

1. Working with a partner, find the missing entries in the following magic square, in which 3.75 is the sum of every row, column, and diagonal.

0.75	1.25	
2.		

Mathematical Reasoning

2. Suppose that a spider is sitting at point *A* on the rectangular web shown. If the spider wants to crawl along the web horizontally and vertically to munch on the delicious fly caught at point *B*, how long is the shortest route that the spider can take?

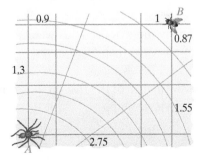

Writing

3. a. How many pairs of whole numbers are there whose sum is 7?
   b. How many pairs of decimals are there whose sum is 0.7?
   c. Explain why (a) and (b) have different answers.

3.3 Multiplying Decimals

OBJECTIVES

A To multiply decimals

B To solve applied problems involving the multiplication of decimals

In this section, we discuss how to multiply two or more decimals, finding both the exact product and an estimated product.

Multiplying Decimals

To find the product of two decimals—say, 1.02 and 0.3—we multiply the same way we multiply whole numbers. But with decimals we need to know where the decimal point goes in the product. To find out, let's change each decimal to its fractional equivalent.

$$
\begin{array}{r}
1.02 \\
\times \ \ 0.3
\end{array}
\Big\}
\quad \text{is equivalent to} \rightarrow \quad
1\frac{2}{100} \times \frac{3}{10}
$$

$$
\rightarrow 306
$$

Where should we place the decimal point?

$$
= \frac{102}{100} \times \frac{3}{10} = \frac{306}{1,000}, \quad \text{or} \quad 0.\underset{\uparrow}{306}
$$

The product is in thousandths, so it has three decimal places.

Looking at the multiplication problem with decimals, note that *the product has as many decimal places as the total number of decimal places in the factors.* This example illustrates the following rule for multiplying decimals.

$$
\begin{array}{r}
1.0\ 2 \\
\underline{0.3} \\
0.3\ 0\ 6
\end{array}
$$

To Multiply Decimals

* Multiply the factors as if they were whole numbers.

* Find the total number of decimal places in the factors.

* Count that many places from the right end of the product, and insert a decimal point.

EXAMPLE 1

Multiply: 6.1×3.7

Solution   First, multiply 61 by 37, ignoring the decimal points.

$$
\begin{array}{r}
6.1 \\
\times \ 3.7 \\
\hline
4\ 2\ 7 \\
1\ 8\ 3 \ \ \\
\hline
2\ 2\ 5\ 7
\end{array}
$$

Then, count the total number of decimal places in the factors.

$$
\begin{array}{r}
6.1 \leftarrow \text{One decimal place} \\
\times \ 3.7 \leftarrow \text{One decimal place} \\
\hline
4\ 2\ 7 \\
1\ 8\ 3 \ \ \\
\hline
2\ 2.5\ 7 \leftarrow \text{Two decimal places} \\
\text{in the product}
\end{array}
$$

Insert the decimal point two places from the right end.
So, 22.57 is the product.

PRACTICE 1

Find the product: 2.81×3.5

EXAMPLE 2

Find the product of 0.75 and 4.

Solution   Let's multiply 0.75 by 4, ignoring the decimal point.

$$\begin{array}{r} 0.75 \\ \times\ \ 4 \\ \hline 300 \end{array}$$

Count the total number of decimal places.

$$\begin{array}{r} 0.75 \leftarrow \text{Two decimal places} \\ \times\ \ 4 \leftarrow \text{Zero decimal places (4 is a whole number)} \\ \hline 3.00 \leftarrow \text{Two decimal places in the product} \end{array}$$

So the product is 3.00, which simplifies to 3.

PRACTICE 2

Multiply: 0.28×5

EXAMPLE 3

Multiply 0.03 and 0.25, rounding the answer to the nearest thousandth.

Solution

$$\begin{array}{r} 0.2\,5 \\ \times\ \ 0.0\,3 \\ \hline 0\,7\,5 \\ 0\,0\,0 \\ \hline 0.0\,0\,7\,5 \end{array}$$

Rounding to the nearest thousandth, we get 0.008.

PRACTICE 3

What is the product of 0.44 and 0.03, rounded to the nearest hundredth?

EXAMPLE 4

Multiply: $(1.1)(3.5)(0.8)$

Solution   To find the product of three factors, we can first multiply the two left factors and then multiply this product by the third factor:

$$(1.1)(3.5)\,(0.8) =$$
$$(3.85)\,(0.8) = 3.08$$

So 3.08 is the final product.

PRACTICE 4

Evaluate: $(0.2)(0.3)(0.4)$

EXAMPLE 5

Simplify: $3 + (1.2)^2$

Solution   Recall that, according to the order of operations rule, we first must find $(1.2)^2$ and then add 3.

$$3 + (1.2)^2 =$$
$$3 + 1.44 = 4.44$$

PRACTICE 5

Evaluate: $10 - (0.3)^2$

EXAMPLE 6

Multiply: 8.274×100

Solution

$\begin{array}{r} 8.274 \leftarrow \text{Three decimal places} \\ \times\ 100 \leftarrow \text{Zero decimal places} \\ \hline 827.400 \leftarrow \text{Three decimal places in the product} \end{array}$

So the product is 827.400, or 827.4 after we drop the extra zeros.

Note that the second factor (100) is a power of 10 ending in two zeros and that the product is identical to the first factor except that the decimal point is moved to the right two places.

PRACTICE 6

Compute: $0.325 \times 1{,}000$

Example 6 suggests the following shortcut:

TIP   To multiply a decimal by a power of 10, move the decimal point to the right the same number of places as the power of 10 has zeros.

EXAMPLE 7

Find the product: $2.89 \times 1{,}000$

Solution   We see that 1,000 is a power of 10 and has three zeros. So to multiply 2.89 by 1,000, we simply move the decimal point in 2.89 to the right three places.

Add a 0 to move three places. $2.89 \times 1{,}000 = 2890.$

So the product is 2,890, with the 0 serving as a placeholder.

PRACTICE 7

Multiply 32.7 by 10,000.

EXAMPLE 8

The popularity of a television show is measured in ratings, where each rating point represents 1,149,000 homes in which the show is watched. After examining the table at the right, answer each question. (*Source:* wikipedia.org)

Show	Rating
1	10.3
2	9.1

a. In how many homes was Show 1 watched?

b. In how many more homes was Show 1 watched than Show 2?

Solution

a. To find the number of homes in which Show 1 was watched, we multiply its rating, 10.3, by 1,149,000, which gives us 11,834,700.

b. To compare the popularity of Show 1 and Show 2, we compute the number of homes in which Show 2 was viewed: $9.1 \times 1{,}149{,}000 = 10{,}455{,}900$. The number of Show 1 homes exceeds the number of Show 2 homes by $11{,}834{,}700 - 10{,}455{,}900$, or 1,378,800 homes.

PRACTICE 8

A chemistry student learns that a molecule is made up of atoms. For instance, the water molecule H_2O consists of two atoms of hydrogen H and one atom of oxygen O. Each of these atoms has an atomic weight.

Atom	Atomic Weight
H	1.008
O	15.999

a. After examining the chart above, compute the weight of the water molecule.

b. Round this weight to the nearest whole number.

Estimating Products

Being able to estimate mentally the product of two decimals is useful for either checking or approximating an exact answer. To estimate, round each factor so that it has only one nonzero digit. Then, multiply the rounded factors.

EXAMPLE 9

Multiply 0.703 by 0.087 and check the answer by estimating.

Solution First, we multiply the factors to find the exact product. Then, we round each factor and multiply them.

$$
\begin{array}{rcl}
0.703 & \approx & 0.7 \leftarrow \text{Rounded to have one nonzero digit} \\
\times \ 0.087 & \approx & \times 0.09 \leftarrow \text{Rounded to have one nonzero digit} \\
\hline
\text{Exact product} \rightarrow 0.061161 & & 0.063 \leftarrow \text{Estimated product}
\end{array}
$$

We see that the exact product and the estimated product are fairly close.

PRACTICE 9

Find the product of 0.0037×0.092, estimating to check.

EXAMPLE 10

Calculate and check: $(4.061)(0.72) + (0.91)(0.258)$

Solution Following the order of operations rule, we begin by finding the two products.

$$(4.061)(0.72) = 2.92392 \qquad (0.91)(0.258) = 0.23478$$

Then, we add these two products.

$$2.92392 + 0.23478 = 3.1587$$

So $(4.061)(0.72) + (0.91)(0.258) = 3.1587$.
   Now, let's check this answer by estimating.

$$(4.061)(0.72) + (0.91)(0.258)$$
$$\downarrow \qquad \downarrow \qquad \downarrow \qquad \downarrow$$
$$(4) \quad (0.7) + (0.9) \ (0.3) = 2.8 + 0.27 = 3.07 \approx 3$$

The estimate 3 is close to 3.1587.

PRACTICE 10

Compute and check:
$(0.488)(9.1) - (3.5)(0.227)$

EXAMPLE 11

The sound waves of an elephant call can travel through both the ground and the air. Through the air, the waves may travel 6.63 miles. If they travel 1.5 times as far through the ground, what is the estimated ground distance? (*Source:* wikipedia.org)

Solution We know that the waves may travel 6.63 miles through the air and 1.5 times as far through the ground. To find the estimated ground distance, we compute this product.

$$
\begin{array}{rcl}
6.63 & \approx & 7 \\
\times \ 1.5 & \approx & \times 2 \\
\hline
& & 14
\end{array}
$$

So the estimated ground distance of the sound waves of an elephant call is about 14 miles.

PRACTICE 11

Earth travels through space at a speed of 18.6 miles per second. Estimate how far Earth travels in 60 seconds. (*Source:* The Diagram Group, *Comparisons*)

Multiplying Decimals on a Calculator

Multiply decimals on a calculator by entering each decimal as you would enter a whole number, but insert a decimal point as needed. If there are too many decimal places in your answer to fit in the display, investigate how your calculator displays the answer.

EXAMPLE 12

Compute 8,278.55 × 0.875, rounding your answer to the nearest hundredth. Then, check the answer by estimating.

Solution

Press	Display
8278.55 ⊠× 0.875 ENTER	8278.55 * 0.875
	7243.73125

Now, 7,243.73125 rounded to the nearest hundredth is 7,243.73. Checking by estimating, we get 8,000 × 0.9, or 7,200, which is close to our exact answer.

PRACTICE 12

Find the product of 2,471.66 and 0.33, rounding to the nearest tenth. Check the answer.

EXAMPLE 13

Find $(1.9)^2$

Solution

Press	Display
1.9 ^ 2 ENTER	1.9 ^ 2
	3.61

Now, let's check by estimating. Since 1.9 rounded to the nearest whole number is 2, $(1.9)^2$ should be close to 2^2, or 4, which is close to our exact answer, 3.61.

PRACTICE 13

Calculate: $(2.1)^3$

Mathematically Speaking

Fill in each blank with the most appropriate term or phrase from the given list.

add	three	factors	five
first factor	four	multiplication	
square	two	division	

1. The operation understood in the expression (3.4) (8.9) is _____ .

2. When multiplying decimals, the number of decimal places in the product is equal to the total number of decimal places in the _____ .

3. To multiply a decimal by 100, move the decimal point _____ places to the right.

4. The product of 0.27 and 8.18 has _____ decimal places.

5. To compute the expression $(8.5)^2 + 2.1$, first _____ .

6. To multiply a decimal by 1,000, move the decimal point _____ places to the right.

A *Insert a decimal point in each product. Check by estimating.*

7. $2.356 \times 1.27 = 299212$

8. $97.26 \times 5.3 = 515478$

9. $3,144 \times 0.065 = 204360$

10. $837 \times 0.15 = 12555$

11. $71.2 \times 35 = 24920$

12. $0.002 \times 37 = 0074$

13. $0.0019 \times 0.051 = 969$

14. $0.0089 \times 0.0021 = 1869$

15. $2.87 \times 1,000 = 287000$

16. $492.31 \times 10 = 492310$

17. $\$4.25 \times 0.173 = \$73525$

18. $11.2 \text{ feet} \times 0.75 = 8400 \text{ feet}$

Find the product. Check by estimating.

19.
$$\begin{array}{r} 0.6 \\ \times\ 0.9 \\ \hline \end{array}$$

20.
$$\begin{array}{r} 0.8 \\ \times\ 0.7 \\ \hline \end{array}$$

21.
$$\begin{array}{r} 0.5 \\ \times\ 0.8 \\ \hline \end{array}$$

22.
$$\begin{array}{r} 0.6 \\ \times\ 0.8 \\ \hline \end{array}$$

23.
$$\begin{array}{r} 0.1 \\ \times\ 0.2 \\ \hline \end{array}$$

24.
$$\begin{array}{r} 0.9 \\ \times\ 0.5 \\ \hline \end{array}$$

25.
$$\begin{array}{r} 0.04 \\ \times\ 0.07 \\ \hline \end{array}$$

26.
$$\begin{array}{r} 0.03 \\ \times\ 0.01 \\ \hline \end{array}$$

27.
$$\begin{array}{r} 2.55 \\ \times\ 0.3 \\ \hline \end{array}$$

28.
$$\begin{array}{r} 8.07 \\ \times\ 0.6 \\ \hline \end{array}$$

29.
$$\begin{array}{r} 0.96 \\ \times\ 2.1 \\ \hline \end{array}$$

30.
$$\begin{array}{r} 0.87 \\ \times\ 3.1 \\ \hline \end{array}$$

31.
$$\begin{array}{r} 38.01 \\ \times\ 0.2 \\ \hline \end{array}$$

32.
$$\begin{array}{r} 12.02 \\ \times\ 0.05 \\ \hline \end{array}$$

33.
$$\begin{array}{r} 125 \\ \times\ 0.004 \\ \hline \end{array}$$

34.
$$\begin{array}{r} 135 \\ \times\ 0.006 \\ \hline \end{array}$$

35. 3.8×1.54

36. 9.51×2.7

37. 13.74×11

38. 12.45×11

39. 12.459×0.3

40. 72.558×0.2

41. $(0.675)(2.66)$

42. $(4.003)(0.59)$

43. 83.127×100

44. 49.247×100

45. $0.0023 \times 10{,}000$

46. $0.0135 \times 10{,}000$

47. $(1.5)(0.6)(0.1)$

48. $(12)(3.5)(0.2)$

49. $(0.03)(1.4)(25)$

50. $(2.6)(0.5)(0.9)$

51. $(0.001)^3$

52. $(0.1)^4$

53. $17 \text{ feet} \times 2.5$

54. $15 \text{ hours} \times 7.5$

55. $3.5 \text{ miles} \times 0.4$

56. $9.1 \text{ meters} \times 1{,}000$

57.
$$\begin{array}{r} 43.87 \\ \times\ 0.975 \\ \hline \end{array}$$

58.
$$\begin{array}{r} 18{,}275.33 \\ \times\ \ \ \ \ 0.39 \\ \hline \end{array}$$

59.
$$\begin{array}{r} 99{,}125 \\ \times\ \ \ \ 2.75 \\ \hline \end{array}$$

60.
$$\begin{array}{r} 3.512 \\ \times\ \ 1.47 \\ \hline \end{array}$$

Simplify.

61. 0.7×10^2

62. 0.6×10^4

63. $30 - 2.5 \times 1.7$

64. $18 - 3.4 \times 1.6$

65. $1 + (0.3)^2$

66. $6 + (1.2)^2$

67. $0.8(1.3 + 2.9) - 0.5$

68. $4 - 2.1(3.5 - 1.8)$

69. $(5.2 - 3.9)(0.9 + 2.14)$

70. $(8 + 4.5)(8 - 4.5)$

71. $0.4(3 - 2.9)(2 + 1.5)$

72. $0.5(1 + 0.2)(1 - 0.2)$

Complete each table.

73.

Input	Output
1	$3.8 \times \mathbf{1} - 0.2 =$
2	$3.8 \times \mathbf{2} - 0.2 =$
3	$3.8 \times \mathbf{3} - 0.2 =$
4	$3.8 \times \mathbf{4} - 0.2 =$

74.

Input	Output
1	$7.5 \times \mathbf{1} + 0.4 =$
2	$7.5 \times \mathbf{2} + 0.4 =$
3	$7.5 \times \mathbf{3} + 0.4 =$
4	$7.5 \times \mathbf{4} + 0.4 =$

Each product is rounded to the nearest hundredth. In each group of three products, one is wrong. Use estimation to explain which product is incorrect.

75. a. $51.6 \times 0.813 \approx 419.51$

b. $2.93 \times 7.283 \approx 21.34$

c. $(5.004)^2 \approx 25.04$

76. a. $0.004 \times 3.18 \approx 0.01$

b. $2.99 \times 0.287 \approx 0.86$

c. $(1.985)^3 \approx 10.82$

77. a. $4.913 \times 2.18 \approx 10.71$

b. $0.023 \times 0.71 \approx 0.16$

c. $(8.92)(1.0027) \approx 8.94$

78. a. $\$138.28 \times 0.075 \approx \$10.37$

b. $0.19 \times \$487.21 \approx \$92.57$

c. $0.77 \times \$6{,}005.79 \approx \$462.45$

Mixed Practice

Solve.

79. Simplify: $9 - (0.5)^2$

80. Compute: $2.1 + 5 \times 0.6$

81. Multiply 0.75 and 0.09, rounding the answer to the nearest thousandth.

82. Multiply: $(2.3)(4.5)(0.6)$

83. Find the product of 0.56 and 8.

84. Find the product: $3.01 \times 1{,}000$

Applications

B *Solve. Check by estimating.*

85. Sound travels at approximately 1,000 feet per second (fps). If a jet is flying at Mach 2.9 (that is, 2.9 times the speed of sound), what is its speed?

86. If insurance premiums of $323.50 are paid yearly for 10 years for a life insurance policy, how much did the policy holder pay altogether in premiums?

87. The planet in the solar system closest to the Sun is Mercury. The average distance between these two bodies is 57.9 million kilometers. Express this distance in standard form. (*Source:* Jeffrey Bennett et al., *The Cosmic Perspective*)

88. According to the first American census in 1790, the population of the United States was approximately 3.9 million. Write this number in standard form. (*Source: The Statistical History of the United States*)

89. A construction company builds custom-designed swimming pools, including the circular pool shown below. The area of the bottom of this pool is approximately 3.14×9^2 square feet. Find this area to the nearest tenth. (*Source:* Pritchett Construction Co.)

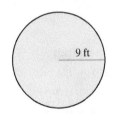

90. Find the area (in square meters) of the floor pictured.

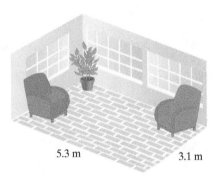

5.3 m   3.1 m

91. Over a 5-day period, a nurse administered 10 tablets to a patient. If each tablet contained 0.125 milligram of the drug Digoxin, how much Digoxin did the nurse administer?

92. Water weighs approximately 62.5 pounds per cubic foot (lb/ft³). If a bathtub contains about 30 ft³ of water, how much does the water in the bathtub weigh?

93. A tennis player weighing 180 pounds burns 10.9 calories per minute while playing singles tennis. How many calories would he burn in 2 hours? (*Source:* caloriesperhour.com)

94. A plumber is paid $37.50 per hour for the first 40 hours worked. She gets time and a half, $56.25, for any time over her 40-hour week. If she works 49 hours in a week, how much is her pay?

95. The sales receipt for a shopper's purchases is as follows:

Purchase	Quantity	Unit Price	Price
Belt	1	$11.99	$____.__
Shirt	3	$16.95	$____.__
Total Price			$____.__

   a. Complete the table.
   b. If the shopper pays for these purchases with four $20 bills, how much change should he get?

96. On an electric bill, *usage* is the difference between the meter's *current reading* and the *previous reading* in kilowatt hours (kWh). The *amount due* is the product of the usage and the *rate per kWh*. Find the two missing quantities in the table, rounding to the nearest hundredth.

Previous Reading	750.07 kWh
Current Reading	1,115.14 kWh
Usage	kWh
Rate per kWh	$0.10
Amount Due	$

97. Scientists have discovered a relationship between the length of a person's bones and the person's overall height. For instance, an adult male's height (in inches) can be predicted from the length of his femur bone by using the formula $(1.9 \times \text{femur}) + 32.0$. With this formula, find the height of the German giant Constantine, whose femur measured 29.9 inches. (*Source: Guinness World Records*)

98. In order to buy a $125,000 house, a couple puts down $25,000 and takes out a mortgage on the balance. To pay off the mortgage, they pay $877.57 per month for the following 360 months. How much more will they end up paying for the house than the original price of $125,000?

• Check your answers on page A-4.

MINDStretchers

Patterns

1. When $(0.001)^{100}$ is multiplied out, how many decimal places will it have?

Mathematical Reasoning

2. Give an example of two decimals
   a. whose sum is greater than their product, and

   b. whose product is greater than their sum.

Groupwork

3. In the product to the right, each letter stands for a different digit. Working with a partner, identify all the digits.

$$
\begin{array}{r}
\text{A.B} \\
\times\,\text{B.A} \\
\hline
\text{C D}
\end{array}
$$

3.4 Dividing Decimals

In this section, we first consider changing a fraction to its decimal equivalent, which involves both division and decimals. We then move on to our main concern—the division of decimals.

Changing a Fraction to the Equivalent Decimal

Earlier in this chapter, we discussed how to change a decimal to its equivalent fraction. Now let's consider the opposite problem—how to change a fraction to its equivalent decimal.

When the denominator of a fraction is already a power of 10, the problem is simple. For example, the decimal equivalent of $\frac{43}{100}$ is 0.43.

But what about the more difficult problem in which the denominator is *not* a power of 10? A good strategy is to find an equivalent fraction that does have a power of 10 as its denominator. Consider, for instance, the fraction $\frac{3}{4}$. Since 4 is a factor of 100, which is a power of 10, we can easily find an equivalent fraction having a denominator of 100.

$$\frac{3}{4} = \frac{3 \cdot 25}{4 \cdot 25} = \frac{75}{100} = 0.75$$

So 0.75 is the decimal equivalent of $\frac{3}{4}$.

There is a faster way to show that $\frac{3}{4}$ is the same as 0.75, without having to find an equivalent fraction. Because $\frac{3}{4}$ can mean $3 \div 4$, we divide the numerator (3) by the denominator (4). Note that if we continue to divide to the hundredths place, there is no remainder.

Insert the decimal point directly above the decimal point in the dividend.

$$
\begin{array}{r}
0.75 \\
4\overline{)3.00} \\
\underline{0} \\
3\,0 \\
\underline{2\,8} \\
20 \\
\underline{20}
\end{array}
$$

← The decimal point is after the 3. Insert enough 0's to continue dividing as far as necessary.

So this division also tells us that $\frac{3}{4}$ equals 0.75.

To Change a Fraction to the Equivalent Decimal

- Divide the denominator of the fraction into the numerator, inserting to its right both a decimal point and enough zeros to get an answer either without a remainder or rounded to a given decimal place.

- Place a decimal point in the quotient directly above the decimal point in the dividend.

EXAMPLE 1

Express $\frac{1}{2}$ as a decimal.

Solution To find the decimal equivalent, we divide the fraction's numerator by its denominator.

$$
\begin{array}{r}
0.5 \\
2\overline{)1.0} \\
\underline{0} \\
1\,0 \\
\underline{1\,0}
\end{array}
$$

Add a decimal point and a 0 to the right of the 1.

So 0.5 is the decimal equivalent of $\frac{1}{2}$.

Check We verify that the fractional equivalent of 0.5 is $\frac{1}{2}$.

$$0.5 = \frac{5}{10} = \frac{1}{2}$$

The answer checks.

PRACTICE 1

Write the fraction $\frac{3}{8}$ as a decimal.

EXAMPLE 2

Convert $2\frac{3}{5}$ to a decimal.

Solution Let's first change this mixed number to an improper fraction: $2\frac{3}{5} = \frac{13}{5}$. We can then change this improper fraction to a decimal by dividing its numerator by its denominator.

$$
\begin{array}{r}
2.6 \\
5\overline{)13.0} \\
\underline{10} \\
3\,0 \\
\underline{3\,0}
\end{array}
$$

So 2.6 is the decimal form of $2\frac{3}{5}$.

Check We convert this answer back from a decimal to its mixed number form.

$$2.6 = 2\frac{6}{10} = 2\frac{3}{5}$$ The answer checks.

PRACTICE 2

Write $7\frac{5}{8}$ as a decimal.

When converting some fractions to decimal notation, we keep getting a remainder as we divide. In this case, we round the answer to a given decimal place.

EXAMPLE 3

Convert $4\frac{8}{9}$ to a decimal, rounded to the nearest hundredth.

Solution First, we change this mixed number to an improper fraction. Then, we convert it to a decimal.

$$4\frac{8}{9} = \frac{44}{9} = 9\overline{)44.000}$$

$$\begin{array}{r} 4.888 \\ 9\overline{)44.000} \\ \underline{36} \\ 8\ 0 \\ \underline{7\ 2} \\ 80 \\ \underline{72} \\ 80 \\ \underline{72} \end{array}$$

← In order to round to the nearest hundredth, we must continue to divide to the thousandths place. So we insert three 0's.

Finally, we round to the nearest hundredth: $4.8\underline{88} \approx 4.89$

PRACTICE 3

Express $83\frac{1}{3}$ as a decimal, rounded to the nearest tenth.

In Example 3, note that if instead of rounding we had continued to divide we would have gotten as our answer the **repeating decimal** 4.88888 . . . (also written $4.\overline{8}$). Can you think of any other fraction that is equivalent to a repeating decimal?

Let's now consider some word problems in which we need to convert fractions to decimals.

EXAMPLE 4

Reformulated gasoline (RFG) is a "cleaner" gasoline required to be used in nine major metropolitan areas of the United States with the worst ozone air pollution problem. In a particular week, the average retail regular gas price for RFG areas was $\$2\frac{7}{8}$. Express this amount in dollars and cents, to the nearest cent. (*Source:* epa.gov and eia.doe.gov)

Solution To solve, we must convert the mixed number $2\frac{7}{8}$ to a decimal.

$$2\frac{7}{8} = \frac{23}{8} = 8\overline{)23.000}$$

$$\begin{array}{r} 2.875 \\ 8\overline{)23.000} \\ \underline{16} \\ 70 \\ \underline{64} \\ 60 \\ \underline{56} \\ 40 \\ \underline{40} \end{array} \approx 2.88$$

So the average price for RFG was $2.88, to the nearest cent.

PRACTICE 4

About $\frac{13}{125}$ of the world's land surface is covered with ice. Express this fraction as a decimal, rounded to the nearest tenth. (*Source:* enotes.com)

Dividing Decimals

Before we turn our attention to dividing one decimal by another, let's consider simpler problems in which we are dividing a decimal by a whole number. An example of such a problem is $0.6 \div 2$. We can write this expression as the fraction $\frac{0.6}{2}$, which can be rewritten as the quotient of two whole numbers by multiplying the numerator and denominator by 10 as follows:

$$\frac{0.6}{2} = \frac{0.6 \times 10}{2 \times 10} = \frac{6}{20}$$

We then convert the fraction $\frac{6}{20}$ to the equivalent decimal, as we have previously discussed.

$$
\begin{array}{r}
0.3 \\
20\overline{)6.0} \\
\underline{0} \\
6\,0 \\
\underline{6\,0}
\end{array}
$$

So $\frac{0.6}{2} = 0.3$

Note that we get the same quotient if we divide the number in the original problem as follows:

$$
\begin{array}{r}
0.3 \leftarrow \text{Quotient} \\
\text{Divisor} \rightarrow 2\overline{)0.6} \leftarrow \text{Dividend} \\
\underline{0} \\
6 \\
\underline{6}
\end{array}
$$

It is important to write the decimal point in the quotient directly above the decimal point in the dividend.

Next, let's consider a division problem in which we are dividing one decimal by another: $0.006 \div 0.02$. Writing this expression as a fraction, we get $\frac{0.006}{0.02}$. Since we have already discussed how to divide a decimal by a whole number, the goal here is to find a fraction equivalent to $\frac{0.006}{0.02}$ where the denominator is a whole number. Multiplying the numerator and denominator by 100 will do just that.

$$0.006 \div 0.02 = \frac{0.006}{0.02} = \frac{0.006 \times 100}{0.02 \times 100} = \frac{0.6}{2}$$

We know from the previous problem that $\frac{0.6}{2} = 0.3$. Since $\frac{0.006}{0.02} = \frac{0.6}{2}$, we conclude $\frac{0.006}{0.02} = 0.3$.

A shortcut to multiplying by 100 in both the divisor and the dividend is to move the decimal point two places to the right.

$$\text{So } 0.02\overline{)0.006}^{\,0.3} \text{ is equivalent to } 2\overline{)0.6}^{\,0.3}$$

As in any division problem, we can check our answer by confirming that the product of the quotient and the *original divisor* equals the *original dividend*.

Division Problem	Check
	0.3
$0.6 \div 2 = 0.3$	$\underline{\times\ 2}$
	0.6
	0.3
$0.006 \div 0.02 = 0.3$	$\underline{\times 0.02}$
	0.006

These examples suggest the following rule:

To Divide Decimals

- Move the decimal point in the divisor to the right end of the number.
- Move the decimal point in the dividend the same number of places to the right as in the divisor.
- Insert a decimal point in the quotient directly above the decimal point in the dividend.
- Divide the new dividend by the new divisor, inserting zeros at the right end of the dividend as necessary.

EXAMPLE 5

What is 0.035 divided by 0.25?

Solution Move the decimal point to the right end, making the divisor a whole number.

$$0.25\overline{)0.035}$$

Move the decimal point in the dividend the same number of places.

Now, we divide 3.5 by 25, which gives us 0.14.

$$\begin{array}{r} 0.14 \\ 25\overline{)3.50} \\ \underline{2\ 5} \\ 1\ 00 \\ \underline{1\ 00} \end{array}$$

Check We see that the product of the quotient and the original divisor is equal to the original dividend.

$$\begin{array}{r} 0.14 \\ \times 0.25 \\ \hline 070 \\ 028 \\ \hline 0.0350 \end{array} = 0.035$$

PRACTICE 5

Divide and check: $2.706 \div 0.15$

EXAMPLE 6

Find the quotient: $6 \div 0.0012$. Check the answer.

Solution

The decimal point is moved four places to the right.

$$0.0012\overline{)6.0000}$$

To move the decimal point four places to the right, we must add four 0's as placeholders.

$$\begin{array}{r} 5,000 \\ 12\overline{)60,000} \end{array}$$

Check
$$\begin{array}{r} 5,000 \\ \times\ 0.0012 \\ \hline 6.0000 \end{array} = 6$$

The answer checks.

PRACTICE 6

Divide $\dfrac{8.2}{0.004}$ and then check.

EXAMPLE 7

Divide and round to the nearest hundredth: $0.7\overline{)40.2}$
Then, check.

Solution $0.7\overline{)40.2}$

$$
\begin{array}{r}
57.428 \approx 57.43 \text{ to the nearest hundredth} \\
7\overline{)402.000} \\
35 \\
\hline
52 \\
49 \\
\hline
3\,0 \\
2\,8 \\
\hline
20 \\
14 \\
\hline
60 \\
56 \\
\hline
4
\end{array}
$$

Check

$$
\begin{array}{r}
57.43 \\
\times\ \ 0.7 \\
\hline
40.201 \approx 40.2
\end{array}
$$

Because we rounded our answer, the check gives us a product only approximately equal to the original dividend.

PRACTICE 7

Find the quotient of 8.07 and 0.11, rounded to the nearest tenth.

EXAMPLE 8

Compute and check: $8.319 \div 1,000$

Solution

$$
\begin{array}{r}
0.008319 \\
1,000\overline{)8.319000} \\
8\,000 \\
\hline
3190 \\
3000 \\
\hline
1900 \\
1000 \\
\hline
9000 \\
9000 \\
\hline
\end{array}
$$

Check

$0.008319 \times 1,000 = 0008.319 = 8.319$

Note that the divisor (1,000) is a power of 10 ending in three zeros, and that the quotient is identical to the dividend except that the decimal point is moved to the left three places.

$$
\frac{8.319}{1,000} = 0.008319
$$

PRACTICE 8

Divide: $100\overline{)3.41}$

Example 8 suggests the following shortcut.

TIP   To divide a decimal by a power of 10, move the decimal point to the left the same number of places as the power of 10 has zeros.

Can you explain the difference between the shortcuts for multiplying and for dividing by a power of 10?

EXAMPLE 9

Compute: $\dfrac{7.2}{100}$

Solution Since we are dividing by 100, a power of 10 with two zeros, we can find this quotient simply by moving the decimal point in 7.2 to the left two places.

$$\frac{7.2}{100} = .072, \quad \text{or} \quad 0.072$$

So the quotient is 0.072.

PRACTICE 9

Calculate: $0.86 \div 1{,}000$

Now, let's try using these skills in some applications.

EXAMPLE 10

The following table gives the area of each of the world's three largest oceans.

Ocean	Area (in millions of square kilometers)
Pacific Ocean	155.6
Atlantic Ocean	76.8
Indian Ocean	68.6

(*Source:* cia.gov)

The area of the Pacific Ocean is how many times as great as the area of the Atlantic Ocean, rounded to the nearest tenth?

Solution The area of the Pacific Ocean is 155.6 and that of the Atlantic Ocean is 76.8 (both in millions of square kilometers). To find how many times as great 155.6 is when compared to 76.8, we find the quotient of these numbers.

$$76.8\overline{)155.6} = 768\overline{)1556}$$

$$
\begin{array}{r}
2.02 \\
768\overline{)1556.00} \\
\underline{1536} \\
20\,0 \\
\underline{0} \\
2000 \\
\underline{1536} \\
464
\end{array}
$$

Rounding to the nearest tenth, we find that the area of the Pacific Ocean is 2.0 times that of the Atlantic Ocean.

PRACTICE 10

The table gives the amount of selected foods consumed per capita in the United States in a recent year.

Food	Annual Per Capita Consumption (in pounds)
Red meat	112.0
Poultry	72.7
Fish and shellfish	16.5

The amount of red meat consumed was how many times as great as the amount of poultry, rounded to the nearest tenth? (*Source:* U.S. Department of Agriculture)

Estimating Quotients

As we have shown, one way to check the quotient of two decimals is by multiplying. Another way is by estimating.

To check a decimal quotient by estimating, we can round each decimal to one nonzero digit and then mentally divide the rounded numbers. But we must be careful to position the decimal point correctly in our estimate.

Mental estimation is also a useful skill for approximating a quotient.

EXAMPLE 11

Divide and check by estimating: $3.36 \div 0.021$

Solution $0.021\overline{)3.360}$

We compute the exact answer.

$$
\begin{array}{r}
160 \\
21\overline{)3{,}360} \\
\underline{2\ 1} \\
1\ 26 \\
\underline{1\ 26} \\
00 \\
\underline{00}
\end{array}
$$

So 160 is our quotient.

Now, let's check by estimating. Because $3.36 \approx 3$ and $0.021 \approx 0.02$, $3.36 \div 0.021 \approx 3 \div 0.02$. We mentally divide to get the estimate.

$$
\begin{array}{r}
150 \\
0.02\overline{)3.00}
\end{array}
$$

Our estimate 150 is reasonably close to our exact answer, 160.

PRACTICE 11

Compute and check by estimating:
$8.229 \div 0.39$

EXAMPLE 12

Calculate and check: $(9.13) \div (0.2) + (4.6)^2$

Solution   Following the order of operations rule, we begin by finding the square and then the quotient.

$$(4.6)^2 = 21.16$$
$$(9.13) \div (0.2) = 45.65$$

Then we add these two results.

$$21.16 + 45.65 = 66.81$$

So $(9.13) \div (0.2) + (4.6)^2 = 66.81$.

Now, let's check this answer by estimating.

$$(9.13) \div (0.2) + (4.6)^2$$

$$\underbrace{9 \div 0.2}_{45} \quad + \quad 25 \ \approx 45 + 25 \approx 70$$

The estimate 70 is close to our answer, 66.81.

PRACTICE 12

Compute and check:
$13.07 + (8.4 \div 0.5)^2$

EXAMPLE 13

The water in a filled aquarium weighs 638.25 pounds. If 1 cubic foot of water weighs 62.5 pounds, estimate how many cubic feet of water there are in the aquarium.

Solution   We know that the water in the aquarium weighs 638.25 pounds. Since 1 cubic foot of water weighs 62.5 pounds, we can estimate the number of cubic feet of water in the aquarium by computing the quotient $638.25 \div 62.5$, which is approximately $600 \div 60$, or 10. So a reasonable estimate for the amount of water in the aquarium is 10 cubic feet.

PRACTICE 13

The following graph shows the number of farms, in a recent year, in five states.

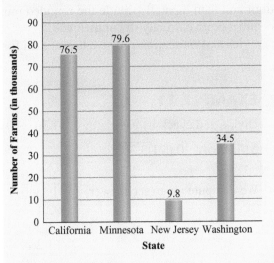

The number of farms in Minnesota is about how many times as great as the number in New Jersey? (*Source:* U.S. Department of Agriculture)

Dividing on a Calculator

When dividing decimals on a calculator, be careful to enter the dividend first and then the divisor. Note that when the dividend is larger than the divisor, the quotient is greater than 1 and when the dividend is smaller than the divisor, the quotient is less than 1.

EXAMPLE 14

Calculate $8.6 \div 1.6$ and round to the nearest tenth.

Solution

Press	Display
8.6 ÷ 1.6 ENTER	8.6/1.6
	5.375

The answer, when rounded to the nearest tenth, is 5.4. As expected, the answer is greater than 1, because $8.6 > 1.6$.

PRACTICE 14

Compute the quotient $8.6\overline{)1.6}$ and round to the nearest tenth.

EXAMPLE 15

Divide $0.3\overline{)0.07}$, rounding to the nearest hundredth.

Solution

Press	Display
0.07 ÷ 0.3 ENTER	0.07/0.3
	0.233333333

The answer, when rounded to the nearest hundredth, is 0.23. As expected, the answer is less than 1, because $0.07 < 0.3$.

PRACTICE 15

Find the quotient, rounding to the nearest hundredth: $0.3 \div 0.07$

Mathematically Speaking

Fill in each blank with the most appropriate term or phrase from the given list.

quotient	three	divisor	decimal
dividend	right	terminating	four
fraction	product	left	repeating

1. To change a fraction to the equivalent _____, divide the numerator of the fraction by its denominator.

2. An example of a(n) _____ decimal is 0.3333 . . . .

3. When dividing decimals, move the decimal point in the divisor to the _____ end.

4. To divide a decimal by 1,000, move the decimal point _____ places to the left.

5. To estimate the _____ of 0.813 and 0.187, divide 0.8 by 0.2.

6. When dividing a decimal by a whole number, the decimal point in the quotient is placed above the decimal point in the _____.

Ⓐ *Change to the equivalent decimal. Then, check.*

7. $\dfrac{1}{2}$

8. $\dfrac{3}{5}$

9. $\dfrac{3}{8}$

10. $\dfrac{1}{8}$

11. $\dfrac{37}{10}$

12. $\dfrac{57}{10}$

13. $1\dfrac{5}{8}$

14. $2\dfrac{7}{8}$

15. $6\dfrac{1}{5}$

16. $8\dfrac{2}{5}$

17. $21\dfrac{3}{100}$

18. $60\dfrac{17}{100}$

Change to the equivalent decimal. Round to the nearest hundredth.

19. $\dfrac{2}{3}$

20. $\dfrac{5}{6}$

21. $\dfrac{7}{9}$

22. $\dfrac{1}{3}$

23. $3\dfrac{1}{9}$

24. $2\dfrac{4}{7}$

25. $5\dfrac{1}{16}$

26. $10\dfrac{11}{32}$

Ⓑ *Divide and check.*

27. $4\overline{)17}$

28. $2\overline{)35}$

29. $5\overline{)21}$

30. $6\overline{)33}$

31. $8\overline{)11}$

32. $6\overline{)9}$

33. $18\overline{)153}$

34. $14\overline{)217}$

Divide. Express any remainder as a decimal rounded to the nearest thousandth.

35. $7\overline{)23}$

36. $9\overline{)41}$

37. $11\overline{)3}$

38. $13\overline{)2}$

39. $7\overline{)46}$

40. $6\overline{)82}$

41. $13\overline{)911}$

42. $12\overline{)208}$

Insert the decimal point in the appropriate place.

43. $0.7\overline{)41.174}$ with quotient 5882

44. $3\overline{)0.0171}$ with quotient 57

45. $0.58\overline{)0.038454}$ with quotient 663

46. $3.9\overline{)26.91}$ with quotient 69

Divide. Check, either by multiplying or by estimating.

47. $8\overline{)23.1}$

48. $8\overline{)24.6}$

49. $7\overline{)2.002}$

50. $6\overline{)4.002}$

51. $\dfrac{17.2}{4}$

52. $\dfrac{18.5}{5}$

53. $\dfrac{0.003}{2}$

54. $\dfrac{0.009}{5}$

55. $8.65 \div 5$

56. $7.74 \div 6$

57. $11.5 \div 4$

58. $16.5 \div 4$

59. $0.2\overline{)0.8}$

60. $0.3\overline{)0.6}$

61. $0.05\overline{)3.52}$

62. $0.04\overline{)1.92}$

63. $\dfrac{47}{0.5}$

64. $\dfrac{86}{0.2}$

65. $\dfrac{5}{0.4}$

66. $\dfrac{9}{0.6}$

67. $0.03 \div 0.1$

68. $0.04 \div 0.2$

69. $0.38 \div 1.9$

70. $0.75 \div 2.5$

71. $95.2 \div 100$

72. $81.6 \div 100$

73. $0.082 \div 100$

74. $0.093 \div 100$

Divide, rounding to the nearest hundredth. Check, either by multiplying or by estimating.

75. $0.8\overline{)307.1}$

76. $0.6\overline{)401.8}$

77. $0.9\overline{)0.0057}$

78. $0.2\overline{)0.0063}$

79. $\dfrac{3.69}{0.4}$

80. $\dfrac{3.98}{0.8}$

81. $\dfrac{87}{0.009}$

82. $\dfrac{23}{0.006}$

83. $41 \div 0.021$

84. $91 \div 0.071$

85. $35.77 \div 0.11$

86. $29.11 \div 0.17$

87. $49.071 \div 0.728$

88. $18.032 \div 0.796$

89. $3 \div 0.0721$

90. $4 \div 0.0826$

Perform the indicated operations.

91. $\dfrac{3.06}{4} + 2$

92. $\dfrac{2.04}{3} + 1$

93. $\dfrac{18.27 - 8.4}{0.3}$

94. $\dfrac{26.77 - 10.1}{0.4}$

95. $\dfrac{13.05}{7.27 - 7.02}$

96. $\dfrac{14.07}{8.41 - 8.01}$

97. $\dfrac{8.1 \times 0.2}{0.4}$

98. $\dfrac{4.7 \times 5.6}{0.8}$

99. $(82.9 - 3.6) \div (0.21 - 0.01)$

100. $(3.21 - 0.207) \div (2.08 - 2.072)$

101. $8.73 \div 0.2 + (2.5)^2$

102. $4.86 \div 0.2 + (3.1)^2$

Complete each table.

103.

Input	Output
1	$1 \div 5 - 0.2 =$
2	$2 \div 5 - 0.2 =$
3	$3 \div 5 - 0.2 =$
4	$4 \div 5 - 0.2 =$

104.

Input	Output
1	$1 \div 4 + 0.4 =$
2	$2 \div 4 + 0.4 =$
3	$3 \div 4 + 0.4 =$
4	$4 \div 4 + 0.4 =$

Each of the following quotients is rounded to the nearest hundredth. In each group of three quotients, one is wrong. Use estimation to identify which quotient is incorrect.

105. a. $5.7 \div 89 \approx 0.06$

b. $0.77 \div 0.0019 \approx 405.26$

c. $31.5 \div 0.61 \approx 516.39$

106. a. $\dfrac{9.83}{4.88} \approx 0.20$

b. $\dfrac{2.771}{0.452} \approx 6.13$

c. $\dfrac{389.224}{1.79} \approx 217.44$

107. a. $61.27 \div 0.057 \approx 1{,}074.91$

b. $0.614 \div 2.883 \approx 2.13$

c. $0.0035 \div 0.00481 \approx 0.73$

108. a. $\$365 \div \$4.89 \approx 7.46$

b. $\$17{,}358.27 \div \$365 \approx 47.56$

c. $\$3{,}000 \div \$2.54 \approx 1{,}181.10$

Mixed Practice

Solve.

109. Express $\frac{4}{5}$ as a decimal.

110. Divide $1.6\overline{)8.5}$ and round to the nearest tenth.

111. Change $1\frac{1}{6}$ to a decimal, rounded to the nearest hundredth.

112. Simplify: $81.5 - \frac{32}{0.4}$

113. What is 0.063 divided by 0.14?

114. Find the quotient: $9 \div 0.0072$

Applications

C *Solve and check.*

115. A stalactite is an icicle-shaped mineral deposit that hangs from the roof of a cave. If it took a thousand years for a stalactite to grow to a length of 3.7 inches, how much did it grow per year?

116. In a strong storm, the damage to 100 houses was estimated at $12.7 million. What was the average damage per house?

117. The women's softball team won 21 games and lost 14. The men's softball team won 22 games and lost 18.
   a. The women's team won what fraction of the games that it played, expressed as a decimal?
   b. The men's team won what fraction of its games, expressed as a decimal?
   c. Which team has a better record? Explain.

118. Yesterday, 0.08 inches of rain fell. Today, $\frac{1}{4}$ inch of rain fell.
   a. How much rain fell today, expressed as a decimal?
   b. Which day did more rain fall? Explain.

119. The table shown gives the highest gasoline mileage for three small SUVs.
   a. For each SUV, compute how many miles it gets per gallon, rounded to the nearest whole number.
   b. Which SUV gives the highest mileage?

SUV	Distance Driven (in miles)	Gasoline Used (in gallons)	Gasoline Mileage (in miles per gallon)
Honda CR-V	40.5	1.9	
Ford Escape Hybrid	62.4	2.4	
GMC Terrain	42.6	2.4	

(*Source: Consumer Reports*)

120. The table shown gives the total number of games played and assists made by three basketball players over the same period of time.

a. Compute the average number of assists per game for each player, expressed as a decimal rounded to the nearest tenth.

b. Decide which player had the highest average.

Player	Number of Games	Number of Assists	Average
Steve Nash	236	2,507	
Chris Paul	203	2,266	
Deron Williams	226	2,385	

(*Source:* nba.com/statistics)

121. On the stock market, shares of Citigroup, Inc. common stock were traded at $3.63 per share. How many shares could have been bought for $7,260? (*Source:* finance.yahoo.com)

122. A light microscope can distinguish two points separated by 0.0005 millimeter, whereas an electron microscope can distinguish two points separated by 0.0000005 millimeter. The electron microscope is how many times as powerful as the light microscope?

123. Typically, the heaviest organ in the body is the skin, weighing about 9 pounds. By contrast, the heart weighs approximately 0.7 pound. About how many times the weight of the heart is that of the skin? (*Source: World of Scientific Discovery*)

124. At a community college, each student enrolled pays a $19.50 student fee per semester. In a given semester, if the college collected $39,000 in student fees, how many students were enrolled?

125. A shopper buys four organic chickens. The chickens weigh 3.2 pounds, 3.5 pounds, 2.9 pounds, and 3.6 pounds. How much less than the average weight of the four chickens was the weight of the lightest one?

126. A dieter joins a weight-loss club. Over a 5-month period, she loses 8 pounds, 7.8 pounds, 4 pounds, 1.5 pounds, and 0.8 pound. What was her average monthly weight loss, to the nearest tenth of a pound?

127. Babe Ruth got 2,873 hits in 8,399 times at bat, resulting in a batting average of $\frac{2,873}{8,399}$, or approximately .342. Another great player, Ty Cobb, got 4,189 hits out of 11,434 times at bat. What was his batting average, expressed as a decimal rounded to the nearest thousandth? (Note that batting averages don't have a zero to the left of the decimal point because they can never be greater than 1.) (*Source:* baseball-reference.com)

128. On January 23, 1960, the Trieste became the only manned deep-diving research vessel ever to reach the bottom of the Mariana Trench. This trench is the deepest part of any ocean on Earth, with a depth of 10,911 meters. At a descent rate of 3,290.4 meters per hour, approximately how long did it take for the Trieste to reach the bottom? Round the answer to the nearest tenth of an hour. (*Source:* absoluteastronomy.com)

• Check your answers on page A-5.

MIND*Stretchers*

Patterns

1. In the *repeating decimal* 0.142847142847142847 . . . , identify the 994th digit to the right of the decimal point.

Groupwork

2. In the following magic square, 3.375 is the *product* of the numbers in every row, column, and diagonal. Working with a partner, fill in the missing numbers.

	0.25	3
		0.5

Writing

3. a. 0.5 ÷ 0.8 = ?

b. 0.8 ÷ 0.5 = ?

c. Find the product of your answers in parts (a) and (b). Explain how you could have predicted this product.

Key Concepts and Skills

CONCEPT   SKILL

Concept/Skill	Description	Example
[3.1] **Decimal**	A number written with two parts: a whole number, which precedes the decimal point, and a fractional part, which follows the decimal point.	Whole-number part ⟶ Fractional part ⟶ 3.721 ↑ Decimal point
[3.1] **Decimal place**	A place to the right of the decimal point.	Decimal places 8.**035** Tenths / Hundredths / Thousandths
[3.1] **To change a decimal to the equivalent fraction or mixed number**	• Copy the nonzero whole-number part of the decimal and drop the decimal point. • Place the fractional part of the decimal in the numerator of the equivalent fraction. • Make the denominator of the equivalent fraction 1 followed by as many zeros as the decimal has decimal places. • Simplify the resulting fraction, if possible.	The decimal 3.25 is equivalent to the mixed number $3\frac{25}{100}$ or $3\frac{1}{4}$.
[3.1] **To compare decimals**	• Rewrite the numbers vertically, lining up the decimal points. • Working from left to right, compare the digits that have the same place value. At the first place value where the digits differ, the decimal which has the largest digit with this place value is the largest decimal.	1.073 1.06999 In the ones place and the tenths place, the digits are the same. But in the hundredths place, 7 > 6, so 1.073 > 1.06999.
[3.1] **To round a decimal to a given decimal place**	• Underline the digit in the place to which the number is being rounded. • The digit to the right of the underlined digit is called the *critical digit*. Look at the critical digit—if it is 5 or more, add 1 to the underlined digit; if it is less than 5, leave the underlined digit unchanged. • Drop all decimal places to the right of the underlined digit.	23.9381 ≈ 23.94 ↑ Critical digit
[3.2] **To add decimals**	• Rewrite the numbers vertically, lining up the decimal points. • Add. • Insert a decimal point in the sum below the other decimal points.	0.035 0.08 C+ 0.00813 0.12313
[3.2] **To subtract decimals**	• Rewrite the numbers vertically, lining up the decimal points. • Subtract, inserting extra zeros in the minuend if necessary for regrouping. • Insert a decimal point in the difference below the other decimal points.	0.90370 C− 0.17052 0.73318

continued

Concept/Skill	Description	Example
[3.3] **To multiply decimals**	• Multiply the factors as if they were whole numbers. • Find the total number of decimal places in the factors. • Count that many places from the right end of the product, and insert a decimal point.	21.07 ← Two decimal places × 0.18 ← Two decimal places 3.7926 ← Four decimal places
[3.4] **To change a fraction to the equivalent decimal**	• Divide the denominator of the fraction into the numerator, inserting to its right both a decimal point and enough zeros to get an answer either without a remainder or rounded to a given decimal place. • Place a decimal point in the quotient directly above the decimal point in the dividend.	$\frac{7}{8} = 8\overline{)7.000}^{\,0.875}$
[3.4] **To divide decimals**	• Move the decimal point in the divisor to the right end of the number. • Move the decimal point in the dividend the same number of places to the right as in the divisor. • Insert a decimal point in the quotient directly above the decimal point in the dividend. • Divide the new dividend by the new divisor, inserting zeros at the right end of the dividend as necessary.	$3.5\overline{)71.05}\; =$ $\;\;20.3$ $35\overline{)710.5}$ $\;\;\underline{70}$ $\;\;\;\;10$ $\;\;\;\;\;\underline{0}$ $\;\;\;\;10\;5$ $\;\;\;\;\underline{10\;5}$

Say Why   *Fill in each blank.*

1. The expression $7\frac{3}{10}$ _____ considered to be a
   is/is not
   decimal because _____
   _____ .

2. In the decimal 2.781, the 2 _____ in a decimal
   is/is not
   place because _____
   _____ .

3. The number 48.726 rounded to the nearest hundredth
   _____ 48.72 because _____
   is/is not
   _____ .

4. We _____ add, subtract, or compare decimals by
   can/cannot
   rewriting them vertically and then lining up the decimal
   points because _____
   _____ .

5. The number 9.1313 _____ a repeating decimal
   is/is not
   because _____ .

6. Without calculating, we know that 0.04 ÷ 0.23
   _____ less than 1 because _____
   is/is not
   _____ .

[3.1] *Name the place that each underlined digit occupies.*

7. 8.3<u>5</u>9
8. 13.<u>0</u>05
9. 8,024.<u>5</u>
10. 0.000<u>3</u>

Express each number as a fraction, mixed number, or whole number.

11. 0.35
12. 8.2
13. 4.007
14. 10.000

Write each decimal in words.

15. 0.72
16. 5.6
17. 3.0009
18. 510.036

Write each decimal in decimal notation.

19. Seven thousandths
20. Two and one tenth
21. Nine hundredths
22. Seven and forty-one thousandths

Between each pair of numbers, insert the appropriate sign, $<$, $=$, or $>$, to make a true statement.

23. 0.037   0.04
24. 2.031   2.0301
25. 5.12   4.71932
26. 2   1.8

Rearrange each group of numbers from largest to smallest.

27. 0.72, 0.8, 1.002
28. 0.003, 0.00057, 0.004

Round as indicated.

29. 7.31 to the nearest tenth
30. 0.0387 to the nearest thousandth
31. 4.3868 to two decimal places
32. $899.09 to the nearest dollar

[3.2] *Perform the indicated operations. Check by estimating.*

33. 8.2 + 3.91
34. 50 + 2.7 + 0.05
35. $8 + $3.25 + $12.88
36. 8.4 m + 3.6 m

37. $30.7 - 1.92$

38. $93 - 5.248$

39. $2.5 - (0.72 - 0.054)$

40. $54.17 - (8 - 2.731)$

41. $5.398 + 8.72 + 92.035 + 0.7723 - 3.714 - 5.008$

42. $\$87,259.39 + \$2,098.35 + \$1,387.92 + \$203.14$

[3.3] *Find the product. Check by estimating.*

43. 7.28×0.4

44. $(288)(3.5)$

45. 0.005×0.002

46. $(3.7)^2$

47. $2.71 \cdot 1,000$

48. 0.0034×10

49. $8 - (1.5)^2$

50. $3(2.4) + 7(0.9)$

51. $18,772.35 \times 0.0836$

52. $(74.862)(5.901)$

[3.4] *Change to the equivalent decimal.*

53. $\dfrac{5}{8}$

54. $90\dfrac{1}{5}$

55. $4\dfrac{1}{16}$

56. $\dfrac{45}{1,000}$

Express each fraction as a decimal. Round to the nearest hundredth.

57. $\dfrac{1}{6}$

58. $\dfrac{2}{7}$

59. $8\dfrac{1}{3}$

60. $11\dfrac{2}{9}$

Divide and check.

61. $2\overline{)1.3}$

62. $\dfrac{4.8}{3}$

63. $0.7 \div 4$

64. $\dfrac{2.77}{10}$

Divide. Round to the nearest tenth.

65. $4.67 \div 0.9$

66. $\dfrac{2.35}{0.73}$

67. $\dfrac{7.11}{0.3}$

68. $0.06\overline{)981.5}$

69. $18.74 \div 9.7$

70. $220 \div 0.61$

71. $81.37\overline{)247.062}$

72. $247.062\overline{)81.37}$

Simplify.

73. $\dfrac{(1.3)^2 - 1.1}{0.5}$

74. $\dfrac{2.5 - (0.4)^2}{0.02}$

75. $\dfrac{13.75}{9.6 - 9.2}$

76. $(2.5)(3.5) \div 6.25$

Mixed Applications

Solve.

77. Recently, a champion swimmer swam 50 meters in 25.2 seconds and then swam 100 meters farther in 29.29 seconds. How long did she take to swim the 150 meters?

78. On a certain day, the closing price of one share of Home Depot was $14.57. If the closing price for the day was $0.43 higher than the opening price, what was the opening price? (*Source:* finance.yahoo.com)

79. The venom of a certain South American frog is so poisonous that 0.0000004 ounce of the venom can kill a person. How is this decimal read?

80. A carpenter is constructing steps leading to a terrace. The cross-section of the steps is shown below. Find the missing dimension.

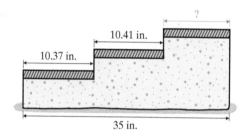

81. Astronomers use the term *astronomical unit* (or AU) for the average distance between Earth and the Sun. The distance 1 AU is about 93,000,000 miles. The average distance from the Sun to Mars is about 140,000,000 miles. Express in astronomical units, rounded to the nearest tenth, the average distance between Mars and the Sun. (*Source*: Jeffrey Bennett et al., *The Cosmic Perspective*)

82. In the United States Congress, there are 100 senators and 435 representatives. How many times as many representatives as senators are there?

83. A supermarket sells a 4-pound package of ground meat for $5.20 and a 5-pound package of ground meat for $6.20. What is the difference between the two prices per pound?

84. A homeowner is making plans to build a patio in her backyard and would like to save money by doing the work herself. The dimensions of the proposed patio are 9.67 yards by 5.33 yards. The labor costs would be about $5 per square yard. Estimate how much money the homeowner would save in labor by building the patio herself.

85. In a chemistry lab, a student weighs a compound three times, getting 7.15 grams, 7.18 grams, and 7.23 grams. What is the average of these weights, to the nearest hundredth of a gram?

86. A team of geologists scaled a mountain. At the base of the mountain, the temperature had been 11°C. The temperature fell 0.75 degrees for every 100 meters the team climbed. After they climbed 1,000 meters, what was the temperature?

🖩 **87.** The following form was adapted from the *U.S. Individual Income Tax Return.* Find the total income in line 22.

7	Wages, salaries, tips, etc.	7	28,774.71
8	Taxable interest income	8	
9	Dividend income	9	232.55
10	Taxable refunds, credits, or offsets of state and local income taxes	10	349.77
11	Alimony received	11	
12	Business income or (loss)	12	
13	Capital gain or (loss)	13	511.74
14	Other gains or (losses)	14	5,052.71
15	IRA distributions: taxable amount	15	
16	Pensions and annuities: taxable amount	16	
17	Rents, royalties, partnerships, estates, trusts, etc.	17	1,240.97
18	Farm income or (loss)	18	
19	Unemployment compensation	19	
20	Social Security benefits	20	
21	Other income	21	
22	Add the amounts shown in the far right column	22	

🖩 **88.** The following table shows the quarterly revenues, in billions of dollars, for Google and Yahoo! for a recent year.

Ending	Google	Yahoo!
June 30	5.523	1.573
September 30	5.945	1.575
December 31	6.674	1.732
March 31	6.775	1.597

(*Source:* finance.yahoo.com)

How much more were Google's earnings than Yahoo!'s for the year?

• Check your answers on page A-5.

CHAPTER 3   Posttest

FOR
EXTRA
HELP

CHAPTER
Test Prep
VIDEOS

The Chapter Test Prep Videos with test solutions are available on DVD,
in MyMathLab, and on You Tube* (search "AkstBasicMath"
and click on "Channels").

To see if you have mastered the topics in this chapter, take this test.

1. In the number 0.79623, which digit occupies the thousandths place?

2. Write in words: 5.102

3. Round 320.1548 to the nearest hundredth.

4. Which is smallest, 0.04, 0.0009, or 0.00028?

5. Express 3.04 as a mixed number.

6. Write as a decimal: four thousandths

Perform the indicated operations.

7. $2.3 + 0.704 + 1.35$

8. $\$5.27 + \$9 - \$8.61$

9. 2.09×10

10. 5.2×1.1

11. $(0.1)^3$

12. $\dfrac{3.52}{2} + \dfrac{4.8}{3}$

13. $2.9 \div 1{,}000$

14. $\dfrac{9.81}{0.3}$

Express as a decimal.

15. $\dfrac{3}{8}$

16. $4\dfrac{1}{6}$, rounded to the nearest hundredth

Solve.

17. The element hydrogen is so light that 1 cubic foot of hydrogen weighs only 0.005611 pound. Round this weight to the nearest hundredth of a pound.

18. Historically, a mile was the distance that a Roman soldier covered when he took 2,000 steps. If a mile is 5,280 feet, how many feet, to the nearest tenth of a foot, was a Roman's step?

19. The Triple Crown consists of three horse races—the Kentucky Derby (1.25 miles), the Preakness Stakes (1.1875 miles), and the Belmont Stakes (1.5 miles). Which race is longest? (*Source: World Almanac 2010*)

20. A part of the real estate tax in Berkeley, California provides funds for the maintenance and servicing of traffic signals and other public lighting. This amount of tax (in dollars) on a house is 0.0108 times the area of the house (in square feet). What is this tax amount on a house that is 3,000 square feet in area? (*Source: ci.berkeley.ca.us*)

• Check your answers on page A-5.

Cumulative Review Exercises

To help you review, solve the following:

1. Round 591,622 to the nearest million.

2. Subtract: $6,063 - 3,987$

3. Multiply: $(409)(67)$

4. Find the area of the shaded region.

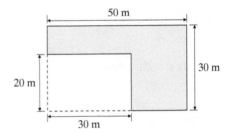

5. Simplify: $22 + 4(9 - 2^2)$

6. List all the factors of 60.

7. Which is larger, $1\frac{1}{2}$ or $1\frac{3}{8}$?

8. Subtract: $5 - 2\frac{1}{3}$

9. Estimate: $7\frac{9}{10} \times 4\frac{1}{13}$

10. Calculate: $\frac{2}{5} + \frac{1}{3} \cdot \frac{1}{2}$

11. Write the equivalent fraction or mixed number for 4.72 in lowest terms.

12. Round 38.363 to one decimal place.

13. Find the difference: $64.99 - 4.777$

14. Divide: $29.89 \div 0.049$

15. How much more than $25 will a shopper need in order to buy items costing, including tax, $8.39, $7.34, and $9.44?

16. A community garden occupies $\frac{1}{5}$ acre on a $\frac{1}{3}$-acre plot of land. What is the area of the land not occupied by the garden?

17. A dating service advertises that it has been introducing thousands of singles for 20 years. On the average, how many successful marriages were arranged per year?

18. A satellite orbiting Earth travels at 16,000 miles per hour. An orbit takes 1.6 hours. How far will the satellite travel once around, to the nearest thousand miles?

19. An electric company charges $0.09693 per kilowatt hour. If a restaurant used 2,000 kilowatt hours of electricity in a certain week, what was its weekly cost?

20. In a recent year, there were 1.596 billion Internet users worldwide. In hundreds of millions, the number of users in Asia was 6.57 and in North America, 2.51. How many times the number of Internet users in North America was the number in Asia, rounded to the nearest tenth? (*Source:* internetworldstats.com)

• Check your answers on page A-5.

CHAPTER 4

4.1   Introduction to Basic Algebra

4.2   Solving Addition and Subtraction Equations

4.3   Solving Multiplication and Division Equations

Basic Algebra: Solving Simple Equations

Algebra and Pressure

Perhaps you have noticed that a woman's high heels sink into soft ground even when the much larger heels of a man's shoes do not. The pressure that a heel exerts on the ground depends not only on the weight of the person walking but also on the area of the heel. Smaller heels result in greater pressure.

Physicists have observed that when a man and a woman have equal weights, the product of the area of their heels and the pressure that they exert on the ground is the same. In this situation, suppose that the man's heels are

10 square inches in area, in contrast to only $\frac{1}{4}$ square inch for the woman's high

heels and that the man's heels each exert 15 pounds per square inch on the ground. We can conclude that:

$$\frac{1}{4}p = 10 \cdot 15$$

Algebra allows us to solve this equation and to find p, the pressure exerted by each of the woman's high heels.

(*Source:* W. Thomas Griffith, *The Physics of Everyday Phenomena*, Dubuque, IA: Wm. C. Brown Publishers, 1992)

To see if you have already mastered the topics in this chapter, take this test.

Write each algebraic expression in words.

1. $t - 4$

2. $\dfrac{y}{3}$

Translate each phrase to an algebraic expression.

3. 8 more than m

4. Twice n

Evaluate each algebraic expression.

5. $\dfrac{x}{4}$, for $x = 16$

6. $5 - y$, for $y = 3\dfrac{1}{2}$

Translate each sentence to an equation.

7. The sum of x and 3 equals 5.

8. The product of 4 and y is 12.

Solve and check.

9. $x + 4 = 10$

10. $t - 1 = 9$

11. $2n = 26$

12. $\dfrac{a}{4} = 3$

13. $8 = m + 1.9$

14. $15 = 0.5n$

15. $m - 3\dfrac{1}{2} = 10$

16. $\dfrac{n}{10} = 1.5$

Write an equation. Solve and check.

17. The planet Jupiter has 36 more moons than the planet Uranus. If Jupiter has 63 moons, how many does Uranus have? (*Source:* NASA)

18. Tickets for all movies shown before 5:00 P.M. at a local movie theater qualify for the bargain matinee price, which is $2.75 less than the regular ticket price. If the bargain price is $6.75, what is the regular price?

19. In Michigan, about two-fifths of the area is covered with water. This portion of the state represents about 39,900 square miles. What is the area of Michigan? (*Source: The New York Times Almanac, 2010*)

20. An 8-ounce cup of regular tea has about 40 milligrams of caffeine, which is 10 times the amount of caffeine in a cup of decaffeinated tea. How much caffeine is in a cup of decaffeinated tea?

• Check your answers on page A-6.

4.1 Introduction to Basic Algebra

What Algebra Is and Why It Is Important

In this chapter, we discuss some of the basic ideas in algebra. These ideas will be important throughout the rest of this book.

In algebra, we use letters to represent unknown numbers. The expression $2 + 3$ is arithmetic, whereas the expression $x + y$ is algebraic, since x and y represent numbers whose values are not known. With *algebraic expressions*, such as $x + y$, we can make general statements about numbers and also find the value of unknown numbers.

We can think of algebra as a *language*: The idea of translating ordinary words to algebraic notation and vice versa is the key. Often, just writing a problem algebraically makes the problem much easier to solve. We present ample proof of this point repeatedly in the chapters that follow.

We begin our discussion of algebra by focusing on what algebraic expressions mean and how to translate and evaluate them.

Translating Phrases to Algebraic Expressions and Vice Versa

To apply mathematics to a real-world situation, we often need to be able to express that situation algebraically. Consider the following example of this kind of translation.

Suppose that you are enrolled in a college course that meets 50 minutes a day for 3 days a week. The course therefore meets for $50 \cdot 3$, or 150 minutes, a week.

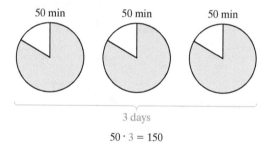

50 min   50 min   50 min

3 days

$50 \cdot 3 = 150$

Now, suppose that in a semester the 50-minute class meets d days but that we do not know what number the letter d represents. How many minutes per semester does the class meet? Do you see that we can express the answer as $50d$, that is, 50 times d days?

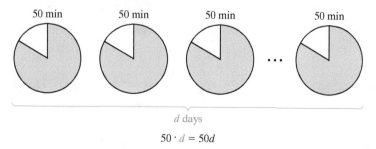

50 min   50 min   50 min   50 min

d days

$50 \cdot d = 50d$

In algebra, a *variable* is a letter, or other symbol, used to represent an unknown number. In the algebraic expression $50d$, for instance, d is a variable and 50 is a *constant*. Note that in writing an algebraic expression, we usually omit any multiplication symbol: $50d$ means $50 \cdot d$.

DEFINITIONS

A **variable** is a letter that represents an unknown number.

A **constant** is a known number.

An **algebraic expression** is an expression that combines variables, constants, and arithmetic operations.

There are many translations of an algebraic expression to words, as the following table indicates.

$x + 4$ translates to	$n - 3$ translates to	$\frac{3}{4} \cdot y$ or $\frac{3}{4}y$ translates to	$z \div 5$ or $\frac{z}{5}$ translates to
• x plus 4	• n minus 3	• $\frac{3}{4}$ times y	• z divided by 5
• x increased by 4	• n decreased by 3		• the quotient of z and 5
• the sum of x and 4	• the difference between n and 3	• the product of $\frac{3}{4}$ and y	• z over 5
• 4 more than x		• $\frac{3}{4}$ of y	
• 4 added to x	• 3 less than n		
	• 3 subtracted from n		

EXAMPLE 1

Translate each algebraic expression in the table to words.

Solution

Algebraic Expression	Translation
a. $\frac{p}{3}$	p divided by 3
b. $x - 4$	4 less than x
c. $5f$	5 times f
d. $2 + y$	the sum of 2 and y
e. $\frac{2}{3}a$	$\frac{2}{3}$ of a

PRACTICE 1

Translate each algebraic expression to words.

Algebraic Expression	Translation
a. $\frac{1}{2}p$	
b. $5 - x$	
c. $y \div 4$	
d. $n + 3$	
e. $\frac{3}{5}b$	

EXAMPLE 2

Translate each word phrase in the table to an algebraic expression.

Solution

Word Phrase	Translation
a. 16 more than m	$m + 16$
b. the product of 5 and b	$5b$
c. the quotient of 6 and z	$6 \div z$
d. a decreased by 4	$a - 4$
e. $\frac{3}{8}$ of t	$\frac{3}{8}t$

PRACTICE 2

Express each word phrase as an algebraic expression.

Word Phrase	Translation
a. x plus 9	
b. 10 times y	
c. the difference between n and 7	
d. p divided by 5	
e. $\frac{2}{5}$ of v	

As we have seen, any letter or symbol can be used to represent a variable. For example, *five less than a number* can be translated to $n - 5$, where n represents the number.

Let's consider the following example.

EXAMPLE 3

Express each phrase as an algebraic expression.

Solution

Word Phrase	Translation
a. 2 less than a number	$n - 2$, where n represents the number
b. an amount divided by 10	$\dfrac{a}{10}$, where a represents the amount
c. $\dfrac{3}{8}$ of a price	$\dfrac{3}{8}p$, where p represents the price

PRACTICE 3

Translate each word phrase to an algebraic expression.

Word Phrase	Translation
a. a quantity increased by 12	
b. the quotient of 9 and an account balance	
c. a cost multiplied by $\dfrac{2}{7}$	

Now, let's look at word problems that involve translations.

EXAMPLE 4

Suppose that p partners share equally in the profits of a business. What is each partner's share if the profit was $2,000?

Solution   Each partner should get the quotient of 2,000 and p, which can be written algebraically as $\dfrac{2,000}{p}$ dollars.

PRACTICE 4

Next weekend, a student wants to study for his four classes. If he has h hours to study in all and he wants to devote the same amount of time to each class, how much time will he study per class?

EXAMPLE 5

At registration, n out of 100 classes are closed. How many classes are not closed?

Solution   Since n classes are closed, the remainder of the 100 classes are not closed. So we can represent the number of classes that are not closed by the algebraic expression $100 - n$.

PRACTICE 5

Of s shrubs in front of a building, 3 survived the winter. How many shrubs died over the winter?

Evaluating Algebraic Expressions

In this section, we look at how to evaluate algebraic expressions. Let's begin with a simple example.

Suppose that the balance in a savings account is $200. If d dollars is then deposited, the balance will be $(200 + d)$ dollars.

To evaluate the expression $200 + d$ for a particular value of d, we replace d with that number. If $50 is deposited, we replace d by 50:

$$200 + d = 200 + 50 = 250$$

So the new balance will be $250.

The following rule is helpful for evaluating expressions:

> ## To Evaluate an Algebraic Expression
> - Substitute the given value for each variable.
> - Carry out the computation.

Now, let's consider some more examples.

EXAMPLE 6

Evaluate each algebraic expression.

Solution

Algebraic Expression	Value
a. $n + 8$, if $n = 15$	$15 + 8 = 23$
b. $9 - z$, if $z = 7.89$	$9 - 7.89 = 1.11$
c. $\frac{2}{3}r$, if $r = 18$	$\frac{2}{3} \cdot 18 = 12$
d. $y \div 4$, if $y = 3.6$	$3.6 \div 4 = 0.9$

PRACTICE 6

Find the value of each algebraic expression.

Algebraic Expression	Value
a. $\frac{s}{4}$, if $s = 100$	
b. $0.2y$, if $y = 1.9$	
c. $x - 4.2$, if $x = 9$	
d. $25 + z$, if $z = 1.6$	

The following examples illustrate how to write and evaluate expressions to solve word problems.

EXAMPLE 7

Power consumption for a period of time is measured in watt-hours, where a watt-hour means 1 watt of power for 1 hour. How many watt-hours of energy will a 60-watt bulb consume in h hours? In 3 hours?

Solution   The expression that represents the number of watt-hours used in h hours is $60h$. So for $h = 3$, the number of watt-hours is $60 \cdot 3$, or 180. Therefore, 180 watt-hours of energy will be consumed in 3 hours.

PRACTICE 7

When deciding how much money to spend on a new car, a good rule of thumb to follow is to budget about one-fifth of your monthly net income for a car payment. How much should you set aside for the monthly car payment if your net income is n dollars per month? If your net income is $3,750? (*Source: automotive.com*)

EXAMPLE 8

Suppose that there are 180 days in the local school year. How many days was a student present at school if she was absent d days? 9 days?

Solution   If d represents the number of days that the student was absent, the expression $180 - d$ represents the number of days that she was present. If she was absent 9 days, we substitute 9 for d in the expression:

$$180 - d = 180 - 9 = 171$$

So the student was present 171 days.

PRACTICE 8

At a coffee shop, a lunch bill was $18.45 plus the tip. What was the total amount of the lunch, including a tip of t dollars? A tip of $3?

4.1 **Exercises**

FOR
EXTRA
HELP
MyMathLab *Math*XL
PRACTICE   WATCH   READ   REVIEW

Mathematically Speaking

Fill in each blank with the most appropriate term or phrase from the given list.

arithmetic	constant	evaluate
translate	variable	algebraic

1. A(n) _____ is a letter that represents an unknown number.

2. A(n) _____ is a known number.

3. A(n) _____ expression combines variables, constants, and arithmetic operations.

4. To _____ an algebraic expression, replace each variable with the given number, and carry out the computation.

Ⓐ *Translate each algebraic expression to two different word phrases.*

5. $t + 9$

6. $8 + r$

7. $c - 12$

8. $x - 5$

9. $c \div 3$

10. $\dfrac{z}{7}$

11. $10s$

12. $11t$

13. $y - 10$

14. $w - 1$

15. $7a$

16. $4x$

17. $x \div 6$

18. $\dfrac{y}{5}$

19. $x - \dfrac{1}{2}$

20. $x - \dfrac{1}{3}$

21. $\dfrac{1}{4}w$

22. $\dfrac{4}{5}y$

23. $2 - x$

24. $8 - y$

25. $1 + x$

26. $n + 7$

27. $3p$

28. $2x$

29. $n - 1.1$

30. $x - 6.5$

31. $y \div 0.9$

32. $\dfrac{n}{2.4}$

Translate each word phrase to an algebraic expression.

33. x plus 10

34. d plus 12

35. 1 less than n

36. 9 less than b

37. the sum of y and 5

38. the sum of x and 11

39. t divided by 6

40. r divided by 2

41. the product of 10 and y

42. the product of 5 and p

43. the difference between w and 5

44. the difference between n and 5

45. n increased by $\dfrac{4}{5}$

46. x increased by $\dfrac{2}{3}$

47. the quotient of z and 3

48. The quotient of n and 10

49. $\dfrac{2}{7}$ of x

50. $\dfrac{2}{3}$ of y

51. 6 subtracted from k

52. 8 subtracted from z

53. 12 more than a number

54. 18 more than a number

55. the difference between a number and 5.1

56. the difference between a number and 8.2

B *Evaluate each algebraic expression.*

57. $y + 7$, if $y = 19$

58. $3 + n$, if $n = 2.9$

59. $7 - x$, if $x = 4.5$

60. $19 - y$, if $y = 6.7$

61. $\dfrac{3}{4}p$, if $p = 20$

62. $\dfrac{4}{5}n$, if $n = 30$

63. $x \div 2$, if $x = 2\dfrac{1}{3}$

64. $\dfrac{n}{3}$, if $n = 7.5$

65. $p - 7.9$, if $p = 9$

66. $y - 20.1$, if $y = 30$

67. $x \div \dfrac{5}{6}$, if $x = \dfrac{1}{6}$

68. $\dfrac{1}{3}y$, if $y = \dfrac{1}{2}$

Complete each table.

69.

x	$x + 8$
1	
2	
3	
4	

70.

x	$x + 10$
1	
2	
3	
4	

71.

n	$n - 0.2$
1	
2	
3	
4	

72.

b	$b - 0.4$
1	
2	
3	
4	

73.

x	$\dfrac{3}{4}x$
4	
8	
12	
16	

74.

n	$\dfrac{2}{3}n$
3	
6	
9	
12	

75.

z	$\dfrac{z}{2}$
2	
4	
6	
8	

76.

y	$\dfrac{y}{5}$
5	
10	
15	
20	

Mixed Practice

Solve.

77. Translate the phrase "7 less than *x*" to an algebraic expression.

78. Evaluate the algebraic expression 0.5*t*, if *t* = 8.

79. Translate the algebraic expression $\frac{n}{2}$ to two different phrases.

80. Evaluate the algebraic expression $\frac{1}{4}y$, if $y = \frac{2}{3}$.

81. Translate the phrase "the product of 3.5 and *t*" to an algebraic expression.

82. Evaluate the algebraic expression *x* + 1, if *x* = 4.

83. Translate the algebraic expression *x* + 6 to two different phrases.

84. Evaluate the algebraic expression *n* − 20, if *n* = 30.

Applications

C *Solve.*

85. A patient receives *m* milligrams of medication per dose. Her doctor orders her medication to be decreased by 25 milligrams. How much medication will she then receive per dose?

86. When a borrower takes out a mortgage, each monthly payment has two parts. One part goes toward the principal and the other toward the interest. If the principal payment is $344.86 and the interest payment is *i*, write an algebraic expression for the total payment.

87. The top of the Flatiron Building in New York City, so called because it is shaped like a clothing iron, is in a form similar to the triangle pictured below. Write an expression for the sum of the measures of the three angles. (*Source:* flatironbid.org)

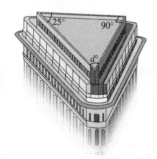

88. Professional land surveyors establish official land, air space, and water boundaries. Below is a sample of a typical lot survey. Write an expression for the sum of the lengths of the sides of the lot. (*Source:* lsrp.com)

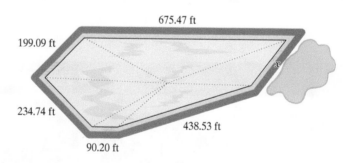

89. If a long-distance trucker drives at a speed of *r* miles per hour for *t* hours, she will travel a distance of *r* · *t* miles. How far will she travel at a speed of 55 miles per hour in 4 hours?

90. If a basketball player makes *b* baskets in *a* attempts, his field goal average is defined to be $\frac{b}{a}$. Find the field goal average of a player who made 12 baskets in 25 attempts.

91. A bank charges customers a fee of $2.50 for each withdrawal made at its ATMs.
   a. Write an expression for the total fee charged to a customer for *w* of these withdrawals
   b. Find the total fee if the customer makes 9 withdrawals.

92. A computer network technician charges $80 per hour for labor.
   a. Write an expression for the cost of *h* hours of work.

   b. Find the cost of a networking job that takes $2\frac{1}{2}$ hours.

• Check your answers on page A-6.

MINDStretchers

Mathematical Reasoning

1. Consider the expression $x + x$.

   a. Why does this expression mean the same as the expression $2x$?

   b. What does the expression $\underbrace{x + x + x + \cdots + x}_{n \text{ times}}$ mean in terms of multiplication?

Groupwork

2. Working with a partner, consider the areas of the following rectangles. For some values of x, the rectangle on the left has a larger area; for other values of x, the rectangle on the right is larger.

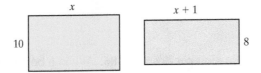

   a. Find a value of x for which the rectangle on the left has the larger area.

   b. Find a value of x for which the area of the rectangle on the right is larger.

Writing

3. Algebra is universal; that is, it is used in all countries of the world regardless of the language spoken. If you know how to speak a language other than English, translate each of the following algebraic expressions to that language.

   a. $7x$ **b.** $x - 2$ **c.** $3 + x$ **d.** $\dfrac{x}{3}$

Cultural Note

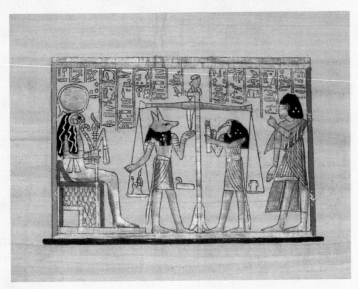

Solving an equation to identify an unknown number is similar to using a balance scale to determine an unknown weight. Egyptians 3,400 years ago used balance scales to weigh objects such as gold rings.

The balance scale is an ancient measuring device. These scales were used by Sumerians for weighing precious metals and gems at least 9,000 years ago.

Source: O. Dilke, *Mathematics and Measurement* (Berkeley: University of California Press/British Museum, 1987).

4.2 Solving Addition and Subtraction Equations

What an Equation Is

An equation contains two expressions separated by an equal sign.

Equal sign
↓
$$\underbrace{x + 3}_{\text{Left side}} = \underbrace{5}_{\text{Right side}}$$

DEFINITION

An **equation** is a mathematical statement that two expressions are equal.

For example,
$$1 + 2 = 3$$
$$x - 5 = 6$$
$$2 + 7 + 3 = 12$$
$$3x = 9$$

are all equations.

Equations are used to solve a wide range of problems. A key step in solving a problem is to translate the sentences that describe the problem to an equation that models the problem. In this section, we focus on equations that involve either addition or subtraction. In the next section, we consider equations involving multiplication or division.

Translating Sentences to Equations

In translating sentences to equations, certain words and phrases mean the same as the equal sign:

- equals
- is the same as
- is
- yields
- is equal to
- results in

Let's look at some examples of translating sentences to equations that involve addition or subtraction and vice versa.

EXAMPLE 1

Translate each sentence in the table to an equation.

Solution

Sentence	Equation
a. The sum of y and 3 is equal to $7\frac{1}{2}$.	$y + 3 = 7\frac{1}{2}$
b. The difference between x and 9 is the same as 14.	$x - 9 = 14$
c. Increasing a number by 1.5 yields 3.	$n + 1.5 = 3$
d. 6 less than a number is 10.	$n - 6 = 10$

PRACTICE 1

Write an equation for each word phrase or sentence.

Sentence	Equation
a. n decreased by 5.1 is 9.	
b. y plus 2 is equal to 12.	
c. The difference between a number and 4 is the same as 11.	
d. 5 more than a number is $7\frac{3}{4}$.	

EXAMPLE 2

In a savings account, the previous balance P plus a deposit of $7.50 equals the new balance of $43.25. Write an equation that represents this situation.

Solution

The previous balance plus the deposit equals the new balance.

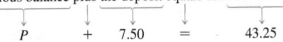

$$P \quad + \quad 7.50 \quad = \quad 43.25$$

So the equation is $P + 7.50 = 43.25$.

PRACTICE 2

The sale price of a jacket is $49.95. This amount is $6 less than the regular price p. Write an equation that represents this situation.

Equations Involving Addition and Subtraction

Suppose that you are told that five *more than some number* is equal to seven. You can find that number by solving the addition equation $x + 5 = 7$. To solve this equation means to find a number that, when substituted for the variable x, makes the equation a true statement. Such a number is called a *solution* of the equation.

To solve the equation $x + 5 = 7$, we can think of a balance scale like the one shown.

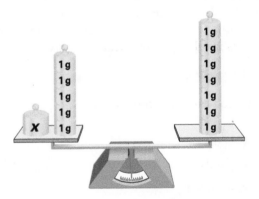

For the balance to remain level, whatever we do to one side, we must also do to the other side. In this case, if we subtract 5 grams from each side of the balance, we can conclude that the unknown weight, x, must be 2 grams, as shown below. So 2 is the solution of the equation $x + 5 = 7$.

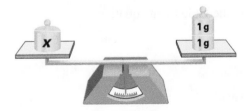

Similarly in the *subtraction equation* $x - 5 = 7$, if we add 5 to each side of the equation, we find that x equals 12.

In solving these and other equations, the key is to **isolate the variable**, that is, to get the variable alone on one side of the equation.

These examples suggest the following rule:

To Solve Addition or Subtraction Equations

- For an addition equation, *subtract* the same number from each side of the equation in order to isolate the variable on one side.

- For a subtraction equation, *add* the same number to each side of the equation in order to isolate the variable on one side.

- In either case, check the solution by substituting the value of the unknown in the original equation to verify that the resulting equation is true.

Because addition and subtraction are **opposite operations**, one operation "undoes" the other. The following examples illustrate how to perform an opposite operation to each side of an equation when you are solving for the unknown.

EXAMPLE 3

Solve and check: $y + 9 = 17$

Solution

$$y + 9 = 17$$
$$y + \underline{9 - 9} = \underline{17 - 9} \qquad \text{Subtract 9 from each side of the equation.}$$
$$\underbrace{y + \quad 0} = \quad 8$$
$$y \quad = \quad 8 \qquad \text{Any number added to 0 is the number.}$$

The solution is 8.

Check $\quad y + 9 = 17$

$$8 + 9 \overset{?}{=} 17 \qquad \text{Substitute 8 for } y \text{ in the original equation.}$$
$$17 \overset{\checkmark}{=} 17 \qquad \text{The equation is true, so 8 is the solution to the equation.}$$

Note that, because 9 was added to y in the original equation, we solved by subtracting 9 from both sides of the equation in order to isolate the variable.

PRACTICE 3

Solve and check: $x + 5 = 14$

EXAMPLE 4

Solve and check: $n - 2.5 = 0.7$

Solution

$$n - 2.5 = 0.7$$
$$n - \underline{2.5 + 2.5} = \underline{0.7 + 2.5} \qquad \text{Add 2.5 to each side of the}$$
$$\underbrace{n - \quad 0} = \quad 3.2 \qquad \text{equation.}$$
$$n \quad = \quad 3.2$$

The solution is 3.2.

Check $\quad n - 2.5 = 0.7$

$$3.2 - 2.5 \overset{?}{=} 0.7 \qquad \text{Substitute 3.2 for } n \text{ in the original equation.}$$
$$0.7 \overset{\checkmark}{=} 0.7$$

Can you explain why checking an answer is important?

PRACTICE 4

Solve and check: $t - 0.9 = 1.8$

EXAMPLE 5

Solve and check: $x + \dfrac{1}{3} = 3\dfrac{1}{2}$

Solution $\quad x + \dfrac{1}{3} = 3\dfrac{1}{2}$

$$x + \dfrac{1}{3} - \dfrac{1}{3} = 3\dfrac{1}{2} - \dfrac{1}{3} \qquad \text{Subtract } \dfrac{1}{3} \text{ from each side of the equation.}$$

$$x = 3\dfrac{1}{6}$$

The solution is $3\dfrac{1}{6}$.

Check $\quad x + \dfrac{1}{3} = 3\dfrac{1}{2}$

$$3\dfrac{1}{6} + \dfrac{1}{3} \stackrel{?}{=} 3\dfrac{1}{2} \qquad \text{Substitute } 3\dfrac{1}{6} \text{ for } x \text{ in the original equation.}$$

$$3\dfrac{1}{2} \stackrel{\checkmark}{=} 3\dfrac{1}{2}$$

PRACTICE 5

Solve and check: $m + \dfrac{1}{4} = 5\dfrac{1}{2}$

Equations are often useful **mathematical models** of real-world situations, as the following examples show. To derive these models, we need to be able to translate word sentences to algebraic equations, which we then solve.

EXAMPLE 6

Write each sentence as an equation. Then, solve and check.

Solution

Sentence	Equation	Check
a. 15 is equal to y increased by 9.	$15 = y + 9$ $15 - 9 = y + 9 - 9$ $6 = y, \text{ or } y = 6$	$15 = y + 9$ $15 \stackrel{?}{=} 6 + 9$ $15 \stackrel{\checkmark}{=} 15$
b. 10 is equal to m decreased by 8.	$10 = m - 8$ $10 + 8 = m - 8 + 8$ $18 = m, \text{ or } m = 18$	$10 = m - 8$ $10 \stackrel{?}{=} 18 - 8$ $10 \stackrel{\checkmark}{=} 10$

Note that we isolated the variable on the right side of the equation instead of the left side. The result is the same.

PRACTICE 6

Translate each sentence to an algebraic equation. Then, solve and check.

a. 11 is 4 less than m.

b. The sum of 12 and n equals 21.

EXAMPLE 7

Suppose that a chemistry experiment requires students to find the weight of the water in a flask. If the weight of the flask with water is 21.49 grams and the weight of the empty flask is 9.56 grams, write an equation to find the weight of the water. Then, solve and check.

Solution Recall that some problems can be solved by representing the given information in a diagram. Let's use that strategy here.

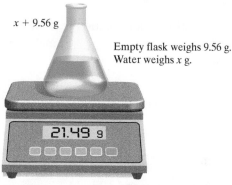

$x + 9.56$ g

Empty flask weighs 9.56 g.
Water weighs x g.

The diagram suggests the equation $21.49 = x + 9.56$, where x represents the weight of the water. Solving this equation, we get:

$$21.49 = x + 9.56$$
$$21.49 - 9.56 = x + 9.56 - 9.56$$
$$11.93 = x, \text{ or } x = 11.93$$

Check $21.49 = x + 9.56$
$21.49 \overset{?}{=} 11.93 + 9.56$
$21.49 \overset{\checkmark}{=} 21.49$

So the weight of the water is 11.93 grams.

An online discount book retailer charges a shipping fee of $3.99. The total cost of a book, including the shipping fee, was $27.18. Write an equation to determine the cost of the book without the shipping fee. Then, solve and check.

EXAMPLE 8

Harvard College (in Cambridge, Massachusetts) and the College of William and Mary (in Williamsburg, Virginia) are the two oldest institutions of higher learning in the United States. Harvard, founded in 1636, is 57 years older than William and Mary. Write an equation to determine when William and Mary was founded. Then, solve and check. (*Source: National Center for Education Statistics*)

Solution Let y represent the year in which William and Mary was founded. We know that 57 years earlier than the year y is 1636, the year in which Harvard was founded. This gives us the equation:

$$y - 57 = 1636$$

Now, we solve for the unknown.

$$y - 57 + 57 = 1636 + 57$$
$$y = 1693$$

Check $y - 57 = 1636$
$1693 - 57 \overset{?}{=} 1636$
$1636 \overset{\checkmark}{=} 1636$

So William and Mary was founded in 1693.

PRACTICE 8

The two U.S. states with the largest area are Alaska and Texas. The area of Texas, 269,000 square miles, is approximately 394,000 square miles smaller than that of Alaska. Write an equation to determine Alaska's area. Then, solve and check. (*Source: The New York Times Almanac, 2010*)

Mathematically Speaking

Fill in each blank with the most appropriate term or phrase from the given list.

constant	subtract	equation
translates	simplifies	variable
add	sentence	

1. A(n) _____ is a mathematical statement that two expressions are equal.

2. A solution of an equation is a number that, when substituted for the _____, makes the equation a true statement.

3. In the equation $x + 2 = 5$, _____ from each side of the equation in order to isolate the variable.

4. The equation $x - 1 = 6$ _____ to the sentence "The difference between x and 1 is 6."

A *Translate each sentence to an equation.*

5. z minus 9 is 25.

6. x minus 7 is 29.

7. The sum of 7 and x is 25.

8. The sum of m and 19 is 34.

9. t decreased by 3.1 equals 4.

10. r decreased by 5.1 equals 6.4.

11. $\frac{3}{2}$ increased by a number yields $\frac{9}{2}$.

12. $\frac{8}{3}$ increased by a number yields $\frac{13}{3}$.

13. $3\frac{1}{2}$ less than a number is equal to 7.

14. $1\frac{1}{2}$ less than a number is equal to $7\frac{1}{4}$.

B *By answering yes or no, indicate whether the value of x shown is a solution of the given equation.*

15.

Equation	Value of x	Solution?
a. $x + 1 = 9$	8	
b. $x - 3 = 4$	5	
c. $x + 0.2 = 5$	4.8	
d. $x - \frac{1}{2} = 1$	$\frac{1}{2}$	

16.

Equation	Value of x	Solution?
a. $x - 39 = 5$	44	
b. $x - 2 = 6$	4	
c. $x + 2.8 = 4$	1.2	
d. $x - \frac{2}{3} = 1$	$1\frac{2}{3}$	

Identify the operation to perform on each side of the equation to isolate the variable.

17. $x + 4 = 6$

18. $x + 10 = 17$

19. $x - 6 = 9$

20. $x - 11 = 4$

21. $x - 7 = 24$

22. $10 = x - 3$

23. $x + 21 = 25$

24. $3 = x + 2$

Solve and check.

25. $a - 7 = 24$

26. $x - 9 = 13$

27. $y + 19 = 21$

28. $z + 23 = 31$

29. $x - 2 = 10$

30. $t - 4 = 19$

31. $n + 9 = 13$

32. $d + 12 = 12$

33. $5 + m = 7$

34. $17 + d = 20$

35. $39 = y - 51$

36. $44 = c - 3$

37. $z + 2.4 = 5.3$

38. $t + 2.3 = 6.7$

39. $n - 8 = 0.9$

40. $c - 0.7 = 6$

41. $y + 8.1 = 9$

42. $a + 0.7 = 2$

43. $x + \dfrac{1}{3} = 9$

44. $z + \dfrac{2}{5} = 11$

45. $m - 1\dfrac{1}{3} = 4$

46. $s - 4\dfrac{1}{2} = 8$

47. $x + 3\dfrac{1}{4} = 7$

48. $t + 1\dfrac{1}{2} = 5$

49. $c - 14\dfrac{1}{5} = 33$

50. $a - 9\dfrac{7}{10} = 27\dfrac{2}{3}$

51. $x - 3.4 = 9.6$

52. $m - 12.5 = 13.7$

53. $5 = y - 1\dfrac{1}{4}$

54. $3 = t - 1\dfrac{2}{3}$

55. $5\dfrac{3}{4} = a + 2\dfrac{1}{3}$

56. $4\dfrac{1}{3} = n + 3\dfrac{1}{2}$

57. $2.3 = x - 5.9$

58. $4.1 = d - 6.9$

59. $y - 7.01 = 12.9$

60. $x - 3.2 = 5.23$

61. $x + 3.443 = 8$

62. $x + 0.035 = 2.004$

63. $2.986 = y - 7.265$

64. $3.184 = y - 1.273$

Translate each sentence to an equation. Solve and check.

65. 3 more than n is 11.

66. 15 more than x is 33.

67. 6 less than y equals 7.

68. 4 less than t equals 1.

69. If 10 is added to n, the sum is 19.

70. 25 added to a number m gives a result of 53.

71. x increased by 3.6 is equal to 9.

72. n increased by 3.5 is equal to 7.

73. A number minus $4\dfrac{1}{3}$ is the same as $2\dfrac{2}{3}$.

74. A number minus $5\dfrac{1}{2}$ is the same as $2\dfrac{1}{2}$.

Choose the equation that best describes the situation.

75. After 6 months of dieting and exercising, an athlete lost $8\dfrac{1}{2}$ pounds. If she now weighs 135 pounds, what was her original weight?

a. $w + 8\dfrac{1}{2} = 135$ **b.** $w - 126\dfrac{1}{2} = 8\dfrac{1}{2}$

c. $w - 8\dfrac{1}{2} = 135$ **d.** $w + 135 = 143\dfrac{1}{2}$

76. A teenager has d dollars. After buying an Xbox 360 Elite for \$299.99, he has \$6.01 left. How many dollars did he have at first?

a. $d + 299.99 = 306$ **b.** $d - 299.99 = 6.01$
c. $d - 299.99 = 306$ **d.** $d + 6.01 = 299.99$

77. According to a 30-day sample, the two most downloaded English-language authors are the British novelist Charles Dickens and the American humorist Mark Twain. In the sample, there were 37,541 downloads of Dickens and 5,268 fewer of Twain. How many downloads of Twain were there? (*Source:* Project Gutenberg)

a. $x + 5,268 = 37,541$ **b.** $x - 5,268 = 37,541$
c. $x + 5,268 = 32,273$ **d.** $x - 37,541 = 5,268$

78. The CN Tower in Canada and Canton Tower in China are two of the tallest telecommunications towers in the world. Of these structures, the CN Tower is 555 meters tall, which is 55 meters shorter than the tower in China. How tall is the Canton Tower? (*Source:* gztvtower.info.com)

a. $x + 55 = 555$ **b.** $x + 555 = 610$
c. $x - 55 = 555$ **d.** $x - 555 = 55$

Mixed Practice   *Solve and check.*

79. $10 = a - 4.5$

80. $x + \dfrac{1}{2} = 6$

Solve.

81. The life expectancy in the United States of a female born in the year 2000 was 79.3 years. For a female born two decades later, it is projected to be 2.6 years greater. Choose the equation to find the life expectancy of a female born in the year 2020. (*Source:* U.S. Census Bureau)

    a. $x + 79.3 = 2.6$ **b.** $x - 2.6 = 79.3$

    c. $x + 2.6 = 79.3$ **d.** $x - 20 = 2.6$

82. The hygienist at a dentist's office cleaned a patient's teeth. The total bill came to $125, which was partially covered by dental insurance. If the patient paid $60 out of pocket toward the bill, choose the equation to find how much of the bill was covered by insurance.

    a. $x + 60 = 125$ **b.** $x - 60 = 125$

    c. $x + 125 = 60$ **d.** $x - 125 = 60$

83. Is 3 a solution to the equation $10 - x = 7$?

84. Is 6 a solution to the equation $x + 4.5 = 7.5$?

85. Translate the sentence "The sum of 4.2 and n is 8" to an equation.

86. Translate the sentence "x decreased by 4 is 10" to an equation.

87. Identify the operation to perform on each side of the equation $y - 1.9 = 5$ to isolate the variable.

88. Identify the operation to perform on each side of the equation $n + 2 = 10$ to isolate the variable.

Applications

C   *Write an equation. Solve and check.*

89. A local community college increased the cost of a credit hour by $12 for this year. If the cost of a credit hour for this year is $106, what was the cost last year?

90. The first algebra textbook was written by the Arab mathematician Muhammad ibn Musa al-Khwarazmi. The title of that book, which gave rise to the word *algebra*, was *Aljabr wa'lmuqabalah*, meaning "the art of bringing together unknowns to match a known quantity." If the book appeared in the year 825, how many years ago was this? (*Source:* R.V. Young, *Notable Mathematicians*)

91. In the triangle shown, angles A and B are complementary, that is, the sum of their measures is 90°. Find x, the number of degrees in angle B.

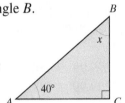

92. In the following diagram, angles ABD and CBD are supplementary, that is, the sum of their measures is 180°. Find y.

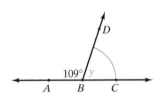

93. An article on Broadway shows reported that this week the box office receipts for a particular show were $621,000. If that amount was $13,000 less than last week's, how much money did the show take in last week?

94. Mount Kilimanjaro, the highest elevation on the continent of Africa, is 299 meters lower than Mount McKinley, the highest elevation on the continent of North America. If Mount Kilimanjaro is 5,895 meters high, how high is Mount McKinley? (*Source: The World Factbook, 2010*)

95. On a state freeway, the minimum speed limit is 45 miles per hour. This is 20 miles per hour lower than the maximum speed limit. What is the maximum speed limit?

96. The melting point of silver is 1,763 degrees Fahrenheit. This is 185 degrees less than the melting point of gold. What is the melting point of gold? (*Source: The New York Times Almanac, 2010*)

97. In a recent year, the U.S. charities that received the greatest private support were two organizations headquartered in Alexandria, Virginia—United Way Worldwide ($4,023,362,895) and the Salvation Army ($1,876,674,000). How much more money did United Way Worldwide receive? (*Source:* philanthropy.com)

98. During a recession, an automobile company laid off 18,578 employees, reducing its workforce to 46,894. How many employees did the company have before the recession?

• Check your answers on page A-6.

MINDStretchers

Groupwork

1. Working with a partner, compare the equations $x - 4 = 6$ and $x - a = b$.
  a. Use what you know about the first equation to solve the second equation for x.

  b. What are the similarities and the differences between the two equations?

Writing

2. Equations often serve as models for solving word problems.
  Write two different word problems corresponding to each of the following equations.
  a. $x + 4 = 9$
  •
  •

  b. $x - 1 = 5$
  •
  •

Critical Thinking

3. In the magic square at the right, the sum of each row, column, and diagonal is the same. Find that sum and write and solve equations to get the values of f, g, h, r, and t.

f	6	11
g	10	h
r	14	t

4.3 Solving Multiplication and Division Equations

OBJECTIVES

Ⓐ To translate sentences involving multiplication or division to equations

Ⓑ To solve multiplication or division equations

Ⓒ To solve applied problems involving multiplication or division equations

Translating Sentences to Equations

In order to translate sentences involving multiplication or division to equations, we must recall the key words that indicate when to multiply and when to divide.

EXAMPLE 1

Translate each sentence in the table to an equation.

Solution

Sentence	Equation
a. The product of 3 and x is equal to 0.6.	$3x = 0.6$
b. The quotient of y and 4 is 15.	$\dfrac{y}{4} = 15$
c. Two-thirds of a number is 9.	$\dfrac{2}{3}n = 9$
d. One-half is equal to some number over 6.	$\dfrac{1}{2} = \dfrac{n}{6}$

PRACTICE 1

Write an equation for each sentence.

Sentence	Equation
a. Twice x is the same as 14.	
b. The quotient of a and 6 is 1.5.	
c. Some number divided by 0.3 is equal to 1.	
d. Ten is equal to one-half of some number.	

EXAMPLE 2

A house sold for $125,000. This amount is twice its assessed value x. Write an equation to represent this situation.

Solution   The selling price of the house is twice its assessed value x.

$$\underbrace{125{,}000} \quad \underset{=}{\downarrow} \quad \underbrace{2x}$$

So the equation is $125{,}000 = 2x$.

PRACTICE 2

The area of a rectangle is equal to the product of its length (3 feet) and its width (w). The rectangle's area is 15 square feet. Represent this relationship in an equation.

Equations Involving Multiplication and Division

As with addition equations, we can also solve *multiplication equations* by thinking of a balance scale like the one shown below at the left.

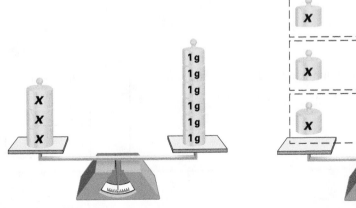
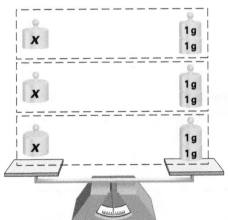

For example, consider the sentence "Three times some number x equals six," which translates to the multiplication equation $3x = 6$. We want to find the number that, when substituted for the variable x, makes this equation a true statement. To keep the balance level, whatever we do to one side we must do to the other side. In this case, dividing each side of the balance by 3 shows that in each group the unknown x must equal 2, as shown on the previous page.

Similarly, in the division equation $\frac{x}{4} = 3$, we can multiply each side of the equation by 4 and then conclude that x equals 12.

These examples suggest the following rule:

To Solve Multiplication or Division Equations

- For a multiplication equation, divide by the same number on each side of the equation in order to isolate the variable on one side.

- For a division equation, multiply by the same number on each side of the equation in order to isolate the variable on one side.

- In either case, check the solution by substituting the value of the unknown in the original equation to verify that the resulting equation is true.

Because multiplication and division are opposite operations, one "undoes" the other. The following examples show how to perform the opposite operation on each side of an equation to solve for the unknown.

EXAMPLE 3

Solve and check: $5x = 20$

Solution $5x = 20$

$\dfrac{5x}{5} = \dfrac{20}{5}$ Divide each side of the equation by 5: $\dfrac{5x}{5} = 1x$, or x.

$x = 4$

The solution is 4.

Check $5x = 20$

$5(4) \stackrel{?}{=} 20$ Substitute 4 for x in the original equation.

$20 \stackrel{\checkmark}{=} 20$ The equation is true, so 4 is the solution to the original equation.

PRACTICE 3

Solve and check: $6x = 30$

In Example 3, can you explain why $1x = x$?

EXAMPLE 4

Solve and check: $5 = \dfrac{y}{2}$

Solution $5 = \dfrac{y}{2}$

Multiply each side of the equation by 2:

$2 \cdot 5 = 2 \cdot \dfrac{y}{2}$ $2 \cdot \dfrac{y}{2} = \dfrac{2}{1} \cdot \dfrac{y}{2} = 1y$, or y.

$10 = y$, or $y = 10$

The solution is 10.

PRACTICE 4

Solve and check: $1 = \dfrac{a}{6}$

EXAMPLE 4 (continued)

Check $5 = \dfrac{y}{2}$

$5 \overset{?}{=} \dfrac{10}{2}$ Substitute 10 for y in the original equation.

$5 \overset{\checkmark}{=} 5$

EXAMPLE 5

Solve and check: $0.2n = 4$

Solution $0.2n = 4$

$\dfrac{0.2n}{0.2} = \dfrac{4}{0.2}$ Divide each side by 0.2: $0.2\overline{)4.0}$ or 20.

$n = 20$

The solution is 20.

Check $0.2n = 4$

$0.2(20) \overset{?}{=} 4$ Substitute 20 for n in the original equation.

$4.0 \overset{?}{=} 4$

$4 \overset{\checkmark}{=} 4$

PRACTICE 5

Solve and check: $1.5x = 6$

EXAMPLE 6

Solve and check: $\dfrac{m}{0.5} = 1.3$

Solution $\dfrac{m}{0.5} = 1.3$

$(0.5)\dfrac{m}{0.5} = (0.5)(1.3)$ Multiply each side by 0.5.

$m = 0.65$

The solution is 0.65.

Check $\dfrac{m}{0.5} = 1.3$

$\dfrac{0.65}{0.5} \overset{?}{=} 1.3$ Substitute 0.65 for m in the original equation.

$1.3 \overset{\checkmark}{=} 1.3$

PRACTICE 6

Solve and check: $\dfrac{a}{2.4} = 1.2$

EXAMPLE 7

Solve and check: $\dfrac{2}{3}n = 6$

Solution

$$\dfrac{2}{3}n = 6$$

$$\dfrac{2}{3}n \div \dfrac{2}{3} = 6 \div \dfrac{2}{3} \qquad \text{Divide each side by } \dfrac{2}{3}.$$

$$\left(\dfrac{2}{3}n\right)\left(\dfrac{3}{2}\right) = 6\left(\dfrac{3}{2}\right)$$

$$\left(\dfrac{2}{3}\right)\left(\dfrac{3}{2}\right)n = 6\left(\dfrac{3}{2}\right)$$

$$n = 9$$

The solution is 9.

Check $\qquad \dfrac{2}{3}n = 6$

$$\dfrac{2}{3}(9) \overset{?}{=} 6 \qquad \text{Substitute 9 for } n \text{ in the original equation.}$$

$$\dfrac{2}{3}\left(\dfrac{9}{1}\right) \overset{?}{=} 6$$

$$6 \overset{\checkmark}{=} 6$$

PRACTICE 7

Solve and check: $\dfrac{3}{4}x = 12$

As in the case of addition and subtraction equations, multiplication and division equations can be useful mathematical models of real-world situations. To derive these models, we translate word sentences to algebraic equations and solve.

EXAMPLE 8

Write each sentence as an algebraic equation. Then, solve and check.

Solution

Sentence	Equation	Check
a. Thirty-five is equal to the product of 5 and x.	$35 = 5x$ $\dfrac{35}{5} = \dfrac{5x}{5}$ $7 = x$, or $x = 7$	$35 = 5x$ $35 \overset{?}{=} 5(7)$ $35 \overset{\checkmark}{=} 35$
b. One equals p divided by 3.	$1 = \dfrac{p}{3}$ $3 \cdot 1 = 3 \cdot \dfrac{p}{3}$ $3 = p$, or $p = 3$	$1 = \dfrac{p}{3}$ $1 \overset{?}{=} \dfrac{3}{3}$ $1 \overset{\checkmark}{=} 1$

PRACTICE 8

Translate each sentence to an equation. Then, solve and check.

Sentence	Equation	Check
a. Twelve is equal to the quotient of z and 6.		
b. Sixteen equals twice x.		

EXAMPLE 9

A baseball player runs 360 feet when hitting a home run.

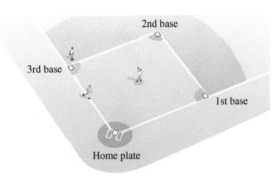

If the distances between successive bases on a baseball diamond are equal, how far is it from third base to home plate? Write an equation. Then, solve and check.

Solution   Let x equal the distance between successive bases. Since these distances are equal, $4x$ represents the distance around the bases. But we know that the distance around the bases also equals 360 feet. So $4x = 360$. We solve this equation for x.

$$4x = 360$$

$$\frac{4x}{4} = \frac{360}{4} \qquad \text{Divide each side by 4.}$$

$$x = 90$$

Check $4x = 360$

$4(90) \stackrel{?}{=} 360$ Substitute 90 for x in the original equation.

$360 \stackrel{\checkmark}{=} 360$

So the distance from third base to home plate is 90 feet.

PRACTICE 9

The Pentagon is the headquarters of the U.S. Department of Defense.

The distance around the Pentagon is about 1.6 kilometers. If each side of the Pentagon is the same length, write an equation to find that length. Then, solve and check. (*Source: Gene Gurney, The Pentagon*)

EXAMPLE 10

At an annual meeting, town officials recommended allocating a sum of money for emergency training to be split evenly among three committees. What was this sum if each committee was to be allocated for emergency training $4,000?

Solution   Let s equal the sum of money allocated. Each committee was allocated $4,000, which is equal to s divided by 3. So we write the following equation:

$$4,000 = \frac{s}{3}$$

PRACTICE 10

At a local club, rock concert tickets sold for $9.50 each. If 87 of them were sold, how much money did the club take in from these tickets? Write an equation. Then, solve and check.

We can solve this equation by multiplying both sides by 3.

$$(3)4{,}000 = (3)\frac{s}{3}$$

$$12{,}000 = s, \text{ or } s = 12{,}000$$

Check $4{,}000 = \dfrac{s}{3}$

$$4{,}000 \overset{?}{=} \frac{12{,}000}{3}$$

$$4{,}000 \overset{\checkmark}{=} 4{,}000$$

So the sum of money allocated for emergency training was $12,000.

EXAMPLE 11

The life expectancy in Zambia is one of the lowest of any country in the world. Zambia's life expectancy is only about 39 years, which is approximately $\frac{1}{2}$ that in the United States. Write an equation to find the life expectancy in the United States. Then, solve and check. (*Source:* cia.gov)

Solution   Let e equal the U.S. life expectancy. Zambia's life expectancy, 39 years, is equal to $\frac{1}{2}$ of e, so we write the following equation:

$$39 = \frac{1}{2}e$$

We can solve this equation by dividing both sides by $\frac{1}{2}$.

$$39 \div \frac{1}{2} = \frac{1}{2}e \div \frac{1}{2}$$

$$(39)\left(\frac{2}{1}\right) = \left(\frac{1}{2}e\right)\left(\frac{2}{1}\right)$$

$$(39)\left(\frac{2}{1}\right) = \left(\frac{1}{2}\right)\left(\frac{2}{1}\right)e$$

$$78 = e, \text{ or } e = 78$$

Check $39 = \dfrac{1}{2}e$

$$39 \overset{?}{=} \frac{1}{2}(78)$$

$$39 \overset{\checkmark}{=} 39$$

So the life expectancy in the United States is approximately 78 years.

PRACTICE 11

Last year, a junior partner in a small law firm received $\frac{3}{8}$ of the firm's profits. What were those profits if she got $150,000? Write an equation. Then, solve and check.

Mathematically Speaking

Fill in each blank with the most appropriate term or phrase from the given list.

divide	expression	equation	evaluating
addition	division	checked	multiply
substituting	solved		

1. In the equation $2x = 6$, _____ each side of the equation by 2 in order to isolate the variable.

2. In the equation $\dfrac{x}{5} = 3$, _____ each side of the equation by 5 in order to isolate the variable.

3. Check whether a number is a solution of an equation by _____ the number for the variable in the equation.

4. An equation is _____ by finding its solution.

5. The equal sign separates the two sides of a(n) _____.

6. Multiplication and _____ are opposite operations.

A *Translate each sentence to an equation.*

7. $\dfrac{3}{4}$ of a number y is 12.

8. $\dfrac{2}{3}$ of a number x is 20.

9. A number x divided by 7 is equal to $\dfrac{7}{2}$.

10. A number z divided by 8 is equal to $\dfrac{8}{3}$.

11. $\dfrac{1}{3}$ of x is 2.

12. $\dfrac{1}{4}$ of x is 6.

13. The quotient of a number and 3 is equal to $\dfrac{1}{3}$.

14. The quotient of a number and 4 is equal to $\dfrac{1}{4}$.

15. The product of 9 and an amount is the same as 27.

16. The product of 8 and an amount is the same as 32.

B *By answering yes or no, indicate whether the value of x shown is a solution of the given equation.*

17.

Equation	Value of x	Solution?
a. $7x = 21$	3	
b. $3x = 12$	36	
c. $\dfrac{x}{4} = 8$	2	
d. $\dfrac{x}{0.2} = 4$	8	

18.

Equation	Value of x	Solution?
a. $\dfrac{x}{3} = 10$	30	
b. $2.5x = 5$	2	
c. $2x = \dfrac{1}{3}$	$\dfrac{1}{6}$	
d. $\dfrac{x}{0.4} = 3$	12	

Identify the operation to perform on each side of the equation to isolate the variable.

19. $3x = 15$

20. $6y = 18$

21. $\dfrac{x}{2} = 9$

22. $\dfrac{y}{6} = 1$

23. $\dfrac{3}{4}a = 21$

24. $\dfrac{2}{3}m = 14$

25. $1.5b = 15$

26. $2.6x = 52$

Solve and check.

27. $5x = 30$

28. $8y = 8$

29. $\dfrac{x}{2} = 9$

30. $\dfrac{n}{9} = 3$

31. $36 = 9n$

32. $125 = 5x$

33. $\dfrac{x}{7} = 13$

34. $\dfrac{w}{10} = 21$

35. $1.7y = 6.8$ **36.** $0.5a = 7.5$ **37.** $2.1b = 42$ **38.** $1.5x = 45$

39. $\dfrac{m}{15} = 10.5$ **40.** $\dfrac{p}{10} = 12.1$ **41.** $\dfrac{t}{0.4} = 1$ **42.** $\dfrac{n}{0.5} = 6$

43. $\dfrac{2}{3}x = 1$ **44.** $\dfrac{1}{8}n = 3$ **45.** $\dfrac{1}{4}x = 9$ **46.** $\dfrac{3}{7}t = 15$

47. $17t = 51$ **48.** $100x = 400$ **49.** $10y = 4$ **50.** $100n = 50$

51. $7 = \dfrac{n}{100}$ **52.** $40 = \dfrac{p}{10}$ **53.** $2.5 = \dfrac{x}{5}$ **54.** $4.6 = \dfrac{z}{2}$

55. $2 = 4x$ **56.** $3 = 5x$ **57.** $\dfrac{14}{3} = \dfrac{7}{9}m$ **58.** $\dfrac{4}{9} = \dfrac{2}{3}a$

Solve. Round to the nearest tenth. Check.

59. $3.14x = 21.3834$ **60.** $2.54x = 78.25$ **61.** $\dfrac{x}{1.414} = 3.5$ **62.** $\dfrac{x}{1.732} = 1.732$

Translate each sentence to an equation. Solve and check.

63. The product of 8 and *n* is 56.

64. The product of 12 and *m* is 3.

65. $\dfrac{3}{4}$ of a number *y* is equal to 18.

66. $\dfrac{1}{3}$ of a number *x* is 16.

67. A number *x* divided by 5 is 11.

68. A number *y* divided by 100 is 10.

69. Twice *x* is equal to 36.

70. 3 times *m* is 90.

71. $\dfrac{1}{2}$ of an amount is 4.

72. $\dfrac{5}{7}$ of a number is 10.

73. A number divided by 5 is equal to $1\dfrac{3}{5}$.

74. An amount divided by 14 is equal to $1\dfrac{1}{2}$.

75. The quotient of a number and 2.5 is 10.

76. A quantity divided by 15 equals 3.6.

Choose the equation that best describes each situation.

77. Suppose that a teenager spends $20, which is $\dfrac{1}{4}$ of his total savings *m*. How much money did he have in the beginning?

  a. $m - \dfrac{1}{4} = 20$ **b.** $4m = 20$

  c. $m + \dfrac{1}{4} = 20$ **d.** $\dfrac{1}{4}m = 20$

78. Find the weight of a child if $\dfrac{1}{3}$ of her weight is 9 pounds.

  a. $3x = 9$ **b.** $\dfrac{1}{3}x = 9$

  c. $x + 3 = 9$ **d.** $x + \dfrac{1}{3} = 9$

79. A high school student plans to buy an MP3 player 8 weeks from now. If the MP3 player costs $140, how much money must the student save each week in order to buy it?

  a. $8c = 140$ **b.** $c + 8 = 140$

  c. $\dfrac{c}{8} = 140$ **d.** $c - 8 = 140$

80. The student government at a college sold tickets to a play. From the ticket sales, they collected $300, which was twice the cost of the play. How much did the play cost?

  a. $\dfrac{n}{2} = 300$ **b.** $n - 2 = 300$

  c. $2n = 300$ **d.** $n + 2 = 300$

Mixed Practice   *Solve and check.*

81. $11 = 2x$

82. $\dfrac{x}{6} = 9$

Solve.

83. The cost of dinner at a restaurant was split evenly among 3 friends. If each friend paid $25.75, choose the equation to find the amount on the check.

   a. $x + 3 = 25.75$
   b. $3x = 25.75$

   c. $x - 3 = 25.75$
   d. $\dfrac{x}{3} = 25.75$

84. According to an Internet speed test, the web connection on a college computer has a download speed of 15 megabits per second (Mbps) and an upload speed of 0.67 Mbps. Choose the equation to find how many times the download speed is the upload speed. (*Source:* compnetworking.about.com)

   a. $\dfrac{x}{0.67} = 15$
   b. $x + 0.67 = 15$

   c. $15x = 0.67$
   d. $x - 0.67 = 15$

85. Is 25 a solution of the equation $0.4x = 10$?

86. Is 2 a solution of the equation $\dfrac{n}{3} = 6$?

87. Translate the sentence "Twice x is 5" to an equation.

88. Translate the sentence "The quotient of y and 3 is 6" to an equation.

89. Identify the operation to perform on each side of the equation $\dfrac{n}{2} = 3$ to isolate the variable.

90. Identify the operation to perform on each side of the equation $4x = 7$ to isolate the variable.

Applications

C *Write an equation. Solve and check.*

91. For a square city block, the perimeter is 60 units. Find the length of one side of the square city block.

92. According to the nutrition label, one packet of regular instant oatmeal has five-eighths the calories of one packet of maple and brown sugar instant oatmeal. If the regular oatmeal has 100 calories, how many calories does the maple and brown sugar oatmeal have?

93. In an Ironman 70.3 triathlon, athletes must complete a 56-mile bike ride. This is one-half the distance of the bike ride in a regular Ironman triathlon. What distance must an athlete bike in a regular Ironman triathlon? (*Source:* World Triathlon Corporation)

94. The town of Ruidoso is located in southeastern New Mexico. During the summer, the population triples, growing to 25,000 as tourists arrive to enjoy the horse racing and the cool mountain air. What is the town's population in the off season, rounded to the nearest thousand? (*Sources:* wikitravel.org and ruidoso.net)

95. An online media rental service charges members a monthly flat rate of $8.99 to watch unlimited TV episodes and movies streamed to their televisions and computers. What does the service charge for 3 months?

96. One plan offered by a long-distance phone service provider charges $0.07 per minute for long-distance phone calls. A customer using this plan was charged $22.26 for long-distance calls this month. How many minutes of long-distance calls did she make this month?

97. A lab technician prepared an alcohol-and-water solution that contained 60 milliliters of alcohol. This was two-fifths of the total amount of the solution.
   a. What was the total amount of solution the lab technician prepared?
   b. How much water was in the solution?

98. A sales representative invested $5,500 of his sales bonus in the stock market. This represents one-third of his total sales bonus.
   a. What was his total sales bonus?
   b. How much of his sales bonus was not invested in the stock market?

99. Unoccupied 25-story condo towers in Orange County, California sold for $\frac{2}{3}$ off their original value. If the towers sold for $128 million, what was their original value? (*Source:* lansner.ocregister.com)

100. Attendance at the Brooklyn Museum in 2009 dropped by a quarter from the previous year to about 340,000. What was the attendance in 2008, to the nearest ten thousand? (*Source: New York Times*)

101. The population density of a country is the quotient of the country's population and its land area. The population density of the United States is approximately 86.8 persons per square mile. If the land area of the United States is 3,537,438 square miles, find the U.S. population to the nearest million. (*Source:* census.gov)

102. In a recent year, the top two U.S. airlines in terms of total passengers were Southwest Airlines and American Airlines. Southwest Airlines flew 101,300,000 passengers, which was about 1.18 times the number of passengers that American flew. To the nearest million, how many passengers did American fly? (*Source:* bts.gov)

• Check your answers on page A-6.

MIND*Stretchers*

Writing

1. Write two different word problems that are applications of each equation.

   a. $4x = 20$
     •
     •

   b. $\dfrac{x}{2} = 5$
     •
     •

Groupwork

2. The equations $\dfrac{r}{7} = 2$ and $\dfrac{7}{r} = 2$ are similar in form. Working with a partner, answer the following questions.

   a. How would you solve the first equation for r?

   b. How can you use what you know about the first equation to solve the second equation for r?

   c. What are the similarities and differences between the two equations?

Critical Thinking

3. In a magic square with four rows and four columns, the sum of the entries in each row, column, and diagonal is the same. If the entries are the consecutive whole numbers 1 through 16, what is the sum of the numbers in each diagonal?

Key Concepts and Skills

Concept/Skill	Description	Example
[4.1] **Variable**	A letter that represents an unknown number.	x, y, t
[4.1] **Constant**	A known number.	$2, \dfrac{1}{3}, 5.6$
[4.1] **Algebraic expression**	An expression that combines variables, constants, and arithmetic operations.	$x + 3, \dfrac{1}{8}n$
[4.1] **To evaluate an algebraic expression**	• Substitute the given value for each variable. • Carry out the computation.	Evaluate $8 - x$ for $x = 3.5$: $8 - x = 8 - 3.5$, or 4.5
[4.2] **Equation**	A mathematical statement that two expressions are equal.	$2 + 4 = 6, x + 5 = 7$
[4.2] **To solve addition or subtraction equations**	• For an addition equation, subtract the same number from each side of the equation in order to isolate the variable on one side. • For a subtraction equation, add the same number to each side of the equation in order to isolate the variable on one side. • In either case, check the solution by substituting the value of the unknown in the original equation to verify that the resulting equation is true.	$y + 9 = 15$ $y + 9 - 9 = 15 - 9$ $y = 6$ Check $\ y + 9 = 15$ $6 + 9 \stackrel{?}{=} 15$ $15 \stackrel{\checkmark}{=} 15$ $w - 6\dfrac{1}{2} = 8$ $w - 6\dfrac{1}{2} + 6\dfrac{1}{2} = 8 + 6\dfrac{1}{2}$ $w = 14\dfrac{1}{2}$ Check $\ w - 6\dfrac{1}{2} = 8$ $14\dfrac{1}{2} - 6\dfrac{1}{2} \stackrel{?}{=} 8$ $8 \stackrel{\checkmark}{=} 8$
[4.3] **To solve multiplication or division equations**	• For a multiplication equation, divide by the same number on each side of the equation in order to isolate the variable on one side. • For a division equation, multiply by the same number on each side of the equation in order to isolate the variable on one side. • In either case, check the solution by substituting the value of the unknown in the original equation to verify that the resulting equation is true.	$1.3r = 26$ $\dfrac{1.3r}{1.3} = \dfrac{26}{1.3}$ $r = 20$ Check $\ 1.3r = 26$ $1.3(20) \stackrel{?}{=} 26$ $26 \stackrel{\checkmark}{=} 26$ $\dfrac{x}{7} = 8$ $7 \cdot \dfrac{x}{7} = 7 \cdot 8$ $x = 56$ Check $\ \dfrac{x}{7} = 8$ $\dfrac{56}{7} \stackrel{?}{=} 8$ $8 \stackrel{\checkmark}{=} 8$

Say Why

Fill in each blank.

1. In the expression $7x + 5$, x _____ a variable
   is/is not
   because _____
   _____.

2. In the expression $6t - 5$, $6t$ _____ a constant
   is/is not
   because _____
   _____.

3. An algebraic expression _____ include a division
   can/cannot
   symbol because _____
   _____.

4. An equation _____ contain exactly one expression
   can/cannot
   because _____
   _____.

5. The number 28 _____ a solution of the equation
   is/is not
   $72 - x = 44$ because _____
   _____.

6. Rewriting $x - 3 = 10$ as $x = 10 + 3$ _____
   is/is not
   an example of isolating the variable because
   _____.

[4.1] *Translate each algebraic expression to words.*

7. $x + 1$

8. $y + 4$

9. $w - 1$

10. $s - 3$

11. $\dfrac{c}{7}$

12. $\dfrac{a}{10}$

13. $2x$

14. $6y$

15. $y \div 0.1$

16. $n \div 1.6$

17. $\dfrac{1}{3}x$

18. $\dfrac{1}{10}w$

Translate each word phrase to an algebraic expression.

19. Nine more than m

20. The sum of b and $\dfrac{1}{2}$

21. y decreased by 1.4

22. Three less than z

23. The quotient of 3 and x

24. n divided by 2.5

25. The product of an amount and 3

26. Twelve times some number

Evaluate each algebraic expression.

27. $b + 8$, for $b = 4$

28. $d + 12$, for $d = 7$

29. $a - 5$, for $a = 5$

30. $c - 9$, for $c = 15$

31. $1.5x$, for $x = 0.2$

32. $1.3t$, for $t = 5$

33. $\dfrac{1}{2}n$, for $n = 3$

34. $\dfrac{1}{6}a$, for $a = 2\dfrac{1}{2}$

35. $w - 9.6$, for $w = 10$

36. $v - 3\dfrac{1}{2}$, for $v = 8$

37. $\dfrac{m}{1.5}$, for $m = 2.4$

38. $\dfrac{x}{0.2}$, for $x = 1.8$

[4.2] *Solve and check.*

39. $x + 11 = 20$

40. $y + 15 = 24$

41. $n - 19 = 7$

42. $b - 12 = 8$

43. $a + 2.5 = 6$

44. $c + 1.6 = 9.1$

45. $x - 1.8 = 9.2$

46. $y - 1.4 = 0.6$

47. $w + 1\frac{1}{2} = 3$

48. $s + \frac{2}{3} = 1$

49. $c - 1\frac{1}{4} = 5\frac{1}{2}$

50. $p - 6 = 5\frac{2}{3}$

51. $7 = m + 2$

52. $10 = n + 10$

53. $39 = c - 39$

54. $72 = y - 18$

55. $38 + n = 49$

56. $37 + x = 62$

57. $4.0875 + x = 35.136$

58. $24.625 = m - 1.9975$

[4.2–4.3] *Translate each sentence to an equation.*

59. n decreased by 19 is 35.

60. 37 less than a equals 234.

61. 9 increased by a number is equal to $15\frac{1}{2}$.

62. 26 more than a number is $30\frac{1}{3}$.

63. Twice y is 16.

64. The product of t and 25 is 175.

65. 34 is equal to n divided by 19.

66. 17 is the quotient of z and 13.

67. $\frac{1}{3}$ of a number equals 27.

68. $\frac{2}{5}$ of a number equals 4.

By answering yes or no, indicate whether the value of x shown is a solution to the given equation.

69.

Equation	Value of x	Solution?
a. $0.3x = 6$	2	
b. $x - \frac{1}{2} = 1\frac{2}{3}$	$2\frac{1}{6}$	
c. $\frac{x}{0.5} = 7$	3.5	
d. $x + 0.1 = 3$	3.1	

70.

Equation	Value of x	Solution?
a. $0.2x = 6$	30	
b. $x + \frac{1}{2} = 1\frac{2}{3}$	$\frac{5}{6}$	
c. $\frac{x}{0.2} = 4.1$	8.2	
d. $x + 0.5 = 7.4$	6.9	

[4.3] *Solve and check.*

71. $2x = 10$

72. $8t = 16$

73. $\frac{a}{7} = 15$

74. $\frac{n}{6} = 9$

75. $9y = 81$

76. $10r = 100$

77. $\frac{w}{10} = 9$

78. $\frac{x}{100} = 1$

79. $1.5y = 30$

80. $1.2a = 144$

81. $\frac{1}{8}n = 4$

82. $\frac{1}{2}b = 16$

83. $\frac{m}{1.5} = 2.1$

84. $\frac{z}{0.3} = 1.9$

85. $100x = 40$

86. $10t = 5$

87. $0.3 = \frac{m}{4}$

88. $1.4 = \frac{b}{7}$

▦ **89.** $0.866x = 10.825$

▦ **90.** $\frac{x}{0.707} = 2.1$

Mixed Applications

Write an algebraic expression for each problem. Then, evaluate the expression for the given amount.

91. The temperature increases 2 degrees an hour. By how many degrees will the temperature increase in *h* hours? In 3 hours?

92. During the fall term, a math tutor works 20 hours per week. What is the tutor's hourly wage if she earns *d* dollars per week? $191 per week?

93. The local supermarket sells a certain fruit for 89¢ per pound. How much will *p* pounds cost? 3 pounds?

94. After having borrowed $3,000 from a bank, a customer must pay the amount borrowed plus a finance charge. How much will he pay the bank if the finance charge is *d* dollars? $225?

Write an equation. Then, solve and check.

95. After depositing $238 in a checking account, the balance will be $517. What was the balance before the deposit?

96. A bowler's final score is the sum of her handicap and scratch score (actual score). If a bowler has a final score of 225 and a handicap of 50, what was her scratch score?

97. Drinking bottled water is more popular in some countries than in others. In a recent year, the per capita consumption of bottled water in the United States was about 100 liters, or approximately 2.9 times as much as it was in the United Kingdom. Find the per capita consumption in the United Kingdom, to the nearest liter. (*Source:* britishbottledwater.org)

98. Hurricane Gilbert was one of the strongest storms to hit the Western Hemisphere in the twentieth century. A newspaper reported that the hurricane left 500,000 people, or about one-fourth of the population of Jamaica, homeless. Approximately what was the population of Jamaica? (*Source:* J. B. Elsner and A. B. Kara, *Hurricanes of the North Atlantic*)

99. On the Moon, a person weighs about one-sixth of his or her weight on Earth. What is the weight on Earth of an astronaut who weighs 30 pounds on the Moon?

100. During an economic recession, a U.S. senator proposed a recovery plan that would cost $3 trillion. Opponents criticized the plan for being too expensive and said that it was 2.5 times the cost of an alternative plan. What was the cost of the alternative plan?

101. The normal body temperature is 98.6 degrees Fahrenheit. An ill patient had a temperature of 101°F. This temperature is how many degrees above normal?

102. This year, a community college received 8,957 applications for admission, which amounts to 256 fewer than were received last year. How many applications did the community college receive last year?

• Check your answers on page A-6.

CHAPTER 4 **Posttest**

FOR EXTRA HELP

CHAPTER Test Prep VIDEOS

The Chapter Test Prep Videos with test solutions are available on DVD, in MyMathLab, and on YouTube (search "AkstBasicMath" and click on "Channels").

To see if you have mastered the topics in this chapter, take this test.

Write each algebraic expression in words.

1. $x + \dfrac{1}{2}$

2. $\dfrac{a}{3}$

Translate each word phrase to an algebraic expression.

3. 10 less than a number

4. The quotient of 8 and p

Evaluate each algebraic expression.

5. $a - 1.5$, for $a = 1.5$

6. $\dfrac{b}{9}$, for $b = 2\dfrac{1}{4}$

Translate each sentence to an equation.

7. The difference between x and 6 is $4\dfrac{1}{2}$.

8. The quotient of y and 8 is 3.2.

Solve and check.

9. $x + 10 = 10$

10. $y - 6 = 6$

11. $81 = 3n$

12. $82 = \dfrac{a}{9}$

13. $m - 1.8 = 6$

14. $1.5n = 75$

15. $10x = 5\dfrac{1}{2}$

16. $\dfrac{n}{100} = 7.6$

Write an equation. Then, solve and check.

17. A recipe for seafood stew requires $2\dfrac{1}{4}$ pounds of fish. After buying $1\dfrac{3}{4}$ pounds of bluefish, a chef decides to fill out the recipe with codfish. How many pounds of codfish should he buy?

18. In a recent year, the federal government removed the Rocky gray wolf from the list of endangered species, resulting in the first Rocky gray wolf hunting season in decades. During this season, about one-fourth of the population, or an estimated 500 wolves, were killed. Approximately how many Rocky gray wolves had lived in the wild before the hunt began? (*Source:* treehugger.com)

19. According to official estimates, the world population in 2045 is projected to be about one-and-a-half times what it was in 1999. If the projected population is 9 billion, what was the population in 1999? (*Source:* census.gov)

20. In chemistry, an *endothermic reaction* is one that absorbs heat. As a result of an endothermic reaction, the temperature of a solution dropped by 19.8 degrees Celsius to 7.6°C. What was the temperature of the solution before the reaction took place? (*Source:* Timberlake, *Chemistry: An Introduction to General, Organic, and Biological Chemistry*)

• Check your answers on page A-7.

Cumulative Review Exercises

To help you review, solve the following:

1. Round 314,159 to the nearest hundreds.

2. One of the three differences below is wrong. Use estimation to identify which difference is incorrect.

   a. $\begin{array}{r} 675,029 \\ -126,384 \\ \hline 548,645 \end{array}$ b. $\begin{array}{r} 539,324 \\ -126,384 \\ \hline 412,940 \end{array}$ c. $\begin{array}{r} 954,736 \\ -365,976 \\ \hline 488,760 \end{array}$

3. Multiply: 804×29

4. Find the quotient and check: $35,020 \div 34$

5. Write the equivalent fraction with the given denominator:
   $$\frac{7}{8} = \frac{}{96}$$

6. Write as a mixed number in simplified form: $\dfrac{56}{40}$

7. Subtract: $8\dfrac{1}{4} - 2\dfrac{7}{8}$

8. Write the decimal 5.239 in words.

9. Insert the appropriate sign, $<$, $=$, or $>$, to make a true statement.   6.356 _____ 6.36

10. Compute: $12 - (3.2 + 4.91)$

11. Find the quotient: $7.5 \div 1,000$

12. Decide whether 2 is a solution of the equation $w + 3 = 5$

13. Solve and check: $n - 3.8 = 4$

14. Solve and check: $\dfrac{x}{2} = 16$

15. In animating a cartoon, artists had to draw 24 images to appear during 1 second of screen time. How many images did they have to draw to produce a 5-minute cartoon?

16. Dental insurance reimbursed a patient $200 on a bill of $700. Did the patient get less or more than $\dfrac{1}{3}$ of his money back? Explain.

17. In a recent review of world energy, the annual oil production of the United States was approximately 300 million tons, or three-fifths of Saudi Arabia's production. Write an equation to find Saudi Arabia's annual oil production. Then solve and check. (*Source: Top 10 of Everything 2010*)

18. According to the Environmental Protection Agency, U.S. residents produce about 4.4 pounds of garbage per person per day. At this rate, how much garbage does a family of 3 produce in a week? (*Source:* epa.gov)

19. Farmers depend on bees to pollinate many crop plants, such as apples and cherries. In the American Midwest, the acreage of crops is large as compared with the number of bees, so farmers are especially concerned if the number of beehives declines. When the number of beehives in the state of Illinois dropped from 101,000 to 46,000, how big a drop was this? (*Source:* ag.uiuc.edu)

20. Due to World War I, the number of U.S. military personnel on active duty in 1918—roughly 2.9 million—was about 4.5 times what it had been the year before. (*Source: The New York Times Almanac 2010*)

a. Write an equation to find the number of personnel in 1917.

b. Solve, rounding the solution to the nearest hundred thousand.

• Check your answers on page A-7.

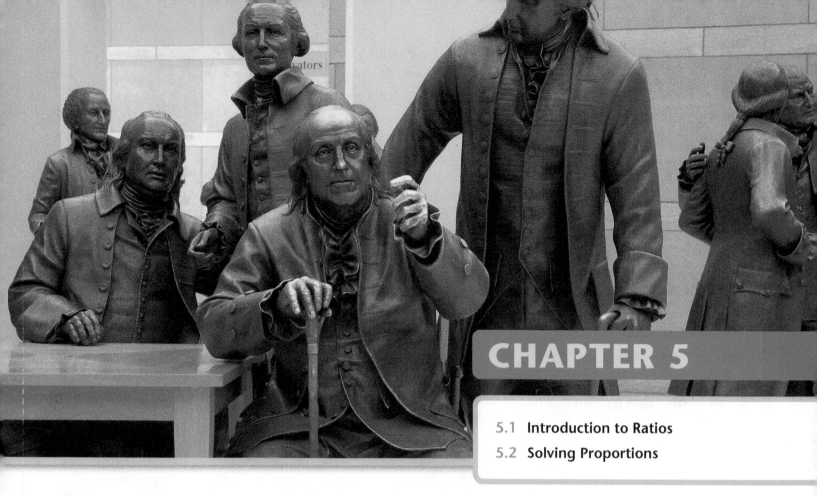

Ratio and Proportion

Ratio, Proportion, and the Connecticut Compromise

One of the most contested issues at the 1787 Constitutional Convention in Philadelphia was how the U.S. Congress was to be structured. The convention delegates from large states, such as Massachusetts, supported the Virginia Plan in which the number of representatives from a state would be *proportional* to its population so that a state with double the population of another would have twice as many representatives. By contrast, the delegates from smaller states, such as Delaware, favored the New Jersey Plan, in which every state has the same number of representatives in Congress.

Finally, after months of heated debate, the convention delegates agreed to the Connecticut Compromise under which Congress would have two chambers whose approval would be required for legislation to pass. In one chamber, the Senate, big and small states alike would have the same number of representatives. In the other chamber, the House of Representatives, representation would be proportional so that for all states the *ratio* of the population to the number of House representatives would be roughly the same. To this day, the Constitution provides that seats in the House are apportioned among the states by population, as determined by the census conducted every ten years.

(*Source:* Douglas Brinkley, *American Heritage History of the United States*, Viking, 1998)

To see if you have already mastered the topics in this chapter, take this test.

Write each ratio or rate in simplest form.

1. 6 to 8

2. 40 to 100

3. $30 to $18

4. 19 feet to 51 feet

5. 48 gallons of water in 15 minutes

6. 10 milligrams every 6 hours

Find the unit rate.

7. 12 dental assistants for every 6 dentists

8. 35 calculators for 35 students

Determine the unit price.

9. $690 for 3 boxes of ceramic tiles

10. 12 bottles of lemon iced tea for $6.00

Determine whether each proportion is true or false.

11. $\dfrac{2}{3} = \dfrac{16}{24}$

12. $\dfrac{32}{20} = \dfrac{8}{3}$

Solve and check.

13. $\dfrac{6}{8} = \dfrac{x}{12}$

14. $\dfrac{21}{x} = \dfrac{2}{3}$

15. $\dfrac{\frac{1}{2}}{4} = \dfrac{2}{x}$

16. $\dfrac{x}{6} = \dfrac{8}{0.3}$

Solve.

17. A contractor combines 80 pounds of sand with 100 pounds of gravel. In this mixture, what is the ratio of sand to gravel?

18. A machine at a potato chip factory can peel 12,000 pounds of potatoes in 60 minutes. At this rate, how many pounds of potatoes can it peel per minute?

19. The *aspect ratio* of an image is the ratio of the image's width to its height. In digital camera photos, a common aspect ratio is 4 to 3. With this ratio, how high is a photo that is 6 inches wide? (*Source:* wikipedia.org)

20. Suppose the scale on a Louisiana map is 3 inches to 31 miles. If two cities, Baton Rouge and New Orleans, are 7.4 inches apart on the map, what is the actual distance, to the nearest mile, between the two cities? (*Source:* ersys.com)

• Check your answers on page A-7.

5.1 Introduction to Ratios

OBJECTIVES

A To write ratios of like quantities in simplest form

B To write rates in simplest form

C To solve applied problems involving ratios

What Ratios Are and Why They Are Important

We frequently need to compare quantities. Sports, medicine, and business are just a few areas where we use **ratios** to make comparisons. Consider the ratios in the following examples.

- The volleyball team won 4 games for every 3 they lost.
- A physician assistant prepared a 1-to-25 boric acid solution.
- The stock's price-to-earnings ratio was 13 to 1.

Can you think of other examples of ratios in your daily life?

The preceding examples illustrate the following definition of a ratio.

DEFINITION

A **ratio** is a comparison of two quantities expressed as a quotient.

There are several ways to write a ratio. For instance, we can write the ratio 3 to 10 as

$$3 \text{ to } 10 \qquad 3{:}10 \qquad \frac{3}{10}$$

No matter which notation we use for this ratio, it is read "3 to 10."

Simplifying Ratios

Because a ratio can be written as a fraction, we can say that, as with any fraction, a ratio is in simplest form (or written in lowest terms) when 1 is the only common factor of the numerator and denominator.

Let's consider some examples of writing ratios in simplest form.

EXAMPLE 1

Write the ratio 10 to 5 in simplest form.

Solution The ratio 10 to 5 expressed as a fraction is $\dfrac{10}{5}$.

$$\frac{10}{5} = \frac{10 \div 5}{5 \div 5} = \frac{2}{1}$$

So the ratio 10 to 5 is the same as the ratio 2 to 1. Note that the ratio 2 to 1 means that the first number is twice as large as the second number.

PRACTICE 1

Write the ratio 8:12 in simplest form.

Frequently, we deal with quantities that have units, such as months or feet. When both quantities in a ratio have the same unit, they are called **like quantities**. In a ratio of like quantities, the units drop out.

EXAMPLE 2

Express the ratio 5 months to 3 months in simplest form.

Solution   The ratio 5 months to 3 months expressed as a fraction is $\frac{5 \text{ months}}{3 \text{ months}}$. Simplifying, we get $\frac{5}{3}$, which is already in lowest terms.

PRACTICE 2

Express in simplest form the ratio 9 feet to 5 feet.

TIP   Note that with ratios we do not rewrite improper fractions as mixed numbers because our answer must be a comparison of *two* numbers. So in Example 2, we write the ratio as $\frac{5}{3}$ rather than as $1\frac{2}{3}$.

EXAMPLE 3

24-karat gold is pure gold. By contrast, 14-karat gold, commonly used to make jewelry, consists of 14 parts out of 24 parts pure gold; the rest is another metal such as copper or silver added for hardness. In 14-karat gold, what is the ratio of gold to the other metal? (*Source:* essortment.com)

Solution   In 14-karat gold, 14 parts of 24 parts are pure gold. First, we calculate the number of parts that are not pure gold.

$$24 - 14 = 10$$

So 10 of 24 parts are the other metal. Next, let's write the ratio of pure gold to the other metal.

$$\frac{\text{Number of parts of pure gold}}{\text{Number of parts of the other metal}} = \frac{14}{10} = \frac{7}{5}$$

We conclude that the ratio of gold to the other metal is 7 to 5.

PRACTICE 3

The Waist to Hip Ratio (WHR) is a ratio, commonly expressed as a decimal, that has been shown to be a good predictor of possible cardiovascular problems in both men and women. If a male has a WHR greater than 1, then he is considered to be at high risk for these problems. Calculate the WHR of a male with a waist measurement of 40 inches and a hip measurement 2 inches less. Is he at high risk? (*Source: The Medical Journal of Australia*)

Now, let's compare **unlike quantities**, that is, quantities that have different units or are different kinds of measurement. Such a comparison is called a **rate**.

DEFINITION
A **rate** is a ratio of unlike quantities.

For instance, suppose that your rate of pay is $52 for each 8 hours of work. Simplifying this rate, we get:

$$\frac{\$52}{8 \text{ hours}} = \frac{\$13}{2 \text{ hours}}$$

So you are paid $13 for every 2 hours that you worked. Note that the units are expressed as part of the answer.

EXAMPLE 4

Simplify each rate.

a. 350 miles to 18 gallons of gas

b. 18 trees to produce 2,000 pounds of paper

Solution

a. 350 miles to 18 gallons $= \dfrac{350 \text{ miles}}{18 \text{ gallons}} = \dfrac{175 \text{ miles}}{9 \text{ gallons}}$

b. 18 trees to 2,000 pounds $= \dfrac{18 \text{ trees}}{2,000 \text{ pounds}} = \dfrac{9 \text{ trees}}{1,000 \text{ pounds}}$

PRACTICE 4

Express each rate in simplest form.

a. 150 milliliters of medication infused every 60 minutes

b. 18 pounds lost in 12 weeks

Examples 1, 2, 3, and 4 illustrate the following rule for simplifying a ratio or rate:

To Simplify a Ratio or Rate

- Write the ratio or rate as a fraction.

- Express the fraction in simplest form.

- If the quantities are like, drop the units. If the quantities are unlike, keep the units.

Frequently, we want to find a particular kind of rate called a *unit rate*. In the rate $\dfrac{\$13}{2 \text{ hours}}$, for instance, it would be useful to know what is earned for each hour (that is, the hourly wage). We need to rewrite $\dfrac{\$13}{2 \text{ hours}}$ so that the denominator is 1 hour.

$$\frac{\$13}{2 \text{ hours}} = \frac{\$13 \div 2}{2 \text{ hours} \div 2} = \frac{\$6.50}{1 \text{ hour}} = \$6.50 \text{ per hour, or } \$6.50/\text{hr}$$

Note that "per" means "divided by."

Here, we divided the numbers in both the numerator and denominator by the number in the denominator.

DEFINITION
A **unit rate** is a rate in which the number in the denominator is 1.

EXAMPLE 5

Write as a unit rate.

a. 275 miles in 5 hours

b. $3,453 for 6 weeks

Solution   First, we write each rate as a fraction. Then, we divide numbers in the numerator and denominator by the number in the denominator, getting 1 in the denominator.

PRACTICE 5

Express as a unit rate.

a. a fall of 192 feet in 4 seconds

b. 15 hits in 40 times at bat

EXAMPLE 5 (continued)

a. 275 miles in 5 hours $= \dfrac{275 \text{ miles}}{5 \text{ hours}} = \dfrac{275 \text{ miles} \div 5}{5 \text{ hours} \div 5} = \dfrac{55 \text{ miles}}{1 \text{ hour}},$

or 55 mph

b. \$3,453 for 6 weeks $= \dfrac{\$3,453}{6 \text{ weeks}} = \dfrac{\$3,453 \div 6}{6 \text{ weeks} \div 6} = \dfrac{\$575.50}{1 \text{ week}},$

or \$575.50 per week

EXAMPLE 6

To reduce expenses, a commuter buys a fuel-efficient car. If the car goes 60 miles on 2.5 gallons of gas, what is its fuel economy, that is, how many miles per gallon does it get?

Solution   To find the car's fuel economy, we calculate the ratio of the distance that it travels (60 miles) to the amount of gas that it uses (2.5 gallons).

$$\text{Fuel economy} = \frac{60 \text{ miles}}{2.5 \text{ gallons}}$$

Next, we simplify by dividing both the numerator and denominator by the number in the denominator, 2.5:

$$\frac{60 \text{ miles}}{2.5 \text{ gallons}} = \frac{24 \text{ miles}}{1 \text{ gallon}}$$

So the car gets 24 miles per gallon.

PRACTICE 6

Because of heavy traffic, a bus took 30 minutes to cover a distance of 20 city blocks. How many minutes per city block did the bus move?

In order to get the better buy, we sometimes compare prices by computing the price of a single item. This **unit price** is a type of unit rate.

> **DEFINITION**
> A **unit price** is the price of one item, or one unit.

To find a unit price, we write the ratio of the total price of the units to the number of units and then, simplify.

$$\text{Unit price} = \frac{\text{Total price}}{\text{Number of units}}$$

Let's consider some examples of unit pricing.

EXAMPLE 7

Find the unit price.

a. \$300 for 12 months of membership

b. 6 credits for \$234

c. 10-ounce box of wheat flakes for \$2.70

PRACTICE 7

Determine the unit price.

a. 4 supersaver flights for \$696

b. \$22 for 8 hours of parking

c. \$19.80 for 20 song downloads

Solution

a. $\dfrac{\$300}{12 \text{ months}} = \$25/\text{month}$

b. $\dfrac{\$234}{6 \text{ credits}} = \$39/\text{credit}$

c. $\dfrac{\$2.70}{10 \text{ ounces}} = \$0.27/\text{ounce}$

In the next example, we apply the concept of unit price to determine which is the better deal.

EXAMPLE 8

For the following two boxes of bandages, which is the better buy?

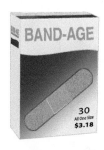 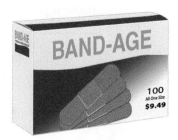

Solution   First, we find the unit price for each box of bandages. Then, we round to the nearest cent and compare the prices.

$$\text{Unit Price} = \frac{\text{Total price}}{\text{Number of units}} = \frac{\$3.18}{30} = \$0.106 \approx \$0.11 \text{ per bandage}$$

$$\text{Unit Price} = \frac{\text{Total price}}{\text{Number of units}} = \frac{\$9.49}{100} = \$0.0949 \approx \$0.09 \text{ per bandage}$$

Since $\$0.09 < \$0.11$, the better buy is the box with 100 bandages.

PRACTICE 8

Which bottle of vitamin C has the lower unit price?

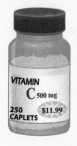

Cultural Note

The shape of a grand piano is dictated by the length of its strings. When a stretched string vibrates, it produces a particular pitch, say C. A second string of comparable tension will produce another pitch, which depends on the ratio of the string lengths. For instance, if the ratio of the second string to the first string is 18 to 16, then plucking the second string will produce the pitch B.

Around 500 B.C., the followers of the mathematician Pythagoras learned to adjust string lengths in various ratios so as to produce an entire scale. Thus the concept of ratio is central to the construction of pianos, violins, and many other musical instruments.

Sources: John R. Pierce, *The Science of Musical Sound* (New York: Scientific American Library, 1983)
David Bergamini, *Mathematics* (New York: Time-Life Books, 1971)

Mathematically Speaking

Fill in each blank with the most appropriate term or phrase from the given list.

weight of a unit	difference	number of units
like	fractional form	denominator
simplest form	unlike	
numerator	quotient	

1. A ratio is a comparison of two quantities expressed as a(n) _____.

2. A rate is a ratio of _____ quantities.

3. A ratio is said to be in _____ when 1 is the only common factor of the numerator and denominator.

4. Quantities that have the same units are called _____ quantities.

5. A unit rate is a rate in which the number in the _____ is 1.

6. To find the unit price, divide the total price of the units by the _____.

A *Write each ratio in simplest form.*

7. 6 to 9

8. 9 to 12

9. 10 to 15

10. 21 to 27

11. 55 to 35

12. 8 to 10

13. 2 to $1\frac{1}{3}$

14. 25 to $1\frac{1}{4}$

15. 2.5 to 10

16. 1.25 to 100

17. 60 minutes to 45 minutes

18. $40 to $25

19. 10 feet to 10 feet

20. 75 tons to 75 tons

21. 30¢ to 18¢

22. 66 years to 32 years

23. 7 miles per hour to 24 miles per hour

24. 21 gallons to 20 gallons

25. 1,000 acres to 50 acres

26. 2,000 miles to 25 miles

27. 8 grams to 7 grams

28. 19 ounces to 51 ounces

29. 24 seconds to 30 seconds

30. 28 milliliters to 42 milliliters

B *Write each rate in simplest form.*

31. 25 telephone calls in 10 days

32. 42 gallons in 4 minutes

33. 288 calories burned in 40 minutes

34. 190 e-mails in 25 days

35. 2 million hits on a website in 6 months

36. 50 million troy ounces of gold produced in 12 months

37. 68 baskets in 120 attempts

38. 18 boxes of cookies for $45

39. 296 points in 16 games

40. 12 knockouts in 16 fights

41. 500 square feet of carpeting for $1,645

42. 300 full-time students to 200 part-time students

43. 48 males for every 9 females

44. 3 case workers for every 80 clients

45. 40 Democrats for every 35 Republicans

46. $12,500 in 6 months

47. 2 pounds of zucchini for 16 servings

48. 57 hours of work in 9 days

49. 1,535 flights in 15 days

50. 25 pounds of plaster for 2,500 square feet of wall

51. 3 pounds of grass seeds for 600 square feet of lawn

52. 684 parts manufactured in 24 hours

Determine the unit rate.

53. 3,375 revolutions in 15 minutes

54. 3,000 houses to 1,500 acres of land

55. 120 gallons of heating oil for 15 days

56. 48 yards in 8 carries

57. 3 tanks of gas to cut 10 acres of lawn

58. 192 meters in 6 seconds

59. 8 yards of material for 5 dresses

60. 648 heartbeats in 9 minutes

61. 20 hours of homework in 10 days

62. $200 for 8 hours of work

63. A run of 5 kilometers in 20 minutes

64. 56 calories in 4 ounces of orange juice

65. 140 fat calories in 2 tablespoons of peanut butter

66. 60 children for every 5 adults

Find the unit price, rounding to the nearest cent if necessary.

67. 12 bars of soap for $5.40

68. 4 credit hours for $200

69. 6 rolls of film that cost $17.70

70. 2 notebooks that cost $6.90

71. 3 plants for $200

72. $240,000 for a 30-second prime time television commercial spot

73. 5 nights in a hotel for $495

74. 60 minutes of Internet access for $3

Complete each table, rounding if necessary. Determine which is the better buy.

75. Honey lemon cough drops

Number of Units	Total Price	Unit Price
30	$1.69	
100	$5.49	

76. Stretchable disposable diapers

Number of Units	Total Price	Unit Price
36	$8.69	
60	$14.99	

77. Staples® Bright White Inkjet paper

Number of Units (Sheets)	Total Price	Unit Price
500	$9.69	
2,500	$42.99	

78. Colgate® Total toothpaste

Number of Units (Ounces)	Total Price	Unit Price
6	$3.59	
7	$4.19	

Fill in the table. Which is the best buy?

79. Glad® trash bags, large, with drawstring

Number of Units	Total Price	Unit Price
14	$8.49	
25	$11.49	
28	$7.49	

80. CVS® AA alkaline batteries

Number of Units	Total Price	Unit Price
4	$2.57	
10	$3.89	
24	$6.89	

Mixed Practice

Solve.

81. To the nearest cent, find the unit price of an 18-ounce jar of creamy peanut butter that costs $2.89.

82. Complete the table. Then, find the best buy.
Starbucks® Cappuccino

Number of units (Fluid ounces)	Total Price	Unit Price
12	$3.15	
16	$3.95	
24	$4.25	

83. Simplify the rate: 4 tutors for every 30 students.

84. Write as a unit rate: 50 lots to 0.2 square mile.

85. Write the ratio 20 to 4 in simplest form.

86. Express $\dfrac{30 \text{ centimeters}}{45 \text{ centimeters}}$ in simplest form.

Applications

Ⓒ *Solve. Simplify if possible.*

87. The number line shown is marked off in equal units. Find the ratio of the length of the distance x to the distance y.

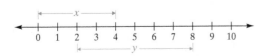

88. In the following rectangle, what is the ratio of the width to the length?

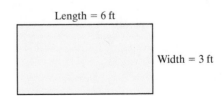

89. In 10 ounces of cashew nuts, there are 1,700 calories. How many calories are there per ounce?

90. For a building valued at $200,000 the property tax is $4,000. Find the ratio of the tax to the building's value.

91. The *cartridge yield* of a computer printer is the number of pages that it will print before the toner runs out. A cartridge that sells for $69.99 has a yield of 2,000 pages. Rounded to the nearest cent, what is the cost per page of printing? (*Source:* smartcomputing.com)

92. A bathtub contains 20 gallons of water. If the tub empties in 4 minutes, what is the rate of flow of the water per minute?

93. In a student government election, 1,000 students cast a vote for the incumbent, 900 voted for the opponent, and 100 cast a protest vote. What was the ratio of the incumbent's vote to the total number of votes?

94. At a college, 4,500 of the 7,500 students are female. What is the ratio of females to males at the college?

95. In finance, the *return on investment* (ROI) is the ratio of profit or loss on an investment relative to the amount of money invested. ROI is commonly calculated to compare the performance of one investment relative to another. Find this ratio for an investment of $9,000 with a profit of $1,500. (*Sources:* investopedia.com and ehow.com)

96. About 15,600 people can ride El Toro, a roller coaster at Six Flags Great Adventure in New Jersey, in 12 hours. Approximately how many people per hour can ride El Toro? (*Source:* wikipedia.org)

97. At the beginning of the 112th U.S. Congress, there were 193 Democrats in the House of Representatives and 51 Democrats in the Senate. For Republicans, there were 242 in the House and 47 in the Senate. Was the ratio of Democrats to Republicans higher in the House or in the Senate? (*Source:* wikipedia.org)

98. The table below shows the breakdown of the number of patients in two hospital units at a local city hospital. Is the ratio of nurses to patients in the intensive care unit higher or lower than the ratio of nurses to patients in the medical unit?

	Intensive Care Unit	Medical Unit
Patients	25	65
Nurses	8	11

99. The following table deals with five of the longest-reigning monarchs in history.

Monarch	Country	Reign	Length of Reign (in years)
King Louis XIV	France	1643–1715	72
King John II	Liechtenstein	1858–1929	71
Emperor Franz-Josef	Austria-Hungary	1848–1916	68
Queen Victoria	United Kingdom	1837–1901	64
Emperor Hirohito	Japan	1926–1989	63

(*Source: The Top 10 of Everything 2006*)

a. What is the ratio of Emperor Hirohito's length of reign to that of Emperor Franz-Josef?

b. What is the ratio of Queen Victoria's length of reign to that of King Louis XIV?

100. The following bar graph deals with popular singers and the number of their albums that "went platinum," that is, sold more than 1 million copies.

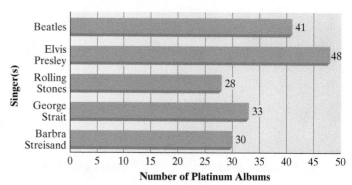

(*Source:* riaa.com)

a. Find the ratio of the number of platinum albums for Elvis Presley as compared to George Strait.

b. What is the ratio of the number of platinum albums for the Rolling Stones as compared to Barbra Streisand?

101. In the insurance industry, a loss ratio is the ratio of total losses paid out by an insurance company to total premiums collected for a given time period.

$$\text{Loss ratio} = \frac{\text{Losses paid}}{\text{Premiums collected}}$$

In 2 months, a certain insurance company paid losses of $6,400,000 and collected premiums of $12,472,000. What is the loss ratio, rounded to the nearest hundredth?

102. Analysts for a brokerage firm prepare research reports on companies with stocks traded in various stock markets. One statistic that an analyst uses is the price-to-earnings (P.E.) ratio.

$$\text{P.E. ratio} = \frac{\text{Market price per share}}{\text{Earnings per share}}$$

Find the P.E. ratio, rounded to the nearest hundredth, for a stock that had a per-share market price of $70.75 and earnings of $5.37 per share.

• Check your answers on page A-7.

MINDStretchers

History

1. For a **golden rectangle**, the ratio of its length to its width is approximately 1.618 to 1 (the **golden ratio**).

1.618

To the ancient Egyptians and Greeks, a golden rectangle was considered to be the ratio most pleasing to the eye. Show that index cards in either of the two standard sizes (3 × 5 and 5 × 8) are close approximations to the golden rectangle.

Investigation

2. The distance around a circle is called its **circumference** (C). The distance across the circle through its center is called its **diameter** (d).

a. Use a string and ruler to measure C and d for both circles shown.

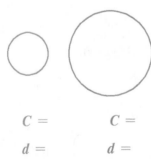

$C =$ $C =$

$d =$ $d =$

b. Compute the ratio of C to d for each circle. Are the ratios approximately equal?

$$\frac{C}{d} = \qquad \frac{C}{d} =$$

Writing

3. Sometimes we use *differences* rather than *quotients* to compare two quantities. Give an example of each kind of comparison and any advantages and disadvantages of each approach.

5.2 Solving Proportions

Writing Proportions

When two ratios—for instance, 1 to 2 and 4 to 8—are equal, they are said to be *in proportion*. We can write "1 is to 2 as 4 is to 8" as $\dfrac{1}{2} = \dfrac{4}{8}$. Such an equation is called a **proportion**.

Proportions are common in daily life and are used in many situations, such as finding the distance between two cities from a map with a given scale or the amount of a worker's pay for four weeks given the weekly pay.

> **DEFINITION**
>
> A **proportion** is a statement that two ratios are equal.

One way to see if a proportion is true is to determine whether the *cross products* of the ratios are equal. For example, we see that the proportion

$$\frac{1}{2} = \frac{4}{8}$$

is true, because $2 \cdot 4 = 1 \cdot 8$, or $8 = 8$. However, the proportion $\dfrac{3}{5} = \dfrac{9}{10}$ is not true, since $5 \cdot 9 \neq 3 \cdot 10$.

EXAMPLE 1

Determine whether the proportion 4 is to 3 as 16 is to 12 is true.

Solution   First, we write the ratios in fractional form: $\dfrac{4}{3} = \dfrac{16}{12}$

$$3 \cdot 16 \overset{?}{=} 4 \cdot 12 \qquad \text{Set the cross products equal.}$$
$$48 \overset{\checkmark}{=} 48$$

So the proportion 4 is to 3 as 16 is to 12 is true.

PRACTICE 1

Are the ratios 10 to 4 and 15 to 6 in proportion?

EXAMPLE 2

Is $\dfrac{15}{9} = \dfrac{8}{5}$ a true proportion?

Solution $\dfrac{15}{9} \overset{?}{=} \dfrac{8}{5}$

$$9 \cdot 8 \overset{?}{=} 15 \cdot 5 \qquad \text{Set the cross products equal.}$$
$$72 \neq 75$$

The cross products are not equal. So the proportion is not true.

PRACTICE 2

Determine whether $\dfrac{15}{6} = \dfrac{8}{3}$ is a true proportion.

EXAMPLE 3

A college claims that the student-to-faculty ratio is 13 to 1. If there are 96 faculty for 1,248 students, is the college's claim true?

Solution   The college claims a student-to-faculty ratio of $\dfrac{13}{1}$, and

the actual ratio of students to faculty is $\dfrac{1,248}{96}$. We want to know if

these two ratios are equal.

$$\begin{array}{l} \text{Students} \rightarrow \dfrac{13}{1} \stackrel{?}{=} \dfrac{1,248}{96} \leftarrow \text{Students} \\ \text{Faculty} \rightarrow \end{array}$$

$$1 \cdot 1,248 \stackrel{?}{=} 13 \cdot 96 \qquad \text{Set the cross products equal.}$$
$$1,248 \stackrel{\checkmark}{=} 1,248$$

Since the cross products are equal, the college's claim is true.

PRACTICE 3

A company has a policy making the compensation of its CEO proportional to the dividends that are paid to shareholders. If the dividends increase from $72 to $80 and the CEO's compensation is increased from $360,000 to $420,000, was the company's policy followed?

Solving Proportions

Suppose that you make $840 for working 4 weeks in a book shop. At this rate of pay, how much money will you make in 10 weeks? To solve this problem, we can write a proportion in which the rates compare the amount of pay to the time worked. We want to find the amount of pay corresponding to 10 weeks, which we call x.

$$\begin{array}{l} \text{Pay} \rightarrow \dfrac{840}{4} = \dfrac{x}{10} \leftarrow \text{Pay} \\ \text{Time} \rightarrow \qquad\quad \leftarrow \text{Time} \end{array}$$

After setting the cross products equal, we find the missing value.

$$\frac{840}{4} = \frac{x}{10}$$
$$4 \cdot x = 840 \cdot 10$$
$$4x = 8,400$$
$$\frac{4x}{4} = \frac{8,400}{4} \qquad \text{Divide each side of the equation by 4.}$$
$$x = 2,100$$

So you will make $2,100 in 10 weeks.

We can check our solution by substituting 2,100 for x in the original proportion.

$$\frac{840}{4} = \frac{x}{10}$$
$$\frac{840}{4} \stackrel{?}{=} \frac{2,100}{10}$$
$$4 \cdot 2,100 \stackrel{?}{=} 840 \cdot 10 \qquad \text{Set the cross products equal.}$$
$$8,400 \stackrel{\checkmark}{=} 8,400$$

Our solution checks.

To Solve a Proportion

- Find the cross products, and set them equal.

- Solve the resulting equation.

- Check the solution by substituting the value of the unknown in the original equation to be sure that the resulting proportion is true.

EXAMPLE 4

Solve and check: $\dfrac{2}{3} = \dfrac{x}{15}$

Solution

$$\dfrac{2}{3} = \dfrac{x}{15}$$

$3 \cdot x = 2 \cdot 15$ Set the cross products equal.

$3x = 30$

$\dfrac{3x}{3} = \dfrac{30}{3}$ Divide each side by 3.

$x = 10$

The solution is 10.

Check

$$\dfrac{2}{3} = \dfrac{x}{15}$$

$\dfrac{2}{3} \overset{?}{=} \dfrac{10}{15}$ Substitute 10 for x.

$3 \cdot 10 \overset{?}{=} 2 \cdot 15$ Set the cross products equal.

$30 \overset{\checkmark}{=} 30$

PRACTICE 4

Solve and check: $\dfrac{x}{6} = \dfrac{12}{9}$

EXAMPLE 5

Solve and check: $\dfrac{\frac{1}{4}}{12} = \dfrac{x}{96}$

Solution

$$\dfrac{\frac{1}{4}}{12} = \dfrac{x}{96}$$

$12 \cdot x = \dfrac{1}{4} \cdot 96$ Set the cross products equal.

$12x = 24$

$\dfrac{12x}{12} = \dfrac{24}{12}$ Divide each side by 12.

$x = 2$

The solution is 2.

Check

$$\dfrac{\frac{1}{4}}{12} = \dfrac{x}{96}$$

$\dfrac{\frac{1}{4}}{12} \overset{?}{=} \dfrac{2}{96}$ Substitute 2 for x.

$12(2) \overset{?}{=} \dfrac{1}{4} \cdot (96)$ Set the cross products equal.

$24 \overset{\checkmark}{=} 24$

PRACTICE 5

Solve and check: $\dfrac{\frac{1}{2}}{2} = \dfrac{3}{x}$

EXAMPLE 6

Forty pounds of sodium hydroxide are needed to neutralize 49 pounds of sulfuric acid. At this rate, how many pounds of sodium hydroxide are needed to neutralize 98 pounds of sulfuric acid? (*Source:* Peter Atkins and Loretta Jones, *Chemistry*)

Solution Let n represent the number of pounds of sodium hydroxide needed. We set up a proportion to compare the amount of sodium hydroxide to the amount of sulfuric acid.

$$\text{Sodium hydroxide} \rightarrow \frac{40}{49} = \frac{n}{98} \longleftarrow \text{Sodium hydroxide}$$
$$\text{Sulfuric acid} \rightarrow \quad \quad \longleftarrow \text{Sulfuric acid}$$

$$49n = 40 \cdot 98 \quad \text{Set the cross products equal.}$$

$$49n = 3,920$$

$$\frac{49n}{49} = \frac{3,920}{49} \quad \text{Divide each side by 49.}$$

$$n = 80$$

Check

$$\frac{40}{49} = \frac{n}{98}$$

$$\frac{40}{49} \stackrel{?}{=} \frac{80}{98} \quad \text{Substitute 80 for } n.$$

$$49 \cdot 80 \stackrel{?}{=} 40 \cdot 98 \quad \text{Set the cross products equal.}$$

$$3,920 \stackrel{\checkmark}{=} 3,920$$

So 80 pounds of sodium hydroxide are needed to neutralize 98 pounds of sulfuric acid.

PRACTICE 6

Saffron is a powder made from crocus flowers and is used in the manufacture of perfume. Some 8,000 crocus flowers are required to make 2 ounces of saffron. How many flowers are needed to make 16 ounces of saffron? (*Source: The World Book Encyclopedia*)

TIP A good way to set up a proportion is to write quantities of the same kind in the numerators and their corresponding quantities of the other kind in the denominators.

EXAMPLE 7

If St. Louis and Cincinnati on the map below are 1.6 inches apart, what is the actual distance between them?

$\frac{1}{2}$ in. = 100 mi

PRACTICE 7

The first aircraft to fly faster than the speed of sound was a research plane piloted by Major Charles E. Yeager of the U.S. Air Force on Oct. 14, 1947. Aircraft speed, especially supersonic, is commonly expressed as a Mach number—the ratio of the speed of the aircraft to the speed of sound (1,066 kilometers per hour). If Yeager's plane reached a top speed of 1,126 kilometers per hour exceeding the speed of sound, what was the Mach speed of the plane, rounded to the nearest hundredth? (*Source:* concorde-jet.com)

Solution   We know that $\frac{1}{2}$ inch corresponds to 100 miles. Let's set up a proportion that compares inches to miles, letting m represent the unknown number of miles.

$$\frac{\frac{1}{2} \text{ inch}}{100 \text{ miles}} = \frac{1.6 \text{ inches}}{m \text{ miles}}$$

$$\frac{\frac{1}{2}}{100} = \frac{1.6}{m}$$

$$\frac{1}{2}m = (100)(1.6) \qquad \text{Set the cross products equal.}$$

$$\frac{1}{2}m = 160$$

$$\frac{1}{2}m \div \frac{1}{2} = 160 \div \frac{1}{2} \qquad \text{Divide each side by } \frac{1}{2}.$$

$$\frac{1}{2}m \times \frac{2}{1} = 160 \times \frac{2}{1}$$

$$m = 320$$

So the cities are 320 miles apart.

Check

$$\frac{\frac{1}{2}}{100} = \frac{1.6}{m}$$

$$\frac{\frac{1}{2}}{100} \stackrel{?}{=} \frac{1.6}{320}$$

$$100(1.6) \stackrel{?}{=} \frac{1}{2} \cdot (320)$$

$$160 \stackrel{\checkmark}{=} 160$$

⊙ **EXAMPLE 8**

In the following diagram, the heights and shadow lengths of the two objects shown are in proportion. Find the height of the tree h.

1.6 m

2.4 m   10.8 m

Solution   The heights and shadow lengths are in proportion, so we write the following:

Height → $\dfrac{h \text{ meters}}{10.8 \text{ meters}} = \dfrac{1.6 \text{ meters}}{2.4 \text{ meters}}$ ← Height
Shadow →   ← Shadow

$$\frac{h}{10.8} = \frac{1.6}{2.4}$$

$$2.4h = (10.8)(1.6)$$

$$\frac{2.4h}{2.4} = \frac{17.28}{2.4}$$

$$h = 7.2$$

So the height of the tree is 7.2 meters.

Check

$$\frac{h}{10.8} = \frac{1.6}{2.4}$$

$$\frac{7.2}{10.8} \stackrel{?}{=} \frac{1.6}{2.4}$$

$$(10.8)(1.6) \stackrel{?}{=} (7.2)(2.4)$$

$$17.28 \stackrel{\checkmark}{=} 17.28$$

PRACTICE 8

A community college in Hawaii has a student-to-faculty ratio of 14 to 1. How many faculty members are at the college if it has 4,200 students? (*Source:* hawaii.edu)

Mathematically Speaking

Fill in each blank with the most appropriate term or phrase from the given list.

equation	check	like
products	solve	cross products
as	proportion	

1. A(n) _____ is a statement that two ratios are equal.

2. To determine if a proportion is true, check whether the _____ of the ratios are equal.

3. The proportion $\frac{4}{5} = \frac{8}{10}$ can be read "4 is to 5 _____ 8 is to 10."

4. To _____ the proportion $\frac{x}{2} = \frac{4}{6}$, find the value of x that makes the proportion true.

A *Indicate whether each statement is true or false.*

5. Thirty is to 9 as 40 is to 12.

6. Nine is to 12 as 12 is to 16.

7. Two is to 3 as 7 is to 16.

8. Three is to 8 as 10 is to 27.

9. One and one-tenth is to 0.3 as 44 is to 12.

10. One and one-half is to 2 as 0.6 is to 0.8.

11. $\frac{3}{6} = \frac{2}{5}$

12. $\frac{4}{7} = \frac{5}{8}$

13. $\frac{12}{28} = \frac{18}{42}$

14. $\frac{28}{24} = \frac{7}{6}$

15. $\frac{6}{1} = \frac{3}{\frac{1}{2}}$

16. $\frac{5}{30} = \frac{\frac{1}{3}}{2}$

Solve and check.

17. $\frac{4}{8} = \frac{10}{x}$

18. $\frac{3}{2} = \frac{42}{x}$

19. $\frac{x}{19} = \frac{10}{5}$

20. $\frac{x}{78} = \frac{1}{6}$

21. $\frac{5}{x} = \frac{15}{12}$

22. $\frac{15}{x} = \frac{6}{10}$

23. $\frac{4}{1} = \frac{52}{x}$

24. $\frac{17}{1} = \frac{51}{x}$

25. $\frac{7}{4} = \frac{14}{x}$

26. $\frac{18}{15} = \frac{6}{x}$

27. $\frac{x}{8} = \frac{3}{6}$

28. $\frac{x}{35} = \frac{5}{7}$

29. $\frac{70}{x} = \frac{21}{6}$

30. $\frac{4}{x} = \frac{92}{23}$

31. $\frac{x}{12} = \frac{25}{20}$

32. $\frac{x}{45} = \frac{20}{25}$

33. $\frac{28}{x} = \frac{36}{27}$

34. $\frac{24}{x} = \frac{27}{63}$

35. $\frac{x}{10} = \frac{4}{3}$

36. $\frac{x}{2} = \frac{6}{5}$

37. $\frac{4}{x} = \frac{\frac{2}{5}}{10}$

38. $\frac{\frac{3}{4}}{6} = \frac{3}{x}$

39. $\frac{x}{27} = \frac{1.6}{24}$

40. $\frac{x}{1.8} = \frac{28}{24}$

41. $\frac{10.5}{x} = \frac{5}{10}$

42. $\frac{9}{x} = \frac{7.2}{32}$

43. $\frac{7}{0.9} = \frac{x}{36}$

44. $\frac{56}{4.8} = \frac{x}{18}$

45. $\dfrac{600}{x} = \dfrac{3}{1\frac{1}{2}}$

46. $\dfrac{12}{x} = \dfrac{5}{2\frac{1}{3}}$

47. $\dfrac{15}{2} = \dfrac{x}{2\frac{2}{3}}$

48. $\dfrac{20}{3} = \dfrac{x}{1\frac{1}{2}}$

49. $\dfrac{\frac{1}{2}}{\frac{1}{5}} = \dfrac{x}{4}$

50. $\dfrac{2}{\frac{4}{5}} = \dfrac{\frac{2}{3}}{x}$

51. $\dfrac{3}{2.7} = \dfrac{6}{x}$

52. $\dfrac{1.5}{6} = \dfrac{x}{1.2}$

53. $\dfrac{\frac{1}{3}}{x} = \dfrac{2}{1.2}$

54. $\dfrac{2.5}{x} = \dfrac{\frac{1}{4}}{50}$

55. $\dfrac{x}{0.16} = \dfrac{0.15}{4.8}$

56. $\dfrac{1.5}{1.25} = \dfrac{x}{0.5}$

Mixed Practice

57. Solve and check: $\dfrac{\frac{3}{4}}{15} = \dfrac{x}{8}$

58. Solve and check: $\dfrac{1.6}{x} = \dfrac{2.4}{27}$

59. Solve and check: $\dfrac{3}{2} = \dfrac{2\frac{2}{5}}{x}$

60. Determine whether the proportion 8 is to 1 as 2 is to $\dfrac{1}{4}$ is true.

61. Is $\dfrac{4}{9} = \dfrac{3}{8}$ a true or false statement?

62. Solve and check: $\dfrac{x}{9} = \dfrac{5}{6}$

Ⓑ Applications

Solve and check.

63. An average adult's heart beats 8 times every 6 seconds, whereas a newborn baby's heart beats 7 times every 3 seconds. Determine whether these rates are the same. (*Source: Mosby's Medical, Nursing, and Allied Health Dictionary*)

64. An intravenous fluid is infused at a rate of 2.5 milliliters per minute. How many milliliters are infused per hour?

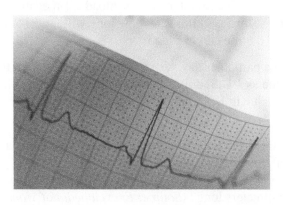

65. A dripping faucet wastes about 15 gallons of water daily. About how much water is wasted in 3 hours? (*Hint:* 1 day = 24 hours)

66. A full-time college student paid tuition of $1,296 for 12 credits, and a part-time student paid $1,008 for 9 credits. Were the tuition rates the same?

67. The recommended daily allowance of protein for adults is 0.8 grams for every 2.2 pounds of body weight. If you weigh 150 pounds, how many grams of protein to the nearest tenth should you consume each day? (*Source: The Nutrition Desk Reference*)

68. A homeowner is preparing a solution of insecticide and water to spray her house plants. The directions on the insecticide bottle instruct her to mix 1 part of insecticide with 50 parts of water. How much water must she mix with 2 tablespoons of insecticide?

69. In carbon dioxide molecules, for every 2 oxygen atoms there is 1 carbon atom. How many oxygen atoms combine with 50 carbon atoms to form carbon dioxide molecules?

71. The following rectangular photo is to be enlarged so that the width of the enlargement is 25 inches. If the dimensions of the photo are to remain in proportion, what should the length of the enlargement be?

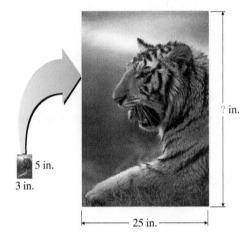

70. The scale on a map is $\frac{1}{4}$ centimeter to 50 kilometers. Find the actual distance between two towns represented by 10 centimeters on the map.

72. Architects now use computers to render their designs. If the actual length of the kitchen shown on the computer-generated floor plan is 10 feet, what is the actual length of the dining area?

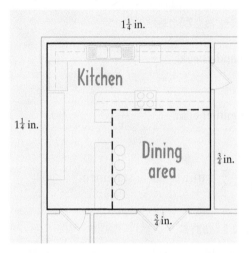

73. A popular scale for building model railroads is the N scale, in which model trains are $\frac{1}{160}$ the size of actual trains. Using this scale, what is the model size of a box-car that is actually 40 feet long?

75. The ratio of your federal income tax to state income tax is 10 to 3. How much is your state income tax if your federal income tax is $2,000?

77. To determine the number of fish in a lake, researchers tagged 150 of them. In a later sample, they found that 6 of 480 fish were tagged. About how many fish were in the lake?

79. A 5-speed bicycle has a chain linking the pedal sprocket and the gears on the rear wheel. The ratio of pedal turns to rear-wheel turns in first gear is 9 to 14. How many times in first gear does the rear wheel turn if the pedals turn 180 times?

81. A tablet of medication consists of two substances in the ratio of 9 to 5. If the tablet contains 140 milligrams of medication, how much of each substance is in the tablet?

74. Thirty gallons of oil flow through a pipe in 4 hours. At this rate, how long will it take 280 gallons to flow through this same pipe?

76. A student's computer can download a 4-megabyte song in 3 seconds. At this rate, how long will it take to download a 6-megabyte song?

78. On a particular day, 89 Japanese yen were worth the same as 1 U.S. dollar. If a shirt cost 1,780 yen, what was its value in U.S. dollars?

80. The tallest land animal is the giraffe. How tall is a giraffe that casts a shadow 320 centimeters long, if a man nearby who is 180 centimeters tall casts a shadow 100 centimeters long? (*Source: Encyclopedia of Mammals*)

82. A certain metal is 5 parts tin and 2 parts lead. How many kilograms of each are there in 28 kilograms of the metal?

83. The nutrition label from a box of General Mills Total cereal indicates that a $\frac{3}{4}$-cup serving contains the following:

Nutrition Facts
Fat 0.5 g
Cholesterol 0 mg
Sodium 190 mg
Potassium 90 mg
Carbohydrates 23 g
Protein 2 g

a. How many grams of carbohydrates are there in 3 cups of cereal?

b. What is the amount of protein in $1\frac{1}{2}$ cups of cereal?

85. A senator reported that 640 metric tons of spent nuclear fuel had produced 660,000 gallons of nuclear waste. At this rate, how many gallons of nuclear waste, to the nearest thousand, would be produced by 810 metric tons of fuel?

84. The following recipe is for Nilla Apple Crisp:

Nilla Apple Crisp	Serves 12
4 large Granny Smith apples (2 pounds), peeled, thinly sliced	
1/2 cup of packed brown sugar	
2 teaspoons of ground cinnamon	
1/3 cup of old-fashioned or quick-cooking oats	
1/4 cup of cold margarine	
25 Reduced Fat Nilla Wafers, crushed (about 1 cup of crumbs)	
1 1/2 cups of thawed Cool Whip Lite Whipped Topping	

(*Source:* Kraftrecipes.com)

a. How many cups of thawed Cool Whip Lite Whipped Topping are needed for 18 servings?

b. What is the number of servings if $1\frac{1}{2}$ cups of packed brown sugar are used and the other ingredients are increased proportionately?

86. A car uses 0.16 gallon of gas to travel through a tunnel 3.6 miles long. At this rate, how many gallons of gas, to the nearest whole number, are needed to travel 2,885 miles across country?

• Check your answers on page A-7.

MINDStretchers

Mathematical Reasoning

1. Pictorial comparisons (called *analogies*) are used on many standardized tests. Fill in the blank.

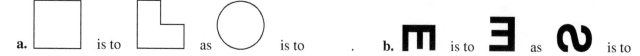

a. ☐ is to ⌐ as ◯ is to ___ .   **b.** m is to Ǝ as 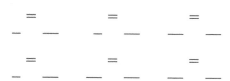 is to ___ .

Groupwork

2. Work with a partner on the following.

a. Complete the following table.

x	0	1	2	3	4
5x					

b. Write as many true proportions as you can, based on the values in the table.

$$\frac{\ }{\ } = \frac{\ }{\ } \quad \frac{\ }{\ } = \frac{\ }{\ } \quad \frac{\ }{\ } = \frac{\ }{\ }$$

$$\frac{\ }{\ } = \frac{\ }{\ } \quad \frac{\ }{\ } = \frac{\ }{\ } \quad \frac{\ }{\ } = \frac{\ }{\ }$$

Technology

3. On the web, there are many currency calculators that convert a given amount of a first currency into the equivalent amount of a second currency. Locate one such calculator. Use your knowledge of proportions to confirm that the currency calculator is working correctly.

Key Concepts and Skills

CONCEPT SKILL

Concept/Skill	Description	Example
[5.1] **Ratio**	A comparison of two quantities expressed as a quotient.	3 to 4, $\frac{3}{4}$, or 3:4
[5.1] **Rate**	A ratio of unlike quantities.	$\dfrac{10 \text{ students}}{3 \text{ tutors}}$
[5.1] **To simplify a ratio**	• Write the ratio as a fraction. • Express the fraction in simplest form. • If the quantities are alike, drop the units. If the quantities are unlike, keep the units.	9:27 is the same as 1:3, because $\dfrac{9}{27} = \dfrac{1}{3}$ 21 hours to 56 hours $= \dfrac{21 \text{ hours}}{56 \text{ hours}} = \dfrac{21}{56} = \dfrac{3}{8}$ 175 miles per 7 gallons $= \dfrac{175 \text{ miles}}{7 \text{ gallons}} = \dfrac{25 \text{ miles}}{1 \text{ gallon}},$ or 25 mpg
[5.1] **Unit rate**	A rate in which the number in the denominator is 1.	$\dfrac{180 \text{ calories}}{1 \text{ ounce}},$ or 180 calories per ounce, or 180 cal/oz
[5.1] **Unit price**	The price of one item, or one unit.	$0.69 per can, or $0.69/can
[5.2] **Proportion**	A statement that two ratios are equal.	$\dfrac{5}{8} = \dfrac{15}{24}$
[5.2] **To solve a proportion**	• Find the cross products, and set them equal. • Solve the resulting equation. • Check the solution by substituting the value of the unknown in the original equation to verify that the resulting proportion is true.	$\dfrac{6}{9} = \dfrac{2}{x}$ $6x = 18$ $x = 3$ **Check** $\dfrac{6}{9} = \dfrac{2}{x}$ $\dfrac{6}{9} \stackrel{?}{=} \dfrac{2}{3}$ $6 \cdot 3 \stackrel{?}{=} 9 \cdot 2$ $18 \stackrel{\checkmark}{=} 18$

Say Why *Fill in each blank.*

1. The ratio $\dfrac{\$25}{\$225}$ _____ is/is not _____ written in simplified form as $\dfrac{\$1}{\$9}$ because _____ _____.

2. The ratio $\dfrac{\$51}{6.8 \text{ hours}}$ _____ is/is not _____ a rate because _____ _____ _____.

3. The rate $\dfrac{1 \text{ mile}}{5,280 \text{ feet}}$ _____ is/is not _____ a unit rate because _____.

4. $10 per foot _____ is/is not _____ an example of a unit price because_____.

5. $\dfrac{2}{3} - \dfrac{x}{5}$ _____ is/is not _____ a proportion because _____ _____ _____.

6. In the proportion $\dfrac{x}{2} = \dfrac{3}{5}$, $2 \cdot 3$ and $5x$ _____ are/are not _____ cross products because_____ _____.

[5.1] *Write each ratio or rate in simplest form.*

7. 10 to 15

8. 28 to 56

9. 3 to 4

10. 50 to 16

11. 10,400 votes to 6,500 votes

12. 9 cups to 12 cups

13. 88 feet in 10 seconds

14. 45 applicants for 10 positions

Write each ratio as a unit rate.

15. 4 pounds of grass seed to plant in 1,600 square feet of lawn

16. 75 billion telephone calls in 150 days

17. 48 yards in 6 downs

18. 3,200 square feet covered by 8 gallons of paint

19. 21,000,000 vehicles produced in 2 years

20. 532,000 commuters traveled in 7 days

Find the unit price for each item.

21. $475 for 4 nights

22. $19.45 for 5 DVD movie rentals

23. $80,000 for 64 computer stations

24. $9,364 for 100 shares of stock

Fill in each table. Which is the better buy?

25. *The New Yorker®* magazine issues

Number of Units	Total Price	Unit Price
47	$39.95	
94	$69.95	

26. Custom laser checks

Number of Units	Total Price	Unit Price
100	$13.95	
250	$37.95	

Complete each table. Determine the best buy.

27. Stop Aging Now® green tea extract capsules

Number of Units	Total Price	Unit Price
30	$16.95	
90	$44.85	
180	$77.70	

28. Johnson's Baby Oil®

Number of Units (fluid ounces)	Total Price	Unit Price
4	$2.78	
14	$3.92	
20	$3.74	

[5.2] *Indicate whether each proportion is true or false.*

29. $\dfrac{15}{25} = \dfrac{3}{5}$

30. $\dfrac{3}{1} = \dfrac{1}{3}$

31. $\dfrac{50}{45} = \dfrac{10}{8}$

32. $\dfrac{15}{6} = \dfrac{5}{2}$

Solve and check.

33. $\dfrac{1}{2} = \dfrac{x}{12}$

34. $\dfrac{9}{12} = \dfrac{x}{4}$

35. $\dfrac{12}{x} = \dfrac{3}{8}$

36. $\dfrac{x}{72} = \dfrac{5}{12}$

37. $\dfrac{1.6}{7.2} = \dfrac{x}{9}$

38. $\dfrac{x}{12} = \dfrac{1.2}{1.8}$

39. $\dfrac{5}{\frac{1}{2}} = \dfrac{7}{x}$

40. $\dfrac{3}{5} = \dfrac{x}{\frac{2}{3}}$

41. $\dfrac{2\frac{1}{4}}{x} = \dfrac{1}{30}$

42. $\dfrac{3}{1\frac{3}{5}} = \dfrac{x}{24}$

43. $\dfrac{\frac{5}{6}}{x} = \dfrac{2}{1.8}$

44. $\dfrac{\frac{2}{3}}{4} = \dfrac{x}{0.9}$

45. $\dfrac{0.36}{4.2} = \dfrac{2.4}{x}$

46. $\dfrac{x}{0.21} = \dfrac{0.12}{0.18}$

Mixed Applications

Solve and check.

47. An airplane has 12 first-class seats and 180 seats in coach. What is the ratio of first-class seats to coach seats?

48. A computer store sells $23,000 worth of desktop computers and $45,000 worth of laptops in a given month. What is the ratio of desktop computer to laptop sales?

49. If a personal care attendant earns $540 for a 6-day workweek, how much does she earn per day?

50. A glacier in Alaska moves about 2 inches in 16 months. How far does the glacier move per month?

51. In a recent year, approximately 200,000,000 of the 300,000,000 people in the United States were Internet users. What is the ratio of Internet users to the total population? (*Source:* internetworldstats.com)

52. A city's public libraries spend about $9.50 in operating expenses for every book they circulate. If their operating expenses amount to $475,000, how many books circulate?

53. In a college's day-care center, the required staff-to-child ratio is 2 to 5. If there are 60 children and 12 staff in the day-care center, is the center in compliance with the requirement?

54. Despite the director's protests, the 1924 silent film *Greed* was edited down from about 42 reels of film to 10 reels. If the original version was about 9 hours long, about how long was the edited version? (*Source: The Film Encyclopedia*)

55. A sports car engine has an 8-to-1 compression ratio. Before compression, the fuel mixture in a cylinder takes up 440 cubic centimeters of space. How much space does the fuel mixture occupy when fully compressed?

56. On an architectural drawing of a planned community, a measurement of 25 feet is represented by 0.5 inches. If two houses are actually 62.5 feet apart, what is the distance between them on the drawing?

57. The *density of a substance* is the ratio of its mass to its volume. To the nearest hundredth, find the density of gasoline if a volume of 317.45 cubic centimeters has a mass of 216.21 grams.

58. The admission rate at a college is the ratio of the number of admitted students to the number of applicants. At Harvard College for the class of 2014, there were 30,489 applicants of whom 2,110 were admitted. Find Harvard's admission rate, expressed as a decimal rounded to the nearest hundredth. (*Source:* news.harvard.edu)

• Check your answers on page A-7.

FOR EXTRA HELP

CHAPTER Test Prep VIDEOS

The Chapter Test Prep Videos with test solutions are available on DVD, in MyMathLab, and on YouTube® (search "AkstBasicMath" and click on "Channels").

To see if you have mastered the topics in this chapter, take this test.

Write each ratio or rate in simplest form.

1. 8 to 12

2. 15 to 42

3. 55 ounces to 31 ounces

4. 180 miles to 15 miles

5. 65 revolutions in 60 seconds

6. 3 centimeters for every 75 kilometers

Find the unit rate.

7. 340 miles in 5 hours

8. 200-meter dash in 25 seconds

Determine the unit price.

9. $4,080 for 30 days

10. 25 greeting cards for $20

Determine whether each proportion is true or false.

11. $\dfrac{8}{21} \overset{?}{=} \dfrac{16}{40}$

12. $\dfrac{7}{3} \overset{?}{=} \dfrac{63}{27}$

Solve and check.

13. $\dfrac{15}{x} = \dfrac{6}{10}$

14. $\dfrac{102}{17} = \dfrac{36}{x}$

15. $\dfrac{0.9}{36} = \dfrac{0.7}{x}$

16. $\dfrac{\frac{1}{3}}{4} = \dfrac{x}{12}$

Solve.

17. To advertise his business, an owner can purchase 3 million e-mail addresses for $120 or 5 million e-mail addresses for $175. Which is the better buy?

18. The Association of American Medical Colleges has called for increasing the number of students attending medical schools so as to reduce projected physician shortages. In a recent year, the entering class of medical schools was about 18,000 students as compared to 16,000 students five years earlier. What is the ratio of the later enrollment to the earlier enrollment? (*Source:* aamc.org)

19. A man $6\frac{1}{4}$ feet tall casts a 5-foot shadow. A nearby tree casts a 20-foot shadow. If the heights and shadow lengths of the man and tree are proportional, how tall is the tree?

20. A nurse takes his patient's pulse. What is the patient's pulse per minute if it beats 12 times in 15 seconds?

• Check your answers on page A-8.

Cumulative Review Exercises

To help you review, solve the following:

1. Add: $93,281 + $8,429 + $6,701

2. Divide: $\dfrac{5,103}{27}$

3. Calculate: $7 \cdot 2^3 - \dfrac{21 - 13}{2}$

4. Write the prime factorization of 168.

5. Find the difference: $3\dfrac{1}{10} - 2\dfrac{7}{10}$

6. Divide: $\dfrac{1}{3} \div 3\dfrac{1}{4}$

7. Simplify: $\dfrac{2}{3} \times 1\dfrac{1}{2} - \dfrac{1}{4}$

8. Multiply: $8.2 \times 1,000$

9. Estimate: $12\dfrac{1}{7} \div 3\dfrac{9}{10}$

10. Solve and check: $x + 6.5 = 9$

11. Solve and check: $\dfrac{3}{10}n = 21$

12. Simplify the ratio: 2.5 to 10

13. Find the unit price: 3 yards for $12

14. Solve and check: $\dfrac{\frac{1}{2}}{4} = \dfrac{x}{6}$

15. What is the area of the singles tennis court shaded in the diagram?

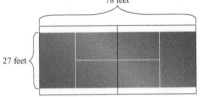

16. A college graduate looking for a teaching position takes a temporary substitute-teaching job. He works two days and makes $178.35. At this rate of pay, how much would he make, to the nearest cent, for teaching five days? (*Source:* okaloosaschools.com)

17. The barometric pressure fell from 30.02 inches to 29.83 inches. By how many inches did it fall?

18. Write the algebraic expression for the number of miles a driver travels if she drives at a speed of r miles per hour for t hours. How far will she travel in 4 hours at a speed of 65 miles per hour?

19. A rule of thumb for growing lily bulbs is to plant them 3 times as deep as they are wide. How deep should a gardener plant a lily bulb that is 2.5 inches wide?

20. In 2010, air traffic between the United States and Western Europe was disrupted because of ash spewing from a volcano in Iceland. On one day alone, 1,000 of 29,000 scheduled flights were cancelled. What fraction of the flights were cancelled? (*Source:* cnn.com)

• Check your answers on page A-8.

CHAPTER 6

6.1 Introduction to Percents

6.2 Solving Percent Problems

6.3 More on Percents

Percents

Percents and Political Polls

In 2007, Barack Obama and Hillary Clinton competed in Iowa for the Democratic nomination for President of the United States. When asked which candidate they would vote for if the Democratic caucus were held that day, 30% of interviewees said Mr. Obama and 26% Mrs. Clinton. But every poll and survey has a *margin of error*. The Iowa poll's margin of error was plus or minus 5%, meaning that support for Mr. Obama was likely between 25% and 35%, and support for Mrs. Clinton between 21% and 31%. The results in Iowa were therefore too close to call—there was essentially a tie. Barack Obama went on to be nominated and to win the election.

(*Source*: *New York Times*, November 28, 2007)

To see if you have already mastered the topics in this chapter, take this test.

Rewrite.

1. 5% as a fraction

2. $37\frac{1}{2}\%$ as a fraction

3. 250% as a decimal

4. 3% as a decimal

5. 0.007 as a percent

6. 8 as a percent

7. $\frac{2}{3}$ as a percent, rounded to the nearest whole percent

8. $1\frac{1}{10}$ as a percent

Solve.

9. What is 75% of 50 feet?

10. Find 110% of 50.

11. 80% of what number is 25.6?

12. 2% of what number is 5?

13. What percent of 10 is 4?

14. What percent of 4 is 10?

15. In a municipal savings account, a city employee earned 3% interest on $350. How much money did the employee earn in interest for 1 year?

16. The number of students enrolled at a community college rose from 2,475 last year to 2,673 this year. What was the percent increase in the college's enrollment?

17. In the depths of the Great Depression, 24% of the U.S. civilian labor force was unemployed. Write this percent as a simplified fraction. (*Source:* census.gov)

18. In a chemistry lab, a student dissolved 10 milliliters of acid in 30 milliliters of water. What percent of the solution was acid?

19. For parties of 8 or more, a restaurant automatically adds an 18% tip to the restaurant check. What tip would be added to a dinner check for a party of 10 if the total bill was $339.50?

20. A patient's health insurance covered 80% of the cost of her operation. She paid the remainder, which came to $2,000. Find the total cost of the operation.

• Check your answers on page A-8.

6.1 Introduction to Percents

What Percents Are and Why They Are Important

Percent means divided by 100. So 50% (read "fifty percent") means 50 divided by 100 (or 50 out of 100).

A percent can also be thought of as a ratio or a fraction with denominator 100. For example, we can look at 50% either as the ratio of 50 parts to 100 parts or as the fraction $\frac{50}{100}$, or $\frac{1}{2}$. Since a fraction can be written as a decimal, we can also think of 50% as 0.50, or 0.5.

In the diagram at the right, 50 of the 100 squares are shaded. This shaded portion represents 50%.

We can use diagrams to represent other percents.

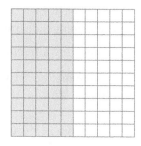

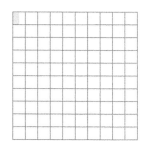

In the diagram to the left, $\frac{1}{2}$% is equivalent to the shaded portion,

$$\frac{\frac{1}{2}}{100}, \text{ or } \frac{1}{200}.$$

The entire diagram at the right is shaded, so 100% means $\frac{100}{100}$, or 1.

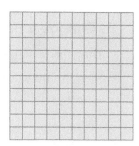

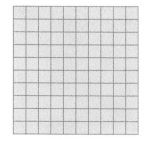 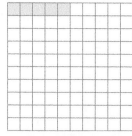

We can express 105% as $\frac{105}{100}$, or $1\frac{1}{20}$, as shown by the shaded portions of the diagrams.

Percents are commonly used, as the following statements taken from a single page of a newspaper illustrate.

- About 10% of the city's budget goes to sanitation.
- Blanket Sale—30% to 40% off!
- The number of victims of the epidemic increased by 125% in just 6 months.

A key reason for using percents so frequently is that they are easy to compare. For instance, we can tell right away that a discount of 30% is larger than a discount of 22%, simply by comparing the whole numbers 30 and 22.

To see how percents relate to fractions and decimals, let's consider finding equivalent fractions, decimals, and percents. In Chapter 3, we discussed two of the six types of conversions:

- changing a decimal to a fraction, and
- changing a fraction to a decimal.

Here, we consider the remaining four types of conversions:

- changing a percent to a fraction,
- changing a percent to a decimal,
- changing a decimal to a percent, and
- changing a fraction to a percent.

Note that each type of conversion changes the way the number is written—but not the number itself.

Changing a Percent to a Fraction

Suppose that we want to rewrite a percent—say, 30%—as a fraction. Because percent means divided by 100, we simply drop the % sign, place 30 over 100, and simplify.

$$30\% = \frac{30}{100} = \frac{3}{10}$$

Therefore, the fraction $\frac{3}{10}$ is just another way of writing the percent 30%. This result suggests the following rule:

To Change a Percent to the Equivalent Fraction

- Drop the % sign from the given percent and place the number over 100.

- Simplify the resulting fraction, if possible.

EXAMPLE 1

Write 7% as a fraction.

Solution   To change this percent to a fraction, we drop the percent sign and write the 7 over 100. The fraction is already in lowest terms.

$$7\% = \frac{7}{100}$$

PRACTICE 1

Find the fractional equivalent of 21%.

EXAMPLE 2

Express 150% as a fraction.

Solution $150\% = \frac{150}{100} = \frac{3}{2}$, or $1\frac{1}{2}$

Note that the answer is larger than 1 because the original percent was more than 100%.

PRACTICE 2

What is the fractional equivalent of 225%?

EXAMPLE 3

Express $\dfrac{1}{10}\%$ as a fraction.

Solution To find the equivalent fraction, we drop the % sign and then put the number over 100.

$$\dfrac{\dfrac{1}{10}}{100} = \dfrac{1}{10} \div 100 = \dfrac{1}{10} \div \dfrac{100}{1} = \dfrac{1}{10} \times \dfrac{1}{100} = \dfrac{1}{1{,}000}$$

So $\dfrac{1}{10}\%$ expressed as a fraction is $\dfrac{1}{1{,}000}$.

PRACTICE 3

Change $\dfrac{2}{3}\%$ to a fraction.

EXAMPLE 4

Express $33\dfrac{1}{3}\%$ as a fraction.

Solution To find the equivalent fraction, we first drop the % sign and then put the number over 100.

$$\dfrac{33\frac{1}{3}}{100} = 33\tfrac{1}{3} \div 100 = 33\tfrac{1}{3} \div \dfrac{100}{1} = \dfrac{100}{3} \div \dfrac{100}{1} = \dfrac{\overset{1}{\cancel{100}}}{3} \times \dfrac{1}{\underset{1}{\cancel{100}}} = \dfrac{1}{3}$$

So $33\dfrac{1}{3}\%$ expressed as a fraction is $\dfrac{1}{3}$.

PRACTICE 4

Change $12\frac{1}{2}\%$ to a fraction.

EXAMPLE 5

The Ring of Fire contains 75% of the volcanoes on Earth. Express this percent as a fraction. (*Source:* nationalgeographic.com)

Ring of Fire

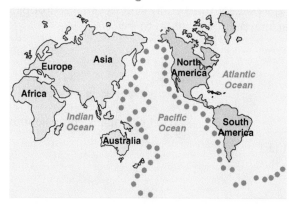

Solution $75\% = \dfrac{75}{100} = \dfrac{3}{4}$

So $\dfrac{3}{4}$ of the volcanoes on Earth are located in the Ring of Fire.

PRACTICE 5

Rwanda is the first country where more than half of the members of the legislature (56%) are women. Express this percent as a fraction. (*Source: Top 10 of Everything, 2010*)

Changing a Percent to a Decimal

Now, let's consider rewriting a percent as a decimal. For instance, take 75%. We begin by writing this percent as a fraction.

$$75\% = \frac{75}{100}$$

Converting this fraction to a decimal, we divide:

$$100\overline{)75.00}^{\,0.75}$$

Note that we could have gotten this answer simply by moving the decimal point two places to the left and dropping the % sign.

$$75\% = 75.\% = .75, \text{ or } 0.75$$

This example suggests the following rule:

To Change a Percent to the Equivalent Decimal

- Drop the % sign from the given percent and divide the number by 100.

EXAMPLE 6

Change 42% to a decimal.

Solution   Drop the % sign from 42% and divide by 100. Recall that to divide a decimal by 100, we can simply move the decimal point two places to the left.

$$42\% = 42.\% = .42, \text{ or } 0.42$$

So the decimal equivalent of 42% is 0.42.

PRACTICE 6

Express 31% as a decimal.

TIP   A shortcut for changing a percent to its equivalent decimal is dropping the percent sign and moving the decimal point *two places* to the *left*.

EXAMPLE 7

Find the decimal equivalent of 1%.

Solution   The unwritten decimal point lies to the right of the 1. Moving the decimal point two places to the left and dropping the % sign, we get:

$$1\% = 01.\% = .01, \text{ or } 0.01$$

Note that we inserted a 0 as a placeholder, because there was only a single digit to the left of the decimal point.

PRACTICE 7

What decimal is equivalent to 5%?

EXAMPLE 8

Convert 37.5% to a decimal.

Solution $37.5\% = .375$, or 0.375

In this problem, the given number is a percent even though it involves a decimal point.

PRACTICE 8

Rewrite 48.2% as a decimal.

EXAMPLE 9

Change $12\frac{1}{2}\%$ to a decimal.

Solution To find the decimal equivalent of $12\frac{1}{2}\%$,

we begin by converting the fraction $\frac{1}{2}$ in the mixed number to its decimal equivalent 0.5. Then, we move the decimal point to the left two places, dropping the % sign.

$$\frac{1}{2} = 2\overline{)1.0}^{\,0.5,\,\text{or}\,.5}$$

$$12\frac{1}{2}\% = 12.5\% = .125, \text{ or } 0.125$$

PRACTICE 9

Express the following percent as a decimal: $62\frac{1}{4}\%$.

EXAMPLE 10

In 1945 at the end of World War II, the public debt of the United States was 602% of what it had been in 1940. Write this percent as a decimal.

Solution $602\% = 602.\%$, or 6.02

The 1945 U.S. debt was 6.02 times what it had been 5 years earlier.

PRACTICE 10

In 1991, the movie sequel *Highlander II* was released and grossed 163.7% of what *Highlander I* had made five years earlier. Express this percent as a decimal. (*Source: Top 10 of Everything, 2010*)

Changing a Decimal to a Percent

Suppose that we want to change 0.75 to a percent. Because 100% is the same as 1, we can multiply this number by 100% without changing its value.

$$0.75 \times 100\% = 75\%$$

We could have gotten this answer simply by moving the decimal point to the right two places and adding the % sign.

$$0.75 = 075.\% = 75\%$$

Note that we dropped the decimal point in the answer because it was to the right of the units digit.

To Change a Decimal to the Equivalent Percent

• Multiply the number by 100 and insert a % sign.

EXAMPLE 11

Write 0.425 as a percent.

Solution We multiply 0.425 by 100 and add a % sign.

$$0.425 = 0.425 \times 100\% = 42.5\%, \text{ or } 42\frac{1}{2}\%$$

PRACTICE 11

What percent is equivalent to the decimal 0.025?

TIP A shortcut for changing a decimal to its equivalent percent is inserting a % sign and moving the decimal point *two places* to the *right*.

EXAMPLE 12

Convert 0.03 to a percent.

Solution $0.03 = 003.\% = 3\%$

PRACTICE 12

Change 0.09 to a percent.

EXAMPLE 13

Express 0.1 as a percent.

Solution   In the given number, only a single digit is to the right of the decimal point. So to move the decimal point two places to the right, we need to insert a 0 as a placeholder.

$$0.1 = 0.10 = 10.\% = 10\%$$

PRACTICE 13

What percent is equivalent to 0.7?

EXAMPLE 14

What percent is equivalent to 2?

Solution   Recall that a whole number such as 2 has a decimal point understood to its right. We move the decimal point two places to the right.

$$2 = 2. = 2.00 = 200.\% = 200\%$$

So the answer is 200%, which makes sense: 200% is double 100%, just as 2 is double 1.

PRACTICE 14

Rewrite 3 as a percent.

EXAMPLE 15

Express 0.2483 as a percent, rounded to the nearest whole percent.

Solution   First, we obtain the exact percent equivalent.

$$0.2\underset{\smile}{4}83 = 24.83\%$$

To round this number to the nearest whole percent, we underline the digit 4. Then, we check the critical digit immediately to its right. This digit is 8, so we round up.

$$2\underline{4}.83\% \approx 25.\% = 25\%$$

PRACTICE 15

Convert 0.714 to a percent, rounded to the nearest whole percent.

EXAMPLE 16

Red blood cells make up about 0.4 of the total blood volume in the human body, whereas 55% of the total blood volume is plasma. Which makes up more of the blood volume—red blood cells or plasma? Explain. (*Source:* Mayo Clinic)

Solution   We want to compare the decimal 0.4 and the percent 55%. One way is to change the decimal to a percent.

$$0.4 = 0.\underset{\smile}{40} = 40.\% = 40\%$$

Since 40% is less than 55%, we conclude that plasma makes up more of the blood volume.

PRACTICE 16

Air is a mixture of many gases. For example, 0.78 of air is nitrogen, and 0.93% is argon. Is there more nitrogen or argon in air? Explain.

Changing a Fraction to a Percent

Now, let's change a fraction to a percent. Consider, for instance, the fraction $\frac{1}{5}$. To convert this fraction to a percent, multiply $\frac{1}{5}$ by 100%, which is equal to 1.

$$\frac{1}{5} = \frac{1}{5} \times 100\% = \frac{1}{\overset{}{\underset{1}{5}}} \times \frac{\overset{20}{\cancel{100}}}{1}\% = 20\%$$

To Change a Fraction to the Equivalent Percent

- Multiply the fraction by 100%.

EXAMPLE 17

Rewrite $\dfrac{7}{20}$ as a percent.

Solution   To change the given fraction to a percent, we multiply by 100%.

$$\frac{7}{20} = \frac{7}{20} \times 100\% = \frac{7}{\underset{1}{20}} \times \frac{\overset{5}{100}}{1}\% = 35\%$$

PRACTICE 17

Convert $\dfrac{4}{25}$ to a percent.

EXAMPLE 18

Which is larger: 130% or $1\dfrac{3}{8}$?

Solution   To compare, let's express $1\dfrac{3}{8}$ as a percent.

$$1\frac{3}{8} = 1\frac{3}{8} \times 100\% = \frac{11}{8} \times \frac{100}{1}\%$$

$$= \frac{11}{\underset{2}{8}} \times \frac{\overset{25}{100}}{1}\% = \frac{275}{2}\% = 137\frac{1}{2}\%$$

Because $137\dfrac{1}{2}\%$ is larger than 130%, so is $1\dfrac{3}{8}$.

PRACTICE 18

True or false: $\dfrac{2}{3} > 60\%$. Justify your answer.

EXAMPLE 19

A student got 28 of 30 questions correct on a test. If all the questions were equal in value, what was the student's grade, rounded to the nearest whole percent?

Solution   The student answered $\dfrac{28}{30}$ of the questions right. To find the student's grade, we change this fraction to a percent.

$$\frac{28}{30} = \frac{28}{30} \times 100\% = \frac{28}{\underset{3}{30}} \times \frac{\overset{10}{100}}{1}\%$$

$$= \frac{280}{3}\% = 93\frac{1}{3}\% = 93.3\ldots\% \approx 93\%$$

Note that the critical digit is 3, so we round down. The rounded grade was therefore 93%.

PRACTICE 19

An administrative assistant spends $490 out of her monthly salary of $1,834 on rent. What percent of her monthly salary is spent on rent, rounded to the nearest whole percent?

Mathematically Speaking

Fill in each blank with the most appropriate term or phrase from the given list.

right	fraction	percent	divide
decimal	left	whole number	multiply

1. A(n) _____ is a ratio or fraction with denominator 100.

2. To change a percent to the equivalent _____, drop the % sign from the given percent, and place the number over 100.

3. To change a percent to the equivalent decimal, move the decimal point two places to the _____ and drop the % sign.

4. To change a fraction to the equivalent percent, _____ the fraction by 100 and insert a % sign.

A *Change each percent to a fraction or mixed number. Simplify.*

5. 8%

6. 3%

7. 250%

8. 110%

9. 33%

10. 41%

11. 18%

12. 44%

13. 14%

14. 45%

15. 65%

16. 92%

17. $\frac{3}{4}\%$

18. $\frac{1}{10}\%$

19. $\frac{3}{10}\%$

20. $\frac{1}{5}\%$

21. $7\frac{1}{2}\%$

22. $2\frac{1}{2}\%$

23. $14\frac{2}{7}\%$

24. $28\frac{4}{7}\%$

Convert each percent to a decimal.

25. 6%

26. 9%

27. 72%

28. 25%

29. 0.1%

30. 0.2%

31. 102%

32. 113%

33. 42.5%

34. 10.5%

35. 500%

36. 400%

37. $106\frac{9}{10}\%$

38. $201\frac{1}{10}\%$

39. $3\frac{1}{2}\%$

40. $2\frac{4}{5}\%$

41. $\frac{9}{10}\%$

42. $\frac{7}{10}\%$

43. $\frac{3}{4}\%$

44. $\frac{1}{4}\%$

B *Express each decimal as a percent.*

45. 0.31

46. 0.37

47. 0.17

48. 0.18

49. 0.3

50. 0.4

51. 0.04

52. 0.05

53. 0.125

54. 0.875

55. 1.29

56. 1.07

57. 2.9

58. 3.5

59. 2.87

60. 3.62

61. 1.016

62. 1.003

63. 9

64. 7

Change each fraction to a percent.

65. $\dfrac{3}{10}$

66. $\dfrac{1}{2}$

67. $\dfrac{1}{10}$

68. $\dfrac{3}{20}$

69. $\dfrac{4}{25}$

70. $\dfrac{6}{25}$

71. $\dfrac{9}{10}$

72. $\dfrac{7}{10}$

73. $\dfrac{3}{50}$

74. $\dfrac{1}{50}$

75. $\dfrac{5}{9}$

76. $\dfrac{2}{9}$

77. $\dfrac{1}{9}$

78. $\dfrac{4}{7}$

79. 6

80. 8

81. $1\dfrac{1}{2}$

82. $2\dfrac{3}{5}$

83. $2\dfrac{1}{6}$

84. $1\dfrac{1}{3}$

Replace ▢ *with* < *or* >.

85. $2\dfrac{1}{4}$ ▢ 240%

86. $3\dfrac{5}{6}$ ▢ 380%

87. $\dfrac{1}{2}\%$ ▢ 50%

88. $\dfrac{1}{40}$ ▢ $\dfrac{1}{4}\%$

Express as a percent, rounded to the nearest whole percent.

89. $\dfrac{4}{9}$

90. $\dfrac{3}{7}$

91. 2.2469

92. 1.1633

Complete each table.

93.

Fraction	Decimal	Percent
		$33\dfrac{1}{3}$
	0.666 …	
	0.25	
		75%
		20%
$\dfrac{2}{5}$		
	0.6	

94.

Fraction	Decimal	Percent
	0.8	
$\dfrac{1}{6}$		
$\dfrac{5}{6}$		
		12.5%
	0.375	
		$62\dfrac{1}{2}\%$
	0.875	

Mixed Practice

Solve.

95. Change 104% to a mixed number.

96. What percent is equivalent to $\dfrac{2}{5}$?

97. Express $3\dfrac{1}{6}$ as a percent.

98. Express $62\dfrac{1}{2}\%$ as a fraction.

99. Convert 27.5% to a decimal.

100. Find the decimal equivalent to $\dfrac{3}{8}\%$.

101. What percent is equivalent to 3.1?

102. Change 0.003 to a percent.

103. Which is smaller, $2\frac{5}{9}$ or 254%?

104. Express 1.2753 to the nearest whole percent.

Applications

⊙ *Solve.*

105. It is estimated that 96% of all e-mail messages received are *spam* (unsolicited junk e-mail). Express this percent as a decimal. (*Source:* govtech.com)

106. According to a recent study, 65% of children have had an imaginary companion by age 7. Express this percent as a fraction. (*Source:* uwnews.org)

107. The following graph shows the percent of people in the United States who get their local news regularly from various sources.

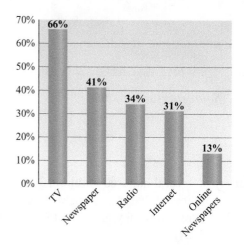

Regular Sources of Local News

(*Source:* people-press.org)

What fraction of people in the U.S. do *not* get their news regularly from TV?

108. The following graph shows the distribution of investments for a retiree. Express as a decimal the percent of investments that are in equities.

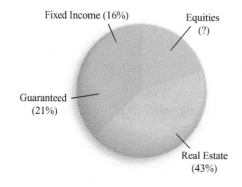

109. According to the nutrition label, one large egg contains 6 grams of protein. This is 10% of the daily value (DV) for protein. Express this percent as a fraction.

110. A bank offers a Visa credit card with a fixed annual percentage rate (APR) of 16.99%. Express the APR as a decimal.

111. Los Angeles has an area 10.05 times that of San Francisco. Express this decimal as a percent. (*Source:* U.S. Census Bureau)

112. In France, the main source of electricity is nuclear power. In a recent year, more than $\frac{3}{4}$ of the country's total electrical production was nuclear. Write this fraction as a percent. (*Source:* International Atomic Energy Agency)

113. When the recession ended, the factory's output grew by 135%. Write this percent as a simplified mixed number.

114. According to a survey, 78% of the arguments that couples have are about money. Express this percent as a decimal.

115. According to a recent U.S. Bureau of Labor Statistics report, 51.5% of all union members are government employees. Convert this percent to a decimal. (*Source:* rsc.tomprice.house.gov)

116. After an oil spill, 15% of the wildlife survived. Express this percent as a fraction.

117. The World Health Organization estimates that in developed countries, $\frac{1}{4}$ of women and 42% of men smoke. In these countries, is smoking more common among women or among men? Explain. (*Source:* americanheart.org)

118. The state sales tax rate in Indiana is 7%, whereas in Iowa it is $\frac{3}{50}$. Which state has a lower sales tax rate? Explain. (*Source:* taxadmin.org)

119. A quality control inspector found 2 defective machine parts out of 500 manufactured.
   a. What percent of the machine parts manufactured were defective?
   b. What percent of the machine parts manufactured were not defective?

120. In a survey of several hundred children, 3 out of every 25 children indicated that they wanted to become professional athletes when they grow up. (*Source: National Geographic Kids*)
   a. What percent of the children wanted to become professional athletes?
   b. What percent of the children did not want to become professional athletes?

121. In the 2008 U.S. presidential election, 131,257,328 people turned out to vote. At the time, there were 189,844,867 registered voters. What percent of the registered voters, to the nearest whole percent, voted? (*Sources:* fec.gov and eac.gov)

122. The first Social Security retirement benefits were paid in 1940 to Ida May Fuller of Vermont. She had paid in a total of $24.85 and got back $20,897 before her death in 1975. Express the ratio of what she got back to what she put in as a percent, rounded to the nearest whole percent. (*Source:* James Trager, *The People's Chronology*)

• Check your answers on page A-8.

MINDStretchers

Mathematical Reasoning

1. By mistake, you move the decimal point to the right instead of to the left when changing a percent to a decimal. Your answer is how many times as large as the correct answer?

Writing

2. A study of the salt content of seawater showed that the average salt content varies from 33‰ to 37‰, where the symbol ‰ (read "per mil") means "for every thousand." Explain why you think the scientist who wrote this study did not use the % symbol.

Critical Thinking

3. What percent of the region shown is shaded in?

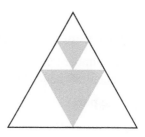

Cultural Note

Throughout history, the concepts of percent and taxation have been interrelated. At the peak of the Roman Empire, the Emperor Augustus instituted an inheritance tax of 5% to provide retirement funds for the military. Another emperor, Julius Caesar, imposed a 1% sales tax on the population. And in Roman Asia, tax collectors exacted a tithe of 10% on crops. If landowners could not pay, the collectors offered to lend them funds at interest rates that ranged from 12% up to 48%.

Roman taxation served as a model for modern countries when these countries developed their own systems of taxation many centuries later.

Sources: Frank J. Swetz, *Capitalism and Arithmetic: The New Math of the 15th Century,* Open Court, 1987; Carolyn Webber and Aaron Wildavsky, *A History of Taxation and Expenditure in the Western World,* Simon and Schuster, 1986.

6.2   Solving Percent Problems

The Three Basic Types of Percent Problems

Frequently, we think of a percent not in isolation but rather in connection with another number. In other words, we take *a percent of a number*.

Consider, for example, the problem of taking 50% of 8. This problem is equivalent to finding $\frac{1}{2}$ of 8, which gives us 4.

Note that this percent problem, like all others, involves three numbers.

$$50\% \quad \text{of} \quad 8 \quad \text{is} \quad 4.$$

Percent   Base   Amount

- The 50% is called the **percent** (or the **rate**). The percent always contains the % sign.
- The 8 is called the **base**. The base of a percent—the number that we are taking the percent of—always follows the word *of* in the statement of the problem.
- The remaining number 4 is called the **amount** (or the **part**).

Percent problems involve finding one of the three numbers. For example, if we omit the 4 in "50% of 8 is 4," we ask the question: What is 50% of 8? Omitting the 8, we ask: 50% of what number is 4? And omitting the 50%, we ask: What percent of 8 is 4?

There are several ways to solve these three basic percent questions. In this section, we discuss two ways—the translation method and the proportion method.

The Translation Method

In the translation method, a percent problem has the form

The percent of the base is the amount.

The percent problem gives only two of the three quantities. To find the missing quantity using the translation method, we translate to a simple equation that we then solve.

This method depends on translating the words in the given problem to the appropriate mathematical symbols.

Word(s)	Math Symbol
What, what number, what percent	*x* (or some other letter)
is	=
of	× or ·
percent, %	Percent value expressed as a decimal or fraction

Let's translate several percent problems to equations.

EXAMPLE 1

Translate each question to an equation, using the translation method.

a. What is 10% of 2?   **b.** 20% of what number is 5?

c. What percent of 8 is 4?

Solution

a. In this problem, we are looking for the amount.

What is 10% of 2?
↓ ↓ ↓ ↓ ↓
$x = 0.1 \cdot 2$

b. Here, we are looking for the base, that is, the number after the word *of*.

20% of what number is 5?
↓ ↓ ↓ ↓ ↓
$0.2 \cdot x = 5$

c. This problem asks "what percent?" So we are looking for the percent.

What percent of 8 is 4?
↓ ↓ ↓ ↓
$x \cdot 8 = 4$

Finding an Amount

Now, let's apply the translation method to solve the type of percent problem in which we are given both the percent and the base and are looking for the amount.

EXAMPLE 2

What is 25% of 8?

Solution First, we translate the question to an equation.

What is 25% of 8?
↓ ↓ ↓ ↓ ↓
$x = \dfrac{1}{4} \cdot 8$

Then, we solve this equation:

$$x = \frac{1}{4} \cdot 8 = \frac{1}{4} \cdot \frac{\overset{2}{\cancel{8}}}{1} = \frac{2}{1}$$
$$= 2$$

So 2 is 25% of 8. Would we have gotten the same answer if we had translated 25% to 0.25?

EXAMPLE 3

Find 200% of 30.

Solution We can reword the problem as a question.

What is 200% of 30?
↓ ↓ ↓ ↓ ↓
$x = 2 \cdot 30$

Solving this equation, we get $x = 60$. So 200% of 30 is 60.

> **TIP** When the percent is less than 100%, the amount is *less* than the base. When the percent is more than 100%, the amount is *more* than the base.

EXAMPLE 4

What is $66\frac{2}{3}\%$ of 15?

Solution First, let's change the percent to a fraction:

$$66\frac{2}{3}\% = \frac{66\frac{2}{3}}{100}$$

$$= 66\frac{2}{3} \div \frac{100}{1}$$

$$= \frac{\overset{2}{\cancel{200}}}{3} \times \frac{1}{\underset{1}{\cancel{100}}} = \frac{2}{3}$$

Translating the question to an equation, we get:

$$
\begin{array}{ccccc}
\text{What} & \text{is} & 66\frac{2}{3}\% & \text{of} & 15? \\
\downarrow & \downarrow & \downarrow & \downarrow & \downarrow \\
x & = & \frac{2}{3} & \cdot & 15
\end{array}
$$

$$= \frac{2}{\underset{1}{\cancel{3}}} \cdot \overset{5}{\cancel{15}} = \frac{10}{1} = 10$$

So $66\frac{2}{3}\%$ of 15 is 10.

PRACTICE 4

Find $33\frac{1}{3}\%$ of 600.

EXAMPLE 5

A marketing account manager has 3.5% of her monthly salary put into a 401(k) plan. How much did she put into the 401(k) plan if her monthly salary is $3,200?

Solution We are looking for the monthly amount placed into the 401(k) plan, which is 3.5% of $3,200.

$$
\begin{array}{ccccc}
\text{What} & \text{is} & 3.5\% & \text{of} & \$3,200? \\
\downarrow & \downarrow & \downarrow & \downarrow & \downarrow \\
x & = & (0.035) & \cdot & (3,200) \\
& = & 112
\end{array}
$$

So she has $112 per month put into the 401(k) plan. Note that this amount has the same unit (dollars) as the base.

PRACTICE 5

Of the 600 workers at a factory, 8.5% belong to a union. How many workers are in the union?

Finding a Base

Now, let's consider some examples of using the translation method to find the base when we know the percent and the amount.

EXAMPLE 6

4% of what number is 8?

Solution   We begin by writing the appropriate equation.

4%	of	what number	is	8?
↓	↓	↓	↓	↓
0.04	·	x	=	8

Next, we solve this equation.

$$0.04x = 8$$

$$\frac{0.04}{0.04}x = \frac{8}{0.04} \qquad \text{Divide each side by 0.04.}$$

$$x = \frac{8}{0.04} = 200 \qquad 0.04\overline{)8.00} = 4\overline{)800.}^{\;200.}$$

So 4% of 200 is 8.

PRACTICE 6

6 is 12% of what number?

EXAMPLE 7

108 is 120% of what number?

Solution   We consider the following question:

120%	of	what number	is	108?
↓	↓	↓	↓	↓
1.2	·	x	=	108

Solving, we get:

$$1.2x = 108$$

$$\frac{1.2}{1.2}x = \frac{108}{1.2}$$

$$x = 90$$

So 108 is 120% of 90.

PRACTICE 7

250% of what number is 18?

EXAMPLE 8

A college awarded financial aid to 3,843 students, which was 45% of the total number of students enrolled at the college. What was the student enrollment at the college?

Solution   We must answer the following question:

45%	of	what number	is	3,843?
↓	↓	↓	↓	↓
0.45	·	x	=	3,843

Next, we solve the equation.

$$0.45x = 3,843$$

$$\frac{0.45x}{0.45} = \frac{3,843}{0.45}$$

$$x = 8,540$$

So 8,540 students were enrolled at the college.

PRACTICE 8

There was a glut of office space in a city, with 400,000 square feet, or 16% of the total office space, vacant. How much office space did the city have?

Finding a Percent

Finally, let's look at the third type of percent problem, in which we are given the base and the amount and are looking for the percent.

EXAMPLE 9

What percent of 80 is 60?

Solution We begin by writing the appropriate equation.

$$\text{What percent} \quad \text{of} \quad 80 \quad \text{is} \quad 60?$$
$$\downarrow \qquad\qquad \downarrow \quad \downarrow \quad \downarrow$$
$$x \qquad \cdot \quad 80 \quad = \quad 60$$

$$80x = 60 \qquad \text{Write the equation in standard form.}$$

$$\frac{80}{80}x = \frac{60}{80} \qquad \text{Divide each side by 80.}$$

$$x = \frac{\overset{3}{\cancel{60}}}{\underset{4}{\cancel{80}}} = \frac{3}{4} \qquad \text{Simplify.}$$

Since we are looking for a percent, we change $\dfrac{3}{4}$ to a percent. So 75% of 80 is 60.

$$x = \frac{3}{4} = \frac{3}{\cancel{4}} \cdot \frac{\overset{25}{\cancel{100}}}{1}\% = 75\%$$

PRACTICE 9

What percent of 6 is 5?

EXAMPLE 10

What percent of 60 is 80?

Solution We begin by writing the appropriate equation, as shown to the right.

$$\text{What percent} \quad \text{of} \quad 60 \quad \text{is} \quad 80?$$
$$\downarrow \qquad\qquad \downarrow \quad \downarrow \quad \downarrow$$
$$x \qquad \cdot \quad 60 \quad = \quad 80$$

$$60x = 80$$

$$\frac{60}{60}x = \frac{80}{60}$$

$$x = \frac{\overset{4}{\cancel{80}}}{\underset{3}{\cancel{60}}} = \frac{4}{3}$$

Finally, we want to change $\dfrac{4}{3}$ to a percent.

$$x = \frac{4}{3} = \frac{4}{3} \cdot \frac{100}{1}\% = \frac{400}{3}\% = 133\frac{1}{3}\%$$

So $133\frac{1}{3}\%$ of 60 is 80.

PRACTICE 10

What percent of 8 is 9?

EXAMPLE 11

A young couple buys a house for $125,000, making a down payment of $25,000 and paying the difference over time with a mortgage. What percent of the cost of the house was the down payment?

Solution We write the question as shown to the right.

What percent of $125,000 is $25,000?

$$x \cdot 125{,}000 = 25{,}000$$

$$125{,}000x = 25{,}000$$

$$\frac{\cancel{125{,}000}}{\cancel{125{,}000}}x = \frac{25{,}000}{125{,}000}$$

$$x = \frac{25}{125} = \frac{1}{5}$$

Next, we change $\frac{1}{5}$ to a percent.

$$x = \frac{1}{5} = \frac{1}{\cancel{5}} \cdot \frac{\overset{20}{\cancel{100}}}{1}\% = 20\%$$

So the down payment was 20% of the total cost of the house.

PRACTICE 11

Of the 400 acres on a farm, 120 were used to grow corn. What percent of the total acreage was used to grow corn?

The Proportion Method

So far, we have used the translation method to solve percent problems. Now, let's consider an alternative approach, the proportion method.

Using the proportion method, we view a percent relationship in the following way.

$$\frac{\text{Amount}}{\text{Base}} = \frac{\text{Percent}}{100}$$

If we are given two of the three quantities, we set up this proportion and then solve it to find the third quantity.

EXAMPLE 12

What is 60% of 35?

Solution The base (the number after the word *of*) is 35. The percent (the number followed by the % sign) is 60. The amount is unknown. We set up the proportion, substitute into it, and solve.

$$\frac{\text{Amount}}{\text{Base}} = \frac{\text{Percent}}{100}$$

$$\frac{x}{35} = \frac{60}{100}$$

$$100x = 60 \cdot 35 \qquad \text{Set cross products equal.}$$

$$\frac{\cancel{100}}{\cancel{100}}x = \frac{2{,}100}{100} \qquad \text{Divide each side by 100.}$$

$$x = 21$$

So 60% of 35 is 21.

PRACTICE 12

Find 108% of 250.

EXAMPLE 13

15% of what number is 21?

Solution   Here, the number after the word *of* is missing, so we are looking for the base. The amount is 21, and the percent is 15. We set up the proportion, substitute into it, and solve.

$$\frac{\text{Amount}}{\text{Base}} = \frac{\text{Percent}}{100}$$

$$\frac{21}{x} = \frac{15}{100}$$

$$15x = 2{,}100 \qquad \text{Set cross products equal.}$$

$$\frac{\cancel{15}}{\cancel{15}}x = \frac{2{,}100}{15} \qquad \text{Divide each side by 15.}$$

$$x = 140$$

So 15% of 140 is 21.

PRACTICE 13

2% of what number is 21.6?

EXAMPLE 14

What percent of $45 is $30?

Solution   We know that the base is 45, the amount is 30, and we are looking for the percent.

$$\frac{30}{45} = \frac{x}{100}$$

$$45x = 3{,}000$$

$$\frac{\cancel{45}}{\cancel{45}}x = \frac{3{,}000}{45}$$

$$x = 66\frac{2}{3}$$

So we conclude that $66\frac{2}{3}\%$ of $45 is $30.

PRACTICE 14

What percent of 63 is 21?

EXAMPLE 15

A car depreciated, that is, dropped in value, by 20% during its first year. By how much did the value of the car decline if it cost $30,500 new?

Solution   The question here is: What is 20% of $30,500? So the percent is 20, the base is $30,500 and we are looking for the amount. We set up the proportion and solve.

$$\frac{x}{30{,}500} = \frac{20}{100}$$

$$100x = 610{,}000$$

$$\frac{\cancel{100}}{\cancel{100}}x = \frac{610{,}000}{100}$$

$$x = 6{,}100$$

So the value of the car depreciated by $6,100.

PRACTICE 15

A credit card company requires a minimum payment of 4% of the balance. What is the minimum payment if the credit card balance is $2,450?

EXAMPLE 16

Each day, an adult takes tablets containing 24 milligrams of zinc. If this amount is 160% of the recommended daily allowance, how many milligrams are recommended? (*Source: Podiatry Today*)

Solution Here, we are looking for the base. The question is: 160% of what amount is 24 milligrams? We set up the proportion and solve.

$$\frac{24}{x} = \frac{160}{100}$$
$$160x = 2{,}400$$
$$\frac{160}{160}x = \frac{2{,}400}{160}$$
$$x = 15$$

Therefore, the recommended daily allowance of zinc is 15 milligrams. Note that this base is less than the amount (24 milligrams). Why must that be true?

PRACTICE 16

According to a newspaper article, a Nobel Prize winner had to pay the Internal Revenue Service $129,200— or 38% of his prize—in taxes. How much was his Nobel Prize worth?

EXAMPLE 17

A college accepted 1,620 of the 4,500 applicants for admission. What was the acceptance rate, expressed as a percent?

Solution The question is: What percent of 4,500 is 1,620?

$$\frac{1{,}620}{4{,}500} = \frac{x}{100}$$
$$4{,}500x = 162{,}000$$
$$\frac{4{,}500}{4{,}500}x = \frac{162{,}000}{4{,}500}$$
$$x = 36$$

So the college's acceptance rate was 36%.

PRACTICE 17

A bookkeeper's annual salary was raised from $38,000 to $39,900. What percent of her original annual salary is her new annual salary?

Percents on a Calculator

Many calculators have a percent key (%), sometimes used with the 2nd function (2nd). However, the percent key functions differently on different models. Check to see if the following approach works on your machine. If it does not, experiment to find an approach that does.

EXAMPLE 18

Use a calculator to find 50% of 8.

Solution

Press	Display
50 2nd % × 8 ENTER	50% * 8
	4.

PRACTICE 18

What is 8.25% of $72.37, to the nearest cent?

Mathematically Speaking

Fill in each blank with the most appropriate term or phrase from the given list.

amount	of	base
is	what	percent

1. The _____ is the number that we are taking the percent of.

2. The _____ is the result of taking the percent of the base.

3. The _____ of the base is the amount.

4. In the translation method of solving a percent problem, _____ is replaced by a multiplication symbol.

A *Find the amount.*

5. What is 75% of 8?

6. What is 50% of 48?

7. Compute 100% of 23.

8. Compute 200% of 6.

9. Find 41% of 7.

10. Find 6% of 9.

11. What is 35% of $400?

12. What is 40% of 10 miles?

13. What is 3.1% of 20?

14. What is 0.5% of 7?

15. Compute 1.8% of 2.5.

16. Compute 3.5% of 4.6.

17. Compute $\frac{1}{2}$% of 20.

18. Compute $\frac{1}{10}$% of 35.

19. What is $12\frac{1}{2}$% of 32?

20. What is $66\frac{2}{3}$% of 33?

21. What is $7\frac{1}{8}$% of $257.13, rounded to the nearest cent?

22. What is 8.9% of 7,325 miles, rounded to the nearest mile?

Find the base.

23. 25% of what number is 8?

24. 30% of what number is 120?

25. $12 is 10% of how much money?

26. $195 is 1% of what salary?

27. 5 is 200% of what number?

28. 14 is 200% of what number?

29. 2% of what amount of money is $5?

30. 20% of how many meters is 8 meters?

31. 15 is $33\frac{1}{3}$% of what number?

32. 85 is $8\frac{1}{2}$% of what number?

33. 3.5 is 200% of what number?

34. 8.1 is 150% of what number?

35. 0.5% of what number is 23?

36. 0.75% of what number is 24?

37. 0.12% of what number is 3.6?

38. 0.25% of what number is 100.4?

39. 6.5% of how much money is $3,200, rounded to the nearest cent?

40. 4,718 is $2\frac{1}{8}$% of what number?

Find the percent.

41. 50 is what percent of 100?

42. 13 is what percent of 52?

43. What percent of 8 is 6?

44. What percent of 50 is 20?

45. What percent of 12 is 10?

46. What percent of 15 is 5?

47. 2 miles is what percent of 8 miles?

48. $16 is what percent of $20?

49. $30 is what percent of $20?

50. 10 is what percent of 8?

51. 9 feet is what percent of 8 feet?

52. 35¢ is what percent of 21¢?

53. 2.5 is what percent of 4?

54. 1.4 is what percent of 8?

55. $1.80 is what percent of $3.60?

56. What percent of 0.3 is 1.5?

57. What percent of 251,749 is 76,801, rounded to the nearest percent?

58. 8,422 is what percent of 11,630, to the nearest percent?

Mixed Practice

Solve.

59. Compute $37\frac{1}{2}\%$ of 160.

60. Calculate 0.01% of 55, rounded to the nearest hundredth.

61. What percent of 15 is 10?

62. What percent of 20 is 30?

63. 20% of what distance is 35 miles?

64. 2.5% of what is 32?

65. 3 feet is what percent of 60 feet?

66. Find 7.2% of $300.

67. 4% of what amount of money is $20?

68. $24 is what percent of $300?

69. What is 40% of 25?

70. $\frac{3}{4}\%$ of what number is 60?

Applications

B *Solve.*

71. During a tournament, a golfer made par on 12 of 18 holes. On what percent of the holes on the course did she make par?

72. In the first quarter of last year, a steel mill produced 300 tons of steel. If this was 20% of the year's output, find that output.

73. A student answered 90% of the questions on a math exam correctly. If she answered 36 questions correctly, how many questions were on the exam?

74. A property management company sold 80% of the condominium units in a new building with 90 units. How many units were sold?

75. Payroll deductions comprise 40% of the gross income of a student working part-time. If his deductions total $240, what is his gross income?

76. In 1862, the U.S. Congress enacted the nation's first income tax, at the rate of 3%. How much in income tax would you have paid if you made $2,500? (*Source:* U.S. Bureau of the Census)

77. According to the report on a country's economic conditions, 1.5 million people, or 8% of the workforce, were unemployed. How large was the workforce?

78. A recipe for cattle feed calls for 1,200 pounds of corn, 400 pounds of oats, 200 pounds of protein, 100 pounds of beet pulp, 75 pounds of cottonseed hulls, and 25 pounds of molasses. What percent of this mixture is corn? (*Source:* cattlepages.com)

79. In basketball, a foul shot is called a *free throw*. The recipient of the most valuable player award on a college basketball team made 75% of 96 free throw attempts. How many free throws did he make? (*Source:* wikipedia.org)

80. According to a recent telephone survey, 424 thousand out of 673 thousand adults interviewed in the U.S. were either overweight or obese. What percent of interviewees, to the nearest whole percent, were either overweight or obese? (*Source:* webmd.com)

81. Flexible-fuel vehicles run on E85, an alternative fuel that is a blend of ethanol and gasoline containing 85% ethanol. How much ethanol is in 12 gallons of E85?

82. Of the 80 classrooms on a community college campus, 75% are equipped with whiteboards. How many classrooms have whiteboards?

83. A company's profits amounted to 10% of its sales. If the profits were $3 million, compute the company's sales.

84. In a recent survey of U.S. colleges, the average tuition and fees at private four-year colleges was approximately $20 thousand, in contrast to about $2 thousand for public two-year colleges. The second figure is what percent of the first figure? (*Source: The Chronicle of Higher Education Almanac*)

85. A math lab coordinator is willing to spend up to 25% of her income on housing. What is the most she can spend if her annual income is $36,000?

86. An office supply warehouse shipped 648 cases of copy paper. If this represents 72% of the total inventory, how many cases of paper did the warehouse have in its inventory?

87. A lab technician mixed 36 milliliters of alcohol with 84 milliliters of water to make a solution. What percent of the solution was alcohol?

88. A shopper lives in a town where the sales tax is 5%. Across the river, the tax is 4%. If it costs her $6 to make the round trip across the river, should she cross the river to buy a $250 television set?

89. The following graph shows the breakdown of the projected U.S population by gender in the year 2020. If the population is expected to be 340 million people, how many more women than men will there be in 2020? (*Source:* census.gov)

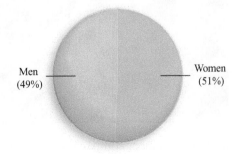

Men (49%)   Women (51%)

90. The graph gives the use of the Internet by U.S. adults, according to a recent national survey. All percents are rounded to the nearest whole percent.

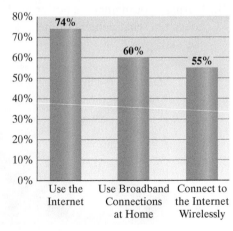

The survey involved tracking a sample of 2,258 adults. How many more adults in this sample use broadband connections at home than those who connect to the internet wirelessly? (*Source:* pewinternet.org)

91. In a company, 85% of the employees are female. If 765 males work for the company, what is the total number of employees?

93. The state of Michigan has an urban population of about 8 million people, with the remaining population of 2 million people living in rural areas. (*Source:* ers.usda.gov)
   a. Approximately what is the total population of Michigan?
   b. Approximately what percent of Michigan's population is urban?

92. A quarterback completed 15 passes or 20% of his attempted passes. How many of his attempted passes did he *not* complete?

94. A homeowner builds a family room addition on his 1,650-square-foot house, increasing the area of the house by 495 square feet.
   a. Calculate the total area of the house with the addition.
   b. What percent of the original area is the total area?

• Check your answers on page A-8.

MIND*Stretchers*

Writing

1. Do you prefer solving percent problems using the translation method or the proportion method? In a few sentences, explain why.

Critical Thinking

2. At a college, 20% of the women commute, in contrast to 30% of the men. Yet more women than men commute. Explain how this result is possible.

Technology

3. On the web, go to the U.S. Bureau of the Census home page (census.gov). Write a percent problem of interest to you involving data from the site, and solve the problem.

6.3 More on Percents

OBJECTIVES

A To solve percent increase or decrease problems

B To solve percent problems involving taxes, commissions, or discounts

C To solve simple or compound interest problems

D To solve applied problems involving percents

Finding a Percent Increase or Decrease

Next, let's consider a type of "what percent" problem that deals with a *changing quantity*. If the quantity is increasing, we speak of a *percent increase*; if it is decreasing, of a *percent decrease*.

Here is an example: Last year, a family paid $2,000 in health insurance, and this year, their health insurance bill was $2,500. By what percent did this expense increase?

Note that this problem states the value of a quantity at two points in time. We are asked to find the percent increase between these two values.

To solve, we first compute the difference between the values, that is, between the *new value* and the *original value*.

$$2{,}500 \quad - \quad 2{,}000 \quad = \quad 500$$

New value   Original value   Change in value

The question posed is expressed as follows:

What percent   of   2,000   is   500?

$$x \quad \cdot \quad 2{,}000 \quad = \quad 500$$

It is important to note that the *base* here—as in all percent change problems—is the original value of the quantity.

Next, we solve the equation.

$$2{,}000x = 500$$

$$\frac{2{,}000}{2{,}000}x = \frac{500}{2{,}000}$$

$$x = \frac{1}{4} = 0.25, \text{ or } 25\%$$

So we conclude that the family's health insurance expense *increased* by 25%.

To Find a Percent Increase or Decrease

- Compute the difference between the new and the original values.

- Compute what percent this difference is of the original value.

EXAMPLE 1

The cost of a marriage license had been $10. Later it rose to $15. What percent increase was this?

PRACTICE 1

To accommodate a flood of tourists, businesses in town boosted the number of hotel beds from 25 to 100. What percent increase is this?

Solution The original cost of the license was $10, and the new cost was $15. The change in cost is, therefore, $15 − $10, or $5. So the question is as follows:

What percent of $10 is $5?

$$x \cdot 10 = 5$$

$$10x = 5$$

$$\frac{\overset{1}{\cancel{10}}}{\cancel{10}}x = \frac{\overset{1}{\cancel{5}}}{\underset{2}{\cancel{10}}}$$

$$x = \frac{1}{2} = 0.5, \text{ or } 50\%$$

So the cost of the license increased by 50%.

EXAMPLE 2

Suppose that an animal species is considered to be endangered if its population drops by more than 60%. If a species' population fell from 40 to 18, should we consider the animal endangered?

Solution The population dropped from 40 to 18, that is, by 22. The question is how the percent decrease compares with 60%. We compute.

What percent of 40 is 22?

$$x \cdot 40 = 22$$

$$40x = 22$$

$$x = \frac{22}{40} = \frac{11}{20} = 0.55, \text{ or } 55\%$$

Since the population decreased by less than 60%, the species is not considered to be endangered.

PRACTICE 2

Major financial crashes took place on both Tuesday, October 29, 1929, and Monday, October 19, 1987. On the earlier date, the stock index dropped from 300 to 230. On the latter date, it dropped from 2,250 to 1,750. As a percent, did the stock index drop more in 1929 or in 1987? (*Source: The Wall Street Journal*)

Business Applications of Percent

The idea of percent is fundamental to business and finance. Percent applications are part of our lives whenever we buy or sell merchandise, pay taxes, and borrow or invest money.

Taxes

Governments levy taxes to pay for a variety of services, from supporting schools to paving roads. There are many kinds of taxes, including sales, income, property, and import taxes.

In general, the amount of a tax that we pay is a percent of a related value. For instance, sales tax is usually computed as a percent of the price of merchandise sold. Thus, in a town where the sales tax rate is 7%, we could compute the tax on any item sold by computing 7% of the price of that item.

Similarly, property tax is commonly computed by taking a given percent (the tax rate) of the property's assessed value. And an import tax is calculated by taking a specified percent of the market value of the imported item.

EXAMPLE 3

The sales tax on a $950 digital camcorder is $71.25. What is the sales tax rate, expressed as a percent?

Solution   We must consider the following question:

$$71.25 \quad \text{is} \quad \text{what percent} \quad \text{of} \quad 950?$$

$$71.25 \quad = \quad x \quad \cdot \quad 950$$

$$950x = 71.25$$

$$\frac{950x}{950} = \frac{71.25}{950}$$

$$x = 0.075, \text{ or } 7.5\%$$

So the rate of the sales tax is 7.5%, or $7\frac{1}{2}\%$.

PRACTICE 3

When registering a new car, the owner paid a 2.5% import tax on the purchase price of $18,500. How much import tax did he pay? (*Source:* justlanded.com)

Commission

To encourage salespeople to make more sales, many of them, instead of receiving a fixed salary, are paid on *commission*. Working on commission means that the amount of money that they earn is a specified percent—say, 10%—of the total sales for which they are responsible. Often salespeople make a flat fee in addition to a commission based on sales.

EXAMPLE 4

The owner of a condo in San Diego sold it for $222,000. On this amount, she paid a real estate agent a commission of 6%.

a. Find the amount of the commission.

b. How much money did the owner make from the sale after paying the agent's fee?

Solution

a. The commission is 6% of $222,000.

$$\text{What} \quad \text{is} \quad 6\% \quad \text{of} \quad \$222,000?$$

$$x \quad = \quad 0.06 \quad \cdot \quad 222,000 = 13,320$$

So the commission amounted to $13,320.

b. The seller made $222,000 − $13,320, or $208,680.

PRACTICE 4

A sales associate at a furniture store is paid a base monthly salary of $1,500. In addition, she earns a 9% commission on her monthly sales. If her total sales this month is $12,500, calculate

a. her commission, and

b. her total monthly income.

Discount

In buying or selling merchandise, the term *discount* refers to a reduction on the merchandise's original price. The rate of discount is usually expressed as a percent of the original price.

EXAMPLE 5

A drugstore gives senior citizens a 10% discount. If some pills normally sell for $16 a bottle, how much will a senior citizen pay?

Solution   Note that, because senior citizens get a discount of 10%, they pay 100% − 10%, or 90%, of the normal price.
   The question then becomes:

$$\text{What} \quad \text{is} \quad 90\% \quad \text{of} \quad \$16?$$
$$x \quad = \quad 0.9 \quad \cdot \quad 16 = 14.4$$

So a senior citizen will pay $14.40 for a bottle of the pills.
   Note that another way to solve this problem is first to compute the amount of the discount (10% of $16) and then to subtract this discount from the original price. With this approach, do we get the same answer?

PRACTICE 5

Find the sale price.

FAMOUS DESIGNER JEANS
REGULARLY $87
20% OFF
TODAY ONLY

Simple Interest

Anyone who has been late in paying a credit card bill or who has deposited money in a savings account knows about *interest*. When we lend or deposit money, we make interest. When we borrow money, we pay interest.
   Interest depends on the amount of money borrowed (the *principal*), the annual rate of interest (usually expressed as a percent), and the length of time the money is borrowed (usually expressed in years). We can compute the amount of interest by multiplying the principal by the rate of interest and the number of years. This type of interest is called *simple interest* to distinguish it from *compound interest* (which we discuss later).

EXAMPLE 6

How much simple interest is earned in 1 year on a principal of $900 at an annual interest rate of 6.5%?

Solution   To compute the interest, we multiply the principal by the rate of interest and the number of years.

$$\underset{\text{Principal}}{} \quad \underset{\substack{\text{Rate of} \\ \text{Interest}}}{} \quad \underset{\substack{\text{Number} \\ \text{of Years}}}{}$$
$$\text{Interest} = 900 \times 0.065 \times 1$$
$$= 58.5$$

So $58.50 in interest is earned.

PRACTICE 6

What is the simple interest on an investment of $20,000 for 1 year at an annual interest rate of 7.25%?

EXAMPLE 7

A customer deposited $825 in a savings account that each year pays 5% in simple interest, which is credited to his account. What is the account balance after 2 years?

Solution   To solve this problem, let's break it into two questions:

- How much interest did the customer make after 2 years?
- What is the sum of the original deposit and that interest?

First, let's find the interest. To do this, we multiply the principal by the rate of interest and the number of years.

$$\text{Interest} = \overset{\text{Principal}}{(825)} \, \overset{\text{Rate of Interest}}{(0.05)} \, \overset{\text{Number of Years}}{(2)}$$
$$= 82.50$$

The customer made $82.50 in interest.

Now, let's find the account balance by adding the amount of the original deposit to the interest made.

$$\text{Account Balance} = \overset{\text{Original Deposit}}{825} + \overset{\text{Interest}}{82.50}$$
$$= 907.50$$

So the account balance after 2 years is $907.50

PRACTICE 7

A bank account pays 6% simple interest on $1,600 for 2 years. Compute the account balance after 2 years.

Compound Interest

As we have seen, simple interest is based on the principal. Most banks, however, pay their customers *compound interest*, which is based on both the principal and the previous interest generated.

For instance, suppose that a bank customer has $1,000 deposited in a savings account that pays 5% interest compounded annually. There were no withdrawals or other deposits. Let's compute the balance in the account at the end of the third year.

The following table shows the account balance after the customer has left the money in the account for 3 years. After 1 year, the account will contain $1,050 (that is, 100% of the original $1,000 added to 5% of $1,000, giving us 105% of $1,000).

Year	Balance at the End of the Year
0	$1,000
1	$1,000 + 0.05 × $1,000 = $1,050.00
2	$1,050 + 0.05 × $1,050 = $1,102.50
3	$1,102.50 + 0.05 × $1,102.50 ≈ $1,157.63

The balance in the account after the third year is $1,157.63, rounded to the nearest cent.

Alternatively, for each year we can multiply the account balance by 1.05 to compute the balance at the end at the next year.

Year	Balance at the End of the Year
0	$1,000
1	1.05 × $1,000 = $1,050.00
2	$(1.05)^2 × $1,000 = $1,102.50
3	$(1.05)^3 × $1,000 ≈ $1,157.63

Note that the balance at the end of the third year is $(1.05)^3 \times \$1,000$, or $\$1,157.63$, in agreement with our previous computation. What would the balance be at the end of the fourth year? What is the relationship between the number of years the money has been invested and the power of 1.05?

In computing the preceding answer, we needed to raise the number 1.05 to a power. Before scientific calculators became available, compound interest problems were commonly solved by use of a compound interest table that contained information such as the following:

Number of Years	4%	5%	6%	7%
1	1.04000	1.05000	1.06000	1.07000
2	1.08160	1.10250	1.12360	1.14490
3	1.12486	1.15763	1.19102	1.22504

When using such a table to calculate a balance, we simply multiply the principal by the number in the table corresponding to the rate of interest and the number of years for which the principal is invested. For instance, after 3 years a principal of $1,000 compounded at 5% per year results in a balance of $1.15763 \times 1,000$, or $\$1,157.63$, as we previously noted.

Today, problems of this type are generally solved on a calculator.

EXAMPLE 8

A couple deposited $7,000 in a bank account and did not make any withdrawals or deposits in the account for 3 years. The interest is compounded annually at a rate of 3.5%. What will be the amount in their account at the end of this period?

Solution   Each year, the amount in the account is $100\% + 3.5\%$, or 1.035 times the previous year's balance. So at the end of 3 years, the number of dollars in the account is calculated as follows:

$$\begin{matrix} & & \text{First} & \text{Second} & \text{Third} \\ \text{Principal} & & \text{Year} & \text{Year} & \text{Year} \\ \downarrow & & \downarrow & \downarrow & \downarrow \\ 7,000 & \times & 1.035 & \times\ 1.035 & \times\ 1.035 \end{matrix}$$

It makes sense to use a calculator to carry out this computation. One way to key in this computation on a calculator is as follows.

Press	Display
7000 $\boxed{\times}$ 1.035 $\boxed{\wedge}$ 3 $\boxed{\text{ENTER}}$	7000 * 1.035 ^ 3
	7761.025 125

So at the end of 3 years, they have $7,761.03 in the account, rounded to the nearest cent.

PRACTICE 8

Find the balance after 4 years on a principal amount of $2,000 invested at a rate of 6% compounded annually.

Mathematically Speaking

Fill in each blank with the most appropriate term or phrase from the given list.

discount	on salary	on commission
interest	simple	compound
final	original	

1. When computing a percent increase or decrease, the _____ value is used as the base of the percent.

2. Sellers who are paid a fixed percent of the sales for which they are responsible are said to work _____.

3. A reduction on the price of merchandise is called a(n) _____.

4. When interest is paid on both the principal and the previous interest generated, it is called _____ interest.

A *Find the percent increase or decrease.*

5.

Original Value	New Value	Percent Increase or Decrease
$10	$12	
$10	$8	
$6	$18	
$35	$70	
$14	$21	
$10	$1	
$8	$6.50	
$6	$5.25	

6.

Original Value	New Value	Percent Increase or Decrease
$5	$6	
$12	$10	
$4	$9	
$25	$45	
$10	$36	
$100	$20	
4 ft	3 ft	
8 lb	4.5 lb	

B *Compute the sales tax. Round to the nearest cent.*

7.

Selling Price	Rate of Sales Tax	Sales Tax
$30.00	5%	
$24.88	3%	
$51.00	$7\frac{1}{2}\%$	
$196.23	4.5%	

8.

Selling Price	Rate of Sales Tax	Sales Tax
$40.00	6%	
$16.98	4%	
$85.00	$5\frac{1}{2}\%$	
$286.38	5%	

Compute the commission. Round to the nearest cent.

9.

Sales	Rate of Commission	Commission
$700	10%	
$450	2%	
$870	$4\frac{1}{2}\%$	
$922	7.5%	

10.

Sales	Rate of Commission	Commission
$400	1%	
$670	3%	
$610	$6\frac{1}{2}\%$	
$2,500	8.25%	

Compute the discount and sale price. Round to the nearest cent.

11.

Original Price	Rate of Discount	Discount	Sale Price
$700.00	25%		
$18.00	10%		
$43.50	20%		
$16.99	5%		

12.

Original Price	Rate of Discount	Discount	Sale Price
$200.00	30%		
$21.00	50%		
$88.88	10%		
$72.50	40%		

C *Calculate the simple interest and the final balance. Round to the nearest cent.*

13.

Principal	Interest Rate	Time (in years)	Interest	Final Balance
$300	4%	2		
$600	7%	2		
$500	8%	2		
$375	10%	4		
$1,000	3.5%	3		
$70,000	6.25%	30		

14.

Principal	Interest Rate	Time (in years)	Interest	Final Balance
$100	6%	5		
$800	4%	5		
$500	3%	10		
$800	6%	10		
$250	1.5%	2		
$300,000	4.25%	20		

Calculate the final balance after compounding the interest annually. Round to the nearest cent.

15.

Principal	Interest Rate	Time (in years)	Final Balance
$500	4%	2	
$6,200	3%	5	
$300	1%	8	
$20,000	4%	2	
$145	3.8%	3	
$810	2.9%	10	

16.

Principal	Interest Rate	Time (in years)	Final Balance
$300	6%	1	
$2,900	5%	4	
$800	3%	5	
$10,000	3%	4	
$250	1.1%	2	
$200	3.3%	5	

Mixed Practice

Complete each table. Round to the nearest whole percent.

17.

Original Value	New Value	Percent Decrease
$5	$4.50	

18.

Original Value	New Value	Percent Increase
$220	$300	

Complete each table. Round to the nearest cent.

19.

Original Price	Rate of Discount	Discount	Sale Price
$87.33	40%		

20.

Assessed Value of a House	Rate of County Property Tax	County Property Tax
$150,000	0.9475%	

21.

Selling Price	Rate of Sales Tax	Sales Tax
$200	7.25%	

22.

Sales	Rate of Commission	Commission
$537.14	10%	

23.

Principal	Interest Rate	Kind of Interest	Time (in years)	Interest	Final Balance
$3,000	5%	simple	5		

24.

Principal	Interest Rate	Kind of Interest	Time (in years)	Final Balance
$259.13	5.8%	compound annually	12	

Applications

D *Solve.*

25. An upscale department-store chain reported that total sales this year were $2.3 billion—up from $1.8 billion last year. Find the percent increase in sales, to the nearest whole percent.

26. Last year, a local team won 20 games. This year, it won 15 games. What was the percent decrease of games won?

27. In 9 years, the number of elderly nursing home residents rose from 200,000 to 1.3 million. By what percent did the number of residents increase?

28. Due to a decrease in demand, a manufacturing plant decreased its production from 2,400 to 1,800 units per day. What was the percent decrease in the number of units produced per day?

29. The first commercial telephone exchange was set up in New Haven, Connecticut, in 1878. Between 1880 and 1890, the number of telephones in the United States increased from 50 thousand to 200 thousand, in round numbers. What percent increase was this? (*Source:* census.gov)

30. A patient's medication was decreased from 250 milligrams to 200 milligrams per dose. What was the percent decrease in the dosage?

31. A customer paid 5% sales tax on a notebook computer that sold for $1,699. Calculate the amount of sales tax that she paid.

32. Last year, a town assessed the value of a residential property at $272,000. If the homeowner paid property tax of $3,264, what was the property tax rate?

33. A customer bought a cell phone for $150. The total selling price of the phone, including sales tax, was $159.75. What was the sales tax rate?

34. In a town, the sales tax rate is 7%. It costs $5 to travel to a nearby town and back where the sales tax is only 5.8%. Is it worthwhile to make this trip to purchase an item that sells in both towns for $800?

35. A pharmaceutical sales representative earns a 12% monthly commission on all her sales above $5,000. Find her commission if her sales this month totaled $27,500.

36. A sales assistant earns a flat salary of $150 plus a 10% commission on sales of $3,000. What were his total earnings?

37. On a restaurant table, a customer leaves $1.35 as a tip. Assuming that the customer left a 15% tip, how much was the bill before the tip?

38. A salesperson receives a 5% commission on the first $2,000 in sales and a 7% commission on sales above $2,000. How much commission does she earn on sales of $3,500?

39. A coupon for an online sporting goods company gives customers a discount on any order. The discounted price on a tennis racquet that normally sells for $180 is $153. What percent is the discount? (*Source:* sportsauthority.com)

40. A car rental company gives members of the organization AARP a 5% discount on standard rates. For a car that ordinarily rents for $43.84 per day, what is the daily rate, to the nearest cent, after the AARP discount? (*Source:* enterprise.com)

41. A store sells a television that lists for $399 at a 35% discount rate. What is the sale price?

42. An appliance store has a sale on all its appliances. A washing machine that originally sold for $800 is on sale for $680. What is the discount rate?

43. A bank customer borrowed $3,000 for 1 year at 5% simple interest to buy a computer. How much interest did the customer pay?

44. How much simple interest is earned on $600 at an 8% annual interest rate for 2 years?

45. A couple deposited $5,000 in a bank. How much interest will they have earned after 1 year if the interest rate is 5%?

46. A student borrowed $2,000 from a friend, agreeing to pay her 4% simple interest. If he promised to repay her the entire amount at the end of 3 years, how much money must he pay her?

47. At a home goods store, a customer bought a down comforter that originally cost $180.

   a. What was the sale price of the comforter?
   b. Calculate the total amount the customer paid after 6% sales tax was added to the purchase.

48. During a sale, a shoe store marked down the price of a pair of sneakers that originally cost $80 by 40%.

   a. What was the sale price of the sneakers?
   b. After two weeks, the store marked down the sale price by another 60%. What percent off the original price was the sale price after the second discount was applied?

49. An investor put $3,000 in an account that pays 4% interest, compounded annually. Find the amount in the account after 2 years.

50. A bank pays 4.5% interest, compounded annually, on a 2-year certificate of deposit (CD) that initially costs $500. What is the value of the CD at the end of the 2 years, rounded to the nearest cent?

51. A city had a population of 4,000. If the city's population increased by 10% per year, what was the population 4 years later?

52. An art dealer bought a painting for $10,000. If the value of the painting increased by 50% per year, what was its value 4 years later?

      • Check your answers on page A-8.

MIND*Stretchers*

Writing

1. Explain the difference between simple interest and compound interest.

Technology

2. Using a spreadsheet, construct a three-column table showing the original price, the 10% discount, and the selling price for items with an original price of any whole number of dollars between $1 and $100.

Mathematical Reasoning

3. If a quantity increases by a given percent and then decreases by the same percent, will the final value be the same as the original value? Explain.

Key Concepts and Skills

Concept/Skill	Description	Example
[6.1] **Percent**	A ratio or fraction with denominator 100. It is written with the % sign, which means divided by 100.	$7\% = \dfrac{7}{100}$ ↑ Percent
[6.1] **To change a percent to the equivalent fraction**	• Drop the % sign from the given percent and place the number over 100. • Simplify the resulting fraction, if possible.	$25\% = \dfrac{25}{100} = \dfrac{1}{4}$
[6.1] **To change a percent to the equivalent decimal**	• Drop the % sign from the given percent and divide the number by 100.	$23.5\% = .235,\text{ or } 0.235$
[6.1] **To change a decimal to the equivalent percent**	• Multiply the number by 100 and insert a % sign.	$0.125 = 12.5\%$
[6.1] **To change a fraction to the equivalent percent**	• Multiply the fraction by 100%.	$\dfrac{1}{5} = \dfrac{1}{5} \times 100\% = \dfrac{1}{\overset{}{5}} \times \dfrac{\overset{20}{100}}{1}\%$ $= 20\%$
[6.2] **Base**	The number that we are taking the percent of. It always follows the word *of* in the statement of a percent problem.	50% of 8 is 4. ↑ Base
[6.2] **Amount**	The result of taking the percent of the base.	50% of 8 is 4. ↑ Amount
[6.2] **To solve a percent problem using the translation method**	• Translate as follows: What number, what percent → x is → $=$ of → $\times$ or $\cdot$ % → decimal or fraction • Set up the equation. The percent of the base is the amount. • Solve.	What is 50% of 8? ↓ ↓ ↓ ↓ ↓ x $=$ 0.5 $\cdot$ 8 $x = 4$ 30% of what number is 6? ↓ ↓ ↓ ↓ ↓ 0.3 $\cdot$ x $=$ 6 $\dfrac{0.3x}{0.3} = \dfrac{6}{0.3}$ $x = \dfrac{6}{0.3} = 20$ What percent of 8 is 2? ↓ ↓ ↓ ↓ x $\cdot$ 8 $=$ 2 $8x = 2$ $x = \dfrac{2}{8} = \dfrac{1}{4} = 25\%$

continued

Concept/Skill	Description	Example
[6.2] **To solve a percent problem using the proportion method**	• Identify the amount, the base, and the percent, if known. • Set up and substitute into the proportion. $$\frac{\text{Amount}}{\text{Base}} = \frac{\text{Percent}}{100}$$ • Solve for the unknown quantity.	50% of 8 is what number? $$\frac{x}{8} = \frac{50}{100}$$ $$100x = 400$$ $$x = 4$$ 30% of what number is 6? $$\frac{6}{x} = \frac{30}{100}$$ $$30x = 600$$ $$x = 20$$ What percent of 8 is 2? $$\frac{2}{8} = \frac{x}{100}$$ $$8x = 200$$ $$x = 25$$ So the answer is 25%.
[6.3] **To find a percent increase or decrease**	• Compute the difference between the new and the original values. • Determine what percent this difference is of the original value.	Find the percent increase for a quantity that changes from 4 to 5. Difference: $5 - 4 = 1$ What percent of 4 is 1? $\downarrow$ $\downarrow$ $\downarrow$ $\downarrow$ $\downarrow$ x $\cdot$ 4 $=$ 1 $$x = \frac{1}{4} = 0.25, \text{ or } 25\%$$

CHAPTER 6   Review Exercises

Say Why
Fill in each blank.

1. $129\frac{1}{2}\%$ and $\dfrac{129\frac{1}{2}}{100}$ _____ equivalent because
   $\underset{\text{are/are not}}{}$

   _____

   _____ .

2. $\dfrac{1}{2}$ and $\dfrac{1}{2}\%$ _____ equivalent because _____
   $\underset{\text{are/are not}}{}$

   _____

   _____ .

3. In "50% of 8 is 4", 8 _____ the base because
   $\underset{\text{is/is not}}{}$

   _____

   _____ .

4. In "50% of 8 is 4", 50 _____ the amount because
   $\underset{\text{is/is not}}{}$

   _____

   _____ .

5. The base of a percent _____ always larger than the
   $\underset{\text{is/is not}}{}$
   amount because _____

   _____ .

6. If 5% of a number is 20, then that number _____
   $\underset{\text{is/is not}}{}$
   greater than 20 because _____

   _____

   _____ .

7. 100% of a number _____ equal to that number
   $\underset{\text{is/is not}}{}$
   because _____

   _____ .

8. If a quantity doubles in value between two points
   in time, then the percent increase _____ 200%
   $\underset{\text{is/is not}}{}$
   because _____

   _____ .

[6.1] *Complete the following tables.*

9.

Fraction	Decimal	Percent
$\frac{1}{4}$		
	0.7	
		$\frac{3}{4}\%$
$\frac{5}{8}$		
		41%
$1\frac{1}{100}$		
		260%
	3.3	
	0.12	
		$66\frac{2}{3}\%$
$\frac{1}{6}$		

10.

Fraction	Decimal	Percent
$\frac{3}{8}$		
	0.49	
		0.1%
		150%
	0.875	
		$83\frac{1}{3}\%$
$2\frac{3}{4}$		
	1.2	
	0.75	
		10%
$\frac{1}{3}$		

[6.2] *Solve.*

11. What is 40% of 30?

12. What percent of 5 is 6?

13. 2 feet is what percent of 4 feet?

14. 30% of what number is 6?

15. What percent of 8 is 3.5?

16. Find 55% of 10.

17. $12 is 200% of what amount of money?

18. 2 is what percent of 10?

19. What is 1.2% of 25?

20. Find 115% of 400.

21. 35% of $200 is what?

22. $\frac{1}{2}$% of what number is 5?

23. 15 is what percent of 0.75?

24. 4.5 is what percent of 18?

25. Calculate $33\frac{1}{3}$% of $600.

26. What percent of $9 is $4?

27. Find 60% of $20.

28. 2.5% of how much money is $40?

29. What percent of $7.99 is $1.35, to the nearest whole percent?

30. 3.5 is $8\frac{1}{4}$% of what number, to the nearest hundredth?

[6.3] *Complete the following tables.*

31.

Original Value	New Value	Percent Decrease
24	16	

32.

Original Value	New Value	Percent Decrease
360 mi	300 mi	

33.

Selling Price	Rate of Sales Tax	Sales Tax
$50	6%	

34.

Sales	Rate of Commission	Commission
$600	4%	

35.

Original Price	Rate of Discount	Discount	Sale Price
$200	15%		

36.

Principal	Interest Rate	Time (in years)	Simple Interest	Final Balance
$200	4%	2		

Mixed Applications

Solve.

37. A compact fluorescent light bulb (CFL) will last up to 8,000 hours. If another CFL lasts 25% longer, what is the life of this bulb? (*Sources:* smarthome.com and bulbs.com)

38. Jonas Salk developed the polio vaccine in 1954. The number of reported polio cases in the United States dropped from 29,000 to 15,000 between 1955 and 1956. What was the percent drop, to the nearest whole percent? (*Source:* census.gov)

39. For their fees, one real estate agent charges 11% of a year's rent and another charges the first month's rent. Which agent charges more?

40. A particular community bank makes available loans with simple interest. How much interest is due on a five-year car loan of $24,000 based on a simple interest rate of 6%?

41. According to a city survey, 49% of respondents approve of how the mayor is handling his job and 31% disapprove. What percent neither approved nor disapproved?

42. Plastics make up about 11% and paper makes up $\frac{9}{25}$ of the solid municipal waste in the United States. Which makes up more of the solid municipal waste? (*Source:* Energy Information Administration)

43. According to a study, 25% of employees do not take all of their vacation time due to the demands of their jobs. Express this percent as a fraction. (*Source:* Families and Work Institute)

44. In a recent year, 16 out of every 25 high school graduates in Ohio took the ACT college entrance exam. Express this fraction as a percent. (*Source: The World Almanac, 2010*)

45. It takes a worker 50 minutes to commute to work. If he has been traveling for 20 minutes, what percent of his trip has been completed?

46. Among left-handed people are a number of U.S. presidents, including Ronald Reagan, George H.W. Bush, Bill Clinton, and Barack Obama. About 3 out of every 20 people are lefties. Express as a percent. (*Sources:* indiana.edu and scientificamerican.com)

47. A couple financed a 30-year mortgage at a fixed interest rate of 6.29%. Express this rate as a decimal.

48. The length of a person's thigh bone is usually about 27% of his or her height. Estimate someone's height whose thigh bone is 20 inches long. (*Source: American Journal of Physical Anthropology*)

49. The following table deals with estimates of the recoverable coal reserves in two states that are leading coal producers.

State	Coal Reserves (in billions of short tons)
West Virginia	17
Illinois	38

The size of West Virginia's reserves is what percent of the size of Illinois' reserves rounded to the nearest percent? (*Source*: nma.org)

50. A clothing store places the following ad in a local newspaper:

At the store, what is the sale price of a suit that regularly sells for $230?

51. The salary of an executive assistant had been $30,000 before she got a raise of $1,000. If the rate of inflation is 5%, has her salary kept pace with inflation?

52. In a scientific study that relates weight to health, people are considered overweight if their actual weight is at least 20% above their ideal weight. If you weigh 160 pounds and have an ideal weight of 130 pounds, are you considered overweight?

53. An airline oversold a flight to Los Angeles by nine seats, or 5% of the total number of seats available on the airplane. How many seats does the airplane have?

54. When an assistant became editor, the magazine's weekly circulation increased from 50,000 to 60,000. By what percent did the circulation increase?

55. The winner of a men's U.S. Open tennis match got $87\frac{1}{2}\%$ of his first serves in. If he had 72 first serves, how many went in?

56. According to a recent survey, there are approximately 78 million owned dogs and 94 million owned cats in the United States. The number of dogs is what percent of the number of cats, to the nearest percent? (*Source:* humanesociety.org)

57. At an auction, a bidder bought a table for $150. The auction house also charged a "buyer's premium"—an extra fee—of 10%. How much did the bidder pay in all?

58. According to the news report, 80 tons of food met only 20% of the food needs in the refugee camp. How much additional food was needed?

59. A traveler needs 14,000 more frequent-flier miles to earn a free trip to Hawaii, which is 20% of the total number needed. How many frequent-flier miles in all does this award require?

60. The sales tax rate on a flat panel TV bought in New Orleans is 9%. What was the selling price (not including the sales tax) if the sales tax amounted to $53.91? (*Source:* forbes.com)

61. A sales representative for wholesale products earned $49,000 per year plus 10% commission on sales totaling $25,000. What was his total income for the year?

62. At the end of the year, the receipts of a retail store amounted to $200,000. Of these receipts, 85% went for expenses; the rest was profit. How much profit did the store make?

63. If a bank customer deposits $7,000 in a bank account that pays a 5.5% rate of interest compounded annually, what will be the balance after 2 years?

64. Suppose that a country's economy expands by 2% per year. By what percent will it expand in 10 years, to the nearest whole percent?

65. Complete the following table which shows the net income for Texas Instruments Inc. in four consecutive quarters.

Quarter Ending	Income (in millions of dollars)	Percent of Total Income (rounded to the nearest tenth of a percent)
Jun 30, 2009	260	
Sep 30, 2009	538	
Dec 31, 2009	655	
Mar 31, 2010	658	
Total		

(*Source:* finance.yahoo.com)

66. The following graph shows the sources from which the federal government received income in a recent year:

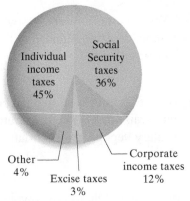

If the total amount of money taken in was $2,500 billion, compute how much money was received from each source, to the nearest billion dollars. (*Source:* taxpolicycenter.org)

• Check your answers on page A-9.

CHAPTER 6   Posttest

FOR EXTRA HELP

CHAPTER Test Prep VIDEOS

The Chapter Test Prep Videos with test solutions are available on DVD, in MyMathLab, and on YouTube (search "AkstBasicMath" and click on "Channels").

To see if you have mastered the topics in this chapter, take this test.

Rewrite.

1. 4% as a fraction

2. $27\frac{1}{2}\%$ as a fraction

3. 174% as a decimal

4. 8% as a decimal

5. 0.009 as a percent

6. 10 as a percent

7. $\frac{5}{6}$ as a percent, rounded to the nearest whole percent

8. $2\frac{1}{5}$ as a percent

Solve.

9. What is 25% of 30 miles?

10. Find 120% of 40.

11. 3% of what number is 9?

12. 8% of what number is 16?

13. What percent of 10 is 6?

14. What percent of 4 is 10?

15. To pay for tuition, a college student borrows $2,000 from a relative for 2 years at 5% simple interest. Find the amount of simple interest that is due.

16. In a parking lot that has 150 spaces, 4% are for handicap parking. How many handicap spaces are in the lot?

17. A customer paid $14.95 in sales tax on an iPhone that sells for $299 (before tax). What was the sales tax rate?

18. Milk is approximately 50% cream. How much milk is needed to produce 2 pints of cream?

19. For some Broadway and off-Broadway performances, TKTS discount booths sell tickets at 30% off the full price plus a $4 per ticket service charge. What is the total cost of three tickets that sell for $98 at full price? (*Source*: tdf.org)

20. A college ended six straight years of tuition increases by raising its tuition from $3,000 to $3,100. Find the percent increase.

• Check your answers on page A-10.

Cumulative Review Exercises

To help you review, solve the following.

1. Express 10,000,000 as a power of 10.

2. Divide: $1,962 \div 18$

3. Find the sum of $3\frac{4}{5}$ and $1\frac{9}{10}$.

4. Find the difference: $32.25 - 4.68$

5. Multiply: 0.2×3.5

6. Express $\frac{5}{6}$ as a decimal, rounded to the nearest hundredth.

7. Divide, rounding to the nearest hundredth: $5.122 \div 0.7$

8. Translate the phrase "the difference between a number and 6.7" into an algebraic expression.

9. Solve and check: $w + 17\frac{2}{5} = 41$

10. Solve for x: $\frac{x}{3} = 2.5$

11. Write as a unit rate: $327.60 for 40 hours.

12. Solve and check: $\frac{1.2}{x} = \frac{1.8}{21}$

13. Change $18\frac{2}{11}\%$ to a fraction.

14. 20% of what amount is $200?

Solve.

15. The government withdrew $\frac{1}{4}$ million of its 2 million troops. What fraction of the total is this?

16. Three FM stations are highlighted on the radio dial shown. These stations have frequencies 99.5 (WBAI), 104.3 (WAXQ), and 105.9 (WQXR). Label the three stations on the dial.

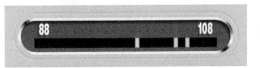

17. At the Westminster Dog Show, the Best in Show prize has been won by terriers three times as often as working group breeds (such as boxers and Great Danes). If terriers have won 45 out of the 103 times that the prize has been awarded, determine how many times working group dogs have won. (*Source*: wikipedia.org)

18. Twitter is a popular social networking service used for tweeting, that is, for sending brief messages. According to a recent survey, 11 of 100 adults who use the internet have tweeted. At this rate among 6,500 such adults, how many would be expected to have tweeted? (*Sources*: wikipedia.org and socialmediatoday.com)

19. In a recent year, about 28% of the 992 thousand U.S. doctors were female. How many female doctors were there, to the nearest thousand? (*Source*: ama.assn.org)

20. Between the years 2010 and 2050, the U.S. population is projected to double. The portion of this population 85 and over is projected to grow more rapidly, increasing from 4 million to 21 million. What percent increase is this? (*Source*: census.gov)

• Check your answers on page A-10.

CHAPTER 7

7.1 **Introduction to Signed Numbers**

7.2 **Adding Signed Numbers**

7.3 **Subtracting Signed Numbers**

7.4 **Multiplying Signed Numbers**

7.5 **Dividing Signed Numbers**

Signed Numbers

Signed Numbers and Chemistry

In chemistry, a valence is assigned to each element in a compound. Valences help us study the ways in which the elements combine to form the compound.

The valence is a positive or negative whole number that expresses the combining capacity of the element. For example in the compound $CaCl_2$ (calcium chloride), the element calcium (Ca) has a valence of $+2$, whereas the element chlorine (Cl) has a valence of -1.

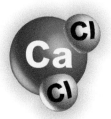

The valences in any chemical compound add up to 0. So if you know how to perform signed number computations, you can predict the chemical formula of any compound.

(*Source:* Karen C. Timberlake, *Basic Chemistry*, Prentice Hall, 2011)

1. Which is larger, -23 or $+7$?

2. A negative number has an absolute value of 4. What is the number?

Compute.

3. $-8 + (-9)$

4. $-20 + 20$

5. $34 - 41$

6. $-9 - (-9)$

7. -5×15

8. -8^2

9. $-\dfrac{3}{4} \times \dfrac{2}{3}$

10. $\left(-\dfrac{1}{2}\right)^2$

11. $-18 \div (-9)$

12. $-1.8 \div (-0.9)$

13. $-2 + 5 + (-3) + 8$

14. $10 + (-3) - (-1)$

15. $-9 - 3^2 \times (-5)$

16. $8 \div (-2) + 3 \cdot (-1)$

Solve.

17. The temperature at noon was 74°F. A cold front moved into the region, causing the temperature to drop an average of 4°F per hour over the next 4 hours. What was the temperature at 4:00 P.M.?

18. A fee of $2.50 is deducted from a student's account each time she uses an ATM on campus. In 1 month, she uses the ATM 7 times. Express as a signed number the impact on her account as a result of the ATM fees.

19. The graph below gives the average December temperatures in degrees Celsius for various cities around the world.

20. The Greek mathematician Pythagoras died about 500 B.C. In the year A.D. 2000, how many centuries had passed since his death? (*Source:* wikipedia.org)

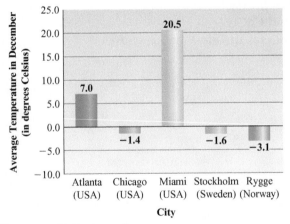

(*Source:* worldclimate.com)

How much greater is the temperature of the warmest city as compared to the coolest city?

• Check your answers on page A-10.

7.1 Introduction to Signed Numbers

OBJECTIVES

Ⓐ Represent signed numbers on the number line

Ⓑ To find the opposite of a signed number

Ⓒ To find the absolute value of a signed number

Ⓓ To compare signed numbers

Ⓔ To solve applied problems involving signed numbers

What Signed Numbers Are and Why They Are Important

In this chapter, we discuss negative numbers and show how they relate to positive numbers—the numbers greater than 0. Negative and positive numbers together are referred to as *signed numbers*.

Here are a few applications of signed numbers.

- In football, a positive number represents yards gained; a negative number, yards lost.
- In terms of time, positive applies to a time after an event took place; negative, to a time before that event.
- In the study of electricity, positive represents one kind of electric charge; negative, the opposite kind of electric charge.

These applications can help you develop intuition in working with signed numbers and understand what they represent.

The Number Line

Our previous discussion of the number line on page 3 included only 0 and the positive numbers. However, the number line can be extended to represent the negative numbers also. If we label the numbers to the right of 0 as positive and extend the line leftward past 0, then we label the numbers to the left of 0 as negative.

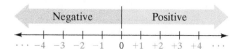

Note that we write "negative two" as -2 and "positive three" as $+3$, or just 3. However, we write no sign before 0 because 0 is neither negative nor positive.

DEFINITIONS

A **positive number** is a number greater than 0.

A **negative number** is a number less than 0.

A **signed number** is a number with a sign that is either positive or negative.

In drawing the number line, we usually label only the integers, that is, the whole numbers and the corresponding negatives.

DEFINITION

The **integers** are the numbers ... , $-4, -3, -2, -1, 0, +1, +2, +3, +4, \ldots$, continuing indefinitely in both directions.

Positive fractions and decimals and their corresponding negatives can also be represented on the number line. Let's look at how to locate the points on the number line that correspond to the numbers $\frac{3}{4}$, 3.8, and -2.4. The following number line shows these locations.

EXAMPLE 1

Locate $\frac{1}{2}$, -2.8, $-\frac{1}{8}$, and 1.2 on the number line.

Solution

PRACTICE 1

Locate $1\frac{9}{10}$, -1, -3.1, and 0 on the number line.

On the number line, we say that -1 and $+1$ (or 1) are the *opposites* of each other. Similarly -50 and $+50$ (or 50) are opposites. What is the opposite of 0?

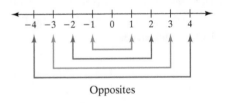

Opposites

DEFINITION

Two numbers that are the same distance from 0 on the number line but on opposite sides of 0 are called **opposites**.

From this definition, we see that opposite numbers have opposite signs.

EXAMPLE 2

Find the opposite of each number in the table.

Solution

Number	Opposite
a. 5	-5
b. $-\frac{1}{2}$	$\frac{1}{2}$
c. 1.5	-1.5
d. -100	100

PRACTICE 2

Find the opposite of each number.

Number	Opposite
a. 9	
b. $-4\frac{9}{10}$	
c. -2.9	
d. 31	

Because the number −2 is negative, it lies 2 units to the left of 0. The number 2, which is positive, lies in the opposite direction: 2 units to the right of 0.

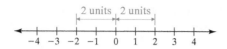

When you locate a number on the number line, the *distance* of that number from 0 is called its *absolute value*. Thus, the absolute value of +2 is 2, and the absolute value of −2 is 2.

DEFINITION

The **absolute value** of a number is its distance from 0 on the number line. The absolute value of a number is represented by the symbol | |.

For example, we write the absolute value of −2 as $|-2|$.

Several properties of absolute value follow from this definition.

- The absolute value of a positive number is the number itself.
- The absolute value of a negative number is its opposite.
- The absolute value of 0 is 0.
- The absolute value of a number is always positive or 0.

These properties help us find the absolute value of any number.

EXAMPLE 3

Compute.

a. $|-8|$ **b.** $|0|$ **c.** $\left|-\dfrac{1}{2}\right|$ **d.** $|5.3|$

Solution

a. Because −8 is negative, its absolute value is its opposite, or 8.

b. The absolute value of 0 is 0.

c. $\dfrac{1}{2}$ **d.** 5.3

PRACTICE 3

Compute.

a. $|9|$ **b.** $\left|1\frac{3}{4}\right|$ **c.** $|-4.1|$ **d.** $|-5|$

EXAMPLE 4

Determine the sign and the absolute value of the number.

a. 25   **b.** −1.9

Solution

a. Sign: +; absolute value: 25

b. Sign: −; absolute value: 1.9

PRACTICE 4

What are the sign and the absolute value of the number?

	Sign	Absolute value
a. −4		
b. $6\frac{1}{2}$		

Comparing Signed Numbers

The number line helps us compare two signed numbers, that is, to decide which number is larger and which is smaller. On the number line, a number to the right is the larger number.

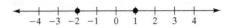

So $1 > -2$.

> ### To Compare Signed Numbers
>
> - Locate the points being compared on the number line; a number to the right is larger than a number to the left.

When comparing signed numbers, remember the following:

- Zero is greater than any negative number because all negative numbers lie to the left of 0.
- Zero is less than any positive number because all positive numbers lie to the right of 0.
- Any positive number is greater than any negative number because all positive numbers lie to the right of all negative numbers.

EXAMPLE 5

Which is larger?

a. $\frac{1}{2}$ or 0   **b.** -1 or -3 **c.** 1.4 or -3

Solution

a. Because $\frac{1}{2}$ (or $+\frac{1}{2}$) is to the right of 0 on the number line, $\frac{1}{2}$ is greater than 0.

b. Because -1 is to the right of -3, $-1 > -3$, that is, -1 is larger.

c. Because 1.4 is to the right of -3, $1.4 > -3$, that is, 1.4 is the larger of the two numbers.

PRACTICE 5

Which is smaller?

a. 0 or 2

b. -5 or -2

c. 2.3 or -4

Now, let's try some practical applications of comparing signed numbers. The key is to be able to determine if a number is negative or positive. You should become familiar with the following words that indicate the sign of a number.

Negative	Positive
Loss	Gain
Below	Above
Decrease	Increase
Down	Up
Withdrawal	Deposit
Past	Future
Before	After

EXAMPLE 6

Express as a signed number: Badwater Basin in Death Valley is the lowest elevation in the Western Hemisphere at 282 feet below sea level. (*Source:* National Park Service)

Solution The number in question represents an elevation below sea level, so we write it as a negative number: -282 feet.

PRACTICE 6

Represent as a signed number: The New York Giants gained 2 yards on a play.

EXAMPLE 7

The following table shows the temperature below which various plants freeze and die.

Plant	Asters	Carnations	Mums
Hardy to	$-20°F$	$-5°F$	$-30°F$

In a very cold climate, which would be planted?
(*Source: The American Horticultural Society A–Z Encyclopedia of Garden Plants*)

Solution First, we compare the temperatures of the asters and the carnations. Because $-20° < -5°$, the asters are hardier than the carnations. Next, we compare the temperatures of the asters and the mums. Because $-20° > -30°$, the mums are hardier. So the mums would be the best of the three to plant.

PRACTICE 7

A student studying astronomy learns that *apparent magnitude* is how bright a star appears when viewed from Earth. The lower the apparent magnitude, the brighter the star appears. The table shows the apparent magnitude for various stars. (*Source: Encyclopedia Britannica Almanac*)

Star	Canopus	Sirius	Alpha Centauri
Apparent Magnitude	-0.72	-1.46	-0.01

Which of these stars is the brightest?

Mathematically Speaking

Fill in each blank with the most appropriate term or phrase from the given list.

larger	smaller	opposites	right
positive number	left	absolute value	integers
signed number	negative number	whole numbers	

1. A number greater than 0 is a(n) _____.

2. A number less than 0 is a(n) _____.

3. A number with a sign that is either positive or negative is called a(n) _____.

4. The _____ are the numbers . . . , −4, −3, −2, −1, 0, 1, 2, 3, 4, . . . , continuing indefinitely in both directions.

5. Two numbers that are the same distance from 0 on the number line but on opposite sides of 0 are called _____.

6. The _____ of a number is its distance from 0 on the number line.

7. For two numbers on the number line, the number on the left is _____ than the number on the right.

8. For two numbers on the number line, the number on the _____ is larger.

Ⓐ *Mark the corresponding point for each number on the number line.*

9. $-2, 2.5, 3$

10. $4, -1, 1.1$

11. $0, -\frac{1}{2}, 1\frac{4}{5}$

12. $-\frac{1}{3}, 2, -3\frac{9}{10}$

Ⓑ *Find the opposite of each number.*

13. 8

14. 3

15. 10.2

16. 8.4

17. -25

18. -5

19. $-5\frac{1}{2}$

20. $-2\frac{1}{3}$

21. -4.1

22. -1.2

23. 0.5

24. 0.8

Ⓒ *Evaluate.*

25. $|-6|$

26. $|-39|$

27. $\left|-\dfrac{4}{5}\right|$

28. $\left|-1\frac{2}{3}\right|$

29. $|2|$

30. $|8|$

31. $|-0.6|$

32. $|-5.8|$

Determine the sign and the absolute value of each number.

	Sign	Absolute Value

33. 8

34. 11

35. −4.3

36. −9.2

37. −7

38. −30

39. $\dfrac{1}{5}$

40. $\dfrac{3}{4}$

Solve.

41. How many numbers have an absolute value of 5?

42. How many numbers have an absolute value of 0.5?

43. Is there a number whose absolute value is −1?

44. Are there three different numbers that have the same absolute value?

D *Circle the larger number in each pair.*

45. −4 and −7

46. −6 and −9

47. 12 and 0

48. 0 and 87

49. −3 and 2

50. −3 and 14

51. −4 and −2$\frac{1}{3}$

52. −6 and −3$\frac{1}{4}$

53. −29 and −2

54. −4 and −27

55. 9 and −22

56. 8 and −15

57. −8 and −2

58. −3 and −14

59. −7 and −7$\frac{1}{4}$

60. −8 and −8$\frac{1}{2}$

61. −8.3 and −8.5

62. −3.9 and −3.4

63. −3$\frac{1}{2}$ and −3$\frac{2}{3}$

64. −7$\frac{1}{2}$ and −7$\frac{1}{4}$

Indicate whether each inequality is true or false.

65. −5 > −7

66. −8 > −9

67. −1 < 3.4

68. −4 < 3.6

69. 0 > −2$\frac{3}{4}$

70. 0 > −5$\frac{3}{4}$

71. 2 > −2

72. 8 > −8

73. −3.5 > −3.4

74. −1.6 < −1.7

75. −4$\frac{1}{3}$ < 0

76. −8$\frac{2}{3}$ < 0

Arrange the numbers in each group from smallest to largest.

77. 3, −3, 0

78. 3.5, −3.1, −3, 0, 4

79. −9, 9, −4.5

80. −2$\frac{1}{2}$, −2, 3, −2.7

Express each quantity as a signed number.

81. A withdrawal of $150 from an account

82. 6 kilometers below sea level

83. A rise in temperature of 14.5°C

84. A gain of 3$\dfrac{1}{4}$ pounds while on a diet

Mixed Practice

Solve.

85. Locate 2$\frac{1}{2}$ and −3.9 on the number line.

86. Find the opposite of −2$\frac{1}{4}$.

87. Write as a signed number:
   a. a withdrawal of $10.98 from a bank account
   b. a deposit of $100 into the account

88. What are the sign and absolute value of the following numbers?
   a. 4   **b.** $-\frac{2}{3}$

	Sign	Absolute Value
a.		
b.		

89. Evaluate: **a.** $|0.5|$ **b.** $|-11|$

90. Which number is larger, -4.95 or -4?

91. Complete using the symbol $<$ or $>$.
   a. -9 ▢ -6 **b.** 0 ▢ $-8\frac{2}{3}$

92. Rewrite -1.7, -2, and $-\frac{3}{4}$ from largest to smallest.

Applications

E *Solve.*

93. The Mariana Trench, the deepest point in the Pacific Ocean, is 11,033 meters below sea level, and the Puerto Rico Trench, the deepest point in the Atlantic Ocean, is 8,648 meters below sea level. Which trench is deeper? (*Source:* marianatrench.com)

94. A small toy company shows a loss of $0.3 million for the second quarter of its business and a loss of $0.9 million for the third quarter. In which quarter did the company show the greater loss?

95. Would a patient be receiving more medication if his dosage is decreased by 50 milligrams or if it is decreased by 25 milligrams?

96. Would a group of passengers be higher if they took the elevator down 2 floors or if they took it down 5 floors?

97. A bone density test is used to determine whether a person has osteoporosis (brittle bone disease). If the result of a bone density test, called the T-score, is below -2.5, then a person has osteoporosis. Does a patient whose T-score is -1.8 have osteoporosis? (*Source:* mayoclinic.com)

98. A bank customer has a checking account with overdraft privileges. The account is currently overdrawn by $109.45. If the customer pays off $100 of the overdraft, will his account still be overdrawn?

99. The following table shows the average surface temperature on several planets.

Planet	Temperature (in degrees Fahrenheit)
Mars	-81
Saturn	-218
Uranus	-323

Which planet is the warmest? (*Source:* nasa.gov)

100. The following graph gives the boiling point (in degrees Celsius) of three liquids.

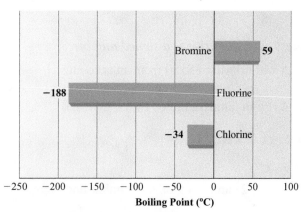

Which of these liquids has the lowest boiling point? (*Source: CRC Handbook of Chemistry and Physics*)

101. In ice hockey, the *plus/minus* statistic is used to rate individual players. If a player is on the ice when *his* team scores a goal, then he gets a *plus* point. If he is on the ice when the *other* team scores a goal, he gets a *minus* point. In theory, the higher a player's plus/minus rating, the better the player. The following table shows an individual hockey player's plus/minus rating for each of the three periods of a certain game. (*Source:* wiki.answers.com)

Period	Plus/Minus Rating
First	−3
Second	1
Third	−2

a. Locate the scores on the number line below. What does 0 on the number line represent?

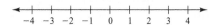

b. In which period were the most goals scored by the other team while the player was on the ice?

102. The following graph shows the estimated change in population of four Midwestern cities during the first decade of the 21st century.

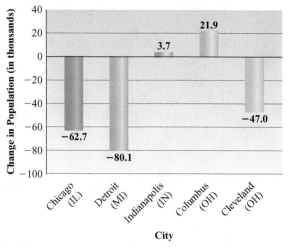

(*Source:* census.gov)

a. Which cities grew in population?

b. Which of the cities had the largest decline in population?

• Check your answers on page A-10.

MINDStretchers

Groupwork

1. a. List several numbers between −2 and −3.

b. How many numbers are there between −2 and −3?

Mathematical Reasoning

2. On the thermometer at the right, highlight all temperatures within 4 degrees of −1°.

Technology

3. Using a computer spreadsheet application such as Microsoft Excel®, enter the numbers

$$-4, 9, 2, 0, -5, -1, 7, 2, 0, 9, 9, 7, -3, -4, 6, 1, 4, 3, 0$$

and sort these numbers in ascending order. Then, sort them in descending order. Is the same number in the middle with both sorts? Explain how you could have predicted this result.

Cultural Note

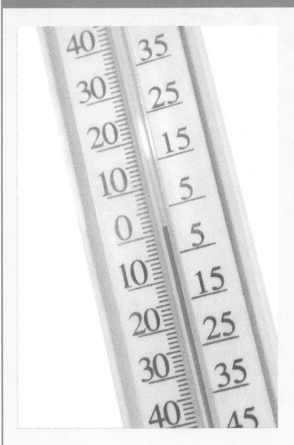

Until the work of sixteenth-century Italian physicists, no one was able to measure temperature. Liquid-in-glass thermometers were invented around 1650, when glassblowers in Florence, Italy, were able to create the intricate shapes that thermometers require. Thermometers from the seventeenth and eighteenth centuries provided a model for working with negative numbers that led to their wider acceptance in the mathematical and scientific communities. Numbers above and below 0 represented temperatures above and below the freezing point of water, just as they do on the Celsius scale today. Before the introduction of these thermometers, a number such as −1 was difficult to interpret for those who believed that the purpose of numbers is to count or to measure.

By contrast, the early Greek mathematicians had rejected negative numbers, calling them absurd. A thousand years later, in the seventh century A.D., the Indian mathematician Brahmagupta argued for accepting negative numbers and put down the first comprehensive rules for computing with them.

Sources: Lancelot Hogben, *Mathematics in the Making* (London: Galahad Books, 1960).

Henri Michel, *Scientific Instruments in Art and History* (New York: Viking Press, 1966).

Calvin C. Clawson, *The Mathematical Traveler* (New York and London: Plenum Press, 1994).

7.2 Adding Signed Numbers

OBJECTIVES

A To add signed numbers

B To solve applied problems involving the addition of signed numbers

Our previous work in addition, subtraction, multiplication, and division was restricted to positive numbers—whether those positive numbers happened to be whole numbers, fractions, or decimals. Now, we consider computations involving *any* signed numbers, starting with the operation of addition.

Suppose that we want to add two negative numbers, say -1 and -2. It is helpful to look at this problem in terms of money. If your hourly wage went down \$1 and down again \$2, altogether it went down \$3. In terms of signed numbers, this example can be expressed as:

$$-1 + (-2) = -3$$

We can also look at this problem on the number line. To add -1 and -2, we start at the point corresponding to the first number, -1. The second number, -2, is *negative*, so we move 2 units to the *left*. We end at -3, which is the answer we expected.

Now, let's consider adding the signed numbers -1 and $+3$. Thinking of this problem in terms of money may make it clearer. If your hourly wage went down \$1 and then up \$3, your total hourly increase is \$2. Using signed numbers, this example can be written as:

$$-1 + 3 = 2$$

We can picture this problem by starting at -1 on the number line. The second number, 3, is *positive*, so we move 3 units to the *right*. We end at 2, which is the answer.

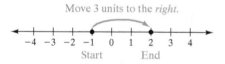

The following rule provides a shortcut for adding signed numbers:

To Add Two Signed Numbers

- If the numbers have the same sign, add the absolute values and keep the sign.

- If the numbers have different signs, subtract the smaller absolute value from the larger and take the sign of the number with the larger absolute value.

EXAMPLE 1

Add: -3 and -2

Solution The sum of the absolute values is 5.

$$|-3| + |-2| = 3 + 2 = 5$$

Both -3 and -2 are negative, so their sum is negative.

$$(-3) + (-2) = -5$$

Check Move 2 units to the *left*.

PRACTICE 1

Combine: -8 and -17

EXAMPLE 2

Find the sum: $(-3.9) + (-0.5)$

Solution $|-3.9| = 3.9$ and $|-0.5| = 0.5$

$$3.9 + 0.5 = 4.4$$

The sum of two negative numbers is negative, so

$$(-3.9) + (-0.5) = -4.4$$

Check   Move 0.5 units to the *left*.

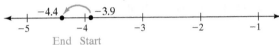

PRACTICE 2

Add: $-3 + (-1\frac{1}{2})$

EXAMPLE 3

Add: $(-1) + 2$

Solution   Here, we are adding numbers with different signs. First, we find the absolute values.

$$|-1| = 1 \quad \text{and} \quad |2| = 2$$

Next, we subtract the smaller absolute value from the larger.

$$2 - 1 = 1$$

Because 2 has the larger absolute value and its sign is positive, the sum is also positive. Our answer is 1, or $+1$.

$$(-1) + 2 = 1$$

Check   Move 2 units to the *right*.

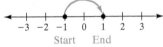

PRACTICE 3

Find the sum of -2 and 9.

Note in Example 3 that, when we added a negative number to 2, we got a smaller result—namely, 1.

EXAMPLE 4

Combine: $(-2) + (+2)$

Solution $|-2| = 2$ and $|+2| = 2$ Find the absolute values.

$$2 - 2 = 0$$ Subtract the absolute values.

Zero is neither positive nor negative, for it has no sign.

$$(-2) + (+2) = 0$$

Check   Move 2 units to the *right*.

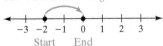

Do you see why the sum of -44 and $+44$ is 0? How about $2.77 + (-2.77)$ or $2\frac{5}{8} + (-2\frac{5}{8})$?

PRACTICE 4

Find the sum: $-35 + 35$

EXAMPLE 5

Add $3\frac{4}{5}$ to $\left(-1\frac{1}{5}\right)$.

Solution $\left|-1\frac{1}{5}\right| = 1\frac{1}{5}$ and $\left|3\frac{4}{5}\right| = 3\frac{4}{5}$ Find the absolute values.

$$
\begin{array}{r}
3\frac{4}{5} \\
-1\frac{1}{5} \\
\hline
2\frac{3}{5}
\end{array}
$$ Subtract the absolute values.

Because $\left|3\frac{4}{5}\right|$ is greater than $\left|-1\frac{1}{5}\right|$, the answer is positive. So

$$3\frac{4}{5} + \left(-1\frac{1}{5}\right) = 2\frac{3}{5}$$

PRACTICE 5

Add: $-2.1 + 0.8$

Some addition problems involve the sum of three or more signed numbers. Rearranging the signed numbers to add the positives and negatives separately can make the addition easier. Note that this rearrangement does not affect the sum because addition is a commutative and associative operation.

EXAMPLE 6

Find the sum: $3 + (-1) + (-8) + 2 + (-11)$

Solution We are adding two positive and three negative numbers. Rearranging the numbers by sign, we get the following.

$$\underbrace{3 + 2}_{\text{Positives}} + \underbrace{(-1) + (-8) + (-11)}_{\text{Negatives}}$$

First, we add the positives. $3 + 2 = 5$

Then, we add the negatives. $(-1) + (-8) + (-11) = -20$

Finally, we combine the positive and the negative subtotals.

$$5 + (-20) = -15$$

So $3 + (-1) + (-8) + 2 + (-11) = -15$.

PRACTICE 6

$-3 + 1 + 8 + (-6) = ?$

EXAMPLE 7

The most famous of all comets is Halley's Comet, which passes by Earth every 76 years. For other comets, however, the length of time between visits is much longer. The Great Comet, for example, comes near Earth only once every 3,000 years. If this comet visited Earth about 1200 B.C., approximately when was its next visit? (*Source:* Mark R. Kidger, "Some Thoughts on Comet Hale-Bopp")

PRACTICE 7

Lake Baikal in Russia is the deepest lake in the world. The deepest point in the lake is 1,187 meters below sea level. If the surface is 1,643 meters above this point, what is the elevation of the surface? (*Source:* bww.irk.ru)

EXAMPLE 7 (continued)

Solution   To help you understand this problem, we draw the number line. Any number line involving time is called a *time line*. On a time line, positive years are A.D. and negative years are B.C.

So 1200 B.C. is represented by -1200. We must add -1200 and $+3000$.

$$|-1200| = 1200 \text{ and } |3000| = 3000 \quad \text{Find the absolute values.}$$
$$3000 - 1200 = 1800 \quad \text{Subtract the absolute values.}$$

Since the absolute value of 3000 is greater than the absolute value of -1200, the answer is positive.

$$(-1200) + 3000 = 1800$$

Therefore, the Great Comet came near Earth in about A.D. 1800.

Check

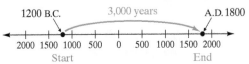

Signed Numbers on a Calculator

The numbers that we have entered so far on a calculator have been positive numbers. To enter a negative number, we need to hit a special key that indicates that the sign of the number is negative. Some calculators have a negative sign key, $\boxed{(-)}$. Others have a change of sign key, $\boxed{+/-}$. Be careful not to confuse either of these keys with the subtraction key, $\boxed{-}$.

EXAMPLE 8

Calculate: $-1.3 + (-5.8)$

Solution

Press

$\boxed{(-)}$ 1.3 $\boxed{+}$ $\boxed{(}$ $\boxed{(-)}$ 5.8 $\boxed{)}$ $\boxed{\text{ENTER} \atop =}$

Display

$$-1.3 + (-5.8)$$
$$-7.1$$

PRACTICE 8

Calculate: $-1.3 + (-5.891) + (4.713)$

Mathematically Speaking

Fill in each blank with the most appropriate term or phrase from the given list.

commutative	right	larger
absolute values	left	distributive
smaller	numbers	

1. To add (-6) and $(+6)$ on the number line, start at (-6) and move 6 units to the _____.

2. To find the sum of two signed numbers with the same sign, add the _____ and keep the sign.

3. To find the sum of two signed numbers with different signs, subtract the smaller absolute value from the larger and take the sign of the number with the _____ absolute value.

4. Rearranging signed numbers to add the positives and negatives separately does not affect the sum, because the operation of addition is associative and _____.

Ⓐ *Find the sum of each pair of numbers. Use the number line as a visual check.*

5. $6 + (-5)$

6. $3 + (-9)$

7. $-2 + 5$

8. $-4 + 9$

9. $-9 + (-2)$

10. $-6 + (-4)$

11. $7 + (-7)$

12. $3 + (-2)$

Find the sum.

13. $67 + (-67)$

14. $2 + (-2)$

15. $-10 + 5$

16. $-12 + 7$

17. $-100 + 300$

18. $-20 + 60$

19. $8 + (-2)$

20. $5 + (-3)$

21. $-60 + (-90)$

22. $-50 + (-40)$

23. $-7 + 2$

24. $-9 + 4$

25. $-27 + 0$

26. $-13 + 0$

27. $-9 + 9$

28. $-2 + 2$

29. $5.2 + (-0.3)$

30. $-0.6 + 1$

31. $-0.2 + 0.3$

32. $-5.5 + 0$

33. $60 + (-0.5)$

34. $-0.7 + 0.7$

35. $-9.8 + 3.9$

36. $6.1 + (-5.9)$

37. $(-5.6) + (-8.9)$

38. $(-0.8) + (-0.5)$

39. $\left(-\frac{1}{2}\right) + \left(-5\frac{1}{2}\right)$

40. $-1\frac{1}{3} + \left(-2\frac{2}{3}\right)$

41. $-1\frac{1}{5} + \frac{3}{5}$

42. $2\frac{1}{6} + \left(-\frac{5}{6}\right)$

43. $-\frac{2}{5} + 2$

44. $-14 + \frac{1}{3}$

45. $1\frac{1}{2} + \left(-1\frac{3}{5}\right)$

46. $1\frac{3}{8} + \left(-2\frac{1}{4}\right)$

47. $(-24) + 20 + (-98)$

48. $35 + (-17) + (-18)$

49. $25 + (-19) + (-16)$

50. $20 + (-8) + (-12)$

51. $-27 + 50 + (-14)$

52. $-34 + (-9) + 15$

53. $12 + (-7) + (-12\frac{1}{2})$

54. $-8 + (-4) + (-8\frac{1}{4})$

55. $(-7) + 12 + 0 + (-7) + 9$

56. $(-3) + 8 + (-9) + 3 + (-4)$

57. $10 + (-9) + (-1) + 0 + 3$

58. $9 + (-3) + 8 + (-4) + 5$

59. $(-5) + (-2) + 6 + (-4) + 5$

60. $-6 + 18 + (-15) + 7 + (-3)$

61. $-0.3 + (-2.6) + (-4)$

62. $-5.25 + (-0.4) + 3$

63. $-12 + 7.58 + 12$

64. $-3.7 + (-1.88) + 5$

65. $8.756 + (-9.08) + (-4.59)$

66. $-5.405 + 6 + (-6.89)$

67. $-3.001 + (-0.59) + 8$

68. $-10 + 5.17 + (-10.002)$

Mixed Practice

Solve.

69. Find the sum of $-6 + 9$ on the number line.

$-6\ -5\ -4\ -3\ -2\ -1\quad 0\quad 1\quad 2\quad 3\quad 4\quad 5\quad 6$

70. Combine 16 and (-24).

71. Add: $9.6 + (-9.6)$

72. Combine: $-4\frac{2}{9} + \left(-2\frac{1}{9}\right)$

73. Add -8, 14, and -10.

74. Find the sum of -1.7, -3.95, and 10.

Applications

B *Solve. Express each answer as a signed number.*

75. The lowest elevation in Africa is Lake Assal at 512 feet below sea level. The highest elevation, Mount Kilimanjaro, is 19,852 feet above Lake Assal. What is the elevation of Mount Kilimanjaro? (*Source: The New York Times Almanac 2010*)

76. A student owes $2,456 on her credit card. After making a payment of $350, what is the balance on her credit card?

77. During a recession, a manufacturer laid off 182 employees. A year later, another 56 employees were laid off. What was the change in the number of employees working for the manufacturer as a result of the two layoffs?

78. A computer retailer decreases the price of a laptop computer by $150 during a sale. As a special promotion, the price is decreased another $75 for customers who trade in their old laptop. What is the total price change for a customer who trades in his old laptop?

79. In a physics class, students study the properties of atomic particles, including protons and electrons. They learn that a proton has an electric charge of $+1$, whereas an electron has an electric charge of -1. What is the total charge of a collection of 3 protons and 4 electrons?

80. Cleopatra became queen of Egypt in 51 B.C. She left the throne 20 years later. In what year was that?

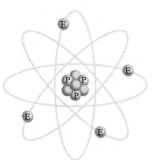

81. Ten years ago, a couple got married. Four years later, they got divorced. When was their divorce?

82. To conduct an experiment, a chemist cooled a substance to −10°C. During the experiment, a chemical reaction took place that raised the temperature of the substance by 15°. What was the final temperature?

83. A football team gained 5 yards on its first down, lost 7 yards on second down, and lost 4 yards on third down. What was the overall change in position after third down?

84. In the last 4 months, a dieter lost 5 pounds, gained 2 pounds, lost 1 pound, and maintained his weight, respectively. What was his overall change in weight?

85. The table below shows for recent years the change from the previous year in the number of union members in the United States.

Year	Change in the Number of Union Members (in millions)
2006	−0.3
2007	+0.3
2008	+0.4
2009	−0.8
2010	−0.6

(*Source:* Barry T. Hirsch and David A. Macpherson; unionstats.com)

a. What was the net change in the number of union members for 2006–2010?

b. If the number of union members in 2006 was 15.7 million, what was the corresponding number in 2010?

86. The following graph shows a company's bottom line (gain or loss) for various quarters, in millions of dollars.

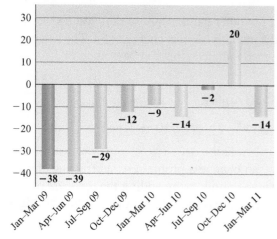

a. What was the company's bottom line for 2010?

b. Was the company's bottom line greater in the last quarter of 2009 or in the first quarter of 2011?

• Check your answers on page A-10.

MINDStretchers

Groupwork

1. Work with a partner on the following.

   a. Fill in the following addition table.

+	+3	−2	−1
+4			
−3			
−1			

   b. Why do the nine numbers that you entered sum to 0?

Writing

2. For signed numbers, does *adding* always mean *increasing*? Explain.

Patterns

3. Find the missing numbers in the following sequence: −5, −7, −6, −8, −7, −9, −8, _____, _____, _____

7.3 Subtracting Signed Numbers

The subtraction of signed numbers is based on two topics previously discussed—adding signed numbers and finding the opposite of a signed number.

Let's first consider a subtraction problem involving money. Suppose that you have $10 in your bank account and withdraw $3. Then $7 will be left in the account. In terms of signed numbers, this can be expressed as

$$10 - (+3) = 7$$

On the other hand, suppose that you had started with $10 in the account and the bank imposed a monthly service charge of $3. The balance in your account once more would be $7. Using signed numbers, this can be written as

$$10 + (-3) = 7$$

The answers to the two problems are the same; so

$$10 - (+3) = 7 \text{ and } 10 + (-3) = 7$$

are equivalent problems.

We can change a problem in subtracting signed numbers to an equivalent problem in adding signed numbers by adding the *opposite* of the number that we want to subtract. The following rule provides a shortcut for subtracting signed numbers:

To Subtract Two Signed Numbers

- Change the operation of subtraction to addition. Then, add the first number and the opposite of the second number.

- Follow the rule for adding signed numbers.

To see if this rule works when the number we are subtracting is negative, consider $4 - (-1)$. Recall that every subtraction problem has a related addition problem. Therefore, $4 - (-1) = 5$ because $5 + (-1) = 4$. Note that we get the same result using the rule for subtracting signed numbers.

$$\underset{\substack{\uparrow \\ \text{Subtract}}}{4} \underset{\substack{\uparrow \\ \text{Negative 1}}}{- \ (-1)} = \underset{\substack{\uparrow \\ \text{Add}}}{4 \ +} \underset{\substack{\uparrow \\ \text{Positive 1}}}{(+1)} = 5$$

EXAMPLE 1

Find the difference: $-2 - (-4)$

Solution   We change the operation of subtraction to addition. Then, we add the first number and the opposite of the second number.

$$-2 - (-4)$$
$$\downarrow \quad \downarrow$$
$$= -2 + (+4)$$

We already know how to add a negative and a positive number. So we get:

$$-2 + 4 = +2, \text{ or } 2$$

PRACTICE 1

Find the difference: $-4 - (-2)$

Note that in Example 1 and Practice 1, the numbers in the differences are the same except for their order. But the answers are quite different: $-2 - (-4) = 2$, whereas $-4 - (-2) = -2$. Why do you think this is so?

EXAMPLE 2

Compute: $3 - (-9)$

Solution   Change negative 9 to its opposite, positive 9.

$$3 - (-9) = 3 + (+9) = +12, \text{ or } 12$$

Change subtraction to addition.

Note that when we subtracted -9 from 3, we got an answer larger than 3.

PRACTICE 2

Subtract: $9 - (-9)$

EXAMPLE 3

Subtract: $-2 - 8\frac{1}{3}$

Solution $-2 - 8\frac{1}{3} = -2 + \left(-8\frac{1}{3}\right) = -10\frac{1}{3}$

PRACTICE 3

Find the difference: $-9 - 12.1$

EXAMPLE 4

Calculate: $5 + (-6) - (-11)$

Solution   This problem involves addition and subtraction. According to the order of operations rule, we work from left to right.

$$\begin{aligned} 5 + (-6) - (-11) &= -1 - (-11) & \text{Add 5 and } (-6). \\ &= -1 + 11 & \text{Subtract } -11. \\ &= 10 & \text{Add 11.} \end{aligned}$$

PRACTICE 4

$-2 - 3 + (-5) = ?$

EXAMPLE 5

Simplify: $4 - [2 - (-3)]$

Solution This problem involves an operation within brackets. According to the order of operations rule, first we work within the brackets.

$$
\begin{aligned}
4 - [2 - (-3)] &= 4 - [2 + 3] && \text{Subtract } -3 \text{ from 2.} \\
&= 4 - 5 && \text{Add 2 and 3.} \\
&= -1 && \text{Subtract 5 from 4.}
\end{aligned}
$$

EXAMPLE 6

Normally we think of oxygen as a gas. However, when cooled to $-183°C$ (its boiling point), oxygen becomes a liquid. If it is cooled further to $-218°C$ (its melting point), oxygen becomes a solid. How much higher is the boiling point of oxygen than its melting point? (*Source: Handbook of Chemistry & Physics*)

Solution We need to compute how much greater is -183 than -218.

$$
\begin{aligned}
(-183) - (-218) &= (-183) + (+218) \\
&= +35
\end{aligned}
$$

The boiling point of oxygen is 35°C higher than its melting point.

PRACTICE 5

Calculate: $7 - [3 + (-2)]$

PRACTICE 6

Paper was invented in China in about 100 B.C. How many years ago was that, to the nearest hundred years? (*Source: World of Invention*)

Mathematically Speaking

Fill in each blank with the most appropriate term or phrase from the given list.

absolute value	order of operations	addition
sum	multiplication	signed numbers
difference	opposite	

1. To subtract two signed numbers, change the operation of subtraction to addition, and change the number being subtracted to its _____. Then, follow the rule for adding signed numbers.

2. Every subtraction problem has a related _____ problem.

3. When a signed number problem involves addition and subtraction, work from left to right according to the _____ rule.

4. When subtracting a negative number, the _____ is greater than the original number.

Ⓐ *Find the difference.*

5. $5 - (-2)$

6. $7 - (-3)$

7. $4 - 8$

8. $5 - 9$

9. $-9 - 5$

10. $-44 - 2$

11. $42 - (-2)$

12. $36 - (-4)$

13. $50 - 75$

14. $44 - 83$

15. $-20 - (-1)$

16. $-18 - (-3)$

17. $3 - (-3)$

18. $4 - (-4)$

19. $0 - 38$

20. $0 - 56$

21. $-13 - 13$

22. $-15 - 15$

23. $13 - (-13)$

24. $14 - (-14)$

25. $8 - 23$

26. $7 - 34$

27. $800 - (-200)$

28. $300 - (-100)$

29. $7 - 8.52$

30. $9.1 - 10.84$

31. $9.2 - (-0.5)$

32. $8.6 - (-0.7)$

33. $-5.2 - (-5.2)$

34. $-0.5 - (-0.5)$

35. $8.6 - (-1.9)$

36. $7.4 - (-3.1)$

37. $-10 - (-9.5)$

38. $-6 - (-8.7)$

39. $4\frac{1}{2} - 9\frac{1}{2}$

40. $6\frac{1}{5} - 8\frac{1}{5}$

41. $10 - 2\frac{1}{4}$

42. $12 - 5\frac{2}{3}$

43. $-7 - \frac{1}{4}$

44. $-9 - \frac{1}{8}$

45. $5\frac{3}{4} - \left(-1\frac{1}{2}\right)$

46. $6\frac{1}{2} - \left(-1\frac{1}{3}\right)$

Combine.

47. $4 + (-6) - (-9)$

48. $10 + (-6) - (-8)$

49. $7 - 7 + (-5)$

50. $8 - 8 + (-9)$

51. $-12 + 3.6 - (-6.5)$

52. $4.6 - (-5) + (-3.6)$

53. $6 + \left(-4\frac{1}{5}\right) + \left(-2\frac{3}{10}\right)$

54. $-2\frac{1}{2} - (-3) + 5\frac{1}{4}$

55. $-8 + (-4) - 9 + 7 + (-1)$

56. $-5 - (-1) + 6 + (-3) - 4$

57. $6 - [5 - (-4)]$

58. $2 - [3 + (-5)]$

59. $7.043 - 9.002 - 1.883$

60. $-6.192 - 0.337 - (-23.94)$

61. $-8.722 + (-3.913) - 3.86$

62. $2.884 - 0.883 + (-6.125)$

Mixed Practice

Solve.

63. Subtract: $-16 - 9$

64. Find the difference: $8.1 - 10.46$

65. Subtract $-19\frac{3}{4}$ from $-19\frac{3}{4}$.

66. From 6 subtract -5.

67. Combine: $-4 + (-5) + 6 - (-4)$

68. Simplify: $3 - [2 + (-9)]$

Applications

B *Solve. Express each answer as a signed number.*

69. Two airplanes take off from the same airport. One flies west and the other east, as shown. How far apart are they?

70. Two friends get on different elevators at the same floor. One goes up 2 floors, the other goes down 4 floors. How many floors are they apart?

71. The highest point on the continent of South America is Mt. Aconcagua at an elevation of 22,834 feet above sea level. The lowest point is the Valdes Peninsula at an elevation of 131 feet below sea level. How much higher is Mt. Aconcagua than the Valdes Peninsula? (*Source: National Geographic Society*)

72. Ethiopia was founded around 1,000 B.C., and the United States in A.D. 1789. About how much older is Ethiopia than the United States? (*Source: The Concise Columbia Encyclopedia*)

73. In business, net income is calculated by subtracting the costs from the revenue. What is a company's net income if its revenues were $2.3 million and its costs were $3.7 million? Express as a signed number.

74. Rapid City, South Dakota, holds the U.S. record for a 2-hour temperature change. On January 12, 1911, the temperature at 6 A.M. was 49°F. If it was 62° colder by 8 A.M., what was the temperature at 8 A.M.? (*Source: crh.noaa.gov*)

75. In St. Louis, Missouri, the water level of the Mississippi River is measured in feet above or below a zero level. On January 16, 1940, the river reached its lowest level, at 6.2 feet below the zero level.

a. Express this measurement as a signed number.

b. The highest level of the Mississippi River in St. Louis, recorded on August 1, 1993, was 49.6 feet above the zero level. What was the difference between the highest and lowest levels? (*Source:* ams.usda.gov)

76. In any year, the U.S. budget surplus or deficit is the difference between what the federal government takes in and what it spends. In 2001 there was a surplus of $127.4 billion, whereas in 2002 there was a deficit of $157.8 billion. (*Source:* gpoaccess.gov)

a. Write each quantity as a signed number.

b. Find the difference between the surplus and the deficit.

77. The bar graph shows the annual precipitation for Phoenix, Arizona for the years from 2005 through 2009. (*Source:* azwater.gov)

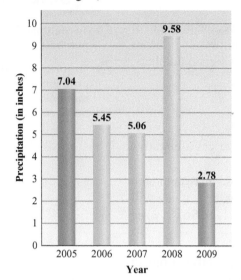

Year

a. The precipitation in 2009 was 5.52 inches below the normal annual precipitation. What is the normal annual precipitation?

b. Find the change in annual precipitation from 2008 to 2009.

78. The bar graph shows the closing price of a share of Whole Foods Market, Inc. stock for a 5-day period in July of 2010. (*Source:* finance.yahoo.com)

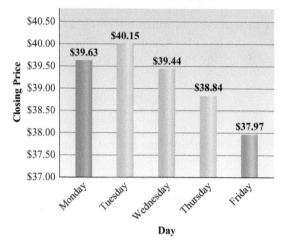

Day

a. Calculate the change in the closing price per share from the previous day for Tuesday through Friday. Express each change as a signed number.

b. If the change in the closing price on Monday was $0.86, what was the closing price the previous day?

• Check your answers on page A-10.

MINDStretchers

Groupwork

1. Working with a partner, rearrange the numbers in the square on the left so that the sum of every row, column, and diagonal is −6.

−3	+2	−2
−5	−4	−6
0	−1	+1

	−2	

Mathematical Reasoning

2. The following two columns of numbers add up to the same sum.

3	7
7	?
1	7
9	8
5	9

What number does the question mark represent?

Writing

3. Consider the following two problems:

$$8 - (-2) = 8 + 2 = 10$$

$$8 \div \frac{4}{7} = 8 \times \frac{7}{4} = 14$$

Explain in what way the two problems are similar.

7.4   Multiplying Signed Numbers

We now turn to the multiplication of signed numbers. Consider, for example, the problem of finding the product of $+4$ and -2, or $4(-2)$. We know that multiplying a number by 4 means the same as adding the number to itself 4 times. Using the rule for adding signed numbers, we get:

$$4(-2) = -2 + (-2) + (-2) + (-2)$$
$$= -8$$

Note that when multiplying a positive number by a negative number, we get a negative product.

Let's take another look at this same problem in practical terms. Suppose that you are on a diet and you lose 2 pounds per month. Compared to your current weight, how much will you weigh 4 months from now? The answer is that you will weigh 8 pounds less. So we write

$$4(-2) = -8$$

Now, we examine a different question. Again assume that you lose 2 pounds per month by dieting. Four months ago, you were heavier than you are now. How much heavier were you? To answer this question, note that each month you lost 2 pounds but that you are going back in time 4 months. So you weighed 8 pounds more than you do now, which can be expressed as

$$-4(-2) = +8, \text{ or } 8$$

Note that when we multiply two negative numbers, we get a positive number.

We can use the following rule to multiply signed numbers:

To Multiply Two Signed Numbers

- Multiply the absolute values of the numbers.

- If the numbers have the same sign, their product is positive; if the numbers have different signs, their product is negative.

Another way to think of multiplying signed numbers is as follows:

Positive · Positive = Positive	Positive · Negative = Negative
Negative · Negative = Positive	Negative · Positive = Negative

EXAMPLE 1

Find the product of -2 and -1.

Solution   First, we find the absolute values.

$$|-2| = 2 \text{ and } |-1| = 1$$

Next, we multiply the absolute values.

$$2 \cdot 1 = 2$$

Since the numbers have the same sign, the product is positive. The answer is $+2$, or 2. So we can write

$$(-2)(-1) = 2$$

PRACTICE 1

Compute: $-8(-4)$

EXAMPLE 2

Calculate: $(5)(-10)$

Solution $|5| = 5$ and $|-10| = 10$ Find the absolute value of each factor.

$5 \cdot 10 = 50$ Multiply the absolute values.

The factors have different signs, so the product is negative.

$$(5)(-10) = -50$$

PRACTICE 2

Multiply: $(-5)(2)$

The next example involves raising signed numbers to a power. Note that in an expression such as $(-7)^2$, the parentheses around the -7 indicate that this negative number is to be squared. By contrast, in the expression -7^2 without parentheses, the positive number 7 is to be squared and the result is preceded by a negative sign.

EXAMPLE 3

Evaluate: **a.** $(-7)^2$ **b.** -7^2

Solution

a. Recall that $(-7)^2$ means $(-7)(-7)$. Because the two factors have the same sign, their product is positive. So $(-7)^2 = 49$.

b. The expression -7^2 means $-(7 \cdot 7)$. So

$$-7^2 = -(7 \cdot 7) = -(49)$$
$$= -49$$

PRACTICE 3

Simplify:

a. $(-1)^2$ **b.** -1^2

Note that in Example 3a, we squared a negative number so that the answer was positive. On the other hand, in Example 3b, we squared a positive number. The square was preceded by a negative sign, giving us a negative answer.

EXAMPLE 4

Find the product of $2\frac{1}{5}$ and -5.

Solution $2\frac{1}{5} \cdot 5 = \frac{11}{5} \cdot \frac{5}{1} = 11$ Multiply the absolute values.

Since the factors $2\frac{1}{5}$ and -5 have different signs, their product is negative.

$$2\frac{1}{5} \cdot (-5) = -11$$

PRACTICE 4

Multiply: $\left(-1\frac{1}{3}\right)\left(-\frac{1}{5}\right)$

EXAMPLE 5

Multiply: $(-1.4)(-0.6)$

Solution $(1.4)(0.6) = 0.84$ Multiply the absolute values.

Since the factors have the same sign, we get:

$$(-1.4)(-0.6) = 0.84$$

PRACTICE 5

Find the product of -2.5 and 8.

EXAMPLE 6

Calculate: $8(-2)(-3)$

Solution   We multiply from left to right.

$$8(-2)(-3) \qquad \text{Positive} \cdot \text{Negative} = \text{Negative}$$
$$= -16 \cdot (-3) \qquad \text{Negative} \cdot \text{Negative} = \text{Positive}$$
$$= 48$$

PRACTICE 6

Multiply: $-8(-2)(-3)$

Comparing Example 6 and Practice 6, we note that both problems have the same absolute values but different signs. The product in Example 6 is positive, because there are two negative factors. By contrast, the answer to Practice 6 is negative, because there are three negative factors. Can you explain why a product is positive if it has an even number of negative factors, whereas a product is negative if it has an odd number of negative factors?

EXAMPLE 7

Simplify: $[8 - 3(-2)]^2$

Solution   Use the order of operations rule.

$$[8 - 3(-2)]^2 = [8 - (-6)]^2 \qquad \text{Multiply 3 by } -2.$$
$$= [8 + 6]^2 \qquad \text{Subtract } -6 \text{ from 8.}$$
$$= [14]^2 \qquad \text{Add.}$$
$$= 196 \qquad \text{Square.}$$

PRACTICE 7

Calculate: $[-3 + 2(-5)]^2$

EXAMPLE 8

An oil company is drilling for oil. Each day, the workers drill down 20 feet farther until they hit a pool of oil, as shown. Will they reach oil by the end of the fifth day?

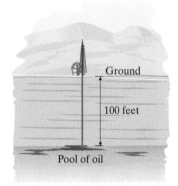

Ground

100 feet

Pool of oil

Solution   Let's represent movement downward by a negative number. Since each of the 5 days they drill 20 feet farther down, we compute $5 \cdot (-20)$. Using the rule for multiplying signed numbers, we get -100. Therefore, the drill will reach 100 feet below ground level by the fifth day—the depth of the pool of oil.

PRACTICE 8

Alvin is a deep submergence vehicle operated by the Woods Hole Oceanographic Institution for marine research. On a research mission, it descends from the surface to the ocean floor 2,000 meters below at a rate of 30 meters per minute. Will *Alvin* reach the ocean floor in 60 minutes? (*Source:* American Geophysical Union)

Mathematically Speaking

Fill in each blank with the most appropriate term or phrase from the given list.

odd	positive	negative	even
product	sum	prime	

1. The product of two numbers with the same sign is _____.

2. The _____ of two numbers with different signs is negative.

3. The product of a(n) _____ number of negative factors is positive.

4. The product of a(n) _____ number of negative factors is negative.

A *Find the product.*

5. $(2)(-5)$

6. $-4 \cdot 9$

7. $-2 \cdot 5$

8. $-3 \cdot 7$

9. $-5 \cdot (-5)$

10. $-4 \cdot (-3)$

11. $-34(-9)$

12. $-35(-7)$

13. $2 \cdot (-8)$

14. $-1 \cdot 5$

15. $907 \cdot (-9)$

16. $-5 \cdot (812)$

17. $5(-8)$

18. $8 \cdot (-53)$

19. $-88 \cdot 2$

20. $20 \cdot (-30)$

21. $(-200)(-4)$

22. $-4 \cdot (-200)$

23. $-80 \cdot 90$

24. $-60 \cdot 40$

25. $(2.5)(-2)$

26. $(0.3)(-0.2)$

27. $(0.2)(-50)$

28. $3 \cdot (-0.3)$

29. $(-1.2)(-4.6)$

30. $(-0.7)(-1.8)$

31. $(5)(-1.6)$

32. $(-40)(2.7)$

33. $-\dfrac{1}{3} \cdot \dfrac{5}{9}$

34. $\left(-\dfrac{5}{6}\right) \cdot \left(\dfrac{2}{3}\right)$

35. $1\dfrac{1}{4}\left(-\dfrac{2}{3}\right)$

36. $-\dfrac{1}{5} \cdot 2\dfrac{1}{2}$

Evaluate.

37. -5^2

38. -6^2

39. $(-100)^2$

40. $(-300)^2$

41. $(-0.5)^2$

42. $(-0.4)^2$

43. $(-0.1)^3$

44. $(-0.2)^3$

45. $\left(-\dfrac{3}{4}\right)^2$

46. $\left(-\dfrac{1}{5}\right)^2$

47. $(-1)^3$

48. $(-4)^3$

49. $(-0.308)^2$

50. $(-7.96)^2$

Multiply.

51. $(9)(12)(-2)$

52. $(2)(-3)(-200)$

53. $(5)(-2)(-1)(3)(-2)$

54. $(-5)(-2)(-1)(3)(-2)$

55. $(-5)(-3)(0)$

56. $(-7)(0)(-10)$

57. $10 \cdot \left(-\dfrac{1}{2}\right) \cdot (-1)$

58. $\left(-\dfrac{1}{2}\right)(-4)\left(-\dfrac{1}{2}\right)$

59. $\dfrac{4}{5} \cdot \left(-\dfrac{8}{9}\right) \cdot \dfrac{1}{3}$

60. $-\dfrac{3}{4} \cdot \dfrac{1}{2} \cdot \left(-\dfrac{5}{7}\right)$

61. $(-2.64)(0.03)(-1.85)$

62. $(5.24)(-0.18)(-2.4)$

Simplify.

63. $(-3)^2 + (-4)$

64. $(-4)^2 + (-5)$

65. $-7 + 3(-3) - 10$

66. $-5 + 2(-8) - 2$

67. $-3(4) + (-6)(-2)$

68. $8 \cdot (-2) + (-3)(-1)$

69. $2(-8) + 3(-4)$

70. $3(-9) + 2(-7)$

71. $(-0.5)^2 + 1^2$

72. $(-0.3)^2 + 0.3^2$

73. $\dfrac{3}{5}(-10) - 6$

74. $\dfrac{1}{5}(-15) + 32$

75. $-5 \cdot (-3 + 1.2)$

76. $-6 \cdot (-4 + 2.7)$

77. $(6 - 8.4) \cdot (3 + 1.5)$

78. $(4.6 - 5) \cdot (-1 + 0.6)$

79. $[-2 + 3(-5)]^2$

80. $[3 - 4(-2)]^2$

81. $-2(8 - 12) + 24 + (-3)^2$

82. $5^2 + 4(-6 - 4) + (-9)(-8)$

Complete each table. Express each answer as a signed number.

83.

Input	Output
a. -2	$(-3)(-2) - 1 =$
b. -1	$(-3)(-1) - 1 =$
c. 0	$(-3)(0) - 1 =$
d. $+1$	$(-3)(+1) - 1 =$
e. $+2$	$(-3)(+2) - 1 =$

84.

Input	Output
a. -2	$(-5)(-2) + 1 =$
b. -1	$(-5)(-1) + 1 =$
c. 0	$(-5)(0) + 1 =$
d. $+1$	$(-5)(+1) + 1 =$
e. $+2$	$(-5)(+2) + 1 =$

Mixed Practice

Solve.

85. Multiply: $805(-6)$

86. Find the product of $-1\dfrac{1}{2}$ and $-1\dfrac{1}{3}$.

87. Calculate: $-(0.01)^2$

88. Compute: $\left(-\dfrac{2}{3}\right)\left(-\dfrac{4}{5}\right)\left(-\dfrac{9}{10}\right)$

89. Simplify: $(-4 + 5) - (-3)^2$

90. Evaluate: $\dfrac{2}{25}(-10)^2 - 6(4 - 7)$

Applications

B *Solve. Express each answer as a signed number.*

91. Tidal gauge measurements show that the sea level at Kodiak Island in Alaska is dropping at a rate of 12 millimeters per year. At this rate, how much will the sea level change in 6 years? (*Source:* National Oceanic and Atmospheric Administration)

92. A patient's dosage of medication is decreased 25 milligrams per day for 1 week. What is the change in her medication at the end of the week?

93. A piece of real estate property dropped $1,475 in value each month. What was the change in value for 3 months?

94. Temperatures can be measured in both the Fahrenheit and Celsius scales. To find the Celsius equivalent of the temperature $-4°F$, we need to compute $\frac{5}{9} \cdot (-4 - 32)$. Simplify this expression.

95. The melting point of a substance is the temperature at which it changes from solid to liquid at standard atmospheric pressure. The melting point of mercury is $-40°C$. Find the melting point of krypton if it is 4 times as great as that of mercury. (*Source: EnvironmentalChemistry.com*)

96. In the 10 basketball games the Panthers played this season, they won 3 games by 2 points, won 2 games by 1 point, lost 4 games by 1 point, and tied in the final game. In these games, what was the difference between the number of points they scored and the number scored by the opposing teams?

97. Two seconds after release, the elevation of an object is $\frac{1}{2}(-32)(2)^2$ feet with respect to the point of release. What is this elevation?

98. During a drought, the water level in a reservoir fell 2 inches per week for 6 straight weeks. What was the change in the water level in the reservoir at the end of this period?

99. The balance in a student's bank account is $1,000. Each month, $150 is withdrawn.
  a. What is the change in the account balance after 6 months?
  b. What is the balance in the account after 6 months?

100. A man lost 1.8 pounds per week through a diet and exercise program.
  a. What was his net change in weight after 15 weeks?
  b. If the man weighed 183 pounds at the start of the program, how much did he weigh after 15 weeks?

• Check your answers on page A-11.

MINDStretchers

Groupwork

1. Ask a partner to think of two negative numbers. Then, you decide which is larger—the product of these numbers or their sum. Switch roles with your partner and repeat the exercise.

Critical Thinking

2. Fill in the following times table.

$\times$	-1	3	-2
2			
-3			
-2			

Verify that the sum of the nine entries is 0. Why is this so?

Writing

3. A salesman says that he loses a little money on each item sold but makes it up in volume. Explain if this is possible.

7.5 Dividing Signed Numbers

OBJECTIVES

Ⓐ To divide signed numbers

Ⓑ To solve applied problems involving the division of signed numbers

Now, let's consider an example of division, the last of the four basic operations. Suppose that you and a friend together owe $8 and you both agree to split the debt evenly. Then, each of you will owe $4.

A debt is considered negative, so this problem requires us to calculate $-8 \div 2$. Recall that every division problem has a related multiplication problem. We see that $-8 \div 2 = -4$ because $-4 \cdot 2 = -8$. Note that when we divide a negative number by a positive number, we get a negative quotient.

Let's look at an example in which we divide one negative number by another negative number. Suppose that your friend owes you $8 and agrees to repay the debt in installments of $2 each. How many installments must your friend pay? The answer, of course, is 4.

This problem asks us to calculate $(-8) \div (-2)$. We know that $4 \cdot (-2) = -8$, so it follows that $(-8) \div (-2) = 4$. This example illustrates that dividing two negative numbers gives a positive quotient.

We can use the following rule for dividing signed numbers:

To Divide Two Signed Numbers

- Divide the absolute values of the numbers.

- If the numbers have the same sign, their quotient is positive; if the numbers have different signs, their quotient is negative.

Another way to think of dividing signed numbers is as follows:

Positive ÷ Positive = Positive   Positive ÷ Negative = Negative
Negative ÷ Negative = Positive   Negative ÷ Positive = Negative

EXAMPLE 1

Find the quotient: $-16 \div (-8)$

Solution   First, find the absolute values.
$$|-16| = 16 \text{ and } |-8| = 8$$
Next, divide the absolute values.
$$16 \div 8 = 2$$
The numbers have the same sign, so the quotient is positive.
$$-16 \div (-8) = 2$$

PRACTICE 1

Divide: $-24 \div (-2)$

EXAMPLE 2

Simplify: $\dfrac{-8}{16}$

Solution $|-8| = 8$ and $|16| = 16$ Find the absolute values.

$\dfrac{8}{16} = \dfrac{1}{2}$ Express the quotient of the absolute values as a fraction.

Because the numbers have different signs, the answer is negative.

$$\dfrac{-8}{16} = -\dfrac{1}{2}$$

PRACTICE 2

Simplify: $\dfrac{9}{-15}$

TIP   When a fraction has a negative sign in its numerator or denominator, we often rewrite the fraction as a negative number. For instance, we write both $\dfrac{-1}{2}$ and $\dfrac{1}{-2}$ as $-\dfrac{1}{2}$.

EXAMPLE 3

$7.4 \div (-2) = ?$

Solution $|7.4| = 7.4$ and $|-2| = 2$ Find the absolute values.

$7.4 \div 2 = 3.7$ Divide the absolute values.

The numbers have different signs, so their quotient is negative.

$$7.4 \div (-2) = -3.7$$

PRACTICE 3

Divide: $-1.5 \div 5$

EXAMPLE 4

Divide: $-8 \div \left(-1\dfrac{3}{5}\right)$

Solution   We divide the absolute values of -8 and $-1\dfrac{3}{5}$.

$$8 \div 1\dfrac{3}{5} = 8 \div \dfrac{8}{5} = \cancel{8} \times \dfrac{5}{\cancel{8}} = 5$$

The quotient of two negative numbers is positive.

$$-8 \div \left(-1\dfrac{3}{5}\right) = 5$$

PRACTICE 4

Find the quotient: $-\dfrac{1}{2} \div 3$

We use the order of operations rule to simplify the following expressions in Example 5.

EXAMPLE 5

Simplify. **a.** $-10 + (-8) \div (-2)$ **b.** $\dfrac{-7 + (-3)^2}{2}$

Solution

a. $-10 + (-8) \div (-2) = -10 + 4$ Perform division before addition.
Divide -8 by -2.

$\qquad\qquad\qquad\qquad = -6$ Add.

b. $\dfrac{-7 + (-3)^2}{2} = \dfrac{-7 + 9}{2}$ Simplify the numerator first.

$\qquad\qquad = \dfrac{2}{2}$ Add -7 and 9.

$\qquad\qquad = 1$ Divide.

PRACTICE 5

Simplify.

a. $6 - (-12) \div (-2)$

b. $\dfrac{5 - (-1)^2}{-4}$

EXAMPLE 6

The federal deficit in 1910 was about \$20 million. Five years later, it was \$60 million. How many times greater was the deficit of 1915 than that of 1910? (*Source:* infoplease.com)

Solution The problem asks us to compute $-60 \div (-20)$. The quotient of numbers with the same sign is positive, so the answer is 3. That is, the 1915 deficit was 3 times as great as the deficit of 1910.

PRACTICE 6

About $\frac{3}{4}$ of Earth's coral reefs are located in the Indian and Pacific Oceans. These reefs are declining at a rate of approximately 600 square miles per year. By how many square miles per month are the reefs declining, expressed as a signed number? (*Source:* news.bbc.co.uk)

EXAMPLE 7

The table shows the change in the closing price of a share of a software company's stock each day over a 5-day period.

Day	Change in Closing Price (in cents)
Monday	+32
Tuesday	-18
Wednesday	-21
Thursday	+16
Friday	-54

What was the average daily change in the closing price of a share of the stock?

Solution To compute the average change, we add the five changes and divide the sum by 5.

$$\frac{+32 + (-18) + (-21) + (+16) + (-54)}{5}$$

Recall from the order of operations rule that we must find the sum in the numerator before dividing by the denominator.

$$\frac{+48 + (-93)}{5} = \frac{-45}{5} = -9$$

So the average daily change over the 5-day period was down 9 cents per share.

PRACTICE 7

A young girl has a fever. The following chart shows how her temperature changed each day this week.

Monday	Up 2°
Tuesday	Up 1°
Wednesday	Down 1°
Thursday	Up 1°
Friday	Down 3°

What was the average daily change in her temperature?

Mathematically Speaking

Fill in each blank with the most appropriate term or phrase from the given list.

addition	positive	negative
unequal	equal	multiplication

1. The quotient of two numbers with the same signs is _____.

2. The quotient of two numbers with different signs is _____.

3. The fractions $\dfrac{-2}{3}$, $\dfrac{2}{-3}$ and $-\dfrac{2}{3}$, are _____ in value.

4. Every division problem has a related _____ problem.

A *Find the quotient. Simplify.*

5. $-20 \div (-4)$

6. $-7 \div (-1)$

7. $0 \div 5$

8. $0 \div 3$

9. $10 \div (-2)$

10. $-9 \div 3$

11. $16 \div (-8)$

12. $-12 \div 4$

13. $-250 \div (-10)$

14. $-300 \div (-3)$

15. $-200 \div 8$

16. $-20 \div 10$

17. $-35 \div (-5)$

18. $-8 \div (-4)$

19. $6 \div (-3)$

20. $-8 \div 2$

21. $-17 \div (-1)$

22. $-20 \div (-2)$

23. $-72 \div (-12)$

24. $-440 \div (-10)$

25. $-2.4 \div 8$

26. $-0.26 \div 2$

27. $-4 \div 0.2$

28. $9 \div (-0.6)$

29. $-4.8 \div (-0.3)$

30. $-2.6 \div (-0.2)$

31. $\left(-\dfrac{2}{3}\right) \div \dfrac{4}{5}$

32. $\left(-\dfrac{5}{6}\right) \div \left(-\dfrac{5}{6}\right)$

33. $7 \div \left(-\dfrac{1}{3}\right)$

34. $9 \div \left(-\dfrac{1}{3}\right)$

35. $-40 \div 2\dfrac{1}{2}$

36. $-30 \div 1\dfrac{1}{2}$

37. $(-15.1214) \div (-2.45)$

38. $-0.749 \div -0.214$

39. $-12.25 \div 3.5$

40. $50.8369 \div (-7.13)$

Simplify.

41. $\dfrac{-1}{5}$

42. $\dfrac{-1}{7}$

43. $\dfrac{-11}{-11}$

44. $\dfrac{-3}{-11}$

45. $\dfrac{4}{-10}$

46. $\dfrac{5}{-10}$

47. $\dfrac{-11}{-2}$

48. $\dfrac{-2}{-11}$

49. $\dfrac{-17}{-4}$

50. $\dfrac{-26}{-5}$

51. $\dfrac{-9}{-12}$

52. $\dfrac{-14}{-16}$

53. $-8 \div (-2)(-2)$

54. $-3(-4) \div (-2)$

55. $(3 - 7)^2 \div (-4)$

56. $(4 - 6)^2 \div (1 - 5)^2$

57. $\dfrac{2^2 - (-6)}{2}$

58. $\dfrac{3^2 - (-7)}{2}$

59. $\dfrac{2^2 + (-6)}{-2}$

60. $\dfrac{3^2 + (-7)}{-1}$

61. $\left(\dfrac{-8}{-2}\right)\left(\dfrac{8}{-2}\right)$

62. $\dfrac{-10}{2} \cdot \dfrac{-6}{5}$

63. $\dfrac{-9 - (-3)}{2}$

64. $\dfrac{-5 - (-7)}{2}$

65. $\dfrac{3(-0.2)^2}{-2}$

66. $\dfrac{(-16)(1.5)^2}{-1}$

67. $(-15) + (-3)^2 - 2 \cdot (-1)$

68. $-12 \cdot 2 + (-2)^2 - (-5) \cdot 3$

69. $24 \div (-8) + (-5) \cdot 6$

70. $-49 \div (-7)^2 - 4 \cdot (-3)$

71. $(-13 - 3) \div (-2 - 6)$

72. $10 + (-8) \div (-4)(-5)$

73. $[18 + (-4)] \div (-2)$

74. $[25 + (-10)] \div (-3)$

Insert parentheses, if needed, to make the expression on the left equal to the number on the right.

75. $9 \div 1 - 4 = -3$

76. $-2 + 8(-12) = -72$

77. $6 \div 3 - 1 - 4 = -1$

78. $-10 + 8 \div 2 - 5 \cdot 3 = -16$

79. $8 - 10 \cdot 2 - (-5) + 13 \div 4 = -6$

80. $12 \div (-5) + 1 + (-6)(-1) + 2 = -9$

Mixed Practice

Solve.

81. Divide: $-\dfrac{4}{5} \div \dfrac{2}{3}$

82. Divide -0.75 by -0.5.

83. Simplify: $\dfrac{19}{-6}$

84. Find the quotient: $-0.06 \div (-0.3)$

85. Evaluate: $(5 - 3)^2 \div (1 - 4)^3$

86. Simplify: $-4 - 9 \div 3(-5) + 2$

Applications

B *Solve. Express each answer as a signed number.*

87. The population of a certain city decreased by 60,989 in 10 years. Find the average annual change in population.

88. A new computer purchased for $1,800 will have a salvage value of $400. If its value decreases $280 per year, in how many years will it reach its salvage value?

89. In the decade between 1990 and 2000, the population of Washington, D.C., dropped from 607 thousand to 572 thousand, rounded to the nearest thousand. During this decade, what was the change in population per year? (*Source:* census.gov)

90. A football running back lost 4 yards on each of several plays. His total yardage lost was 24 yards. How many plays were involved?

91. The altitude of a plane decreased from 25,000 feet to 19,000 feet in 6 minutes. At what rate did the altitude of the plane change?

92. Over a 5-year period, the height of a cliff eroded by 3.5 feet. By how many feet did it change per year?

93. A meteorologist is expected to accurately predict the average high temperature for the next 5 days. This week the high temperatures were 3°, 0°, −8°, −11°, and 1°. If her prediction for these days was −3°, was it correct?

94. In a statistics course, a student needs to carry out the following computation.

$$\dfrac{(-0.5)^2 + (0.3)^2 + (0.2)^2}{3}$$

Find this number, rounded to the nearest hundredth.

95. The bar graph shows the daily high temperature in degrees Fahrenheit in Fairbanks, Alaska, for the first week of January in a recent year. (*Source:* climate.gi.alaska.edu)

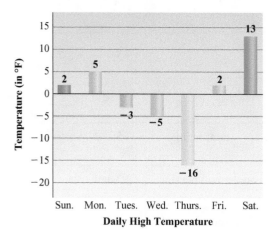

Daily High Temperature

a. Which day of the first week was the coldest? The warmest?

b. To the nearest degree, what was the average daily high temperature that week?

96. The table below shows the stockholders' equity for Ford Motor Co. in each of four consecutive quarters.

Quarter	Stockholders' Equity (in billions)
1	−$11
2	−$9
3	−$8
4	−$6

(*Sources:* investopedia.com and finance.yahoo.com)

a. Find the average quarterly stockholders' equity for the first two quarters.

b. If the stockholders' equity had been $2 billion more in the fourth quarter, what would the average for the four quarters have been?

● Check your answers on page A-11.

MINDStretchers

Patterns

1. Find the missing numbers in the following sequence.

$$+1296, +648, -216, -108, +36, +18, -6, \underline{\quad}, \underline{\quad}, \underline{\quad}$$

Groupwork

2. Do the following with a partner.

- Take your partner's age in years.
- Square it.
- Subtract 9.
- Divide the result by 3 less than your partner's age.
- Subtract 53.
- Add your partner's age.
- Divide by 2.
- Add 5^2.

Verify that you wind up where you started—with your partner's age.

Writing

3. Explain the difference between the *opposite* of a number and the *reciprocal* of a number.

Key Concepts and Skills

Concept/Skill	Description	Example
[7.1] Positive number	A number greater than 0.	$5, \frac{1}{3}, 2.7$
[7.1] Negative number	A number less than 0.	$-5, -\frac{1}{3}, -2.7$
[7.1] Signed number	A number with a sign that is either positive or negative.	$5, -5, \frac{1}{3}, -\frac{1}{3}, 2.7, -2.7$
[7.1] Integers	The numbers . . . , $-4, -3, -2, -1, 0, 1, 2, 3, 4, \ldots$ continuing indefinitely in both directions.	$+5, -5$
[7.1] Opposites	Two numbers that are the same distance from 0 on the number line but on opposite sides of 0.	$+2$ and -2
[7.1] Absolute value	The distance of a number from 0 on the number line, represented by the symbol $\lvert \; \rvert$.	$\lvert -2 \rvert = 2, \quad \lvert +2 \rvert = 2$
[7.1] To compare signed numbers	• Locate the points being compared on the number line. A number to the right is larger than a number to the left.	$2 > -1$
[7.2] To add two signed numbers	• If the numbers have the same sign, add the absolute values and keep the sign. • If the numbers have different signs, subtract the smaller absolute value from the larger and take the sign of the number with the larger absolute value.	$-0.5 + (-1.7) = -2.2$ because $\lvert -0.5 \rvert + \lvert -1.7 \rvert =$ $0.5 + 1.7 = 2.2$ $3\frac{1}{2} + (-9) = -5\frac{1}{2}$ because $\lvert -9 \rvert > \left\lvert +3\frac{1}{2} \right\rvert$ and $9 - 3\frac{1}{2} = 5\frac{1}{2}$
[7.3] To subtract two signed numbers	• Change the operation of subtraction to addition. Then add the first number and the opposite of the second number. • Follow the rule for adding signed numbers.	$-2 - (-5) = -2 + 5$ $= +3$, or 3
[7.4] To multiply two signed numbers	• Multiply the absolute values of the numbers. • If the numbers have the same sign, their product is positive; if the numbers have different signs, their product is negative.	$(-8)\left(-\frac{1}{2}\right) = +4$, or 4 $-0.2 \times 4 = -0.8$
[7.5] To divide two signed numbers	• Divide the absolute values of the numbers. • If the numbers have the same sign, their quotient is positive; if the numbers have different signs, their quotient is negative.	$\dfrac{-8}{-4} = +2$, or 2 $18 \div (-2) = -9$

Say Why
Fill in each blank.

1. The number $\dfrac{7}{9}$ _____ a signed number because
   __is/is not__
   _____.

2. The number -17 _____ less than 0 because
   __is/is not__
   _____

3. The number -8.2 _____ an integer because
   __is/is not__
   _____
   _____.

4. The numbers -28.7 and 28.7 _____ opposites
   __are/are not__
   because _____
   _____.

5. The number -3 _____ the absolute value of any
   __is/is not__
   number because _____
   _____.

6. When we add -1 to a signed number, the sum
   _____ larger than that signed number because
   __is/is not__
   _____
   _____.

[7.1] *Mark the corresponding point for each number on the number line.*

7. -3 8. 1.5

$$\overset{\longleftarrow \; | \quad | \quad | \quad | \quad | \quad | \quad | \quad | \quad | \; \longrightarrow}{\quad -4 \; -3 \; -2 \; -1 \quad 0 \quad 1 \quad 2 \quad 3 \quad 4}$$

Find the opposite signed number.

9. $+6$ 10. -4 11. $-7\dfrac{1}{2}$ 12. 10.1

Find the absolute value.

13. $|10|$ 14. $|+2.5|$ 15. $\left|-1\dfrac{1}{5}\right|$ 16. $|-7|$

Circle the larger number.

17. -11 and -15 18. -15 and 10 19. 9 and $-5\dfrac{1}{3}$ 20. -6.75 and -2

Arrange the numbers in each group from smallest to largest.

21. $-8, 8, -3.5$ 22. $9, -6, -9.7$ 23. $-2\dfrac{1}{2}, 0, -2.9$ 24. $-4, -1\dfrac{1}{4}, 0$

Express each quantity as a signed number.

25. Ten feet above sea level   26. A loss of $350 on an investment

[7.2] *Find the sum.*

27. $-10 + (-10)$ 28. $8 + (-10)$ 29. $-5\dfrac{1}{2} + 12$

30. $-\dfrac{1}{4} + \left(-\dfrac{3}{4}\right)$ 31. $0.9 + (-5)$ 32. $-1.2 + (-0.8)$

33. $-8 + 5 + (-4)$ 34. $12 + (-12) + \left(-\dfrac{1}{4}\right)$

[7.3] *Find the difference.*

35. $-10 - (-10)$ 36. $14 - (-14)$ 37. $5 - 15$

38. $-2 - 9$ 39. $2.5 - (-0.5)$ 40. $-\dfrac{1}{8} - 4$

[7.4] *Find the product.*

41. $-10(-10)$

42. $-15 \cdot 3$

43. $\dfrac{-2}{-3}\left(\dfrac{+10}{-11}\right)$

44. $3.5 \times (-2.1)$

45. $4(-3)(-6)$

46. $-2(-3)(-5)$

Evaluate.

47. $\left(\dfrac{1}{4}\right)^2$

48. $(-0.7)^2$

49. $(-6)^2$

50. -9^2

[7.5] *Find the quotient.*

51. $-35 \div (-7)$

52. $-80 \div 8$

53. $20 \div (-4)$

54. $-\dfrac{1}{8} \div (-4)$

55. $15 \div (-0.3)$

56. $\dfrac{-10}{-5}$

[7.2–7.5] *Simplify.*

57. $-8 - (-3) + 20$

58. $12 \cdot (-3)^2 - (-6)$

59. $(-7 + 3) \cdot (-5)^2$

60. $(20 - 30) \div (-10)$

61. $\dfrac{(-9.1)(-0.6)}{2}$

62. $\dfrac{-8 - 5.1}{5}$

63. $10^2 + \dfrac{-8 - 2}{2} + (-3)^2$

64. $\dfrac{10}{2} - (5 - 9)^2(-1)$

65. $6 - [5 + (-9)]$

66. $8 - [4 - (-6)]$

67. $[10 - 5(-1)]^2$

68. $[-2 + 3(-6)]^2$

Mixed Applications

Solve.

69. After answering a question incorrectly, a contestant on *Jeopardy* had $1,000 deducted from his score of $600. What was his new score?

70. The Chou dynasty ruled China between 1027 B.C. and 256 B.C. The philosopher Confucius was born in about 551 B.C. and died in about 479 B.C. Was the Chou dynasty in power throughout Confucius's lifetime? (*Source: Asian History on File*)

71. A customer has his monthly car payment automatically deducted from his checking account. If his monthly car payment is $235, express the annual change in balance in his checking account as a signed number.

72. An administrative assistant had a balance of $1,498.56 on her credit card. What is her new balance after charges totaling $378.12, a payment of $250, and a finance charge of $23.15 are included?

73. A meteorologist reports that today's low temperature was −5°F and that the normal low for the day is 23°F. How far below the normal low temperature is the low temperature today?

74. An instructor deducts 4 points for each incorrect answer on an exam. If a student received 92 out of a possible 120 points on the exam, how many questions did he answer incorrectly?

75. An investor bought 100 shares of a media company's stock for $3,500. The value of the stock was $3,380 after one month. Express the investor's change in value per share as a signed number.

76. Two of the most influential math books in history were *The Elements*, which Euclid wrote in 323 B.C., and *The Principia*, which Isaac Newton wrote in A.D 1687. How many years apart were these books written? (*Source: Notable Mathematicians from Ancient Times to the Present*)

77. Buddha was born in 563 B.C. and died in 483 B.C. Was he alive in 500 B.C.? (*Source: Compton's Encyclopedia*)

78. On a diver's first day of scuba diving, he dove to a depth of 30 feet below the surface of the sea. If on the next day he dove to a depth 3 times as great, how deep did he dive on that day?

79. Golf scores are commonly expressed as over or under *par*—the number of expected strokes on each hole. To *birdie* a hole is to take 1 less stroke than par, to *eagle* is to take 2 fewer strokes than par, and to *bogie* is to take 1 more stroke than par. With 3 birdies, 2 eagles, 1 par, and 2 bogies, how far over or under par is the golfer altogether?

80. Physicists have shown that, if an object is thrown upward at a speed of 100 feet per second, its elevation after 5 seconds will be

$$-16 \times 5^2 + 100 \times 5$$

feet relative to the point at which the object was thrown. How far above or below that point will the object be at that time?

81. The following bar graph shows the record low temperatures for selected states.

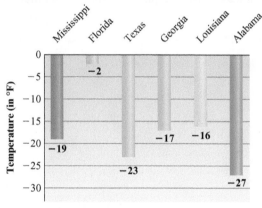

(*Source: National Climatic Data Center*)

a. Which state had the coldest record low temperature?

b. How much higher than the record low temperature in Louisiana was the record low temperature in Florida?

82. The following table shows the net income for American International Group, Inc. (AIG) for three consecutive years.

Year	Net Income (in billions of dollars)
2007	−6.2
2008	−99.3
2009	−10.9

a. What was the company's total net income for the three years?

b. What was the average annual net income for the company?

• Check your answers on page A-11.

CHAPTER 7   Posttest

FOR
EXTRA
HELP

CHAPTER
Test Prep
VIDEOS

The Chapter Test Prep Videos with test solutions are available on DVD, in MyMathLab, and on You Tube ® (search "AkstBasicMath" and click on "Channels").

To see if you have mastered the topics in this chapter, take this test.

1. Which is smaller, -10 or -4?

2. A number has an absolute value of $\frac{1}{2}$ and is negative. What is the number?

Evaluate.

3. $-8 + 8$

4. $4.5 + (-5)$

5. $42 - 91$

6. $-12 - (-12)$

7. -23×9

8. -0.5×0.2

9. -12^2

10. $\left(-\dfrac{1}{4}\right)^2$

11. $-64 \div 16$

12. $\dfrac{1}{2} \div (-4)$

13. $-4 + 6 + (-7) + 9$

14. $15 - (-7) + (-1)$

15. $-8 - 4^2 \cdot (-3)$

16. $(2 - 8)^2 \div (-2)$

Solve.

17. A dieter on a weight-loss program lost 12 pounds in the first month. Over the next 5 months, he lost an additional 39 pounds. Express as a signed number the total change in weight in 6 months.

18. A copier that was purchased new for $6,900 is worth $4,700 four years later. If the copier changes in value by the same amount each year, what is the rate at which its value changes, expressed as a signed number?

19. On April 20, 2010, Deepwater Horizon, an oil rig owned by British Petroleum (BP), exploded off the coast of Louisiana, sending oil gushing into the Gulf of Mexico from the well nearly a mile below the water's surface. The graph below shows the percent change in stock prices for the top five oil companies in the world from the day of the explosion to two weeks after.

20. At 36,000 feet, the temperature outside an airplane had been $-56°C$. When the plane landed, the temperature outside rose to $20°C$. How much greater was the temperature outside the plane on the ground than in the air?

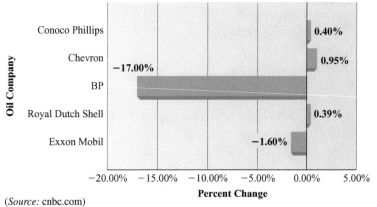

(*Source:* cnbc.com)

Rank these companies in order from biggest loss to biggest gain in their stock prices.

• Check your answers on page A-11.

Cumulative Review Exercises

To help you review, solve the following:

1. Round 2,891 to the nearest thousand.

2. $(5 - 9)^2 \div (-6 + 2)$

3. Multiply: $(4)\left(2\frac{1}{2}\right)$

4. Add: $8 + 2.1 + 3.9$

5. Find the product: $(3.7)(0.4)(2.1)$

6. Perform the indicated operations: $\dfrac{32.44 - 11.8}{6}$

7. Solve for x: $x + 7.5 = 9$

8. Translate the sentence "$\frac{5}{9}$ of x is 40" to an equation.

9. Solve for n: $\dfrac{1.4}{7} = \dfrac{13}{n}$

10. Change 1.125 to a percent.

11. What percent of 2.5 is 0.5?

12. Find the sum: $-7.84 + (-0.3) + 2.1$

13. Simplify: $(-0.5)^2 + (0.5)^2$

14. Divide: $\dfrac{5}{12} \div \left(-\dfrac{3}{4}\right)$

15. In a varsity baseball game, the starting pitcher pitched $6\frac{1}{3}$ innings before he was relieved. The relief pitcher lasted until the end of the 9th inning. How many innings was the relief pitcher in the game? (*Source: Kern Valley Sun*)

Solve.

16. A patient is to be given a total of 480 milligrams of medication per day. If the medication is to be administered every 4 hours, how much medication should be administered with each dose?

17. A patient has a total cholesterol level of 200 and an HDL (also called "good") cholesterol level of 50, both in terms of milligrams per deciliter. Find the ratio of total cholesterol to HDL cholesterol. (*Source:* americanheart.org)

18. When mortgage rates dropped, the number of housing starts rose from 4,000 to 5,000. What percent increase is this?

19. Three of the coldest temperature readings ever recorded on Earth were $-89°C$, $-68°C$, and $-63°C$. Of these three temperatures, which was the coldest? (*Source: Time Almanac, 2010*)

20. Nitrogen gas, when cooled, becomes liquid at $-196°C$. This liquid becomes solid at $-210°C$. At $-200°C$, is nitrogen a gas, a liquid or a solid? (*Source:* nasa.gov)

• Check your answers on page A-11.

CHAPTER 8

8.1 **Introduction to Basic Statistics**

8.2 **Tables and Graphs**

Basic Statistics

Statistics and the Law

Lawyers make frequent use of statistical evidence to win their cases.

Statistics on the distribution of blood and hair types in the general population are commonly used as evidence in physical assault and robbery trials. For those plaintiffs who claim that they are suffering from exposure to a toxic agent, their lawyers often present statistical evidence about the general incidence of their illness. And cases of race and sex discrimination typically focus on such statistics as the proportion of people who are admitted to a college or hired by a company or the average length of time that employees have spent in positions before being promoted.

This use of statistics in the U.S. legal system goes back to a landmark nineteenth-century trial, wherein the claim was made that the signature of Sylvia Howland on her will was forged. The turning point of the case was the testimony of an expert witness—a Harvard mathematician—who developed a system of statistically analyzing the degree of similarity among 42 signatures of the deceased. On the basis of these statistics, he testified that the signature on the will was unreasonably similar to another of Ms. Howland's from which it had probably been traced.

(*Source:* Jack B. Weinstein, "Litigation and Statistics," *Statistical Science*, 3, (3), 1988, pp. 286–297)

To see if you have already mastered the topics in this chapter, take this test.

1. In the 2009 World Series, the Philadelphia Phillies, champions of the National League, played the New York Yankees, champions of the American League. The Yankees defeated the Phillies four games to two, as indicated in the following table of runs scored in the six games.

Team	Game 1	Game 2	Game 3	Game 4	Game 5	Game 6
Philadelphia Phillies	6	1	5	4	8	3
New York Yankees	1	3	8	7	6	7

(*Source:* mlb.com)

Was the range of runs that the Phillies scored in a Series game the same as that for the Yankees?

2. What is the mode of the number of days in a month? (*Reminder:* February has 28 or 29 days; April, June, September, and November have 30 days; and January, March, May, July, August, October, and December have 31 days.)

3. A local fire department tracks its emergency response times. Last month, the response times were: 12 minutes, 7 minutes, 20 minutes, 10 minutes, 6 minutes, 15 minutes, 8 minutes, 12 minutes, and 9 minutes. What was the mean response time?

4. The following table shows the amount of rainfall (in millimeters) each month for a recent year in London. (*Source:* worldweather.org)

Jan	Feb	Mar	Apr	May	June
53	36	48	47	51	50

July	Aug	Sept	Oct	Nov	Dec
48	54	53	57	57	57

What was the median amount of monthly rainfall?

5. Late in the spring term, your grades were: Spanish I (3 credits)—A; Music (2 credits)—A; Social Science (4 credits)—C; and Physical Education (1 credit)—B. The grades are assigned the following points: A = 4, B = 3, C = 2, D = 1, and F = 0. Calculate your GPA.

In each case, use the given table or graph to answer the question.

6. The following mortality table gives estimates for the life spans of individuals (in years), taking into account such factors as year of birth and gender. (*Source:* U.S. National Center for Health Statistics)

Year of Birth	1920	1930	1940	1950	1960	1970	1980	1990	2000	2010
Male	53.6	58.1	60.8	65.6	66.6	67.1	70.0	71.8	74.3	75.6
Female	54.6	61.6	65.2	71.1	73.1	74.7	77.5	78.8	79.7	81.4

For which years was the difference between male and female life spans greater than in 1950?

7. The following graph shows the percent of American cancer patients surviving 5 or more years, during various periods of time.

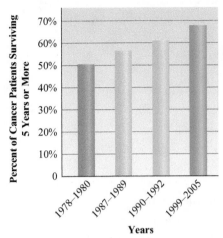

(*Source:* National Cancer Institute)

In which period(s) of time shown did more than three-fifths of the cancer patients survive 5 or more years?

8. The following pictograph shows the average circulation of some major newspapers across the United States in a recent year.

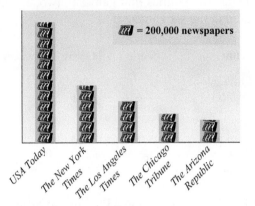

(*Source: Top Ten of Everything, 2010*)

What was the approximate daily circulation of *The New York Times*?

9. The first automated teller machine (ATM) in the United States was installed in 1971 at the Citizens & Southern National Bank in Atlanta. Overall, the number of ATMs has grown rapidly. The following graph shows the number in recent years.

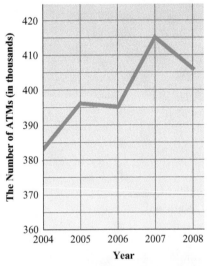

(*Source:* Insurance Information Institute)

In the year 2008, approximately how many ATMs were there in the United States?

10. The graph shows the breakdown of days of school missed in a recent 12-month period due to illness or injury for U.S. children 5–17 years of age.

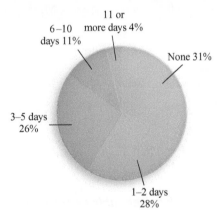

(*Source:* cdc.gov)

What percent of children missed 3 or more days of school?

• Check your answers on page A-11.

Cultural Note

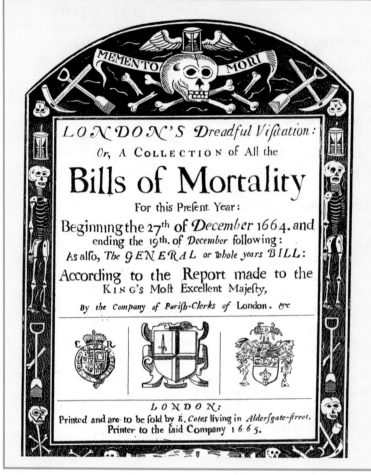

A seventeenth-century English clothing salesman named John Graunt had the insight to apply a numerical approach to major social problems. In 1662, he published a book entitled *Natural and Political Observations upon the Bills of Mortality*, and thus founded the science of statistics.

Graunt was curious about the periodic outbreaks of the bubonic plague in London, and his book analyzed the number of deaths in London each week due to various causes. He was the first to discover that, at least in London, the number of male births exceeded the number of female births. He also found that there was a higher death rate in urban areas than in rural areas and that more men than women died violent deaths. Graunt summarized large amounts of information to make it understandable and made conjectures about large populations based on small samples. Graunt was also a pioneer in examining expected life span—a statistic that became vital to the insurance companies formed at the end of the seventeenth century.

Sources: Morris Kline, *Mathematics, a Cultural Approach* (Reading, Mass.: Addison-Wesley Publishing Company, 1962), p. 614.

F. N. David, *Games, Gods and Gambling* (New York: Hafner Publishing Company, 1962).

8.1 Introduction to Basic Statistics

OBJECTIVES

A To find the mean, median, or mode(s) of a set of numbers

B To find the range of a set of numbers

C To solve applied problems involving basic statistics

What Basic Statistics Is and Why It Is Important

Statistics is the branch of mathematics that deals with ways of handling large quantities of information. The goal is to make this information easier to interpret.

With unorganized data, spotting trends and making comparisons is difficult. The study of statistics teaches you how to organize data in various ways in order to make the data more understandable.

One approach is to calculate special numbers, also called statistics, which describe the data. In this section, we consider four statistics: the mean, the median, the mode, and the range.

You have already seen that another way to organize data is to display the information in the form of a table or graph. We will discuss tables and graphs in greater detail in the next section of this chapter.

Many situations lend themselves to the application of statistical techniques. Wherever there are large quantities of information—from sports to business—statistics can help us to find meaning where, at first glance, there seems to be none, and to become more quantitatively literate.

Averages

We begin our introduction to statistics by revisiting the meaning of "average." Previously, we defined the average of a set of numbers to be the sum of the numbers divided by however many numbers are in the set. This statistic, which is more precisely called the *arithmetic mean*, or just the **mean**, is what most people think of as the average. However, it is not the only kind of average used to represent the numbers in a set.

A second average, the *median*, may describe a set of numbers better than the mean when there is an unusually large or unusually small number in the set to be averaged. The third average, the *mode*, has a special property—unlike the mean and the median, it is always in the set of numbers being averaged.

Mean

Let's look at an example of the mean.

EXAMPLE 1

The area of the United States is about 3,800,000 square miles.

a. Approximately what is the average area of each of the 50 states?

b. Is Michigan above or below average in area?

Michigan
Area: 97,000 sq mi

Solution

a. The mean area of a state is $\dfrac{3,800,000}{50}$, or 76,000 square miles.

b. Since 97,000 is greater than 76,000, Michigan is above average in area.

PRACTICE 1

Reggie Jackson hit five home runs in the 1977 World Series, which lasted six games. By contrast, Lou Gehrig hit four home runs in the 1928 World Series, a four-game series. On the average, which baseball player hit fewer home runs per game?

Note that a property of the mean is that it is changed substantially if even a single number in a set of numbers is replaced by one much larger or much smaller. For instance, if five people each make $10 per hour, then their mean hourly wage is $10. However, if the hourly wage of one of these individuals jumps to $500, then the mean wage skyrockets to $108, more than 10 times the previous mean.

Another kind of mean, called the *weighted average*, is used when some numbers in a set count more heavily than others. Weighted average comes into play, for instance, if you want to compute the average of your test scores in a class and the final exam counts twice as much as any of the other tests. Or, if you are computing your grade point average (GPA) and some courses carry more credits than others.

EXAMPLE 2

Last term, a student's grades were as follows.

Course	Credits	Grade	Grade Equivalent
Psychology	4	A	4
English	4	C	2
Art	3	B	3
Physical Education	1	B	3

If the student's GPA is 3.5 this term, did she have a higher or lower GPA last term?

Solution   To calculate the GPA for last term, we first multiply the number of credits each course carries by the numerical grade equivalent received. We then add these products to find the total number of grade points. Finally, we divide this sum by the total number of credits.

Number of credits for the first course
Grade equivalent of the first course

$$GPA = \frac{4 \cdot 4 + 4 \cdot 2 + 3 \cdot 3 + 1 \cdot 3}{12}$$

Total number of credits

$$= \frac{16 + 8 + 9 + 3}{12} = \frac{36}{12} = 3$$

A GPA of 3 is less than a GPA of 3.5. So the student had a lower GPA last term.

PRACTICE 2

The following table shows the test scores that a classmate earned.

Exam	Score
1	95
2	80
3	80
Final	90

If the final exam is equivalent to two other exams, did the classmate earn an exam average above or below 85?

Median

As we have seen, a very large number can affect the mean of a set of numbers to such an extent that it is not representative of the set. Another kind of average, the *median*, is used when we wish to reduce the impact of an extreme number in the set, for instance, in computing average salary.

DEFINITION

In a set of numbers arranged in numerical order, the **median** of the numbers is the number in the middle. If there are two numbers in the middle, the median is the mean of the two middle numbers.

EXAMPLE 3

Find the median.

a. 6, 8, 2, 1, and 5   **b.** 6, 8, 2, and 5

Solution

a. We arrange the numbers from smallest to largest.

The middle number
↓

1   2   5   6   8

So the median is 5. If we arrange the numbers from largest to smallest, we get the same answer.

The middle number
↓

8   6   5   2   1

The median is still 5.

b. We order the numbers from smallest to largest.

2   5   6   8

Since four numbers are on the list and four is even, no single number is in the middle. In this case, the median is the mean of the two middle numbers.

Two middle numbers
↓

2   5   6   8
↓

$$\frac{5 + 6}{2} = 5.5$$

So 5.5 is the median.

PRACTICE 3

Compute the median.

a. 7, 2, 8, 5, 10, 7, 9, 10, 2, 5, 8, and 6

b. 0, 4, 1, 5, 7, 2, 5, 9, and 3

EXAMPLE 4

The first 11 justices on the U.S. Supreme Court served the following numbers of years: 5, 8, 1, 20, 5, 9, 0, 13, 4, 15, and 30. (*Source: Time Almanac 2010*)

a. What was the median number of years that they served on the court?

b. The next appointed justice served on the court for 3 years. With the addition of this new justice, by how much did the median number of years that the justices served change?

Solution

a. To compute the median of the years of service, let's first arrange these numbers in increasing order:

The middle number
↓

0   1   4   5   5   8   9   13   15   20   30

Because 8 is the middle number, the median number of years of service was 8.

PRACTICE 4

The weekend box office receipts (in millions of dollars) for five leading movies was:

25   16   9   12   26

a. What was the median box office receipt for these movies?

b. A sixth movie also took in $9 million at the box office. How does the median box office receipt of the six movies compare with that of the five movies?
(*Source: Variety*)

b. Let's arrange the 12 numbers in increasing order:

Two middle numbers
↓

0 1 3 4 5 5 8 9 13 15 20 30

The numbers 5 and 8 are in the middle. So the median is $\frac{5 + 8}{2}$, or 6.5. Since the median decreased from 8 to 6.5, it dropped by 1.5, that is, by 1.5 years.

Mode

The last type of average that we consider is the mode. Note that a set of numbers can have one mode, more than one mode, or even no mode.

> **DEFINITION**
> The **mode** of a set of numbers is the number (or numbers) occurring most frequently in the set.

EXAMPLE 5

Compute the mode(s).

a. 8, 6, 10, 8, 10, 8, 9, and 6

b. 2, 9, 3, 5, 7, 12, 3, 2, 18, 12, 2, and 3

c. 4, 10, 1, 5, 12, and 7

Solution

a. When we count how often each number occurs on this list, we see that 6 occurs twice, 8 occurs three times, 9 once, and 10 twice. Because there are more 8's than any other number, 8 is the mode.

b. Here, 2 occurs three times, 3 occurs three times, 5 once, 7 once, 9 once, 12 twice, and 18 once. So both 2 and 3, occurring most frequently, are modes.

c. No number occurs more than once. There is no mode.

PRACTICE 5

Find the mode(s).

a. 7, 2, 5, 1, 2, 5, and 2

b. 9, 1, 0, 4, 9, 4, 1, 5, 9, and 4

c. 8, 13, 9, and 2

EXAMPLE 6

Every U.S. state has a maximum posted speed limit for driving passenger vehicles. One state has a limit of 45 miles per hour, another one has a limit of 50 miles per hour, 26 have a limit of 55 miles per hour, 3 have a limit of 60 miles per hour, 16 have a limit of 65 miles per hour, and 3 have a limit of 70 miles per hour. What is the mode of these speed limits? (*Source:* iihs.org)

Solution The speed limit 55 miles per hour occurs more frequently than any other limit (26 times). So 55 miles per hour is the mode of the state speed limits.

PRACTICE 6

Students in a class discussed the number of hours in their college schedules. One student had a weekly schedule consisting of 3 hours of classes, 2 students had 6 hours, 15 had 12 hours, 1 had 13 hours, and 1 had 14 hours. Find the mode of the number of hours in these schedules.

Range

The last statistic that we consider is called the *range*. The range is not an average because it does not represent a typical number in the set. Instead, the range is a measure of the spread of the numbers in the set.

> **DEFINITION**
>
> The **range** of a set of numbers is the *difference* between the largest and the smallest number in the set.

EXAMPLE 7

Find the range of the numbers 3, 13, 2, 5, 9, and 2.

Solution   The largest number in the set is 13, and the smallest is 2. So the range is $13 - 2$, or 11.

PRACTICE 7

What is the range of 8, 10, 3, and 8?

EXAMPLE 8

Americans have seen a great deal of variability in gasoline prices at the pumps. The U.S. average retail prices (in dollars) for all grades of gasoline, including taxes, during the first six months of a recent year were as follows:

Jan	Feb	Mar	Apr	May	June
3.10	3.08	3.29	3.51	3.82	4.11

The average retail prices for gasoline during the last six months of the year were:

July	Aug	Sept	Oct	Nov	Dec
4.11	3.83	3.76	3.11	2.21	1.75

(*Source:* tonto.eia.doe.gov)

In which of the two six-month periods was the spread on gasoline prices greater?

Solution   During the first six-month period, the highest average gas price was $4.11 and the lowest was $3.08. Therefore the range of gas prices was $4.11 − $3.08, or $1.03. For the second period, the highest average gas price was $4.11 and the lowest was $1.75. So the range was $4.11 − $1.75, or $2.36. Since the second period had a larger range, its spread was greater.

PRACTICE 8

In a couple of years, each of the 45 states in the U.S. with a state minimum hourly wage rate had one of the following rates: $8.06, $7.25, $7.30, $8.55, $5.15, $7.24, $7.75, $6.25, $6.15, $8.25, $8.40, $7.50, $8.00, $7.40. What is the range of these rates? (*Source:* dol.gov)

Mathematically Speaking

Fill in each blank with the most appropriate term or phrase from the given list.

range	weighted	mean
median	statistics	arithmetic
mode	algebra	

1. The branch of mathematics that deals with handling large quantities of information is called _____.

2. The sum of the numbers in a set divided by however many numbers are in the set is called the _____.

3. When some numbers in a set count more heavily than other numbers in the set, the average is said to be _____.

4. The middle number in a set of numbers arranged in numerical order is called the _____.

5. The _____ is the number (or numbers) occurring most frequently in a set of numbers.

6. The _____ is the difference between the largest number and the smallest number in a set of numbers.

A *Compute the indicated statistics. Round to the nearest tenth, where necessary.*

7.

Numbers	Mean	Median	Mode(s)
a. 8, 2, 9, 4, 8			
b. 3, 0, 0, 3, 10			
c. 4, 6, 9, 1, 1, 3			
d. 7.5, 9, 8.5, 5.5, 8.1			
e. $3\frac{1}{2}, 3\frac{3}{4}, 4, 3\frac{1}{2}, 3\frac{1}{4}$			
f. 4, −2, −1, 0, −1			

8.

Numbers	Mean	Median	Mode(s)
a. 5, 3, 5, 5, 3			
b. 7, 0, 7, 6, 0			
c. 5, 1, 0, 7, 7, 4			
d. 2.1, 3.6, 1.4, 2.5, 2.4			
e. $4\frac{1}{2}, 3\frac{3}{4}, 4, 4\frac{1}{2}, 4\frac{1}{4}$			
f. −1, −3, −3, −2, 4			

9. Calculate the mean, rounded to the nearest cent.
$9,125.88 $11,724.87 $12,705 $11,839.75
$13,500.79 $14,703.71

10. Find the mean, rounded to the nearest foot, of the following measurements.
3,725 ft   3,719 ft   3,740 ft   3,726 ft   3,729 ft
3,734 ft   3,725 ft

B *Complete each table.*

11.

Numbers	Range
a. 20, 11, 3, 4, 16	
b. 2.3, 5.7, 10.2, 6.1, 0.9	
c. $6\frac{5}{6}, 5\frac{1}{2}, \frac{1}{3}, 8, 5\frac{3}{4}$	
d. −2, 6, −4, −1, −4	

12.

Numbers	Range
a. 8, 0, 14, 3, 11	
b. 7.4, 2.9, 3.5, 8.6, 4.1	
c. $3\frac{1}{4}, 4\frac{2}{3}, 6\frac{1}{2}, \frac{9}{10}, 3\frac{7}{8}$	
d. −2, 4, −5, −2, 0	

Applications

C *Solve and check.*

13. Here are a student's grades last term: A in College Skills (2 credits), B in World History (4 credits), C in Music (2 credits), A in Spanish (3 credits), and B in Physical Education (1 credit). Did the student make the Dean's List, which requires a GPA of 3.5? Explain. (*Reminder:* A = 4, B = 3, C = 2, and D = 1.)

14. On a test, 9 students earned 80, 10 students earned 70, and 1 student earned 75. Was the grade of 75 below the class average (mean), exactly average, or above the class average? Explain.

15. A grandmother leaves a total of $1,000,000 to her 10 grandchildren. What is the mean amount left to each grandchild? Can you compute the median amount with the given information? Explain.

16. A woman and four men are riding in an elevator. Two men are taller than the woman, and two are shorter. Who has the median height of the people in the elevator?

17. In the U.S. House of Representatives, 435 members of Congress represent the 50 states. The table below shows the number of representatives of 8 states.

State	Number of Representatives
Maine	2
Indiana	9
Wisconsin	8
Hawaii	2
Colorado	7
North Carolina	13
Tennessee	9
Nebraska	3

(*Source:* 2010.census.gov)

Which of these 8 states has representation that is above the average for all 50 states?

18. The table shows the quarterly revenues for Ford Motor Company in a recent year.

Quarter	Revenue (in billions)
1	$31.7
2	$35.4
3	$31.6
4	$35.1

(*Source:* finance.yahoo.com)

What was the median quarterly revenue?

19. The table shows the salary of six teachers based on the number of years of service at a local school.

Years of Service	Salary
6	$44,424
10	$57,418
1	$37,925
4	$42,656
13	$58,358
18	$70,852

a. Find the median salary.

b. What is the range?

20. The table shows the prime interest rate on June 1st of the years 2000 through 2010.

2000	2001	2002	2003	2004	2005
9.50%	7.00%	4.75%	4.25%	4.00%	6.00%

2006	2007	2008	2009	2010
8.00%	8.25%	5.00%	3.25%	3.25%

(*Source:* moneycafe.com)

a. What is the mode of the interest rates for the given years?

b. Find the range.

21. The diameters for the eight planets of the solar system, rounded to the nearest 1,000 miles, are as follows:

Planet	Diameter (in thousands of miles)
Mercury	3
Venus	8
Earth	8
Mars	4
Jupiter	89
Saturn	75
Uranus	32
Neptune	31

(*Source: Encyclopedia Americana*)

Find each of the following distances, rounded to the nearest 1,000 miles:

a. mean diameter

b. median diameter

c. mode(s) of the diameters

d. range of the diameters

23. In the year 1990, when the number of U.S. residents was about 249 million, the U.S. Postal Service delivered some 166 billion pieces of mail. By 2003, when the population had grown to 292 million, the Service delivered approximately 202 billion pieces of mail. On the average, how many more pieces of mail, to the nearest whole number, did a resident receive in 2003 than in 1990? (*Source:* U.S. Bureau of the Census)

22. Consider the following utility bills for the past 10 months:

Month	Utility Bill
January	$90
February	$80
March	$90
April	$70
May	$100
June	$110
July	$140
August	$140
September	$100
October	$90

Find each of the following:

a. the mean bill

b. the median bill

c. the mode(s) of the bills

d. the range of the bills

24. Students earned the following grades on a college math test:

85   90   60   45   95   70   60   90   100   25   85   70   80

75   55   85   100   40   95   50   75   65   90   75   60   50

Using the mean as the average, how far above or below the class average, to the nearest whole number, was the test score of 75?

• Check your answers on page A-11.

MINDStretchers

Groupwork

1. Working with a partner, construct an example of a set of 10 numbers

   a. whose mean, median, and mode are equal.

   b. whose mean is less than its median.

   c. that has two modes.

Mathematical Reasoning

2. Can the range of a set of numbers be equal to a negative number? Explain.

Investigation

3. In your college library or on the web, research the legal drinking age in 10 countries of your choosing. Then, determine the mean, median, mode, and range of these ages.

8.2   Tables and Graphs

What Tables and Graphs Are and Why They Are Important

We frequently present data in the form of tables or graphs. A **table** is a rectangular display of data. A **graph** is a picture or diagram of the data.

Organizing data in a table or graph makes it easier for a reader to make comparisons, to understand relationships, to spot trends, and to gain a sense of the data.

Graphs generally provide less accurate information than tables because we often have to read a graph by estimating. However, graphs are pictorial, so they make a more lasting impression than a table.

Tables and graphs are used in many different situations. Train schedules, insurance premium charts, and accountants' spreadsheets are common examples of tables. Graphs, such as a bar graph of a changing population, a line graph of fluctuating stock prices, and a circle graph of budget allocations, appear regularly in newspapers, magazines, and reports.

Tables

A table consists of rows and columns. Rows run horizontally, and columns run vertically. The nature of the entries in a row or column is described with labels called *headings*.

To read a table, first identify a particular row and column, and then locate the entry at their intersection. Consider the following table that shows the typical heartbeat rates for people of various ages:

	Person's Age	**Heartbeats per Minute**
Heading →		Column
Row →	Newborn	135
	2	110
	6	95
	10	87
	20	71
	40	72
Entry →	60	74

As the headings indicate, the entries in the first column are a person's age. The second column gives the number of times per minute that the heart of a person of that age typically beats.

As given in the table, the heart of a 20-year-old beats 71 times a minute. Does this table suggest that a child's heart beats more quickly than the heart of an adult? How many times per minute would you estimate that the heart of an 8-year-old beats?

Example 1 illustrates both reading and drawing conclusions from tables.

EXAMPLE 1

The following is the schedule of math classes this term:

Course	Section	Day/Time	Room	Professor
010	090	Tu W Th 9–10:50	516	Einstein
011	091	M W Th 9–9:50	518	Banneker
011	611	Tu Th 6–7:15	516	Kovalevski
051	111	M Tu W Th 11–11:50	523	Noether
051	711	M W 7–8:40	518	Hilbert
056	131	M W Th 1–2:50	516	Banneker
100	121	M Tu W Th 12–12:50	511	Hilbert
104	081	M W Th 8–8:50	511	Einstein
104	111	M W Th 11–11:50	511	Newton
150	091	M Tu W Th 9–9:50	511	Newton
150	511	M W 5:25–7:05	511	Kovalevski
206	131	M Tu W Th 1–1:50	523	Noether
301	141	M Tu W Th 2–2:50	523	Hilbert
302	511	Tu Th 5:25–7:05	520	Gauss

a. In what room does Math 301, Section 141 meet?

b. Is Professor Kovalevski teaching a section of Math 056 this term?

c. Today is Monday, and a student needs to speak to Professor Einstein. When and where is he teaching?

Solution

a. Math 301, Section 141 meets in room 523.

b. No, Professor Kovalevski is not teaching Math 056.

c. Professor Einstein is in room 511 from 8 to 8:50.

PRACTICE 1

A mail-order catalog contains the following chart for determining shipping and handling (S&H) charges:

Amount of Merchandise	Up to $5	$5.01–$15	$15.01–$25*
Charges	$2.95	$3.95	$4.95

*Add $0.10 for each additional $1 of merchandise over $25.

a. What are the S&H charges on $23.45 worth of merchandise?

b. How much must a customer pay in all for merchandise that, excluding S&H charges, sells for $3?

c. How much are the S&H charges on merchandise selling for $30?

Graphs

Now, let's discuss displaying data in the form of graphs. We deal with five kinds of graphs: pictographs, bar graphs, histograms, line graphs, and circle graphs.

Pictographs

A **pictograph** is a kind of graph in which images such as people, books, or coins are used to represent and to compare quantities. A *key* is given to explain what each image represents.

Pictographs are visually appealing. However, they make it difficult to distinguish between small differences—say, between a half and a third of an image.

EXAMPLE 2

The following graph shows the number of degrees awarded in the United States in a recent year:

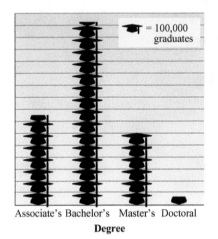

= 100,000 graduates

Associate's Bachelor's Master's Doctoral

Degree

(*Source:* census.gov)

a. What does the symbol 🎓 mean in the key at the top of the graph?

b. About how many master's degrees were awarded?

c. About how many more bachelor's degrees than associate's degrees were awarded?

Solution

a. According to the key, the symbol 🎓 represents 100,000 graduates.

b. The number of master's degrees awarded was about 6(100,000), or 600,000.

c. About 15(100,000), or 1,500,000, bachelor's degrees were awarded, in contrast to about $7\frac{1}{2}$ (100,000), or 750,000, associate's degrees.

So there were approximately 750,000 more bachelor's degrees awarded.

PRACTICE 2

The following pictograph shows the number of passengers who departed from or arrived at four busy U.S. airports in a recent year.

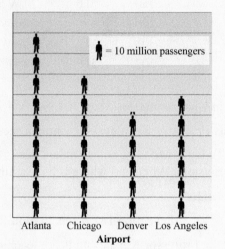

= 10 million passengers

Atlanta Chicago Denver Los Angeles

Airport

(*Source: The World Almanac 2010*)

a. What does the symbol 🧍 represent?

b. Which of the four airports was the busiest in terms of passengers?

c. Approximately how many passengers did the Los Angeles airport serve?

Bar Graphs

On a **bar graph**, quantities are represented by thin, parallel rectangles called bars. The length of each bar is proportional to the quantity that it represents.

On some graphs, the bars extend to the right. On other graphs, they extend upward or downward. Sometimes, bar lengths are labeled. Other times, they are read against an *axis*—a straight line parallel to the bars and similar to a number line.

Bar graphs are especially useful for making comparisons or contrasts among a few quantities, as the following example illustrates.

EXAMPLE 3

The graph shows the net income of Delta Air Lines Inc. in recent years.

a. What was the approximate net income of the company in fiscal year 2009?

b. About how much greater was the net income in fiscal year 2007 than in fiscal year 2006?

c. Describe the information shown by the graph.

Solution

a. In 2009, the net income of the company was about −$1.2 billion, that is, a loss of about $1.2 billion.

b. In 2006, the net income was about −$6.2 billion. The next year, it was about $1.6 billion. So the net income for 2007 was approximately $7.8 billion greater than in 2006.

c. The company operated at a profit in 2007. In other years, however, it operated at a loss, especially in 2008.

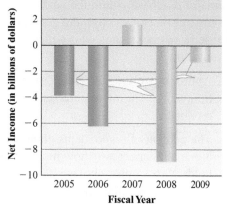

(*Source:* dailyfinance.com)

PRACTICE 3

The following graph shows the value of five leading farm commodities in California for a recent year.

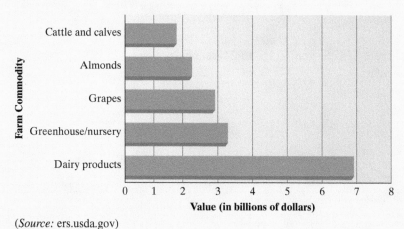

(*Source:* ers.usda.gov)

a. Which commodity had the greatest value?

b. What was the approximate value of grapes?

c. About how much greater was the value of greenhouse/nursery than almonds?

The next graph is an example of a *double-bar graph*. This kind of graph is used to compare two sets of data in various ways, as the following example illustrates.

EXAMPLE 4

The graph shows the percent of U.S. respondents according to a recent poll who were planning to make a major purchase within the next six months. The poll compares responses from the general population with those from households whose incomes exceeded $100 thousand.

a. Approximately what percent of the general population were planning to purchase home improvements/repairs?

b. The percent of respondents planning to purchase home appliances was how much greater from households with income above $100 thousand than from the general population?

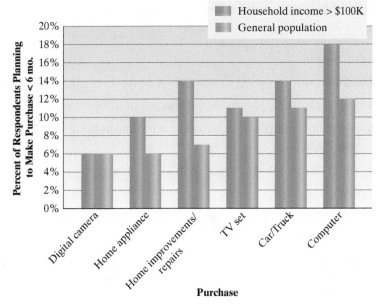

(*Source: Adweek*)

Solution

a. The percent of respondents from the general population who were planning to purchase home improvements/repairs was approximately 7%.

b. The percent of respondents planning to purchase home appliances was about 10% for households with income above $100 thousand and about 6% for the general population. So the difference was approximately 4%.

PRACTICE 4

The following graph shows the unemployment rate of U.S. youth (16- to 24-year-olds) versus adults (ages 25 and over) for five years.

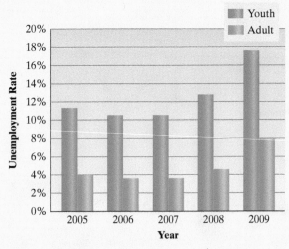

(*Source*: bls.gov)

a. For the year 2006, approximately what was the unemployment rate for youth?

b. For the year 2009, approximately what was the difference between the unemployment rate for youth and that for adults?

Histograms

Now, let's consider another kind of bar graph called a **histogram**. To understand what a histogram is, we consider an example.

Suppose that in a math class, 24 students take a final exam. The results are organized into a *frequency table*, as shown to the left. In the left column, note that the scores are grouped into *class intervals* (ranges of numbers) all of the same width and that these class intervals are written in increasing order. The right column shows the *class frequencies*, that is, the number of students who earned scores that fall into the class interval on the left. How would you have predicted the sum of the class frequencies in the right column?

A histogram is a graph of a frequency table. In a histogram, adjacent bars touch. For each bar, the width represents a class interval, and the height stands for the corresponding class frequency. Consider the following histogram, which corresponds to the frequency table, as shown above to the right.

Score (Class Interval)	Frequency (Class Frequency)
40–49	2
50–59	2
60–69	6
70–79	4
80–89	6
90–99	4

Note that according to the histogram, 4 students scored between 70 and 79, as given in the frequency table. Can you explain how the histogram shows that 10 students scored 80 or above?

EXAMPLE 5

The following graph shows the number of earthquakes worldwide in a recent year with magnitude 1.0 or greater.

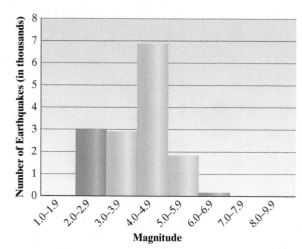

(*Source:* earthquake.usgs.gov)

PRACTICE 5

The following histogram summarizes the ages of the first 44 U.S. presidents at the time of their initial inauguration.

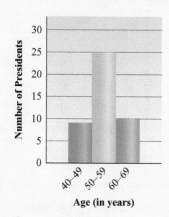

(*Source:* wikipedia.org)

EXAMPLE 5 (continued)

a. Approximately how many earthquakes were there with magnitude between 5.0 and 5.9?

b. To the nearest thousand, how many earthquakes were there with magnitude 4.9 or below?

c. What is the approximate ratio in simplified form of the number of earthquakes with magnitude 4.0–4.9 to those with magnitude 3.0–3.9?

Solution

a. The height of the bar for the class interval 5.0–5.9 is approximately 1,800. So there were about 1,800 earthquakes with magnitude between 5.0 and 5.9.

b. The number of earthquakes with magnitude 4.9 or below is the sum of the height of the bar for the class interval 4.0–4.9, as well as the height of all bars to the left. To the nearest thousand, this sum is 13,000.

c. The ratio of the number of earthquakes with magnitude 4.0–4.9 to those with magnitude 3.0–3.9 is about 7 to 3.

a. Approximately how many presidents were in their fifties when they were first inaugurated?

b. Were any presidents younger than 40 at their initial inauguration?

c. About how many presidents were 59 or younger when they were first inaugurated?

Line Graphs

On a **line graph**, points are connected by straight-line segments. The position of any point on a line graph is read against the vertical axis and the horizontal axis.

A line graph, also called a **broken-line graph**, is commonly used to highlight changes and trends over a period of time. Especially when we have data for many points in time, we are more likely to use a line graph than a bar graph.

EXAMPLE 6

The following graph shows the number of Americans 65 years of age and older from 1900 to 2010.

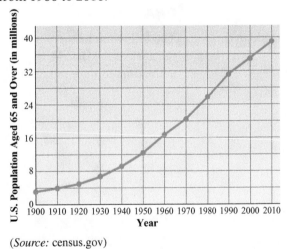

(*Source:* census.gov)

a. Approximately how big was this population in the year 2000?

b. In what year did this population number about 21 million?

c. In the year 2000, the U.S. population overall was approximately 4 times as large as it had been in the year 1900. Did the population shown in the graph grow more quickly?

PRACTICE 6

The following graph shows the mean temperatures in Chicago over a 30-year period for each month of the year.

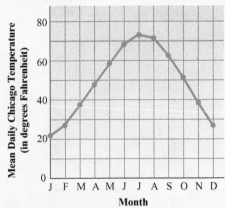

(*Source:* The U.S. National Climatic Data Center)

a. Which month in Chicago has the highest mean temperature?

Solution

a. In 2000, there were about 35 million Americans aged 65 and above.

b. There were approximately 21 million Americans aged 65 and above in the year 1970.

c. In 2000, the overall U.S. population was 4 times what it had been in 1900. But the population shown in the graph grew by a factor of about 10 and so grew more quickly.

b. Approximately what is the mean temperature in February?

c. What trend does the graph show?

Comparison line graphs show two or more changing quantities, as Example 7 illustrates.

EXAMPLE 7

The graph gives the number of male and female participants in high school athletic programs in the U.S. for selected years.

a. Estimate the number of females who participated in high school athletic programs in 2005–06.

b. Was the difference between the number of male and the number of female participants greater in 1985–86 or 1995–96?

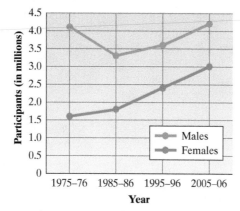

(*Source:* infoplease.com)

c. Describe the trend that this graph shows.

Solution

a. In 2005–06, the number of female participants in high school athletic programs was approximately 3 million.

b. In 1985–86, the number of male participants was about 3.3 million and the number of female participants about 1.8 million. So the difference was about 1.5 million. By contrast in 1995–96, there were about 3.6 million males and 2.4 million females, with a difference of approximately 1.2 million. Since 1.5 million is larger than 1.2 million, the difference was greater in 1985–86.

c. Each year, there were more male participants than female participants. The number of female participants increased each year. The number of male participants decreased in 1985–86 and then increased in subsequent years.

PRACTICE 7

The following graph shows the mean precipitation for the cities of Seattle, Washington and Orlando, Florida in selected months.

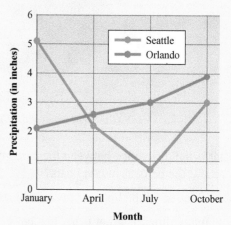

(*Source:* weatherbase.com)

a. On the average, does it rain more in Seattle or in Orlando during the month of October?

b. Approximately what is the average precipitation in Seattle for the month of January?

c. What trend does this graph show?

Circle Graphs

Circle graphs are commonly used to show how a whole amount—say, an entire budget or population—is broken into its parts. The graph resembles a pie (the whole amount) that has been cut into slices (the parts).

Each slice (or *sector*) is proportional in size to the part of the whole that it represents. Each slice is appropriately labeled with either its actual count or the percent of the whole that it represents.

The following example illustrates how to read and interpret the information given by a circle graph.

EXAMPLE 8

The following graph shows the percents of American households that own a single kind of pet:

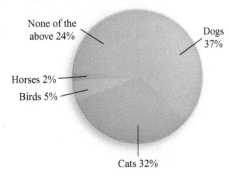

(*Source: Statistical Abstract of the United States, 2010*)

a. What is the difference between the percent of households owning dogs and the percent owning cats?

b. What fraction of the households own birds?

c. How many times as great is the percent of households owning cats as the percent owning horses?

Solution

a. Dog owners comprise 37% of the households, in contrast to 32% for cats. So the difference is 5%.

b. 5%, or 5 out of every 100, of the households own birds, which is equivalent to $\frac{5}{100}$, or $\frac{1}{20}$.

c. 32% of the households own cats, and 2% own horses. So the percent of households that owns cats is 16 times the percent that owns horses.

PRACTICE 8

A sample of U.S. e-mail users were asked how frequently they check their e-mail. The following graph summarizes their responses.

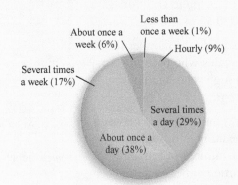

(*Source:* digitalcenter.org)

a. What fraction of the respondents check their e-mail about once a week?

b. What percent check their e-mail at least several times a day?

c. How many times as great is the percent of users who check their e-mail hourly than the percent who check their e-mail less than once a week?

Mathematically Speaking

Fill in each blank with the most appropriate term or phrase from the given list.

line graph	circle graph	heading
rows	columns	histogram
bar graph	graph	
pictograph	table	

1. A _____ is a rectangular display of data.

2. A _____ is a picture or diagram of data.

3. In a table, _____ run horizontally.

4. On a _____, images such as people, books or coins are used to represent quantities.

5. On a _____, quantities are represented by thin, parallel rectangles.

6. A _____ is a graph of a frequency table.

7. A _____ is commonly used to highlight changes and trends over a period of time.

8. A _____ resembles a pie (the whole) that has been cut into slices (the parts).

Applications

Ⓐ *Read each table and solve.*

9. The following table shows how to determine a stockbroker's commission in a stock transaction. The commission depends on both the number of shares sold and the price per share.

Price per Share	Number of Shares				
	100	200	300	400	500
$1–$20	$40	$50	$60	$70	$80
>$20	$40	$60	$80	$90	$100

a. What is the broker's commission on a sale of 300 shares of stock at $15.75 a share?

b. What is the commission on a sale of 500 shares of stock at $30 a share?

c. Will an investor pay her broker a lower commission if she sells 400 shares of stock in a single deal or 200 shares of stock in each of two deals?

10. The table shows the 2009 federal income tax schedule for single filers.

If taxable income is over	But not over	The tax is
$0	$8,350	10% of the amount over $0
$8,350	$33,950	$835 plus 15% of the amount over $8,350
$33,950	$82,250	$4,675 plus 25% of the amount over $33,950
$82,250	$171,550	$16,750 plus 28% of the amount over $82,250
$171,550	$372,950	$41,754 plus 33% of the amount over $171,550
$372,950	No limit	$108,216 plus 33% of the amount over $372,950

(*Source:* irs.gov)

a. What is the tax for a person whose taxable income was $33,950?

b. Compute the tax for a person whose taxable income is $27,000.

11. An atlas contains a table of road distances (in miles) between various U.S. cities.

	Los Angeles	Chicago	Houston
Los Angeles	—	2,112	1,556
Chicago	2,112	—	1,092
Houston	1,556	1,092	—

(*Source: Road McNally Road Atlas*)

a. According to this table, how far is Los Angeles from Houston?

b. Chicago is how much closer to Houston than to Los Angeles?

c. What is the meaning of the blanks in the table?

12. At a college, the math courses that students take depend on their scores on the Arithmetic and Algebra Placement Test. Test scores get translated into course placements as follows.

		Arithmetic Score		
		0–10	**11–15**	**16–28**
	0–10	Math 1 and then Math 3	Math 2 and then Math 3	Math 3
Algebra Score	**11–15**	Math 1 and then Math 3	Math 4	Math 3
	16–20	Math 1	Math 2	Math 5

a. If you score 12 in arithmetic and 8 in algebra, what should you take?

b. Suppose that you score 8 in arithmetic and 12 in algebra. What is your placement?

c. What must you score to take Math 5?

B *Read each graph and solve.*

13. The pictograph shows the projected employment for five major U.S. industries in the year 2018.

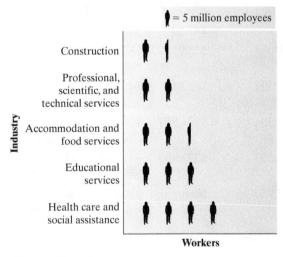

(*Source:* bls.gov)

a. Which of the industries will employ the most people in 2018?

b. Approximately how many workers will be employed in the accommodation and food services industry in 2018?

14. The following pictograph shows the percent of adults by age group who have accessed the internet wirelessly, according to a recent survey.

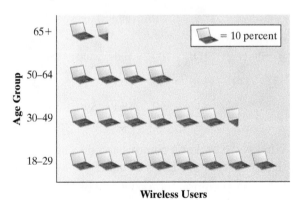

Wireless Users

(*Source:* pewinternet.org)

a. Approximately what percent of 30–49 year olds have accessed the internet wirelessly?

b. For those adults who accessed the internet wirelessly, estimate the ratio of the percent of those 65 and over to the percent of 50–64 year olds.

15. In chemistry, the pH scale measures how acidic or basic a solution is. A solution with a pH of 7 is considered neutral. Solutions with a pH less than 7 are acids, and solutions with a pH greater than 7 are bases. The graph below shows the pH of various solutions.

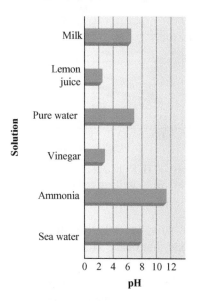

a. Which of the solutions are acids?

b. Approximate the pH of sea water.

c. Which solution is neutral?

17. The following histogram shows the waiting time for applicants while at a passport office:

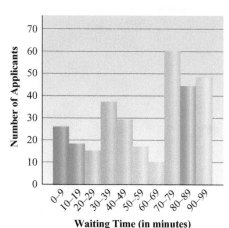

a. Did more applicants wait less than 10 minutes or more than 89 minutes?

b. Approximately how many applicants waited 80 minutes or more?

c. About how many applicants waited between 60 and 79 minutes?

16. The following graph shows the percent changes in the U.S. consumer price index (CPI) for energy types between November and December 2009 and between May and June 2010.

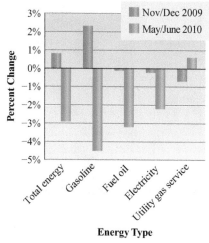

(*Source:* bls.gov)

a. Estimate the percent increase in the CPI for total energy between November and December 2009.

b. Between May and June 2010, the CPI for which type of energy increased?

c. According to the graph, which type of energy between which consecutive months had the greatest percent increase in CPI?

18. The histogram shows the number of 2009 college-bound high school seniors taking the SAT by family income.

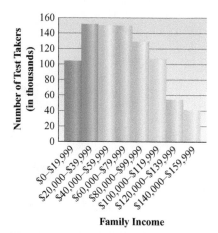

(*Source:* professionals.collegeboard.com)

a. About how many 2009 college-bound seniors with family incomes less than $60,000 took the SAT?

b. About how many 2009 college-bound seniors with family incomes between $80,000 and $119,999 took the SAT?

c. Describe the trend in this histogram.

19. The following graph shows the number of cell phone subscribers (in millions) for recent years.

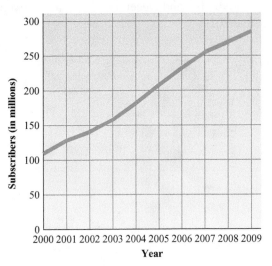

(*Source:* CTIA)

a. About how many subscribers were there in the year 2008?

b. In what year did the number of subscribers first exceed 200 million?

c. Describe the trend shown in the graph.

21. The graph shows the percent of Americans affiliated with various political parties, according to a recent poll.

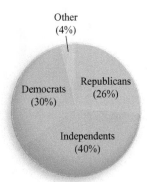

(*Source:* gallup.com)

a. According to this graph, are there more Americans who consider themselves Democrats or Republicans?

b. What fraction of Americans consider themselves Independent?

c. If 15,000 people were polled, how many of these considered themselves neither Republicans, Democrats, nor Independents?

20. A human child and a chimp were raised together. Scientists graphed the number of words that the child and the chimp understood at different ages.

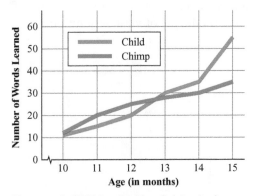

(*Sources:* A. H. Kritz, *Problem Solving in the Sciences;* W. N. Kellogg and L. A. Kellogg, *The Ape and the Child*)

a. At about what age was the child's vocabulary first better than that of the chimp?

b. At age 15 months, about how many more words did the child know than the chimp?

22. The following circle graph shows the percent of social security recipients receiving various types of payment in a recent month:

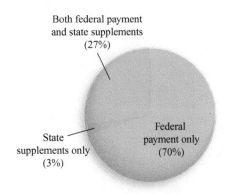

(*Source:* ssa.gov)

a. What percent of the recipients received both federal payment and state supplements?

b. What percent of the recipients received state supplements?

c. Is it true that the number of recipients who received federal payment only was more than ten times as great as the number of recipients who received state supplements only?

• Check your answers on page A-11.

MINDStretchers

Technology

1. On a computer, use a spreadsheet program to draw a circle graph that represents the following data, showing the percent of men and the percent of women at a party:

Gender	Number of Guests at a Party
Men	12
Women	8

Writing

2. A *stacked bar graph* not only allows comparisons between quantities but also shows how each quantity is divided into parts. For example, the following stacked bar graph deals, for each month of a year, with a company's total revenue, which is generated partly in store and partly online. In a few sentences, describe some of the main trends that this graph implies.

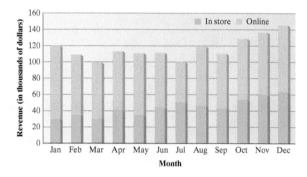

Mathematical Reasoning

3. Consider the following two bar graphs. They both represent the same data, namely the percent of voters in the presidential election of 2008 who voted either Democratic or Republican. (*Source:* wikipedia.org)

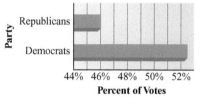

   a. Explain the difference between the impression that the top graph gives and the impression the bottom graph gives.

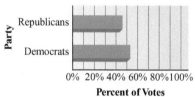

   b. How is this difference in impression achieved?

   c. Why would someone prefer to give one impression more than the other?

Key Concepts and Skills

CONCEPT   SKILL

Concept/Skill	Description	Example
[8.1] **Mean**	Given a set of numbers, the sum of the numbers divided by however many numbers are in the set.	For 0, 0, 1, 3, and 5, the mean is: $$\frac{0 + 0 + 1 + 3 + 5}{5}$$ $$= \frac{9}{5} = 1.8$$
[8.1] **Median**	Given a set of numbers arranged in numerical order, the number in the middle. If there are two numbers in the middle, the mean of the two middle numbers.	For 0, 0, 1, 3, and 5, the median is 1.
[8.1] **Mode**	Given a set of numbers, the number (or numbers) occurring most frequently in the set.	For 0, 0, 1, 3, and 5, the mode is 0.
[8.1] **Range**	Given a set of numbers, the difference between the largest and the smallest number in the set of numbers.	For 0, 0, 1, 3, and 5, the range is $5 - 0$, or 5.
[8.2] **Table**	A rectangular display of data.	
[8.2] **Pictograph**	A graph in which images such as people, books, or coins are used to represent the quantities.	
[8.2] **Bar graph**	A graph in which quantities are represented by thin, parallel rectangles called bars. The length of each bar is proportional to the quantity that it represents.	
[8.2] **Histogram**	A graph of a frequency table.	

(CONCEPT) (SKILL)

Concept/Skill	Description	Example
[8.2] **Line graph**	A graph in which points are connected by straight-line segments. The position of any point on a line graph is read against the vertical axis and the horizontal axis.	
[8.2] **Circle graph**	A graph that resembles a pie (a whole amount) that has been cut into slices (the parts).	

CHAPTER 8   Review Exercises

Say Why
Fill in each blank.

1. A set of numbers _____ have more than one mean
   can/cannot
   because _____
   _____.

2. A set of numbers _____ have more than one mode
   can/cannot
   because _____
   _____.

3. The range in the set 1, 4, 4, 4 _____ the same as
   is/is not
   the range in the set 401, 404, 404, 404 because
   _____
   _____.

4. A table _____ provide more exact information
   does/does not
   than a graph because _____
   _____.

5. A pictograph _____ typically used to represent
   is/is not
   small differences because _____
   _____.

6. A circle graph _____ used to make comparisons or
   is/is not
   contrasts among quantities because _____
   _____.

[8.1] *Compute the desired statistic for each list of numbers.*

7.
List of Numbers	Mean	Median	Mode	Range
a. 6, 7, 4, 10, 4, 5, 6, 8, 7, 4, 5				
b. 1, 3, 4, 4, 2, 3, 1, 4, 5, 1				

Mixed Applications

8. The following table shows how long the first five American presidents and their wives lived:

President	Age	President's Wife	Age
George Washington	67	Martha Washington	70
John Adams	90	Abigail Adams	74
Thomas Jefferson	83	Martha Jefferson	34
James Madison	85	Dolley Madison	81
James Monroe	73	Eliza Monroe	62

(*Source: Presidents, First Ladies, and Vice Presidents*)

   a. Using the median as the average, did the husbands or the wives live longer?

   b. By how many years?

   c. What was the range of the ages of the presidents?

9. The median age of National Public Radio (NPR) listeners is 55 years. (*Source:* npr.org)
   a. Explain what this statement means.
   b. By how many years is the age of a 25-year-old listener above or below the median?

10. A soda machine is considered reliable if the range of the amounts of soda that it dispenses is less than 2 fluid ounces. In 10 tries, a particular machine dispensed the following amounts (in fluid ounces).

    8.1 7.8 8.6 8.1 8.4 7.8 8 7.7 6.9 8.4

    Is the machine reliable? Explain.

11. In order for a small local zoo to be profitable, it must average a minimum of at least 12,500 paying visitors per month. For the past 5 months, the number of paying visitors was as follows:

    14,912 9,873 11,025 15,207 14,528

    Using the mean as the average, determine whether the zoo was profitable.

12. In a recent year, the amount of cargo (in tons) that the five busiest U.S. ports handled was as follows:

Port	Cargo (in tons)		
	Total	Domestic	Foreign
Port of South Louisiana, LA	229,040,085	121,549,984	107,490,101
Houston, TX	216,064,325	70,721,886	145,342,439
New York, NY and NJ	157,202,043	65,780,088	91,421,955
Long Beach, CA	85,939,895	15,383,519	70,556,376
Beaumont, TX	81,383,531	24,339,637	57,043,894

(*Source:* U.S. Army Corps of Engineers)

   a. To the nearest 10,000 tons, how much domestic cargo did Houston handle?
   b. Which of these five ports handled the least foreign cargo?
   c. To the nearest 10,000 tons, how much more domestic cargo did New York handle than Beaumont?
   d. Which of these ports handled more foreign than domestic cargo?

13. The following pictograph shows the number of monthly domestic flights in the U.S. during recent years.

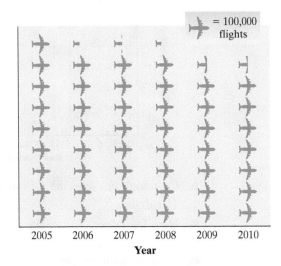

(*Source: Newsweek*)

   a. About how many monthly domestic flights were there in 2007?

   b. In which year shown were there the most monthly domestic flights?
   c. About how many more monthly domestic flights were there in 2008 than in 2010?

14. The following graph shows the seven largest libraries in the United States and the number of volumes held by each.

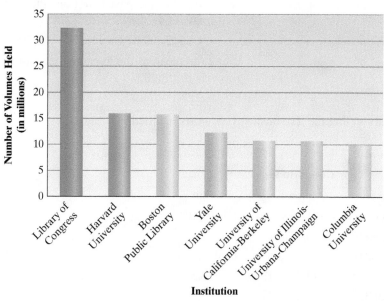

(*Source:* ala.org)

   a. Approximately how many volumes are held in the library at Columbia University?

   b. About how many more volumes does the Boston Public Library hold than the University of California–Berkeley?

   c. Which libraries appear to hold half the number of volumes that the Library of Congress holds?

15. The following histogram displays the number of U.S. licensed drivers in a recent year, aged 20 through 84, according to their age.

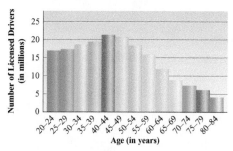

(*Source:* fhwa.dot.gov)

   a. About how many licensed drivers were between 35 and 49 years of age?

   b. If the total number of licensed drivers was about 200 million, approximately what percent of these were between the ages of 35 and 39?

   c. Describe the trend in this graph.

16. Consider the following learning curve that shows how long a rat running through a maze takes on each run:

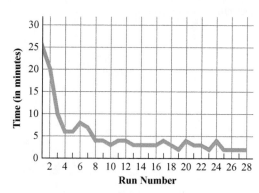

   a. On which run does the rat run through the maze in 10 minutes?

   b. How long does the rat take on the tenth run?

   c. What general conclusion can you draw from this learning curve?

17. The graph shows the health care expenditures from out-of-pocket and insurance sources.

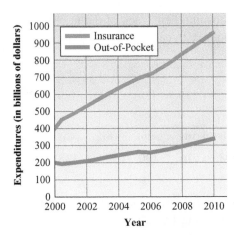

(*Source:* Centers for Medicare and Medicaid Services)

a. In what year were the insurance expenditures approximately $600 billion?

b. In the year 2000, what was the approximate ratio of out-of-pocket expenditures to insurance expenditures?

c. Express in words the trend the graph is illustrating.

19. In a college algebra course, each of two tests counts 20% of a student's course average, whereas the final exam counts 60% of the course average. Find the course average of a student who scored 80 and 90 on her tests and 70 on the final exam.

18. The following graph shows the number of organ transplants performed in the United States for a recent year.

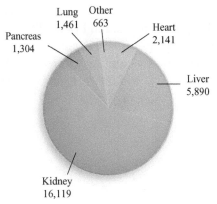

(*Source:* ustransplant.org)

a. How many transplants in all were performed?

b. How many more liver transplants than lung transplants were performed?

c. What percent of all transplants performed were kidney transplants, to the nearest whole percent?

20. A survey was conducted on thousands of households throughout the United States comparing the views of internet users with non-users on whether communication technology has made the world a better place. The graph below summarizes their responses.

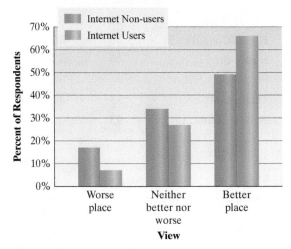

(*Source:* digitalcenter.org)

Did a greater percent of Internet users or non-users indicate that communication technology has made the world a better place?

• Check your answers on page A-12.

CHAPTER 8   Posttest

FOR EXTRA HELP   CHAPTER Test Prep VIDEOS The Chapter Test Prep Videos with test solutions are available on DVD, in MyMathLab, and on YouTube™ (search "AkstBasicMath" and click on "Channels").

To see whether you have mastered the topics in this chapter, take this test.

1. At the end of your first term, your grades were as follows: English Composition I (4 credits)—A, College Skills and Freshman Orientation (2 credits)—B, History (3 credits)—C, and Art (1 credit)—A. If $A = 4, B = 3, C = 2, D = 1$, and $F = 0$, calculate your GPA.

2. A local hospital kept track of the number of babies born each month last year.

Jan	Feb	Mar	Apr	May	June
106	115	138	165	189	202

July	Aug	Sept	Oct	Nov	Dec
208	216	190	172	138	105

What was the mean number of babies born at the hospital in a month last year?

3. A math instructor records the following exam scores for students in her Math 110 course:

86   78   96   82   74   56   72   76
88   60   48   76   100   98   64   80

What was the median exam score?

4. The weights (in pounds) of the 25 players on the active roster for the San Diego Padres during a recent season were as follows:

195   250   200   200   210   200   225   215   200   240
205   230   205   200   175   225   190   210   205   210
195   220   200   160   210

(*Source:* mlb.com)

What are the mode and range of the weights?

5. Shown in the following table is the fuel economy in miles per gallon (mpg) of the six most fuel-efficient vehicles for the model year 2010.

Vehicle	City (mpg)	Highway (mpg)
Toyota Prius	51	48
Honda Civic Hybrid	40	45
Honda Insight	40	43
Ford Fusion Hybrid	41	36
Smart for Two	33	41
Nissan Altima Hybrid	35	33

(*Source:* thedailygreen.com)

Which vehicles have better fuel efficiency for city driving than for highway driving?

6. A sample of adults were asked how they try to avoid catching the flu. The following graph summarizes their responses.

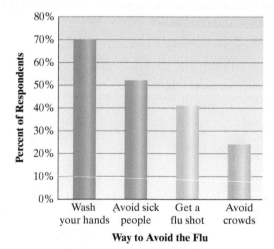

(*Source:* usatoday.com)

Approximately how much greater was the percent of respondents who avoid the flu by washing their hands than by getting a flu shot?

7. The following graph shows the number of U.S. adult victims of identity fraud for the years 2003 through 2009.

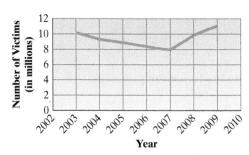

(*Source:* identitytheftassistance.org)

About how many more victims of identity fraud were there in 2009 than in 2007?

8. The graph below shows music sales for the years 2000–2009, including album sales, digital track sales, and overall music purchases.

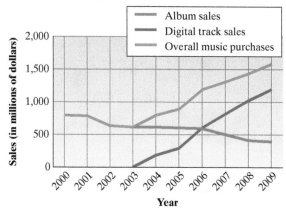

(*Source:* narm.com)

a. In what year were digital track sales first higher than album sales?

b. Describe the relationship between album, digital track, and overall music purchases. Use this relationship to describe overall music purchases for the year 2006.

9. The following circle graph shows the breakdown of the U.S. coastline (in miles) by region:

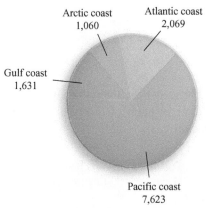

(*Source:* National Oceanic and Atmospheric Administration, U.S. Department of Commerce)

To the nearest 10%, what percent of the U.S. coastline is on the Pacific coast?

10. The following graph shows the number of Nobel prizes awarded in the sciences for research conducted in the United States and in the United Kingdom.

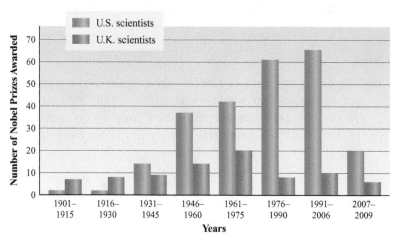

(*Source:* wikipedia.org)

In which period of time did scientists in the United States receive about twice as many prizes as scientists in the United Kingdom?

• Check your answers on page A-12.

Cumulative Review Exercises

To help you review, solve the following.

1. Simplify: $3 + 4(7 - 2)$

2. Simplify: $\dfrac{20}{25}$

3. Combine and simplify: $4\dfrac{17}{100} - 2\dfrac{3}{10}$

4. Estimate the following product: $\left(8\dfrac{1}{10}\right)\left(4\dfrac{9}{10}\right)$

5. Compute: $7.34 - (2.46 + 2.07)$

6. $(3.01)(1,000) = ?$

7. Solve for x: $x - 7\dfrac{1}{4} = 10$

8. Is 24 a solution to the equation $\dfrac{x}{0.4} = 6$?

9. Solve for n: $\dfrac{7}{10} = \dfrac{n}{30}$

10. Which is larger, 462% or $4\dfrac{5}{8}$?

11. What is $12\dfrac{1}{2}\%$ of 16?

12. What are the sign and the absolute value of $-\dfrac{7}{4}$?

13. Find the quotient and simplify: $-8 \div \left(\dfrac{4}{9}\right)$

14. Find the mean, median, mode(s), and range of 3.6, 3.9, 3.3, 3.8, and 3.9.

15. Recently in the United States, there were 14.9 million students enrolled in public high schools and 1.4 million students enrolled in private high schools. How many times the second enrollment is the first, rounded to the nearest tenth? (*Source:* National Center for Educational Statistics)

16. There were 480 unemployed people for 60 job openings. How many jobless people were there per opening?

17. Between July 2009 and July 2010, the number of full-time workers in the United States dropped from 114 million to 112 million. Find the percent decrease, to the nearest percent. (*Source:* bls.gov)

Solve.

18. The Great Pyramid of Khufu—the last surviving wonder of the ancient world—was built around 2680 B.C. To the nearest thousand years, how long ago was this pyramid built? (*Source: The Concise Columbia Encyclopedia*)

19. The following table shows the maximum number of home runs hit by a player in each of the two major baseball leagues during recent years.

Year	National League	American League
2005	48	51
2006	54	58
2007	54	50
2008	37	48
2009	39	47

(*Source:* baseball-almanac.com)

Was the median number of home runs higher in the National League or in the American League?

20. Many Americans vacation in Australia. The graph below shows the age and gender of visitors to Australia from the United States for a recent year.

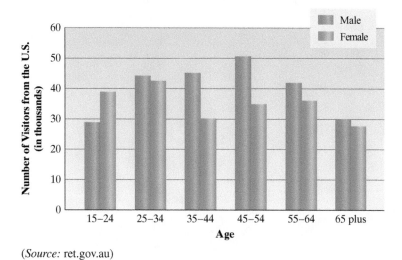

(*Source:* ret.gov.au)

In terms of gender and age, which was the largest group of visitors from the U.S. to Australia?

11.6 Square Roots and the Pythagorean Theorem

OBJECTIVES

In Section 11.3, we found the area of a square by squaring the length of one of its sides. In this section, we look at the opposite of squaring a number, that is, finding its *square root.*

A To find the square root of a number

Finding the Square Root of a Number

B To find the unknown side of a right triangle, using the Pythagorean theorem

Consider the following problem. Suppose that a square has an area of 25 ft^2. What is the length s of each side?

C To solve applied problems involving a square root or the Pythagorean theorem

Recall that, for the area of a square, $A = s^2$. So for $25 = s^2$, we need to determine what whole number when multiplied by itself equals 25. Because $25 = 5 \cdot 5$, the whole number is 5. So a square with an area of 25 ft^2 has sides of length 5 feet.

Squaring the whole number 5 gives 25. So we say that 25 is the *square* of 5, or that 5 is the (principal) *square root* of 25 (written $\sqrt{25} = 5$).

Since 25 is the square of a whole number, it is called a *perfect square.* Perfect squares play a special role in the discussion of square roots.

DEFINITIONS

A **perfect square** is a number that is the square of a whole number.

The (principal) **square root** of a number n, written $\sqrt{n}$, is the positive number whose square is n.

Since $36 = 6^2$, $\sqrt{36} = 6$. And since $4 = 2^2$, $\sqrt{4} = 2$. Squaring and taking a square root are opposite operations, since one operation undoes the other.

EXAMPLE 1	PRACTICE 1
Find the square root.	What is the square root of each perfect square?

EXAMPLE 1

Find the square root.

a. $\sqrt{64}$ **b.** $\sqrt{100}$

Solution In each case, we need to find the whole number that when squared gives us the number under the square root sign.

a. $\sqrt{64} = 8$ because $8 \cdot 8 = 64$.

b. $\sqrt{100} = 10$ because $10 \cdot 10 = 100$.

PRACTICE 1

What is the square root of each perfect square?

a. $\sqrt{49}$

b. $\sqrt{144}$

In Example 1, note that $100 > 25$ and $\sqrt{100} > \sqrt{25}$. In general, larger numbers have larger square roots.

Many numbers are not perfect squares. For instance, 28 is not a perfect square because there is no whole number that when multiplied by itself equals 28. If a number is not a perfect square, we can either estimate or use a calculator to find its approximate square root.

EXAMPLE 2

$\sqrt{28}$ lies between which two consecutive whole numbers?

Solution To begin, let's find the two consecutive perfect squares that 28 lies between. The number 28 is more than 25 and less than 36, which are consecutive perfect squares.

Because 28 lies between 5^2 and 6^2, $\sqrt{28}$ lies between 5 and 6.

PRACTICE 2

Between which two consecutive whole numbers does $\sqrt{47}$ lie?

EXAMPLE 3

Using a calculator, approximate each square root. Round to the nearest tenth.

a. $\sqrt{75}$ **b.** $\sqrt{21}$

Solution

a. Press

2nd   √   75   ENTER

Display

√(75
                8.660254038

So $\sqrt{75} \approx 8.7$.

b. Press

2nd   √   21   ENTER

Display

√(21
                4.582575695

Therefore, $\sqrt{21} \approx 4.6$.

PRACTICE 3

Using a calculator, approximate each square root. Round to the nearest hundredth.

a. $\sqrt{56}$

b. $\sqrt{12}$

The Pythagorean Theorem

Recall that a right triangle is a triangle that has one 90° angle. In a right triangle, the side opposite the right angle is called the **hypotenuse**. The other two sides are called **legs**.

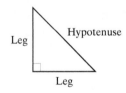

The lengths of the three sides of a right triangle are related in a special way. To understand this relationship, consider the areas of the squares on the legs and on the hypotenuse, as in the following example:

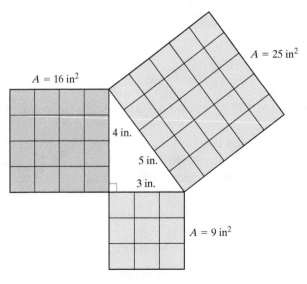

$$9 \text{ in}^2 + 16 \text{ in}^2 = 25 \text{ in}^2$$

| Area of the square on one leg | $+$ | Area of the square on the other leg | $=$ | Area of the square on the hypotenuse |

In general, if we let a and b represent the lengths of the legs and c represent the length of the hypotenuse, then $a^2 + b^2 = c^2$.

This relationship is called the *Pythagorean theorem*.

The Pythagorean Theorem

For every right triangle, the sum of the squares of the lengths of the two legs equals the square of the length of the hypotenuse, that is,

$$a^2 + b^2 = c^2$$

where a and b are the lengths of the legs, and c is the length of the hypotenuse.

We can use the Pythagorean theorem to find the third side of a right triangle if we know the other two sides.

EXAMPLE 4

Find the length of the hypotenuse.

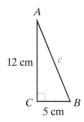

Solution   To find the length of the hypotenuse, we use the Pythagorean theorem.

$$a^2 + b^2 = c^2$$
$$5^2 + 12^2 = c^2$$
$$25 + 144 = c^2$$
$$169 = c^2$$
$$\sqrt{169} = c \qquad \text{Taking a square root is the opposite of squaring.}$$
$$13 = c, \text{ or } c = 13$$

So the hypotenuse is 13 centimeters long.

PRACTICE 4

Find the length of the unknown side in $\triangle ABC$.

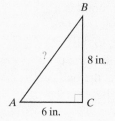

EXAMPLE 5

If b equals 1 centimeter and c equals 2 centimeters, what is a in a right triangle, where a and b are the lengths of the legs and c is the length of the hypotenuse? Round the answer to the nearest tenth of a centimeter.

PRACTICE 5

In a right triangle, one leg equals 2 feet and the hypotenuse equals 4 feet. Approximate the length of the missing leg. Round the answer to the nearest tenth of a foot.

EXAMPLE 5 (continued)

Solution   First, we draw a diagram.

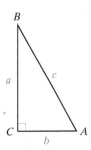

Then, we use the Pythagorean theorem and substitute the given values to obtain the following:

$$a^2 + b^2 = c^2$$
$$a^2 + 1^2 = 2^2$$
$$a^2 + 1 = 4$$
$$a^2 + 1 - 1 = 4 - 1$$
$$a^2 = 3$$
$$a = \sqrt{3} \qquad \text{Taking a square root is the opposite of squaring.}$$

To express the answer as a decimal, we use a calculator. Rounding to the nearest tenth, we find that $\sqrt{3}$ is 1.7. So $a \approx 1.7$ centimeters.

EXAMPLE 6

A baseball diamond is a square with sides 90 feet long. How far, to the nearest foot, must the third baseman throw the ball to reach the first baseman?

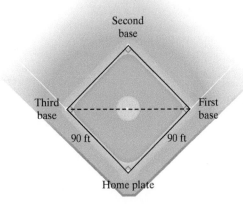

Solution   The sides of the diamond together with the diagonal from third base to first base form a right triangle. To find the distance from third base to first base, we use the Pythagorean theorem.

$$a^2 + b^2 = c^2$$
$$90^2 + 90^2 = c^2$$
$$8,100 + 8,100 = c^2$$
$$16,200 = c^2$$
$$\sqrt{16,200} = c$$
$$c = \sqrt{16,200}$$

We use a calculator and round to find that $\sqrt{16,200}$ is approximately 127 feet. So the third baseman must throw the ball approximately 127 feet to reach the first baseman.

PRACTICE 6

Stair stringers, the structural supporting parts of staircases, are used by carpenters in building stairs. What is the length, to the nearest tenth of a foot, of the stair stringer shown in the diagram below? (*Source:* wikipedia.org)

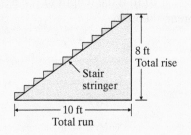

Mathematically Speaking

Fill in each blank with the most appropriate term or phrase from the given list.

squaring	leg	hypotenuse
multiple	Area of three squares	prime
consecutive		perfect square
doubling	Pythagorean theorem	square root

1. The number 5 is the _____ of 25.

2. Finding a square root is the opposite of _____ the number.

3. The square of a whole number is said to be a(n) _____.

4. The whole numbers 5 and 6 are _____.

5. In a right triangle, the longest side is called the _____.

6. If a and b are the lengths of the legs of a right triangle and c is the length of the hypotenuse, then the _____ states that $a^2 + b^2 = c^2$.

Ⓐ *Find each square root.*

7. $\sqrt{9}$

8. $\sqrt{4}$

9. $\sqrt{16}$

10. $\sqrt{36}$

11. $\sqrt{81}$

12. $\sqrt{64}$

13. $\sqrt{169}$

14. $\sqrt{121}$

15. $\sqrt{400}$

16. $\sqrt{225}$

17. $\sqrt{256}$

18. $\sqrt{900}$

Determine between which two consecutive whole numbers each square root lies.

19. $\sqrt{50}$

20. $\sqrt{7}$

21. $\sqrt{80}$

22. $\sqrt{31}$

23. $\sqrt{39}$

24. $\sqrt{2}$

25. $\sqrt{14}$

26. $\sqrt{105}$

⊞ *Approximate each square root. Round to the nearest tenth, if needed.*

27. $\sqrt{5}$

28. $\sqrt{11}$

29. $\sqrt{37}$

30. $\sqrt{74}$

31. $\sqrt{139}$

32. $\sqrt{165}$

33. $\sqrt{9,801}$

34. $\sqrt{8,649}$

Ⓑ ⊞ *Find each missing length. Round to the nearest tenth, if needed.*

35.
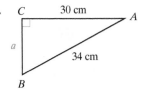

36.
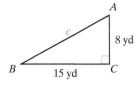

37.
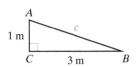

38.

Given a right triangle with legs a and b, and hypotenuse c, find the missing side.
Round to the nearest tenth, if needed.

	a	*b*	*c*
39.	24 m		25 m
40.	5 in.	12 in.	
41.	6 ft		10 ft
42.		4 cm	5 cm
43.	12 m	16 m	
44.		9 in.	15 in.
45.	7 cm	9 cm	
46.	2 yd	5 yd	
47.		18 ft	20 ft
48.	2 in.	2 in.	

Mixed Practice

Solve.

49. Find $\sqrt{196}$.

50. Determine between which two consecutive whole numbers $\sqrt{95}$ lies.

51. Find the missing length.

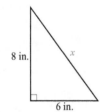

52. Find the missing length.

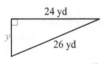

53. Find the missing length. Round to the nearest tenth.

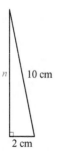

54. Find $\sqrt{41}$ to the nearest tenth.

Applications

C *Solve. Use a calculator, if needed.*

55. A contractor leans a ladder against the side of a building. How high up the building does the ladder reach?

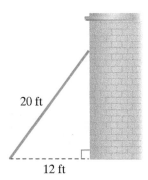

20 ft

12 ft

56. A scuba diver swims away from the boat and then dives, as shown. How far from the boat, to the nearest foot, will he be?

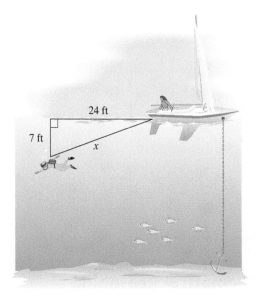

24 ft

7 ft

x

57. What is the length of the rectangular plot of land shown?

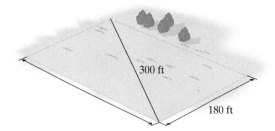

300 ft

180 ft

58. *ABCE* is a rectangular picnic area, with a picnic table at point *B* and the entrance at point *D*. The lengths *BC*, *CD*, and *BE* are as shown below:

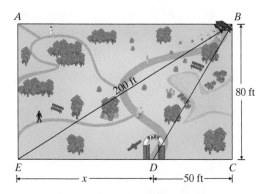

A   *B*

200 ft

80 ft

E   *D*   *C*

|←——— *x* ———→|←—50 ft—→|

Find the distance between the entrance and point *E*.

59. A builder constructed a roof of wooden beams. According to the diagram, what is the length of the sloping beam?

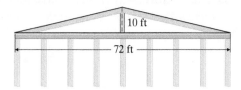

60. A college is constructing an access ramp to a door in one of its buildings, as shown. Find the length of the ramp.

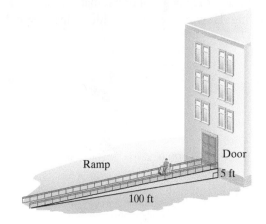

• Check your answers on page A-14.

MINDStretchers

Mathematical Reasoning

1. Give an example of a number that is smaller than its square root.

Writing

2. Thousands of years ago, the ancient Egyptians used a clever way of creating a right angle for their construction projects. For example, to create a right triangle with side lengths 3, 4, and 5, they would use a rope tying it in a circle with 12 equally spaced knots, as shown:

   Explain why this procedure would create the right triangle. (*Source:* Peter Tompkins, *Secrets of the Great Pyramids*)

Investigation

3. Choose a whole number. Use a calculator to determine whether it is a perfect square.

[11.6] *Find the square root.*

33. $\sqrt{9}$ **34.** $\sqrt{64}$ **35.** $\sqrt{121}$ **36.** $\sqrt{900}$

Determine between which two consecutive whole numbers each square root lies.

37. $\sqrt{3}$ **38.** $\sqrt{84}$ **39.** $\sqrt{40}$ **40.** $\sqrt{10}$

Find the square root. Round to the nearest hundredth.

41. $\sqrt{8}$ **42.** $\sqrt{1{,}235}$ **43.** $\sqrt{195}$ **44.** $\sqrt{29}$

For a given triangle, the lengths of the legs are a and b, and the length of the hypotenuse is c. Find the length of the missing side. Round to the nearest tenth, if needed.

	a	b	c
45.	9 ft		15 ft
46.		24 in.	26 in.
47.	8 yd	5 yd	
48.	2 ft	2 ft	

5.2   More Laws of Exponents and Scientific Notation

In this section, we consider several additional laws of exponents, as well as an important application of exponents known as scientific notation.

A To simplify an expression by using the power rule

Additional Laws of Exponents

In the previous section, we discussed the product rule for the product of powers and the quotient rule for the quotient of powers. We now consider a third rule known as the *power rule*. The power rule deals with expressions in which a power is raised to a power.

Let's consider, for instance, the expression $(x^2)^3$. Using the definition of an exponent gives us:

$$(x^2)^3 = \underbrace{x^2 \cdot x^2 \cdot x^2}_{\text{3 factors of } x^2} = x^{2+2+2} = x^6$$

So $(x^2)^3 = x^6$. We can generalize this result as follows:

B To simplify an expression by raising a product to a power

C To simplify an expression by raising a quotient to a power

D To write a number in scientific notation or standard notation

E To solve applied problems involving laws of exponents or scientific notation

Power Rule of Exponents

For any nonzero real number x and any integers a and b,

$$(x^a)^b = x^{ab}.$$

In words, to raise a power to a power, *multiply* the exponents and *keep the base the same.*

EXAMPLE 1

Simplify using the power rule of exponents.

a. $(5^2)^2$ **b.** $(2^{-3})^2$ **c.** $-(p^4)^5$ **d.** $(q^2)^{-1}$

Solution   We apply the power rule and then simplify.

a. $(5^2)^2 = 5^{2 \cdot 2} = 5^4 = 625$

b. $(2^{-3})^2 = 2^{-3 \cdot 2}$
$= 2^{-6}$
$= \dfrac{1}{2^6}$ Take the reciprocal of 2^{-6}, and change the exponent from -6 to 6.
$= \dfrac{1}{64}$

c. $-(p^4)^5 = -(p^{4 \cdot 5}) = -p^{20}$

d. $(q^2)^{-1} = q^{2 \cdot (-1)} = q^{-2} = \dfrac{1}{q^2}$

PRACTICE 1

Simplify using the power rule of exponents.

a. $(2^3)^2$

b. $(7^3)^{-1}$

c. $(q^2)^4$

d. $-(p^3)^{-5}$

TIP   Be sure to distinguish between the *product* rule and the *power* rule.

Product rule: $x^a \cdot x^b = x^{a+b}$ **Power rule:** $(x^a)^b = x^{ab}$

Add the exponents. ⌐   Multiply the exponents. ⌐

Another law of exponents has to do with *raising a product to a power*.
For instance, consider the expression $(5x)^3$.

Rearrange the factors.

$$(5x)^3 = (5x)(5x)(5x) = (5 \cdot 5 \cdot 5)(x \cdot x \cdot x) = 5^3 \cdot x^3 = 125x^3$$

So we see that $(5x)^3$ is the same as 5^3 times x^3. We can generalize this result as follows:

Raising a Product to a Power

For any nonzero real numbers x and y and any integer a,

$$(xy)^a = x^a \cdot y^a.$$

In words, to raise a product to a power, raise each factor to that power.

EXAMPLE 2

Simplify using the rule for raising a product to a power.

a. $(2y)^4$ **b.** $(-3a)^2$ **c.** $-(3a)^2$

Solution   We apply the rule for raising a product to a power, and then simplify.

a. $(2y)^4 = 2^4 \cdot y^4 = 16y^4$

b. $(-3a)^2 = (-3)^2(a)^2 = 9a^2$

c. $-(3a)^2 = -3^2 \cdot a^2 = -9a^2$

PRACTICE 2

Simplify.

a. $(7a)^2$

b. $(-4x)^3$

c. $-(4x)^3$

EXAMPLE 3

Simplify.

a. $(2x^4)^5$ **b.** $(p^3q^5)^3$ **c.** $-7(m^5n^{10})^2$ **d.** $(5a^{-2}c^4)^{-2}$

Solution

a. $(2x^4)^5 = 2^5(x^4)^5$ Use the rule for raising a product to a power.

$= 32x^{20}$ Use the power rule.

b. $(p^3q^5)^3 = (p^3)^3(q^5)^3 = p^9q^{15}$

c. $-7(m^5n^{10})^2 = -7(m^5)^2(n^{10})^2 = -7m^{10}n^{20}$

d. $(5a^{-2}c^4)^{-2} = 5^{-2}(a^{-2})^{-2}(c^4)^{-2}$ Use the rule for raising a product to a power.

$= 5^{-2}(a^4)(c^{-8})$ Use the power rule.

$= \dfrac{1}{25} \cdot a^4 \cdot \dfrac{1}{c^8}$ Use the definition of a negative exponent.

$= \dfrac{a^4}{25c^8}$

PRACTICE 3

Simplify.

a. $(-6a^9)^2$

b. $(q^8r^{10})^2$

c. $-2(ab^7)^3$

d. $(7a^{-1}c^{-5})^2$

The final law of exponents that we discuss is *raising a quotient to a power*. For instance, consider the expression $\left(\dfrac{a}{b}\right)^4$, where a divided by b is raised to the fourth power. By the definition of exponent, we get:

$$\left(\frac{a}{b}\right)^4 = \frac{a}{b} \cdot \frac{a}{b} \cdot \frac{a}{b} \cdot \frac{a}{b} = \frac{a \cdot a \cdot a \cdot a}{b \cdot b \cdot b \cdot b} = \frac{a^4}{b^4}$$

So $\left(\dfrac{a}{b}\right)^4 = \dfrac{a^4}{b^4}$. We generalize this result as follows:

Raising a Quotient to a Power

For any nonzero real numbers x and y and any integer a,

$$\left(\frac{x}{y}\right)^a = \frac{x^a}{y^a}.$$

In words, to raise a quotient to a power, raise both the numerator and the denominator to that power.

EXAMPLE 4

Simplify by using the rule for raising a quotient to a power.

a. $\left(\dfrac{x}{5}\right)^3$ **b.** $\left(\dfrac{-a}{b}\right)^4$ **c.** $\left(\dfrac{5}{x}\right)^{-3}$ **d.** $\left(\dfrac{-3r^2}{st^4}\right)^3$ **e.** $\left(\dfrac{9u}{v^{-1}}\right)^2$

Solution Here we use the rule for raising a quotient to a power, and then simplify.

a. $\left(\dfrac{x}{5}\right)^3 = \dfrac{x^3}{5^3} = \dfrac{x^3}{125}$ **b.** $\left(\dfrac{-a}{b}\right)^4 = \dfrac{(-a)^4}{b^4} = \dfrac{a^4}{b^4}$

c. $\left(\dfrac{5}{x}\right)^{-3} = \dfrac{5^{-3}}{x^{-3}}$

$= 5^{-3} \cdot \dfrac{1}{x^{-3}}$

$= \dfrac{1}{5^3} \cdot x^3$

$= \dfrac{x^3}{125}$

d. $\left(\dfrac{-3r^2}{st^4}\right)^3 = \dfrac{(-3r^2)^3}{(st^4)^3} = \dfrac{(-3)^3(r^2)^3}{s^3(t^4)^3} = \dfrac{-27r^6}{s^3t^{12}}$

e. $\left(\dfrac{9u}{v^{-1}}\right)^2 = \dfrac{(9u)^2}{(v^{-1})^2}$

$= \dfrac{9^2u^2}{v^{-2}}$

$= 81u^2 \cdot \dfrac{1}{v^{-2}}$

$= 81u^2v^2$

PRACTICE 4

Simplify.

a. $\left(\dfrac{y}{3}\right)^2$ **b.** $\left(\dfrac{-u}{v}\right)^{10}$

c. $\left(\dfrac{3}{y}\right)^{-2}$ **d.** $\left(\dfrac{-10a^5}{3b^2c}\right)^2$

e. $\left(\dfrac{5x}{y^{-2}}\right)^3$

Note that the simplified form of the expression in Example 4(a) is the same as the simplified form of the expression in Example 4(c). Since $\left(\dfrac{5}{x}\right)^{-3} = \dfrac{x^3}{125}$ and $\left(\dfrac{x}{5}\right)^3 = \dfrac{x^3}{125}$, we conclude that $\left(\dfrac{5}{x}\right)^{-3} = \left(\dfrac{x}{5}\right)^3$. This conclusion leads us to another law of exponents—*raising a quotient to a negative power.*

Raising a Quotient to a Negative Power

For any nonzero real numbers x and y and any integer a,

$$\left(\frac{x}{y}\right)^{-a} = \left(\frac{y}{x}\right)^{a}.$$

In words, to raise a quotient to a negative power, take the reciprocal of the quotient and change the sign of the exponent.

EXAMPLE 5

Simplify.

a. $\left(\dfrac{2}{x}\right)^{-3}$ b. $\left(\dfrac{3r}{10s}\right)^{-1}$ c. $\left(\dfrac{x^4}{y^2}\right)^{-2}$

Solution   Use the rule for raising a quotient to a negative power.

a. $\left(\dfrac{2}{x}\right)^{-3} = \left(\dfrac{x}{2}\right)^3 = \dfrac{x^3}{2^3} = \dfrac{x^3}{8}$

b. $\left(\dfrac{3r}{10s}\right)^{-1} = \left(\dfrac{10s}{3r}\right)^1 = \dfrac{10s}{3r}$

c. $\left(\dfrac{x^4}{y^2}\right)^{-2} = \left(\dfrac{y^2}{x^4}\right)^2 = \dfrac{(y^2)^2}{(x^4)^2} = \dfrac{y^4}{x^8}$

PRACTICE 5

Simplify.

a. $\left(\dfrac{5}{a}\right)^{-2}$

b. $\left(\dfrac{4u}{v}\right)^{-1}$

c. $\left(\dfrac{a^5}{b^3}\right)^{-2}$

Scientific Notation

Scientific notation is an important application of exponents—whether they are positive, negative, or zero. Scientists use this notation to abbreviate very large or very small numbers. Note that scientific notation is based on powers of 10.

Example	Standard Notation	Scientific Notation
The speed of light	983,000,000 ft/sec	9.83×10^8 ft/sec
The length of a virus	0.000000000001 m	1×10^{-12} m

Scientific notation has several advantages over standard notation. For example, when a number contains a long string of 0's, writing it in scientific notation can take fewer digits. Also, numbers written in scientific notation can be relatively easy to multiply or divide.

DEFINITION

A number is in **scientific notation** if it is written in the form

$$a \times 10^n$$

where n is an integer and a is greater than or equal to 1 but less than 10 ($1 \leq a < 10$).

Note that any value of a that satisfies the inequality $1 \leq a < 10$ must have *one nonzero digit* to the left of the decimal point. For instance, 7.3×10^5 is written in scientific notation. Do you see why the numbers 0.83×10^2, 5×3^7, and 13.8×10^{-4} are *not* written in scientific notation?

> **TIP** When written in scientific notation, large numbers have positive powers of 10, whereas small numbers have negative powers of 10. For instance, 3×10^{23} is large, whereas 3×10^{-23} is small.

Let's now consider how to change a number from scientific notation to standard notation.

EXAMPLE 6

Change the number 2.41×10^5 from scientific notation to standard notation.

Solution To express this number in standard notation, we need to multiply 2.41 by 10^5. Since $10^5 = 100{,}000$, multiplying 2.41 by 100,000 gives:

$$2.41 \times 10^5 = 2.41 \times 100{,}000 = 241{,}000.00 = 241{,}000$$

The number 241,000 is written in standard notation.

Note that the power of 10 here is *positive* and that the decimal point is moved five places *to the right*. So a shortcut for expressing 2.41×10^5 in standard notation is to move the decimal point in 2.41 five places to the right.

$$2.41 \times 10^5 = 2\,4\,1\,0\,0\,0. = 241{,}000$$

PRACTICE 6

Express 2.539×10^2 in standard notation.

EXAMPLE 7

Convert 3×10^{-5} to standard notation.

Solution Using the definition of a negative exponent, we get:

$$3 \times 10^{-5} = 3 \times \frac{1}{10^5}, \text{ or } \frac{3}{10^5}$$

Since $10^5 = 100{,}000$, dividing 3 by 100,000 gives us:

$$\frac{3}{10^5} = \frac{3}{100{,}000} = 0.00003$$

Here we note that the power of 10 is *negative* and that the decimal point, which is understood to be at the right end of a whole number, is moved five places *to the left*. So a shortcut for expressing 3×10^{-5} in standard notation is to move the decimal point in 3. five places to the left.

$$3 \times 10^{-5} = 3. \times 10^{-5} = .0\,0\,0\,0\,3 = .00003, \text{ or } 0.00003$$

PRACTICE 7

Change 4.3×10^{-9} to standard notation.

> **TIP** When converting a number from scientific notation to standard notation, move the decimal point to the *right* if the power of 10 is *positive* and to the *left* if the power of 10 is *negative*.

Now, let's consider the reverse situation, namely changing a number in standard notation to scientific notation.

EXAMPLE 8

Express 37,000,000,000 in scientific notation.

Solution   For a number to be written in scientific notation, it must be of the form

$$a \times 10^n$$

where n is an integer and $1 \le a < 10$. We know that 37,000,000,000 and 37,000,000,000. are the same. We move the decimal point *to the left* so that there is one nonzero digit to the left of the decimal point. The power of 10 by which we multiply is the same as the number of places moved.

$$37{,}000{,}000{,}000 = 3.7\,0\,0\,0\,0\,0\,0\,0\,0\,0 \times 10^{10}$$

Move 10 places to the *left*.

$$= 3.7 \times 10^{10}$$

Since 3.7 and 3.7000000000 are equivalent, we can drop the trailing zeros. So 37,000,000,000 expressed in scientific notation is 3.7×10^{10}.

PRACTICE 8

Write 8,000,000,000,000 in scientific notation.

EXAMPLE 9

Convert 0.00000000000000002 to scientific notation.

Solution   We must write the number 0.00000000000000002 in the form

$$a \times 10^n$$

where n is an integer and $1 \le a < 10$. We move the decimal point *to the right* so that there is one nonzero digit to the left of the decimal point. The power of 10 by which we multiply is the number of places moved, preceded by a *negative* sign.

$$0.00000000000000002 = 0\,0\,0\,0\,0\,0\,0\,0\,0\,0\,0\,0\,0\,0\,0\,0\,2. \times 10^{-17}$$

Move 17 places to the *right*.

$$= 2. \times 10^{-17} = 2 \times 10^{-17}$$

PRACTICE 9

Express 0.000000000071 in scientific notation.

Next, let's consider calculations involving numbers written in scientific notation. We focus on the operations of multiplication and division.

EXAMPLE 10

Calculate, writing the result in scientific notation.

a. $(4 \times 10^{-1})(2.1 \times 10^6)$

b. $(1.2 \times 10^5) \div (2 \times 10^{-4})$

PRACTICE 10

Calculate, writing the result in scientific notation.

a. $(7 \times 10^{-2})(3.52 \times 10^3)$

b. $(2.4 \times 10^3) \div (6 \times 10^{-9})$

EXAMPLE 10 (continued)

Solution

a. $(4 \times 10^{-1})(2.1 \times 10^6)$

$\quad = (4 \times 2.1)(10^{-1} \times 10^6)$ Regroup the factors.

$\quad = 8.4 \times 10^{-1+6}$ Use the product rule.

$\quad = 8.4 \times 10^5$

b. $(1.2 \times 10^5) \div (2 \times 10^{-4})$

$\quad = \dfrac{1.2 \times 10^5}{2 \times 10^{-4}}$

$\quad = \dfrac{1.2}{2} \times \dfrac{10^5}{10^{-4}}$ Rewrite the quotient as a product of quotients.

$\quad = 0.6 \times 10^{5-(-4)}$

$\quad = 0.6 \times 10^9$ Use the quotient rule.

Note that 0.6×10^9 is not in scientific notation because 0.6 is not between 1 and 10, that is, it does not have one nonzero digit to the left of the decimal point. To write 0.6×10^9 in scientific notation, we convert 0.6 to scientific notation and then simplify the product.

$\quad 0.6 \times 10^9 = (6 \times 10^{-1}) \times 10^9$ Convert 0.6 to scientific notation.

$\quad\quad\quad\quad\quad\; = 6 \times (10^{-1} \times 10^9)$

$\quad\quad\quad\quad\quad\; = 6 \times 10^8$ Use the product rule.

So the answer is 6×10^8.

EXAMPLE 11

There are about 5×10^6 red blood cells per cubic millimeter of blood. Each of these red blood cells contains about 2×10^8 hemoglobin molecules. Calculate the approximate number of hemoglobin molecules per cubic millimeter of blood, writing the result in scientific notation. (*Source:* Sylvia Mader, *Inquiry into Life*)

Solution   We need to find the product of the number of red blood cells per cubic millimeter of blood and the number of hemoglobin molecules per red blood cell:

$$(5 \times 10^6)(2 \times 10^8) = \underbrace{(5 \times 2)}\underbrace{(10^6 \times 10^8)}$$

$$= \quad 10 \quad \times \quad 10^{6+8}$$

$$= \quad 10 \quad \times \quad 10^{14}$$

To write this number in scientific notation, we convert 10 to scientific notation and then simplify the product.

$$10 \times 10^{14} = (1.0 \times 10^1) \times 10^{14}$$

$$= 1.0 \times (10^1 \times 10^{14})$$

$$= 1.0 \times 10^{15}$$

So there are approximately 1×10^{15} hemoglobin molecules per cubic millimeter of blood.

PRACTICE 11

The number of hairs on the average human head is estimated to be about 1.5×10^5. If there are approximately 6×10^9 people in the world, estimate the number of human head hairs in the world. (*Source: Time Almanac 2011*)

EXAMPLE 12

A certain DVD holds 9.4×10^9 bytes of information. How many files, each containing 9.4×10^6 bytes, can the DVD hold?

Solution   To determine the number of files that will fit on the DVD, we divide:

$$(9.4 \times 10^9) \div (9.4 \times 10^6) = \frac{9.4 \times 10^9}{9.4 \times 10^6}$$

$$= \frac{9.4}{9.4} \times \frac{10^9}{10^6}$$

$$= 1 \times 10^{9-6}$$

$$= 1 \times 10^3$$

So the DVD can hold 1×10^3, or 1000 files.

PRACTICE 12

At the very best, a light microscope can distinguish points 2×10^{-7} m apart, whereas an electronic microscope can distinguish points that are 2×10^{-10} m apart. The second number is how many times the first number? (*Source:* Sylvia Mader, *Inquiry into Life*)

Calculators and Scientific Notation

Calculators vary as to how numbers are displayed or entered in scientific notation.

Display

In order to avoid an overflow error, many calculator models change to scientific notation an answer that is either too small or too large to fit into the calculator's display. Calculators generally use the base 10 *without displaying it. Some calculators display scientific notation with either an E or e, and others show a space. For example, 3.1E–4 or 3.1   –4 can represent* 3.1×10^{-4}. *What other differences do you see between written scientific notation and displayed scientific notation?*

EXAMPLE 13

Multiply 1,000,000,000 by 2,000,000,000.

Solution

Press	Display
1000000000 ⊠ 2000000000 ⌷ENTER⌷	*1000000000 * 2000000000* *2 E 18*

Does your calculator display the product in scientific notation, that is, as 2E18, 2e18, or 2.   18?

PRACTICE 13

Square 0.000000005. How is the answer displayed?

Enter

Some calculators give the wrong answer to a computation if very large or very small numbers are entered in standard form rather than in scientific notation. To enter a number in scientific notation, many calculators have a key labeled $\boxed{\text{EE}}$, $\boxed{\text{EXP}}$, *or* $\boxed{\text{EEX}}$. *For a negative exponent, a key labeled* $\boxed{+/-}$ *or* $\boxed{(-)}$ *must be pressed either before or after the exponent key, depending on the calculator.*

EXAMPLE 14

Enter the number 5,000,000,000,000 in scientific notation.

Solution

Press   **Display**

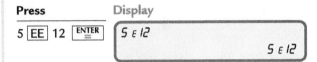

PRACTICE 14

In your calculator, enter in scientific notation the number 0.00000000073.

EXAMPLE 15

Multiply 3.5×10^4 by 2.1×10^7 on a calculator.

Solution

Press   **Display**

So the answer is 7.35×10^{11}. If your calculator has enough places in the display, it may give the answer to this problem in standard form: 735,000,000,000.

PRACTICE 15

Use a calculator to divide 9.2×10^{12} by 2×10^4.

The following table summarizes the laws of exponents considered in Sections 5.1 and 5.2. For any nonzero numbers x and y, and any integers a and b:

Exponent 1	$x^1 = x$ (x can be any real number.)
Exponent 0	$x^0 = 1$
Product rule of exponents	$x^a \cdot x^b = x^{a+b}$
Quotient rule of exponents	$\dfrac{x^a}{x^b} = x^{a-b}$
Negative exponents	$x^{-a} = \dfrac{1}{x^a}$
Reciprocal of x^{-a}	$\dfrac{1}{x^{-a}} = x^a$
Power rule of exponents	$(x^a)^b = x^{ab}$
Raising a product to a power	$(xy)^a = x^a \cdot y^a$
Raising a quotient to a power	$\left(\dfrac{x}{y}\right)^a = \dfrac{x^a}{y^a}$
Raising a quotient to a negative power	$\left(\dfrac{x}{y}\right)^{-a} = \left(\dfrac{y}{x}\right)^a$

Mathematically Speaking

Fill in each blank with the most appropriate term or phrase from the given list.

> add the factors
> right
> terms
> power form
> scientific notation
>
> raise both the numerator and the denominator
> raise each factor to that power
> add the powers
>
> left
> factors
> multiply the exponents
> raise the reciprocal of the quotient

1. The expression $(x^3)^2$ contains two _____ of x^3.

2. The power rule of exponents states that to raise a power to a power, _____ and leave the base the same.

3. To raise a product to a power, _____.

4. To raise a quotient to a power, _____ to that power.

5. To raise a quotient to a negative power, _____ to the opposite of the given power.

6. A number is written in _____ if it is in the form $a \times 10^n$, where n is an integer and a is greater than or equal to 1 but less than 10.

7. To convert a number from scientific to standard notation, move the decimal point to the _____ if the power of 10 is negative.

8. To convert a number from standard to scientific notation, move the decimal point to the _____ if the number is less than 1.

A *Simplify.*

9. $(2^2)^4$
10. $(3^3)^2$
11. $(5^2)^2$
12. $(2^3)^3$
13. $(10^5)^2$
14. $(0^5)^3$
15. $(4^{-2})^2$
16. $(2^{-3})^4$
17. $(x^4)^6$
18. $(p^2)^{10}$
19. $(y^4)^2$
20. $(n^3)^3$
21. $(x^{-2})^3$
22. $(y^{-5})^6$
23. $(n^{-2})^{-2}$
24. $(a^{-5})^{-4}$

B *Express in simplest form.*

25. $(4x)^3$
26. $(2y)^5$
27. $(-8y)^2$
28. $(-7a)^2$
29. $-(4n^5)^3$
30. $-(5x^3)^3$
31. $4(-2y^2)^4$
32. $2(-3t)^3$
33. $(3a)^{-2}$
34. $-(5t)^{-3}$
35. $(pq)^{-7}$
36. $(mn)^{-6}$
37. $(r^2t)^6$
38. $(a^3b^5)^4$
39. $(-2p^5q)^2$
40. $(-3a^2b^3)^4$
41. $-2(m^4n^8)^3$
42. $4(x^2y^3)^2$
43. $(-4m^5n^{-10})^3$
44. $(3a^{-3}c^8)^2$
45. $(a^3b^2)^{-4}$
46. $(p^3q^4)^{-2}$
47. $(4x^{-2}y^3)^2$
48. $(2x^{-2}y^3)^2$

C *Simplify.*

49. $\left(\dfrac{5}{b}\right)^3$
50. $\left(\dfrac{x}{4}\right)^2$
51. $\left(\dfrac{c}{b}\right)^2$
52. $\left(\dfrac{t}{s}\right)^5$
53. $-\left(\dfrac{a}{b}\right)^7$
54. $-\left(\dfrac{x}{y}\right)^3$
55. $\left(\dfrac{a^2}{3}\right)^3$
56. $\left(\dfrac{y^6}{4}\right)^3$

57. $\left(-\dfrac{p^3}{q^2}\right)^5$ 　　**58.** $\left(-\dfrac{x^2}{y^3}\right)^4$ 　　**59.** $\left(\dfrac{a}{4}\right)^{-1}$ 　　**60.** $\left(\dfrac{b}{3}\right)^{-1}$

61. $\left(\dfrac{2x^5}{y^2}\right)^3$ 　　**62.** $\left(\dfrac{n^2}{3w^5}\right)^2$ 　　**63.** $\left(\dfrac{pq}{p^2q^2}\right)^5$ 　　**64.** $\left(\dfrac{s^2t^3}{st^2}\right)^2$

65. $\left(\dfrac{3x}{y^{-3}}\right)^4$ 　　**66.** $\left(\dfrac{p^{-1}}{5q^5}\right)^2$ 　　**67.** $\left(\dfrac{-u^2v^3}{4vu^4}\right)^2$ 　　**68.** $\left(\dfrac{2xy^3}{xy^2}\right)^4$

69. $\left(-\dfrac{x^{-2}y}{2z^{-4}}\right)^4$ 　　**70.** $-\left(\dfrac{4a^{-4}}{bc^{-2}}\right)^2$ 　　**71.** $\left(\dfrac{r^5}{t^6}\right)^{-2}$ 　　**72.** $\left(\dfrac{y^3}{x^3}\right)^{-2}$

73. $\left(\dfrac{2a^4}{b^2}\right)^{-3}$ 　　**74.** $\left(\dfrac{q^5}{5p^4}\right)^{-2}$

D *Express in standard notation.*

75. 3.17×10^8 　　**76.** 9.1×10^5 　　**77.** 1×10^{-6} 　　**78.** 8.33×10^{-4}

79. 6.2×10^6 　　**80.** 7.55×10^{10} 　　**81.** 4.025×10^{-5} 　　**82.** 2.1×10^{-3}

Express in scientific notation.

83. 420,000,000 　　**84.** 100,000,000 　　**85.** 0.0000035 　　**86.** 0.00017

87. 217,000,000,000 　　**88.** 154,800,000,000 　　**89.** 0.00000000731 　　**90.** 0.00000005672

Complete each table.

91.

Standard Notation	Scientific Notation (written)	Scientific Notation (displayed on a calculator)
975,000,000		
	4.87×10^8	
		1.652E−10
0.000000067		
	1×10^{-13}	
		3.281E9

92.

Standard Notation	Scientific Notation (written)	Scientific Notation (displayed on a calculator)
975,000,000,000		
	5×10^8	
		4.988E−7
0.0000048		
	9.34×10^{-9}	
		9.772E6

▦ *Calculate, writing the result in scientific notation.*

93. $(3 \times 10^2)(3 \times 10^5)$

94. $(5 \times 10^4)(7.1 \times 10^3)$

95. $(2.5 \times 10^{-2})(8.3 \times 10^{-3})$

96. $(9.1 \times 10^{-13})(6.3 \times 10^{-10})$

97. $(2.1 \times 10^4)(8 \times 10^{-4})$

98. $(8.6 \times 10^9)(4.4 \times 10^{-12})$

99. $(2.5 \times 10^8) \div (2 \times 10^{-2})$

100. $(3.0 \times 10^4) \div (1 \times 10^3)$

101. $(6 \times 10^5) \div (2 \times 10^3)$

102. $(4.8 \times 10^{-3}) \div (8 \times 10^2)$

103. $(9.6 \times 10^{20}) \div (3.2 \times 10^{12})$

104. $(8.4 \times 10^6) \div (4.2 \times 10^7)$

Mixed Practice

Simplify.

105. Express 3.067×10^{-4} in standard notation.

106. Express 895,600,000 in scientific notation.

▦ **107.** Complete the table.

Standard Notation	Scientific Notation (written)	Scientific Notation (displayed on a calculator)
428,000,000,000		
	3.24×10^6	
		5.224E−6
0.000000057		
	6.82×10^{-7}	
		4.836E7

Simplify, using only positive exponents.

108. $(a^{-3})^5$

109. $\left(\dfrac{a^2}{3b^5}\right)^{-2}$

110. $(2r^7s^{-3})^3$

111. $-(4y)^{-3}$

112. $\left(-\dfrac{m^2}{n^3}\right)^5$

113. $-\left(\dfrac{2x^{-2}}{y^{-3}z}\right)^4$

114. $2(-3x^4)^3$

▦ *Calculate, writing the result in scientific notation.*

115. $(6.3 \times 10^{-4}) \div (9 \times 10^3)$

116. $(4.1 \times 10^{-3})(2.7 \times 10^{-2})$

Applications

E *Solve.*

117. Consider the two boxes shown. How many times the volume of the smaller box is the volume of the larger box?

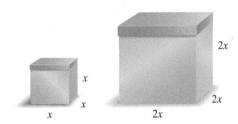

118. The infectious part of a virus is typically between 2.5×10^{-8} m and 2×10^{-7} m in size. Express these quantities in standard notation. (*Source:* Sylvia Mader, *Inquiry into Life*)

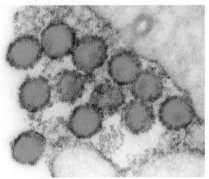

119. A DVD holds between 4×10^9 and 1.7×10^{10} bytes of data. Express these quantities in standard notation.

120. After a flood, the radius of a circular pond doubles. How does the area of the pond change?

121. The wavelength of red light is 0.0000007 m. Write this length in scientific notation.

122. In a recent year, the U.S. federal budget had a deficit of $1,400,000,000,000. Express this amount in scientific notation. (*Source: The 2011 Statistical Abstract of the United States*)

123. The cell is considered the basic unit of life. Each day, the body destroys and replaces more than 200 billion cells. Write this quantity in scientific notation.

124. The diameter of an atom is about 1.1×10^{-10} m. What is this quantity in standard notation? (*Source:* Peter J. Nolan, *Fundamentals of College Physics*)

125. The mass of a proton is about 1.7×10^{-24} g. Rewrite this quantity in standard notation. (*Source:* Karen Timberlake, *Chemistry*)

126. To measure vast distances, astronomers use a unit called a *parsec*, which is equal to about 3.086×10^{18} cm. Express this quantity in standard form. (*Source:* Derek McNally, *Positional Astronomy*)

127. The world population is projected to be 7.6×10^9 in 2020. What is this population expressed in standard notation? (*Source:* census.gov)

128. The diameter of a water molecule is about 2.8 angstroms, where one angstrom is 0.00000001 cm. What is the radius of a water molecule in centimeters, expressed in scientific notation? (*Source:* answers.com)

129. For each pound of body weight, a human body contains about 3.2×10^4 microliters (μL) of blood. In turn, a microliter of blood contains about 5×10^6 red blood cells. A person weighing 100 lb has approximately how many red blood cells?

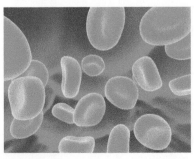

130. On the television series *Star Trek: The Next Generation*, the android Data could carry out 60 trillion operations per second. Express this rate in scientific notation.

131. Light travels through a vacuum at a speed of 186,000 mi/sec.

    a. Express this speed in scientific notation.

    b. How long will it take for light to travel to Earth from the star Vega, which is 1.58×10^{14} mi from Earth? (*Source: The New York Times Almanac 2011*)

132. There are 26,890,000,000,000,000,000 molecules of a gas in a cubic meter.

    a. Rewrite this quantity in scientific notation.

    b. What volume is required for 3.4×10^{20} molecules of the gas?

• Check your answers on page A-20.

MINDStretchers

Investigation

  1. On a scientific calculator, enter the number 2. Double that number. Then, keep doubling the result. After how many doublings does your calculator display the number in scientific notation? Explain how you could have predicted that result.

Critical Thinking

  2. What is the mathematical relationship between $(a^m)^n$ and $(a^m)^{-n}$? Justify your answer.

Research

  3. In your college library or on the Web, determine the annual national debt for the United States for 5 consecutive years. Would you use scientific notation or standard notation to express these amounts? Explain why.

Appendix

Scientific Notation

Frequently, scientists deal with numbers that are either very large or very small. For instance, in astronomy, they study the distance to the nearest star; in biology, the length of a virus.

    40,000,000,000,000 kilometers ← The distance between the Sun and Proxima Centauri

    0.0000000000001 meters ⟵ The length of a virus

Scientists commonly write such numbers not in standard notation, but rather in *scientific notation*. Also, scientific and graphing calculators generally use scientific notation to show answers that are too long to fit in their display.

Scientific notation is based on powers of 10. ***A positive number is said to be in scientific notation if it is written as the product of a decimal factor whose absolute value is greater than or equal to 1 but less than 10 and an integer power of 10.***

For instance, the number 7.35×10^5 is written in scientific notation, because the decimal factor 7.35 is between 1 and 10, and 10^5 is a power of 10. However, the number 81.45×2^6 is not in scientific notation, because the base of the exponent is not 10, and the decimal factor 81.45 is not between 1 and 10.

> **TIP** A number written in scientific notation has one nonzero digit to the left of the decimal point in its decimal factor.

Let's consider how to change a number from scientific notation to standard notation and vice versa. First, we will look at *large numbers*.

EXAMPLE 1

Change the number 7.34×10^5 from scientific notation to standard notation.

Solution   To express 7.34×10^5 in standard notation, we need to multiply 7.34 by 10^5 or 100,000.

$$7.34 \times 10^5 = 7.34 \times 100,000 = 734,000.$$

So 7.34×10^5 written in standard notation is 734,000.

PRACTICE 1

Express 2.539×10^7 in standard notation.

In Example 1, note that the power of 10 is *positive*, and that the decimal point is moved five places *to the right*. So a shortcut for writing 7.34×10^5 in standard notation is to move the decimal point in 7.34 five places to the right, where 5 is the power of 10.

$$7.34 \times 10^5 = 7\underset{\text{5 places}}{34000.} = 734,000$$

To change a number from standard notation to scientific notation, the process is reversed.

EXAMPLE 2

Rewrite 3,700,000,000 in scientific notation.

Solution   We know that for a number to be written in scientific notation, it must be the product of a decimal factor whose absolute value is greater than or equal to 1 but less than 10 and an integer power of 10. Recall that 3,700,000,000 and 3,700,000,000. are the same. We move the decimal point *to the left* so that there is one nonzero digit to its left. The number of places moved is the power of 10 by which we need to multiply.

$$3{,}700{,}000{,}000. = 3.\underbrace{700000000}_{9 \text{ places}} \times 10^9 = 3.7 \times 10^9$$

Note that we dropped the extra zeros in 3.700000000. So 3,700,000,000 expressed in scientific notation is 3.7×10^9.

PRACTICE 2

Write 8,000,000,000,000 in scientific notation.

Now, let's turn our attention to writing *small numbers* in scientific notation. The key is an understanding of *negative exponents*. Until now, we have only considered exponents that were positive integers. What meaning should we attach to a negative exponent? To the exponent 0? The following pattern, in which each number is $\frac{1}{10}$ of the previous number, suggests an answer.

$$10^3 = 1{,}000$$
$$10^2 = 100$$
$$10^1 = 10$$
$$10^0 = 1$$
$$10^{-1} = \frac{1}{10}$$
$$10^{-2} = \frac{1}{100}$$
$$10^{-3} = \frac{1}{1{,}000}$$

Notice that 10^{-1}, or $\frac{1}{10}$, is the reciprocal of 10^1 or 10. So in general, *a number raised to a negative exponent is defined to be the reciprocal of that number raised to the corresponding positive exponent. Also, a number raised to the power 0 is 1.*

When written in scientific notation, large numbers have positive powers of 10, whereas small numbers have negative powers of 10. For instance, 3×10^5 is large, whereas 3×10^{-5} is small.

Next, let's look at how we change *small* numbers from scientific notation to standard notation and vice versa.

EXAMPLE 3

Convert 3×10^{-5} to standard notation.

Solution Using the meaning of negative exponents, we get:

$$3 \times 10^{-5} = 3 \times \frac{1}{10^5}, \quad \text{or} \quad \frac{3}{10^5}$$

Since $10^5 = 100{,}000$, dividing 3 by 10^5 gives us:

$$\frac{3}{10^5} = \frac{3}{100{,}000} = 0.00003$$

So 3×10^{-5} written in standard notation is 0.00003.

PRACTICE 3

Change 4.3×10^{-9} to standard notation.

In Example 3, note that the power of 10 is *negative*, and the decimal point, which is understood to be at the right end of a whole number, was moved five places *to the left*. So just as with 7.34×10^5, there is a shortcut for expressing 3×10^{-5} in standard notation. To do this, we move the decimal point five places *to the left*:

$$3 \times 10^{-5} = 3. \times 10^{5} = \underset{\text{5 places}}{.\,0\,0\,0\,0\,3} = .00003, \text{ or } 0.00003.$$

TIP When converting a number from scientific notation to standard notation, move the decimal point to the *left* if the power of 10 is *negative* and to the *right* if the power of 10 is *positive*. The number of places the decimal point is moved is the absolute value of the power of 10.

EXAMPLE 4

Write 0.00000000000000002 in scientific notation.

Solution To write 0.00000000000000002 in scientific notation, we move the decimal point *to the right* until there is one nonzero digit to the left of the decimal point. The number of places moved, preceded by a *negative* sign, is the power of 10 that we need.

$$0.00000000000000002 = \underset{\text{17 places}}{0\,0\,0\,0\,0\,0\,0\,0\,0\,0\,0\,0\,0\,0\,0\,0\,2.} \times 10^{-17}$$

$$= 2 \times 10^{-17}$$

PRACTICE 4

Express 0.000000000071 in scientific notation.

Computation Involving Scientific Notation

Now, let's consider how to perform calculations on numbers written in scientific notation. We focus on the operations of multiplication and division.

Multiplying and dividing numbers written in scientific notation can best be understood in terms of two *laws of exponents*—the *product rule* and the *quotient rule*.

- The *product rule of exponents* states that when we multiply a base raised to a power by the same base raised to another power, we add the exponents and leave the base the same. For example,

$$10^3 \cdot 10^2 = 10^{3+2} = 10^5$$

    → Add the exponents.

    → Keep the base.

This result is reasonable, since $10^3 \times 10^2 = 1{,}000 \times 100 = 100{,}000 = 10^5$.

- The *quotient rule of exponents* states that when we divide a base raised to a power by the same base to another power, we subtract the second power from the first power, and leave the base the same. For instance,

Subtract the exponents.

$$10^5 \div 10^2 = 10^{\overbrace{5-2}} = 10^3$$

Keep the base.

We would have expected this result even if we did not know the quotient rule, since

$$\frac{10^5}{10^2} = \frac{100,000}{100} = \frac{1,000}{1} = 1,000 = 10^3.$$

EXAMPLE 5

Calculate, writing the result in scientific notation.

a. $(4 \times 10^{-1})(2.1 \times 10^6)$

b. $(1.2 \times 10^5) \div (2 \times 10^{-4})$

Solution

a. $(4 \times 10^{-1})(2.1 \times 10^6)$

$= (4 \times 2.1)(10^{-1} \times 10^6)$ Change the order of the factors and regroup.

$= (8.4)(10^{-1} \times 10^6)$ Multiply the decimal factors.

$= 8.4 \times 10^{-1+6}$ Use the product rule of exponents.

$= 8.4 \times 10^5$ Simplify.

b. $(1.2 \times 10^5) \div (2 \times 10^{-4})$

$= \dfrac{1.2 \times 10^5}{2 \times 10^{-4}}$

$= \dfrac{1.2}{2} \times \dfrac{10^5}{10^{-4}}$ Write as the product of fractions.

$= 0.6 \times \dfrac{10^5}{10^{-4}}$ Divide the decimal factors.

$= 0.6 \times 10^{5-(-4)}$ Use the quotient rule of exponents.

$= 0.6 \times 10^9$ Simplify.

Note that 0.6×10^9 is not written in scientific notation, because 0.6 is not between 1 and 10, that is, it does not have one nonzero digit to the left of the decimal point. To write 0.6×10^9 in scientific notation, we convert 0.6 to scientific notation and simplify the product.

$0.6 \times 10^9 = 6 \times 10^{-1} \times 10^9$

$= 6 \times 10^{-1+9}$ Use the product rule of exponents.

$= 6 \times 10^8$

So the quotient, written in scientific notation, is 6×10^8.

PRACTICE 5

Calculate, expressing the answer in scientific notation.

a. $(7 \times 10^{-2})(3.52 \times 10^3)$

b. $(5.01 \times 10^3) \div (6 \times 10^{-9})$

Exercises

Express in standard notation.

1. 3.17×10^8

2. 9.1×10^5

3. 1×10^{-6}

4. 8.013×10^{-4}

5. 4.013×10^{-5}

6. 2.1×10^{-3}

Express in scientific notation.

7. 400,000,000

8. 10,000,000

9. 0.0000035

10. 0.00017

11. 0.00000000031

12. 218,000,000,000

Multiply, and write the result in scientific notation.

13. $(3 \times 10^2)(3 \times 10^5)$

14. $(5 \times 10^6)(1 \times 10^3)$

15. $(2.5 \times 10^{-2})(8.3 \times 10^{-3})$

16. $(2.1 \times 10^4)(8 \times 10^{-4})$

Divide, and write the result in scientific notation.

17. $(2.5 \times 10^8) \div (2 \times 10^{-2})$

18. $(3.0 \times 10^4) \div (1 \times 10^3)$

19. $(1.2 \times 10^5) \div (3 \times 10^3)$

20. $(4.88 \times 10^{-3}) \div (8 \times 10^2)$

Answers

CHAPTER 1

Chapter 1 Pretest, p. 2

1. Two hundred five thousand, seven **2.** 1,235,000 **3.** Hundred thousands **4.** 8,100 **5.** 8,226 **6.** 4,714 **7.** 185 **8.** 29,124
9. 260 **10.** 308 R6 **11.** 2^3 **12.** 36 **13.** 5 **14.** 43
15. 75 years old **16.** $55 **17.** 68 **18.** 324 sec **19.** $36
20. Room C, which measures 126 sq ft

Section 1.1 Practices, pp. 4–8

1, *p. 4:* **a.** Thousands **b.** Hundred thousands **c.** Ten millions **2**, *p. 4:*
Eight billion, three hundred seventy-six thousand, fifty-two **3**, *p. 4:*
$7,372,050 Seven million, three hundred seventy-two thousand, fifty
dollars **4**, *p. 5:* $95,000,003 **5**, *p. 5:* $375,000 **6**, *p. 6:*
a. 2 ten thousands + 7 thousands + 0 hundreds + 1 ten + 3 ones =
20,000 + 7,000 + 0 + 10 + 3 or 20,000 + 7,000 + 10 + 3
b. 1 million + 2 hundred thousands + 7 ten thousands + 9 tens +
3 ones = 1,000,000 + 200,000 + 70,000 + 90 + 3 **7**, *p. 7:* **a.** 52,000
b. 50,000 **8**, *p. 8:* 420,000,000 **9**, *p. 8:* **a.** One million, six hundred
ninety-nine thousand, two hundred **b.** 1,960,000

Exercises 1.1, pp. 9–13

1. whole numbers **3.** odd **5.** standard form **7.** placeholder
9. expanded form **11.** 4,867 **13.** 316 **15.** 28,461,013 **17.** Hundred
thousands **19.** Hundreds **21.** Billions **23.** Four hundred eighty-seven
thousand, five hundred **25.** Two million, three hundred fifty thousand
27. Nine hundred seventy-five million, one hundred thirty-five thousand
29. Two billion, three hundred fifty-two **31.** One billion **33.** 10,120
35. 150,856 **37.** 6,000,055 **39.** 50,600,195 **41.** 400,072
43. 3 ones = 3 **45.** 8 hundreds + 5 tens + 8 ones = 800 + 50 + 8
47. 2 millions + 5 hundred thousands + 4 ones = 2,000,000 +
500,000 + 4 **49.** 670 **51.** 7,100 **53.** 30,000 **55.** 700,000
57. 30,000
59.

To the nearest	135,842	2,816,533
Hundred	135,800	2,816,500
Thousand	136,000	2,817,000
Ten thousand	140,000	2,820,000
Hundred thousand	100,000	2,800,000

61. 1 ten thousand + 2 thousands + 5 tens + 1 one =
10,000 + 2,000 + 50 + 1 **63.** 40,059 **65.** 1,056,100; one million,
fifty-six thousand, one hundred **67.** Nine hundred thousand **69.** forty-
eight thousand, three hundred eighty-one **71.** Three hundred million
73. 100,000,000,000 **75.** 3,288 **77.** 3,233,300,000,000 **79.** 150 ft
81. 20,000 mi **83.** 1,900 **85. a.** Three million, six hundred thousand,
nine hundred thirty sq mi **b.** 301,000 sq mi

Section 1.2 Practices, pp. 15–23

1, *p. 15:* 385 **2**, *p. 16:* 10,436 **3**, *p. 17:* 16 mi **4**, *p. 18:* 651
5, *p. 19:* 4,747 **6**, *p. 20:* 750 plant species **7**, *p. 20:* **a.** 286,000
b. 193,000 **c.** Less **8**, *p. 22:* 9,477 **9**, *p. 22:* 2,791 **10**, *p. 23:*
20,000 ft

Calculator Practices, pp. 23–24

11, *p. 23:* 49,532 **12**, *p. 24:* 31,899 **13**, *p. 24:* 2,499 ft

Exercises 1.2, pp. 25–31

1. right **3.** sum **5.** Associative Property of Addition **7.** subtrahend
9. 177,778 **11.** 14,710 **13.** 14,002 **15.** 56,188 **17.** 6,978 **19.** 4,820
21. 413 **23.** 14,865 **25.** 15,509 m **27.** 82 hr **29.** $104,831
31. $12,724 **33.** 31,200 tons **35.** 13,296,657 **37.** 1,662,757
39.

+	400	200	1,200	300	Total
300	700	500	1,500	600	3,300
800	1,200	1,000	2,000	1,100	5,300
Total	1,900	1,500	3,500	1,700	8,600

41.

+	389	172	1,155	324	Total
255	644	427	1,410	579	3,060
799	1,188	971	1,954	1,123	5,236
Total	1,832	1,398	3,364	1,702	8,296

43. a; possible estimate: 12,800 **45.** a; possible estimate: $900,000
47. 217 **49.** 90 **51.** 362 **53.** 68,241 **55.** 2,285 **57.** 52,999
59. 2,943 **61.** 203,465 **63.** 368 **65.** 4,996 **67.** 982 **69.** 1,995 mi
71. $669 **73.** $3,609 **75.** 273 books **77.** 209 m **79.** 2,001,000
81. 813,429 **83.** c; possible estimate: 40,000,000 **85.** a; possible estimate: $200,000 **87.** 7,065 **89.** 1,676 **91.** 5,186 **93.** 281,000,000
95. 3,400,000 sq mi **97. a.** Austria, 16; Canada, 26; Germany 30;
Norway, 23; United States, 37 **b.** United States **99.** About 43 years
old **101.** No, the elevator is not overloaded. The total weight of passengers is 963 lb. **103.** 180°F **105.** 151 mi **107.** 19,403,000
109. 1,454 **111. a.** Less (2,804) **b.** 2,932 seats **113. a.** 280,000
species **b.** 1,060,000 species **c.** 260,000 species **115.** $28,576

Section 1.3 Practices, pp. 34–37

1, *p. 34:* 608 **2**, *p. 34:* 4,230 **3**, *p. 35:* 480,000 **4**, *p. 35:* 205,296
5, *p. 36:* 107 sq ft **6**, *p. 36:* 112,840 **7**, *p. 37:* No; possible
estimate = 20,000

Calculator Practices, p. 38

8, *p. 38:* 1,026,015 **9**, *p. 38:* 345,546

Exercises 1.3, pp. 39–43

1. product **3.** Identity Property of Multiplication **5.** addition **7.** 400
9. 142,000 **11.** 170,000 **13.** 7,000,000 **15.** 12,700 **17.** 418
19. 3,248,000 **21.** 65,268 **23.** 817 **25.** 34,032 **27.** 3,003
29. 3,612 **31.** 57,019 **33.** 243,456 **35.** 200,120 **37.** 149,916
39. 144,500 **41.** 123,830 **43.** 3,312 **45.** 2,106 **47.** 40,000
49. 23,085 **51.** 3,274,780 **53.** 54,998,850 **55.** c; possible estimate:
480,000 **57.** b; possible estimate: 80,000 **59.** 2,880 **61.** 230,520
63. 1,071,000 **65.** 300,000 **67.** 3,300 yr **69. a.** 3,000,000
b. 1,000,000 **71.** Yes **73.** 5,775 sq in. **75.** 1,750 mi **77.** $442
79. a. 294 mi **b.** 1,470 mi **81.** Colorado; area ≈ 106,700 sq mi

Section 1.4 Practices, pp. 46–50

1, *p. 46:* 807 **2**, *p. 46:* 7,002 **3**, *p. 47:* 5,291 R1 **4**, *p. 48:* 79 R1
5, *p. 48:* 94 R10 **6**, *p. 49:* 607 R3 **7**, *p. 49:* 200 **8**, *p. 50:* 967
9, *p. 50:* 5 times

Calculator Practice, p. 51

10, *p. 51:* 603

Exercises 1.4, pp. 52–54

1. divisor **3.** multiplication **5.** 400 **7.** 2,560 **9.** 301 **11.** 3,003
13. 8,044 **15.** 500 **17.** 30 **19.** 14 **21.** 42 **23.** 400 **25.** 159
27. 5,353 **29.** 1,002 **31.** 6,944 **33.** 1,001 **35.** 3,050 **37.** 907
39. 1,201 **41.** 651 R2 **43.** 11 R7 **45.** 116 R83 **47.** 700 R2
49. 723 R19 **51.** 428 R8 **53.** 1,010 R10 **55.** 928 R24 **57.** 721
59. 155 **61.** c; possible estimate: 800 **63.** a; possible estimate: 7,000
65. 907 R1 **67.** 2,000 **69.** 2,400 **71.** 370 **73.** $135 **75.** 2 times
77. 300 people per square mile **79.** 6 calories **81. a.** 304 tiles **b.** 26
boxes **c.** $468

Section 1.5   Practices, pp. 55–59

1, *p. 55:* $5^5 \cdot 2^2$ **2,** *p. 56:* **a.** 1 **b.** 1,331 **3,** *p. 56:* 784 **4,** *p. 56:* 10^9
5, *p. 57:* 28 **6,** *p. 58:* 146 **7,** *p. 58:* 4 **8,** *p. 58:* 130 **9,** *p. 59:* 60 ft
10, *p. 59:* $40 **11,** *p. 59:* **a.** 61 fatalities **b.** 2006 and 2009

Calculator Practices, p. 60

12, *p. 60:* 140,625; **13,** *p. 60:* 131

Exercises 1.5, pp. 61–65

1. base **3.** adding
5.

n	0	2	4	6	8	10	12
n^2	0	4	16	36	64	100	144

7.

n	0	2	4	6	8
n^3	0	8	64	216	512

9. 10^2 **11.** 10^4 **13.** 10^6 **15.** $2^2 \cdot 3^2$ **17.** $4^3 \cdot 5^1$ **19.** 900 **21.** 1,568
23. 18 **25.** 4 **27.** 13 **29.** 14 **31.** 35 **33.** 225 **35.** 250 **37.** 36
39. 5 **41.** 28 **43.** 6 **45.** 99 **47.** 99 **49.** 4 **51.** 39 **53.** 16 **55.** 93
57. 67 **59.** 18 **61.** 529 **63.** 419 **65.** 137,088
67. $\boxed{4} \cdot 3 + \boxed{6} \cdot 5 + \boxed{6} \cdot 7 = 98$ **69.** $(\boxed{8})(3 + \boxed{4}) - 2 \cdot \boxed{6} = 44$
71. $\boxed{8} + 10 \times \boxed{4} - \boxed{6} \div 2 = 45$ **73.** $(5 + 2) \cdot 4^2 = 112$
75. $(5 + 2 \cdot 4)^2 = 169$ **77.** $(8 - 4) \div 2^2 = 1$
79. 242 sq cm **81.** 3,120 sq in.
83.

Input	Output
0	$21 + 3 \times 0 = 21$
1	$21 + 3 \times 1 = 24$
2	$21 + 3 \times 2 = 27$

85. 25 **87.** 40 **89.** 4 **91.** 2,412 mi **93.** 8 **95.** 10^8 **97.** 289
99. 48 **101.** 8 **103.** 625 sq ft **105.** $5^2 + 12^2 = 13^2$; 25 + 144 = 169
107. 10^6 **109. a.** $21,500 **b.** $1,050 **111. a.** 69 **b.** At home; the average score for home games was higher than the average score for away games. **113. a.** 108,000 workers **b.** 1,969,000 workers; below average
115. Yes, because the average number of customers is 502.

Section 1.6   Practices, pp. 67–69

1, *p. 67:* 10,670 employees **2,** *p. 68:* 2 yr **3,** *p. 68:* 1,551 students
4, *p. 69:* 180 lb

Exercises 1.6, pp. 70–71

1. $2,150 **3.** 27 mi **5.** 75 times **7.** 5,882 mi **9.** 528,179
immigrants **11.** 300¢, or $3 **13.** $17,000 **15.** $6,036 **17.** $1,458
19. 8 extra pens **21.** 1952 was closer by 31 votes. **23.** $983

Chapter 1   Review Exercises, pp. 75–79

1. are; possible answer: both digits are in the hundreds place
2. is not; possible answer: the critical digit 6 is greater than 5
3. is not; possible answer: the perimeter is the sum of the lengths of the figure's sides **4.** is not; possible answer: 8 times 7 is 56
5. is; possible answer: the area of a rectangle is the product of its length and its width **6.** is not; possible answer: 9 is the base which is raised to the power 2 **7.** is; possible answer: of the distributive property
8. is; possible answer: 10 divided by 5 is 2 **9.** is not; possible answer: the sum of the numbers should be divided by 3 and not by 2 since there are three numbers **10.** before; possible answer: of the order of operations rule **11.** Ones **12.** Ten thousands **13.** Hundred millions **14.** Ten billions **15.** Four hundred ninety-seven
16. Two thousand, fifty **17.** Three million, seven **18.** Eighty-five
billion **19.** 251 **20.** 9,002 **21.** 14,000,025 **22.** 3,000,003,000
23. 2 millions + 5 hundred thousands = 2,000,000 + 500,000
24. 4 ten thousands + 2 thousands + 7 hundreds + 7 ones = 40,000 + 2,000 + 700 + 7 **25.** 600 **26.** 1,000 **27.** 380,000
28. 70,000 **29.** 9,486 **30.** 65,692 **31.** 173,543 **32.** 150,895
33. 1,957,825 **34.** $223,067 **35.** 445 **36.** 10,016 **37.** 11,109
38. 5,510 **39.** 11,042,223 **40.** $2,062,852 **41.** 11,006 **42.** 2,989
43. 432 **44.** 1,200 **45.** 149,073 **46.** 12,000,000 **47.** 477,472
48. 1,019,000 **49.** 1,397,508 **50.** 188,221,590 **51.** 39 **52.** 307 R3
53. 37 R10 **54.** 680 R8 **55.** 25,625 **56.** 957 **57.** 343 **58.** 1
59. 72 **60.** 300,000 **61.** 5 **62.** 169 **63.** 5 **64.** 19 **65.** 12 **66.** 18
67. 10,833,312 **68.** 2,694 **69.** $7^2 \cdot 5^2$ **70.** $2^2 \cdot 5^3$ **71.** 39 **72.** 7
73. 6 **74.** 5 **75.** Two million, four hundred thousand **76.** 150,000,000
77. $3,009,000,000,000 **78.** 1985 **79.** 300,000 sq mi
80. 32,000,000 iPods **81.** 9 **82.** possible answer; 24 times
83. 2,717 **84.** 23 flats **85.** $307 per week
86.

Net sales	$430,000
− Cost of merchandise sold	− 175,000
Gross margin	$255,000
− Operating expenses	− 135,000
Net profit	$120,000

87. 6,675 sq m **88.** 272 legs **89.** 1968 to 1972 (15,385,031
votes) **90.** 4,341 points **91. a.** 1,949 km **b.** 1,683 km
92. a. 14,994,000 **b.** The average would increase by 62,000.
93. 29 sq mi **94.** 162 cm

Chapter 1   Posttest, p. 80

1. 225,067 **2.** 1,768,405 **3.** One million, two hundred five thousand,
seven **4.** 200,000 **5.** 1,894 **6.** 607 **7.** 147 **8.** 297,496 **9.** 509
10. 622 R19 **11.** 625 **12.** $4^3 \cdot 5^2$ **13.** 84 **14.** 2 **15.** 5,600,000 sq mi
16. 46,177,500 acres **17.** $469 **18.** $123 **19.** $1,380 **20.** 26 g of fat

CHAPTER 2

Chapter 2   Pretest, p. 82

1. 1, 2, 4, 5, 10, 20 **2.** $2 \times 2 \times 2 \times 3 \times 3$, or $2^3 \times 3^2$ **3.** $\frac{2}{5}$ **4.** $\frac{61}{3}$
5. $1\frac{1}{30}$ **6.** $\frac{3}{4}$ **7.** 20 **8.** $\frac{1}{8}$ **9.** $1\frac{1}{5}$ **10.** $12\frac{5}{6}$ **11.** $2\frac{1}{4}$ **12.** $4\frac{5}{8}$ **13.** $3\frac{1}{2}$
14. 60 **15.** $\frac{2}{3}$ **16.** $3\frac{2}{3}$ **17.** $\frac{2}{21}$ **18.** 6 students **19.** 6 mi **20.** 69 g

Section 2.1   Practices, pp. 83–89

1, *p. 83:* 1, 7 **2,** *p. 84:* 1, 3, 5, 15, 25, 75 **3,** *p. 85:* 1, 2, 3, 5, 6, 9, 10, 15,
18, 30, 45, 90 **4,** *p. 85:* Yes; 24 is a multiple of 3. **5,** *p. 86:* **a.** Prime
b. Composite **c.** Prime **d.** Composite **e.** Prime **6,** *p. 87:* $2^3 \times 7$
7, *p. 87:* 3×5^2 **8,** *p. 88:* 18 **9,** *p. 89:* 66 **10,** *p. 89:* 12
11, *p. 89:* 6 yr

Exercises 2.1, pp. 90–91

1. factors **3.** prime **5.** prime factorization **7.** 1, 3, 7, 21 **9.** 1, 17 **11.** 1, 2, 3, 4, 6, 12 **13.** 1, 31 **15.** 1, 2, 3, 4, 6, 9, 12, 18, 36 **17.** 1, 29 **19.** 1, 2, 4, 5, 10, 20, 25, 50, 100 **21.** 1, 2, 4, 7, 14, 28 **23.** Prime **25.** Composite (2, 4, 8) **27.** Composite (7) **29.** Prime **31.** Composite (3, 9, 27) **33.** 2^3 **35.** 7^2 **37.** $2^3 \times 3$ **39.** 2×5^2 **41.** 7×11 **43.** 3×17 **45.** 5^2 **47.** 2^5 **49.** 3×7 **51.** $2^3 \times 13$ **53.** 11^2 **55.** 2×71 **57.** $2^2 \times 5^2$ **59.** 5^3 **61.** $3^3 \times 5$ **63.** 15 **65.** 40 **67.** 90 **69.** 110 **71.** 72 **73.** 360 **75.** 300 **77.** 84 **79.** 105 **81.** 60 **83.** 3×5^2 **85.** 1, 2, 3, 4, 6, 8, 9, 12, 18, 24, 36, and 72 **87. a.** No, because 2015 is not a multiple of 10 **b.** Yes, because 2020 is a multiple of 10 **89.** No **91.** 30 students **93.** 30 days

Section 2.2 Practices, pp. 93–102

1, ***p. 94:*** $\frac{5}{8}$ **2,** ***p. 94:*** $\frac{7}{30}$ **3,** ***p. 94:*** $\frac{3}{4}$
4, ***p. 95:***

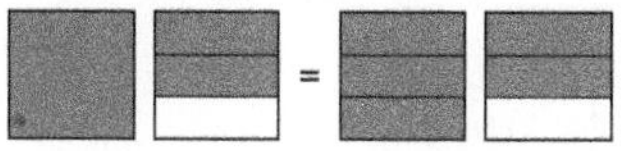

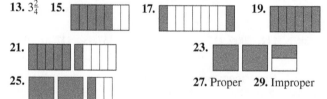

5, ***p. 95:*** **a.** $\frac{16}{3}$ **b.** $\frac{102}{5}$ **6,** ***p. 96:*** **a.** 2 **b.** $5\frac{5}{9}$ **c.** $2\frac{2}{3}$ **7,** ***p. 98:*** Possible answer: $\frac{4}{10}, \frac{6}{15}, \frac{8}{20}$ **8,** ***p. 98:*** $\frac{45}{72}$ **9,** ***p. 99:*** $\frac{2}{3}$ **10,** ***p. 99:*** $\frac{7}{3}$ **11,** ***p. 99:*** $\frac{5}{16}$ **12,** ***p. 101:*** $\frac{11}{16}$ **13,** ***p. 102:*** $\frac{8}{15}, \frac{23}{30}, \frac{9}{10}$ **14,** ***p. 102:*** Country stations

Exercises 2.2, pp. 103–108

1. proper fraction **3.** equivalent **5.** like fractions **7.** $\frac{1}{3}$ **9.** $\frac{3}{6}$ **11.** $1\frac{1}{4}$ **13.** $3\frac{2}{4}$ **15.**

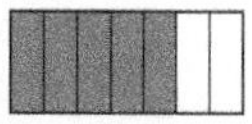

17.

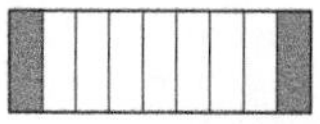

19.

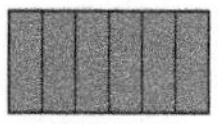

21.

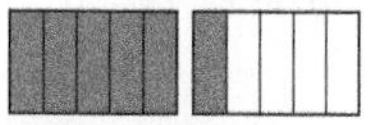

23.

25.

27. Proper **29.** Improper

31. Mixed **33.** Improper **35.** Proper **37.** Mixed **39.** $\frac{13}{5}$ **41.** $\frac{55}{9}$ **43.** $\frac{57}{5}$ **45.** $\frac{5}{1}$ **47.** $\frac{59}{8}$ **49.** $\frac{88}{9}$ **51.** $\frac{27}{2}$ **53.** $\frac{98}{5}$ **55.** $\frac{14}{1}$ **57.** $\frac{54}{11}$ **59.** $\frac{115}{14}$ **61.** $\frac{202}{25}$ **63.** $1\frac{1}{3}$ **65.** $1\frac{1}{9}$ **67.** 3 **69.** 1 **71.** $19\frac{4}{5}$ **73.** $9\frac{1}{9}$ **75.** 1 **77.** $8\frac{2}{9}$ **79.** $13\frac{1}{2}$ **81.** $11\frac{1}{9}$ **83.** 27 **85.** 8 **87.** Possible answers: $\frac{2}{16}, \frac{3}{24}$ **89.** Possible answers: $\frac{4}{22}, \frac{6}{33}$ **91.** Possible answers: $\frac{6}{8}, \frac{9}{12}$ **93.** Possible answers: $\frac{2}{18}, \frac{3}{27}$ **95.** 9 **97.** 15 **99.** 40 **101.** 36 **103.** 40 **105.** 54 **107.** 36 **109.** 42 **111.** 6 **113.** 49 **115.** 32 **117.** 30 **119.** $\frac{2}{3}$ **121.** 1 **123.** $\frac{1}{3}$ **125.** $\frac{9}{20}$ **127.** $\frac{1}{4}$ **129.** $\frac{1}{8}$ **131.** $\frac{5}{4}$, or $1\frac{1}{4}$ **133.** $\frac{33}{16}$, or $2\frac{1}{16}$ **135.** $\frac{9}{16}$ **137.** $\frac{7}{24}$ **139.** 3 **141.** $\frac{1}{7}$ **143.** $3\frac{2}{3}$ **145.** 3 **147.** $<$ **149.** $>$ **151.** $=$ **153.** $<$ **155.** $\frac{1}{4}, \frac{1}{3}, \frac{1}{2}$ **157.** $\frac{7}{12}, \frac{2}{3}, \frac{5}{6}$ **159.** $\frac{3}{5}, \frac{2}{3}, \frac{8}{9}$ **161.** $\frac{5}{6}$ **163.** Possible answers: $\frac{4}{18}, \frac{6}{27}$ **165.** $\frac{12}{15}$ **167.** $2\frac{1}{5}$ hr per day **169. a.** $\frac{20}{401}$ **b.** $\frac{381}{401}$ **171.** $\frac{50}{103}$ **173.** The plain yogurt, because $\frac{2}{5}$ is greater than $\frac{1}{10}$. **175. a.** $\frac{1}{16}$ **b.** $\frac{1}{2}$ **177.** $250\frac{1}{2}$ lb

Section 2.3 Practices, pp. 109–124

1, ***p. 109:*** $\frac{2}{3}$ **2,** ***p. 110:*** $1\frac{7}{40}$ **3,** ***p. 110:*** $\frac{2}{5}$ **4,** ***p. 110:*** **a.** $\frac{3}{5}$ g **b.** $\frac{2}{5}$ g **5,** ***p. 112:*** $1\frac{2}{3}$ **6,** ***p. 112:*** $\frac{3}{10}$ **7,** ***p. 112:*** $\frac{71}{72}$ **8,** ***p. 113:*** $2\frac{1}{30}$ mi **9,** ***p. 114:*** $34\frac{2}{5}$ **10,** ***p. 114:*** $7\frac{1}{2}$ **11,** ***p. 115:*** 4 lengths **12,** ***p. 115:*** $7\frac{5}{8}$ **13,** ***p. 116:*** $11\frac{5}{24}$ **14,** ***p. 117:*** $4\frac{2}{5}$ **15,** ***p. 117:*** $1\frac{2}{5}$ in. **16,** ***p. 118:*** $4\frac{7}{12}$ **17,** ***p. 118:*** $1{,}439\frac{7}{10}$ mi **18,** ***p. 119:*** $1\frac{2}{7}$ **19,** ***p. 120:*** $5\frac{1}{6}$ **20,** ***p. 121:*** $12\frac{1}{2}$ **21,** ***p. 121:*** No, there will be only $1\frac{5}{8}$ yd left. **22,** ***p. 122:*** $10\frac{11}{20}$ **23,** ***p. 123:*** $1\frac{3}{8}$ **24,** ***p. 124:*** $6\frac{3}{4}$

Exercises 2.3, pp. 125–128

1. numerators **3.** regroup **5.** $1\frac{1}{4}$ **7.** $1\frac{1}{2}$ **9.** $\frac{4}{5}$ **11.** $\frac{3}{5}$ **13.** $1\frac{1}{6}$ **15.** $\frac{7}{8}$ **17.** $\frac{77}{100}$ **19.** $\frac{37}{40}$ **21.** $1\frac{5}{18}$ **23.** $1\frac{17}{100}$ **25.** $\frac{3}{4}$ **27.** $\frac{53}{80}$ **29.** $1\frac{7}{72}$ **31.** $1\frac{13}{40}$ **33.** $3\frac{1}{3}$ **35.** $15\frac{2}{5}$ **37.** $14\frac{1}{5}$ **39.** 15 **41.** $10\frac{5}{12}$ **43.** $3\frac{11}{15}$ **45.** $13\frac{13}{15}$ **47.** $6\frac{19}{24}$ **49.** $20\frac{1}{4}$ **51.** $10\frac{3}{100}$ **53.** $11\frac{3}{8}$ **55.** $36\frac{3}{50}$ **57.** $91\frac{7}{12}$ **59.** $6\frac{1}{2}$ **61.** $10\frac{33}{40}$ **63.** $11\frac{3}{8}$ **65.** $\frac{1}{5}$ **67.** $\frac{2}{5}$ **69.** $\frac{4}{25}$ **71.** $\frac{1}{2}$ **73.** 2 **75.** $\frac{1}{12}$ **77.** $\frac{5}{18}$ **79.** $\frac{1}{20}$ **81.** $\frac{1}{14}$ **83.** $\frac{5}{72}$ **85.** $\frac{1}{4}$ **87.** $4\frac{2}{7}$ **89.** $1\frac{3}{4}$ **91.** 20 **93.** $4\frac{1}{10}$ **95.** $3\frac{1}{3}$ **97.** $3\frac{3}{10}$ **99.** $6\frac{1}{3}$ **101.** $5\frac{1}{2}$ **103.** $4\frac{1}{2}$ **105.** $3\frac{1}{4}$ **107.** $11\frac{4}{5}$ **109.** $6\frac{2}{3}$ **111.** $7\frac{5}{6}$ **113.** $3\frac{13}{24}$ **115.** $15\frac{7}{18}$ **117.** $2\frac{29}{30}$ **119.** $\frac{1}{4}$ **121.** $5\frac{5}{12}$ **123.** $13\frac{39}{40}$ **125.** $\frac{3}{8}$ **127.** $1\frac{11}{40}$ **129.** $16\frac{23}{30}$ **131.** $5\frac{1}{5}$ **133.** $18\frac{11}{20}$ **135.** $4\frac{1}{8}$ **137.** $8\frac{1}{3}$ **139.** $2\frac{14}{15}$ **141.** $\frac{1}{8}$ in. **143. a.** $1\frac{1}{2}$ mi **b.** $\frac{1}{4}$ mi **145.** 5 hr **147.** $790\frac{1}{4}$ ft **149.** $\frac{1}{10}$ **151.** 1 lb

Section 2.4 Practices, pp. 131–140

1, ***p. 131:*** $\frac{15}{28}$ **2,** ***p. 131:*** $\frac{81}{100}$ **3,** ***p. 131:*** 20 **4,** ***p. 131:*** $\frac{7}{22}$ **5,** ***p. 132:*** $\frac{2}{9}$ **6,** ***p. 132:*** $5\frac{1}{4}$ hr **7,** ***p. 132:*** \$20,769 **8,** ***p. 133:*** $7\frac{7}{8}$ **9,** ***p. 133:*** 28 **10,** ***p. 134:*** $25\frac{1}{2}$ sq in. **11,** ***p. 135:*** $18\frac{1}{4}$ **12,** ***p. 136:*** 6 **13,** ***p. 137:*** 8 **14,** ***p. 137:*** $2\frac{2}{3}$ yr **15,** ***p. 138:*** $1\frac{3}{5}$ **16,** ***p. 138:*** $\frac{7}{16}$ **17,** ***p. 138:*** 6 lb **18,** ***p. 139:*** 6 **19,** ***p. 140:*** $4\frac{1}{2}$

Exercises 2.4, pp. 141–144

1. multiply **3.** reciprocal **5.** invert **7.** $\frac{2}{15}$ **9.** $\frac{5}{12}$ **11.** $\frac{9}{16}$ **13.** $\frac{8}{25}$ **15.** $\frac{35}{32} = 1\frac{3}{32}$ **17.** $\frac{45}{16} = 2\frac{13}{16}$ **19.** $\frac{2}{9}$ **21.** $\frac{7}{12}$ **23.** $\frac{3}{40}$ **25.** $\frac{31}{30} = 1\frac{1}{30}$ **27.** $\frac{40}{3} = 13\frac{1}{3}$ **29.** $\frac{40}{3} = 13\frac{1}{3}$ **31.** 16 **33.** 4 **35.** 4 **37.** $\frac{35}{4} = 8\frac{3}{4}$ **39.** $1\frac{5}{16}$ **41.** $2\frac{1}{8}$ **43.** $\frac{25}{27}$ **45.** $2\frac{2}{3}$ **47.** 1 **49.** $\frac{7}{8}$ **51.** $1\frac{13}{35}$ **53.** $4\frac{41}{100}$ **55.** $7\frac{4}{5}$ **57.** 375 **59.** 8 **61.** 3 **63.** $41\frac{2}{3}$ **65.** $113\frac{1}{3}$ **67.** $1\frac{1}{6}$ **69.** $\frac{7}{12}$ **71.** $\frac{77}{100}$ **73.** $3\frac{3}{8}$ **75.** $\frac{9}{10}$ **77.** $\frac{32}{35}$ **79.** $3\frac{1}{2}$ **81.** $4\frac{4}{9}$ **83.** $1\frac{1}{2}$ **85.** $2\frac{1}{3}$ **87.** $1\frac{1}{5}$ **89.** $\frac{1}{4}$ **91.** $\frac{2}{21}$ **93.** $\frac{1}{9}$ **95.** 40 **97.** $16\frac{1}{3}$ **99.** $13\frac{1}{3}$ **101.** 7 **103.** $6\frac{11}{18}$ **105.** $1\frac{2}{3}$ **107.** $9\frac{22}{27}$ **109.** $100\frac{1}{2}$ **111.** $\frac{7}{90}$ **113.** $\frac{5}{26}$ **115.** $3\frac{1}{5}$ **117.** $\frac{21}{200}$ **119.** $\frac{35}{44}$ **121.** $1\frac{47}{115}$ **123.** $\frac{14}{27}$ **125.** $2\frac{1}{4}$ **127.** $1\frac{7}{18}$ **129.** $4\frac{13}{15}$ **131.** $\frac{87}{160}$ **133.** $3\frac{19}{27}$ **135.** $4\frac{1}{5}$ **137.** $3\frac{1}{8}$ **139.** $11\frac{1}{6}$ **141.** $\frac{1}{20}$ **143.** $\frac{1}{9}$ **145.** $20\frac{13}{16}$ **147.** $2\frac{5}{22}$ **149.** $\frac{21}{40}$ **151.** 8 **153.** $\frac{7}{12}$ **155.** \$1,340 **157.** \$1,116 **159.** $6\frac{1}{4}$ **161.** $\frac{27}{64}$ **163.** 7 times **165. a.** The scented candle **b.** The unscented candle

Chapter 2 Review Exercises, pp. 148–154

1. is; possible answer: it has more than two factors: 1, 3, 9, and 27 **2.** is not; possible answer: 4 is not a prime number **3.** is not; possible answer: the denominator of a fraction must be nonzero **4.** is; possible answer: the numerator, 12, is greater than the denominator, 11 **5.** is; possible answer: if you divide both the numerator and the denominator by the same number, 16, you get $\frac{1}{3}$ **6.** are; possible answer: they have different denominators **7.** is; possible answer: 24 is the least common multiple of 8 and 12 **8.** is not; possible answer: the reciprocal, $\frac{8}{6}$, is formed by switching the numerator and the denominator **9.** 1, 2, 3, 5, 6, 10, 15, 25, 30, 50, 75, 150 **10.** 1, 2, 3, 4, 5, 6, 9, 10, 12, 15, 18, 20, 30, 36, 45, 60, 90, 180 **11.** 1, 3, 19, 57 **12.** 1, 2, 5, 7, 10, 14, 35, 70 **13.** Prime **14.** Composite **15.** Composite **16.** Prime **17.** $2^2 \times 3^2$ **18.** 3×5^2 **19.** $3^2 \times 11$ **20.** 2×3^3 **21.** 42 **22.** 10 **23.** 72 **24.** 60 **25.** $\frac{2}{4}$ **26.** $\frac{6}{12}$ **27.** $1\frac{1}{6}$ **28.** $2\frac{3}{5}$ **29.** Mixed **30.** Proper **31.** Improper **32.** Improper **33.** $\frac{23}{3}$ **34.** $\frac{9}{5}$ **35.** $\frac{91}{10}$ **36.** $\frac{59}{7}$ **37.** $6\frac{1}{2}$ **38.** $4\frac{2}{3}$ **39.** $2\frac{3}{4}$ **40.** 1 **41.** 84 **42.** 4 **43.** 5 **44.** 27 **45.** $\frac{1}{2}$ **46.** $\frac{5}{7}$ **47.** $\frac{2}{3}$ **48.** $\frac{3}{4}$ **49.** $5\frac{1}{2}$ **50.** $8\frac{2}{3}$ **51.** $6\frac{2}{7}$ **52.** $8\frac{5}{7}$ **53.** $>$ **54.** $>$ **55.** $<$ **56.** $>$ **57.** $>$ **58.** $>$ **59.** $>$ **60.** $>$ **61.** $\frac{2}{7}, \frac{3}{8}, \frac{1}{2}$ **62.** $\frac{2}{15}, \frac{1}{5}, \frac{1}{3}$ **63.** $\frac{3}{4}, \frac{4}{5}, \frac{9}{10}$ **64.** $\frac{13}{18}, \frac{7}{9}, \frac{7}{8}$ **65.** $\frac{6}{5} = 1\frac{1}{5}$ **66.** $\frac{3}{4}$ **67.** $\frac{15}{8} = 1\frac{7}{8}$ **68.** $\frac{3}{5}$ **69.** $\frac{11}{15}$ **70.** $1\frac{17}{24}$ **71.** $1\frac{4}{5}$ **72.** $1\frac{37}{40}$ **73.** $5\frac{7}{8}$ **74.** $9\frac{1}{2}$ **75.** $10\frac{3}{5}$ **76.** 8 **77.** $12\frac{1}{3}$ **78.** $4\frac{3}{10}$ **79.** $5\frac{7}{10}$ **80.** $17\frac{13}{24}$ **81.** $23\frac{5}{12}$ **82.** $46\frac{3}{8}$ **83.** $20\frac{3}{4}$ **84.** $56\frac{1}{24}$ **85.** $\frac{1}{4}$ **86.** $\frac{2}{3}$ **87.** 1 **88.** 0 **89.** $\frac{1}{4}$ **90.** $\frac{3}{8}$ **91.** $\frac{7}{20}$ **92.** $\frac{7}{30}$ **93.** $7\frac{1}{2}$ **94.** $2\frac{3}{10}$ **95.** $3\frac{3}{4}$ **96.** $18\frac{1}{2}$ **97.** $6\frac{1}{2}$ **98.** $1\frac{7}{10}$ **99.** $2\frac{2}{3}$ **100.** $\frac{1}{5}$ **101.** $1\frac{4}{5}$ **102.** $\frac{3}{4}$ **103.** $2\frac{1}{2}$ **104.** $3\frac{1}{3}$ **105.** $\frac{3}{10}$ **106.** $2\frac{7}{8}$ **107.** $\frac{7}{12}$ **108.** $3\frac{8}{9}$ **109.** $\frac{2}{3}$ **110.** $9\frac{9}{20}$ **111.** $\frac{3}{16}$ **112.** $\frac{7}{16}$ **113.** $\frac{5}{8}$ **114.** $\frac{1}{6}$ **115.** $5\frac{1}{3}$

A-4 Answers

116. $\frac{7}{10}$ 117. $\frac{1}{125}$ 118. $\frac{8}{27}$ 119. $\frac{1}{4}$ 120. $\frac{7}{120}$ 121. $\frac{24}{25}$ 122. $1\frac{5}{9}$ 123. $2\frac{2}{3}$
124. $\frac{2}{3}$ 125. 6 126. $18\frac{5}{12}$ 127. $8\frac{7}{16}$ 128. $21\frac{1}{4}$ 129. $\frac{9}{20}$ 130. $1\frac{9}{16}$
131. $37\frac{1}{27}$ 132. $3\frac{3}{8}$ 133. $3\frac{1}{8}$ 134. $1\frac{41}{90}$ 135. $2\frac{1}{10}$ 136. $7\frac{1}{5}$ 137. $\frac{3}{2}$
138. $\frac{2}{3}$ 139. $\frac{1}{8}$ 140. 4 141. $\frac{7}{40}$ 142. $\frac{5}{81}$ 143. $\frac{2}{15}$ 144. $\frac{1}{200}$ 145. $\frac{3}{4}$
146. $1\frac{1}{3}$ 147. 30 148. $8\frac{3}{4}$ 149. $1\frac{1}{6}$ 150. $1\frac{4}{5}$ 151. 2 152. 4 153. $1\frac{3}{4}$
154. $\frac{4}{7}$ 155. $1\frac{7}{12}$ 156. $\frac{12}{19}$ 157. $5\frac{1}{2}$ 158. $2\frac{11}{20}$ 159. 2 160. 3 161. $9\frac{3}{4}$
162. $1\frac{3}{10}$ 163. $5\frac{1}{3}$ 164. $7\frac{5}{9}$ 165. No 166. 50¢ 167. $\frac{1}{4}$ 168. $\frac{2}{9}$
169. The Filmworks camera 170. $\frac{7}{12}$ 171. The patient got back more than $\frac{1}{3}$, because $\frac{275}{700} = \frac{11}{28} = \frac{33}{84}$, which is greater than $\frac{1}{3} = \frac{28}{84}$. 172. Yes it should, because $\frac{23}{32}$ is greater than $\frac{2}{3}$. $\frac{23}{32} = \frac{69}{96}$, whereas $\frac{2}{3} = \frac{64}{96}$ 173. a. $\frac{12}{23}$ b. $\frac{3}{4}$ 174. a. Lisa Gregory b. Monica Yates 175. $\frac{3}{4}$ 176. $\frac{11}{12}$ oz
177. $\frac{1}{4}$ carat 178. $\frac{3}{5}$ 179. 12 women 180. 2,685 undergraduate students 181. 2 awardees 182. 7 lb 183. \$1,050 184. 2 times 185. 19 fish
186. $11\frac{3}{4}$ mi 187. $11\frac{1}{2}$ ft 188. $7\frac{5}{12}$ hr 189. 1,500 fps 190. 500 lb/sq in.
191. $281\frac{1}{4}$ lb 192. 3,100,000 193. 8 orbits 194. $25\frac{5}{8}$ sq mi
195.

Employee	Saturday	Sunday	Total
L. Chavis	$7\frac{1}{2}$	$4\frac{1}{4}$	$11\frac{3}{4}$
R. Young	$5\frac{3}{4}$	$6\frac{1}{2}$	$12\frac{1}{4}$
Total	$13\frac{1}{4}$	$10\frac{3}{4}$	24

196.

Worker	Hours per Day	Days Worked	Total Hours	Wage per Hour	Gross Pay
Maya	5	3	15	\$7	\$105
Noel	$7\frac{1}{4}$	4	29	\$10	\$290
Alisa	$4\frac{1}{2}$	$5\frac{1}{2}$	$24\frac{3}{4}$	\$9	$\$222\frac{3}{4}$

197. $10\frac{10}{11}$ lb 198. $22\frac{1}{2}$ cups 199. 3,200 mi 200. 6 times

Chapter 2 Posttest, p. 155

1. 1, 3, 7, 9, 21, 63 2. 2×3^3 3. $\frac{4}{9}$ 4. $\frac{12}{1}$ 5. $10\frac{1}{4}$ 6. $\frac{7}{8}$ 7. $\frac{5}{10}$ 8. 24
9. $1\frac{13}{24}$ 10. $8\frac{7}{40}$ 11. $4\frac{2}{7}$ 12. $5\frac{23}{30}$ 13. $\frac{1}{81}$ 14. 12 15. $\frac{7}{9}$ 16. $7\frac{5}{6}$ 17. $\frac{10}{11}$
18. $19\frac{1}{5}$ mi 19. $\frac{5}{6}$ hr 20. \$94

Chapter 2 Cumulative Review, p. 156

1. Five million, three hundred fifteen 2. 1,900,000 3. 581,400 4. 908
5. 1 6. $\frac{1}{25}$ 7. $2^2 \times 3 \times 7$ 8. 120 9. $\frac{3}{4}$ 10. $\frac{3}{8}$ 11. $1\frac{11}{24}$ 12. $6\frac{2}{5}$ 13. 7
14. $1\frac{5}{11}$ 15. \$37 billion 16. 1 million times 17. 12 above
18. Yes. The room has 370 square feet of wall area. 19. $\frac{1}{3}$ 20. 4 pieces

CHAPTER 3

Chapter 3 Pretest, p. 158

1. Hundredths 2. Four and twelve thousandths 3. 3.1 4. 0.0029
5. 21.52 6. 7.3738 7. 11.69 8. 9.81 9. 8,300 10. 18.423
11. 0.0144 12. 7.1 13. 0.00605 14. 32.7 15. 0.875 16. 2.83
17. One with a pH value of 2.95 18. \$58.44 billion 19. 3 times
20. \$3.74

Section 3.1 Practices: pp. 160–167

1, *p. 160:* a. The tenths place b. The ten-thousandths place
c. The thousandths place 2, *p. 161:* $\frac{7}{8}$ 3, *p. 161:* $2\frac{3}{100}$ 4, *p. 162:* a. $5\frac{3}{5}$
b. $5\frac{3}{5}$ 5, *p. 162:* a. $7\frac{3}{1,000}$ b. $4\frac{1}{10}$ 6, *p. 162:* a. Sixty-one hundredths
b. Four and nine hundred twenty-three thousandths c. Seven and five hundredths 7, *p. 163:* a. 0.043 b. 10.26 8, *p. 163:* 3.14

9, *p. 164:* 0.8297 10, *p. 164:* 3.51, 3.5, 3.496 11, *p. 165:* The one with the rating of 8.1, because $9 > 8.2 > 8.1$ 12, *p. 166–167:* a. 748.1
b. 748.08 c. 748.077 d. 748 e. 700 13, *p. 167:* 7.30 14, *p. 167:* 11.7 m

Exercises 3.1, pp. 168–172

1. right 3. hundredths 5. greater 7. 2.78 9. 9.01 11. 2.00175
13. 823.001 15. Tenths 17. Hundredths 19. Thousandths 21. Ones
23. Fifty-three hundredths 25. Three hundred five thousandths
27. Six tenths 29. Five and seventy-two hundredths 31. Twenty-four and two thousandths 33. 0.8 35. 1.041 37. 60.01 39. 4.107
41. 3.2 m 43. $\frac{3}{5}$ 45. $\frac{39}{100}$ 47. $1\frac{1}{2}$ 49. 8 51. $5\frac{5}{250}$ 53. > 55. <
57. > 59. = 61. < 63. 7, 7.07, 7.1 65. 4.9, 5.001, 5.2
67. 9.1 mi, 9.38 mi, 9.6 mi 69. 17.4 71. 3.591 73. 37.1 75. 0.40
77. 7.06 79. 9 mi
81.

To the Nearest	8.0714	0.9916
Tenth	8.1	1.0
Hundredth	8.07	0.99
Ten	10	0

83. 0.024 85. 870.06 87. 2.04 m, 2.14 m, 2.4 m 89. Twenty-three and nine hundred thirty-four thousandths 91. Eighteen and seven tenths; eighteen and eight tenths 93. Two hundred eleven and seven tenths, sixty-nine and four tenths, one hundred eighty-nine and eight tenths, one hundred ninety-three and five tenths, forty-seven and five tenths 95. One hundred-thousandth; eight hundred-thousandths 97. 1.2 acres 99. 74.59 mph
101. 14.7 lb 103. 9.6 V 105. 352.1 kWh 107. Evgeni Plushenko
109. Last winter 111. 2005 113. Husband's 115. \$57.03 117. 0.001
119. 1.4

Section 3.2 Practices: pp. 173–177

1, *p. 173:* 10.387 2, *p. 173:* 39.3 3, *p. 174:* 102.1°F 4, *p. 174:* 46.2125
5, *p. 175:* \$485.43 6, *p. 175:* 16.9 mi 7, *p. 175:* 22.13 mi 8, *p. 176:* 0.863
9, *p. 176:* 0.079 10, *p. 176:* 0.5744 11, *p. 177:* Possible estimate: \$480
12, *p. 177:* Possible estimate: \$2 million

Calculator Practices, p. 178

13, *p. 178:* 79.23; 14, *p. 178:* 0.00002

Exercises 3.2, pp. 179–182

1. decimal points 3. sum 5. 9.33 7. 0.9 9. 8.13 11. 21.45
13. 7.67 15. \$77.21 17. 1.08993 19. 24.16 21. 44.422
23. 20.32 mm 25. 16.682 kg 27. 23.30595 29. 0.7 31. 16.8
33. 18.41 35. 75.63 37. 22.324 39. 0.17 41. 0.1142 43. 6.2
45. 15.37 47. 5.9 49. 6.21 51. 1.85 lb 53. 4.9°F 55. 39.752
57. 27.9 mg 59. 3.205 61. 21.19896 63. c; possible estimate: 0.084
65. b; possible estimate: 0.06 67. 7.771 69. 7.75 lb 71. 11.6013
73. \$1.03 75. 56.8 centuries 77. \$1.7 million 79. 6.84 in.
81. Yes; $2.8 + 2.9 + 2.6 + 1.6 = 9.9$
83. a.

Gymnast	VT	UB	BB	FX	AA
Nastia Liukin (U.S.)	15.1	15.95	15.975	15.35	62.375
Yang Yilin (China)	15.2	16.65	15.5	15	62.35
Shawn Johnson (U.S)	16	15.325	15.975	15.425	62.725

b. Shawn Johnson 85. A total of 16.2 mg of iron; no, she needs 1.8 mg more

Section 3.3 Practices: pp. 183–186

1, *p. 183:* 9.835 2, *p. 184:* 1.4 3, *p. 184:* 0.01 4, *p. 184:* 0.024
5, *p. 184:* 9.91 6, *p. 185:* 325 7, *p. 185:* 327,000 8, *p. 185:* a. 18.015
b. 18 9, *p. 186:* 0.0003404; possible estimate: $0.004 \times 0.09 = 0.00036$
10, *p. 186:* 3.6463 11, *p. 186:* Possible answer: 1,200 mi

Calculator Practices, p. 187
12, *p. 187:* 815.6   **13,** *p. 187:* 9.261

Exercises 3.3, pp. 188–191
1. multiplication   **3.** two   **5.** square   **7.** 2.99212   **9.** 204.360
11. 2,492.0   **13.** 0.0000969   **15.** 2,870.00   **17.** $0.73525   **19.** 0.54
21. 0.4   **23.** 0.02   **25.** 0.0028   **27.** 0.765   **29.** 2.016   **31.** 7.602
33. 0.5   **35.** 5.852   **37.** 151.14   **39.** 3.7377   **41.** 1.7955
43. 8,312.7   **45.** 23   **47.** 0.09   **49.** 1.05   **51.** 0.000000001
53. 42.5 ft   **55.** 1.4 mi   **57.** 42.77325   **59.** 272,593.75   **61.** 70
63. 25.75   **65.** 1.09   **67.** 2.86   **69.** 3.952   **71.** 0.14
73.

Input	Output
1	$3.8 \times 1 - 0.2 = 3.6$
2	$3.8 \times 2 - 0.2 = 7.4$
3	$3.8 \times 3 - 0.2 = 11.2$
4	$3.8 \times 4 - 0.2 = 15$

75. a; possible estimate: 50   **77.** b; possible estimate: 0.014   **79.** 8.75
81. 0.068   **83.** 4.48   **85.** 2,900 fps   **87.** 57,900,000 km
89. 254.3 sq ft   **91.** 1.25 mg   **93.** 1,308 calories
95. a.

Purchase	Quantity	Unit Price	Price
Belt	1	$11.99	$11.99
Shirt	3	$16.95	$50.85
Total Price			$62.84

b. $17.16   **97.** 88.81 in.

Section 3.4   Practices: pp. 193–199
1, *p. 193:* 0.375   **2,** *p. 193:* 7.625   **3,** *p. 194:* 83.3   **4.** *p. 194:* 0.1
5, *p. 196:* 18.04   **6,** *p. 196:* 2,050   **7,** *p. 197:* 73.4   **8,** *p. 197:* 0.0341
9, *p. 198:* 0.00086   **10,** *p. 198:* 1.5   **11,** *p. 199:* 21.1; possible estimate: 20
12, *p. 199:* 295.31   **13,** *p. 199:* 8 times as great

Calculator Practices, p. 200
14, *p. 200:* 0.2   **15,** *p. 200:* 4.29

Exercises 3.4, pp. 201–204
1. decimal   **3.** right   **5.** quotient   **7.** 0.5   **9.** 0.375   **11.** 3.7   **13.** 1.625
15. 6.2   **17.** 21.03   **19.** 0.67   **21.** 0.78   **23.** 3.11   **25.** 5.06
27. 4.25   **29.** 4.2   **31.** 1.375   **33.** 8.5   **35.** 3.286   **37.** 0.273
39. 6.571   **41.** 70.077   **43.** 58.82   **45.** 0.0663   **47.** 2.8875
49. 0.286   **51.** 4.3   **53.** 0.0015   **55.** 1.73   **57.** 2.875   **59.** 4
61. 70.4   **63.** 94   **65.** 12.5   **67.** 0.3   **69.** 0.2   **71.** 0.952
73. 0.00082   **75.** 383.88   **77.** 0.01   **79.** 9.23   **81.** 9,666.67
83. 1,952.38   **85.** 325.18   **87.** 67.41   **89.** 41.61   **91.** 2.765
93. 32.9   **95.** 52.2   **97.** 4.05   **99.** 396.5   **101.** 49.9
103.

Input	Output
1	$1 \div 5 - 0.2 = 0$
2	$2 \div 5 - 0.2 = 0.2$
3	$3 \div 5 - 0.2 = 0.4$
4	$4 \div 5 - 0.2 = 0.6$

105. c; possible estimate: 50   **107.** b; possible estimate: 0.2   **109.** 0.8
111. 1.17   **113.** 0.45   **115.** 0.0037 in. per yr   **117. a.** 0.6 **b.** 0.55
c. The women's team has a better record. The team won $\frac{3}{5}$, or 0.6, of the
games played, and the men's team won $\frac{11}{20}$, or 0.55, of the games played.

119. a.

SUV	Distance Driven (in miles)	Gasoline Used (in gallons)	Gasoline Mileage (miles per gallon)
Honda CR-V	40.5	1.9	21
Ford Escape Hybrid	62.4	2.4	26
GMC Terrain	42.6	2.4	18

b. Ford Escape Hybrid   **121.** 2,000 shares   **123.** 13 times   **125.** 0.4 lb
127. .366

Chapter 3   Review Exercises, pp. 207–210
1. is not; possible answer: it does not have a decimal point (or it is written
in fractional form).   **2.** is not; possible answer: decimal places are to the
right of the decimal point, and this digit is to the left.   **3.** is not; possible
answer: the number to the right of the critical digit 2 is 6, so we round up,
getting 48.73   **4.** can; possible answer: then each column will contain digits with the same place value.   **5.** is not; possible answer: no digits repeat
indefinitely.   **6.** is; possible answer: the dividend is smaller than the
divisor.   **7.** Hundredths   **8.** Tenths   **9.** Tenths   **10.** Ten-thousandths
11. $\frac{7}{20}$ **12.** $8\frac{1}{5}$ **13.** $4\frac{7}{1,000}$ **14.** 10   **15.** Seventy-two hundredths
16. Five and six tenths   **17.** Three and nine ten-thousandths
18. Five hundred ten and thirty-six thousandths   **19.** 0.007   **20.** 2.1
21. 0.09   **22.** 7.041   **23.** <   **24.** >   **25.** >   **26.** >
27. 1.002, 0.8, 0.72   **28.** 0.004, 0.003, 0.00057   **29.** 7.3   **30.** 0.039
31. 4.39   **32.** $899   **33.** 12.11   **34.** 52.75   **35.** $24.13   **36.** 12 m
37. 28.78   **38.** 87.752   **39.** 1.834   **40.** 48.901   **41.** 98.2033
42. $90,948.80   **43.** 2.912   **44.** 1,008   **45.** 0.00001   **46.** 13.69
47. 2,710   **48.** 0.034   **49.** 5.75   **50.** 13.5   **51.** 1,569.36846
52. 441.760662   **53.** 0.625   **54.** 90.2   **55.** 4.0625   **56.** 0.045
57. 0.17   **58.** 0.29   **59.** 8.33   **60.** 11.22   **61.** 0.65   **62.** 1.6
63. 0.175   **64.** 0.277   **65.** 5.2   **66.** 3.2   **67.** 23.7   **68.** 16,358.3
69. 1.9   **70.** 360.7   **71.** 3.0   **72.** 0.3   **73.** 1.18   **74.** 117
75. 34.375   **76.** 1.4   **77.** 54.49 sec   **78.** $14.14   **79.** Four ten-mil-
lionths   **80.** 14.22 in.   **81.** 1.5 AU.   **82.** 4.35 times   **83.** $0.06
84. $250   **85.** 7.19 g   **86.** 3.5°C   **87.** 36,162.45
88.

Period Ending	Google	Yahoo!
June 30	5.523	1.573
September 30	5.945	1.575
December 31	6.674	1.732
March 31	6.775	1.597

$18.440 billion

Chapter 3   Posttest, p. 211
1. 6   **2.** Five and one hundred two thousandths   **3.** 320.15
4. 0.00028   **5.** $3\frac{1}{25}$ **6.** 0.004   **7.** 4.354   **8.** $5.66   **9.** 20.9
10. 5.72   **11.** 0.001   **12.** 3.36   **13.** 0.0029   **14.** 32.7   **15.** 0.375
16. 4.17   **17.** 0.01 lb   **18.** 2.6 ft   **19.** Belmont Stakes   **20.** $32.40

Chapter 3   Cumulative Review, p. 212
1. 1,000,000   **2.** 2,076   **3.** 27,403   **4.** 900 sq m   **5.** 42   **6.** 1, 2, 3, 4,
5, 6, 10, 12, 15, 20, 30, 60   **7.** $1\frac{1}{2}$ **8.** $2\frac{2}{3}$ **9.** 32   **10.** $\frac{17}{30}$ **11.** $4\frac{18}{25}$
12. 38.4   **13.** 60.213   **14.** 610   **15.** $0.17   **16.** $\frac{2}{15}$ acre   **17.** 325
18. 26,000 mi   **19.** $193.86   **20.** 2.6

ANSWERS

CHAPTER 4

Chapter 4 Pretest, p. 214

1. Possible answer: four less than t **2.** Possible answer: quotient of y and three **3.** $m + 8$ **4.** $2n$ **5.** 4 **6.** $1\frac{1}{2}$ **7.** $x + 3 = 5$
8. $4y = 12$ **9.** $x = 6$ **10.** $t = 10$ **11.** $n = 13$ **12.** $a = 12$
13. $m = 6.1$ **14.** $n = 30$ **15.** $m = 13\frac{1}{2}$, or 13.5 **16.** $n = 15$
17. $63 = x + 36$; 27 moons **18.** $6.75 = x - 2.75$; \$9.50
19. $\frac{2}{5}x = 39{,}900$; 99,750 sq mi **20.** $40 = 10x$; 4 mg

Section 4.1 Practices: pp. 216–218

1, p. 216: Answers may vary **a.** One-half of p **b.** x less than 5 **c.** y divided by 4 **d.** 3 more than n **e.** $\frac{3}{5}$ of b **2, p. 216: a.** $x + 9$ **b.** $10y$ **c.** $n - 7$
d. $p \div 5$ **e.** $\frac{2}{5}v$ **3, p. 217: a.** $q + 12$, where q represents the quantity
b. $\frac{9}{a}$, where a represents the account balance **c.** $\frac{2}{7}c$, where c represents the cost **4, p. 217:** $\frac{h}{4}$ hr **5, p. 217:** $s - 3$ **6, p. 218: a.** 25 **b.** 0.38 **c.** 4.8
d. 26.6 **7, p. 218:** $\frac{1}{5}n$ dollars; \$750 **8, p. 218:** The total amount was $(18.45 + t)$ dollars; \$21.45 for $t = \$3$

Exercises 4.1, pp. 219–221

1. variable **3.** algebraic **5.** 9 more than t; t plus 9 **7.** c minus 12; 12 subtracted from c **9.** c divided by 3; the quotient of c and 3; **11.** 10 times s; the product of 10 and s **13.** y minus 10; 10 less than y
15. 7 times a; the product of 7 and a **17.** x divided by 6; the quotient of x and 6 **19.** x minus $\frac{1}{2}$; $\frac{1}{2}$ less than x **21.** $\frac{1}{4}$ times w; $\frac{1}{4}$ of w **23.** 2 minus x; the difference between 2 and x **25.** 1 increased by x; x added to 1
27. 3 times p; the product of 3 and p **29.** n decreased by 1.1; n minus 1.1
31. y divided by 0.9; the quotient of y and 0.9 **33.** $x + 10$
35. $n - 1$ **37.** $y + 5$ **39.** $t \div 6$ **41.** $10y$ **43.** $w - 5$ **45.** $n + \frac{4}{5}$
47. $z \div 3$ **49.** $\frac{2}{7}x$ **51.** $k - 6$ **53.** $n + 12$ **55.** $n - 5.1$ **57.** 26
59. 2.5 **61.** 15 **63.** $1\frac{1}{6}$ **65.** 1.1 **67.** $\frac{1}{5}$

69.

x	$x + 8$
1	9
2	10
3	11
4	12

71.

n	$n - 0.2$
1	0.8
2	1.8
3	2.8
4	3.8

73.

x	$\frac{3}{4}x$
4	3
8	6
12	9
16	12

75.

z	$\frac{z}{2}$
2	1
4	2
6	3
8	4

77. $x - 7$ **79.** Possible answers: n over 2; n divided by 2 **81.** $3.5t$
83. Possible answers: 6 more than x; the sum of x and 6
85. $(m - 25)$ mg **87.** $25° + 90° + d°$, or $115° + d°$ **89.** 220 mi
91. a. $2.5w$ dollars **b.** \$22.50

Section 4.2 Practices: pp. 223–227

1, p. 223: a. $n - 5.1 = 9$ **b.** $y + 2 = 12$ **c.** $n - 4 = 11$
d. $n + 5 = 7\frac{3}{4}$ **2, p. 224:** $p - 6 = 49.95$, where p is the regular price.
3, p. 225: $x = 9$; **4, p. 225:** $t = 2.7$; **5, p. 226:** $m = 5\frac{1}{4}$;
6, p. 226: a. $11 = m - 4$; $m = 15$ **b.** $12 + n = 21$; $n = 9$
7, p. 227: $x + 3.99 = 27.18$; \$23.19 **8, p. 227:**
$269{,}000 = x - 394{,}000$; 663,000 sq mi

Exercises 4.2, pp. 228–231

1. equation **3.** subtract **5.** $z - 9 = 25$ **7.** $7 + x = 25$
9. $t - 3.1 = 4$ **11.** $\frac{3}{2} + y = \frac{9}{2}$ **13.** $n - 3\frac{1}{2} = 7$
15. a. Yes **b.** No **c.** Yes **d.** No **17.** Subtract 4. **19.** Add 6.
21. Add 7. **23.** Subtract 21. **25.** $a = 31$ **27.** $y = 2$ **29.** $x = 12$
31. $n = 4$ **33.** $m = 2$ **35.** $y = 90$ **37.** $z = 2.9$ **39.** $n = 8.9$
41. $y = 0.9$ **43.** $x = 8\frac{2}{3}$ **45.** $m = 5\frac{1}{3}$ **47.** $x = 3\frac{3}{4}$ **49.** $c = 47\frac{1}{5}$
51. $x = 13$ **53.** $y = 6\frac{1}{4}$ **55.** $a = 3\frac{5}{12}$ **57.** $x = 8.2$ **59.** $y = 19.91$
61. $x = 4.557$ **63.** $y = 10.251$ **65.** $n + 3 = 11$; $n = 8$
67. $y - 6 = 7$; $y = 13$ **69.** $n + 10 = 19$; $n = 9$

71. $x + 3.6 = 9$; $x = 5.4$ **73.** $n - 4\frac{1}{3} = 2\frac{2}{3}$; $n = 7$ **75.** Equation c
77. Equation a **79.** $a = 14.5$ **81.** Equation b **83.** Yes
85. $4.2 + n = 8$ **87.** Add 1.9. **89.** $x + 12 = 106$; \$94
91. $40° + x = 90°$; 50° **93.** $621{,}000 = x - 13{,}000$; \$634,000
95. $45 = x - 20$; 65 mph **97.** $m + 1{,}876{,}674{,}000 = 4{,}023{,}362{,}895$;
\$2,146,688,895

Section 4.3 Practices, pp. 232–237

1, p. 232: a. $2x = 14$ **b.** $\frac{a}{6} = 1.5$ **c.** $\frac{n}{0.3} = 1$ **d.** $10 = \frac{1}{2}n$
2, p. 232: $15 = 3w$ **3, p. 233:** $x = 5$ **4, p. 233:** $a = 6$
5, p. 234: $x = 4$ **6, p. 234:** $a = 2.88$ **7, p. 235:** $x = 16$ **8, p. 235:**
a. $12 = \frac{z}{6}$, $z = 72$; $12 \overset{?}{=} \frac{72}{6}$, $12 \overset{\checkmark}{=} 12$ **b.** $16 = 2x$, $8 = x$, or $x = 8$;
$16 \overset{?}{=} 2(8)$, $16 \overset{\checkmark}{=} 16$ **9, p. 236:** $1.6 = 5x$; 0.32 km **10, p. 236:**
$\frac{x}{25.5} = 87$; \$2,218.50 **11, p. 237:** $\frac{3}{8}p = 150{,}000$; \$400.000

Exercises 4.3, pp. 238–241

1. divide **3.** substituting **5.** equation **7.** $\frac{3}{4}y = 12$ **9.** $\frac{x}{7} = \frac{7}{2}$
11. $\frac{1}{3}x = 2$ **13.** $\frac{n}{3} = \frac{1}{3}$ **15.** $9a = 27$ **17. a.** Yes **b.** No **c.** No **d.** No
19. Divide by 3. **21.** Multiply by 2. **23.** Divide by $\frac{3}{4}$, or multiply by $\frac{4}{3}$.
25. Divide by 1.5. **27.** $x = 6$ **29.** $x = 18$ **31.** $n = 4$ **33.** $x = 91$
35. $y = 4$ **37.** $b = 20$ **39.** $m = 157.5$ **41.** $t = 0.4$ **43.** $x = \frac{3}{2}$, or
$1\frac{1}{2}$ **45.** $x = 36$ **47.** $t = 3$ **49.** $y = \frac{2}{5}$ **51.** $n = 700$ **53.** $x = 12.5$
55. $x = \frac{1}{2}$ **57.** $m = 6$ **59.** $x \approx 6.8$ **61.** $x \approx 4.9$ **63.** $8n = 56$; $n = 7$
65. $\frac{3}{4}y = 18$; $y = 24$ **67.** $\frac{x}{5} = 11$; $x = 55$ **69.** $2x = 36$; $x = 18$
71. $\frac{1}{2}a = 4$; $a = 8$ **73.** $\frac{n}{5} = 1\frac{3}{5}$; $n = 8$ **75.** $\frac{n}{2.5} = 10$; $n = 25$
77. Equation d **79.** Equation a **81.** $x = 5.5$ **83.** Equation d
85. Yes **87.** $2x = 5$ **89.** Multiply by 2. **91.** $4s = 60$; 15 units
93. $56 = \frac{1}{2}x$; 112 mi **95.** $\frac{c}{3} = 8.99$; \$26.97 **97. a.** $\frac{2}{5}x = 60$; 150 ml
b. 90 ml **99.** $\frac{1}{3}x = 128$; \$384 million **101.** $\frac{p}{3{,}537{,}438} = 86.8$; 307,000,000
people

Chapter 4 Review Exercises, pp. 243–245

1. is; possible answer: x represents an unknown number **2.** is not; possible answer: constants are known numbers such as 6 or -5 **3.** can; possible answer: algebraic expressions combine constants, variables, and algebraic operations **4.** cannot; possible answer: an equation is a mathematical statement that two expressions are equal **5.** is; possible answer: substituting 28 for x makes the equation $72 - 28 = 44$ a true statement
6. is; possible answer: x is alone on one side of the equation **7.** x plus 1
8. Four more than y **9.** w minus 1 **10.** Three less than s
11. c divided by 7 **12.** The quotient of a and 10 **13.** Two times x
14. The product of 6 and y **15.** y divided by 0.1 **16.** The quotient of n and 1.6 **17.** One-third of x **18.** One-tenth of w **19.** $m + 9$
20. $b + \frac{1}{2}$ **21.** $y - 1.4$ **22.** $z - 3$ **23.** $\frac{3}{x}$ **24.** $n \div 2.5$ **25.** $3n$
26. $12n$ **27.** 12 **28.** 19 **29.** 0 **30.** 6 **31.** 0.3 **32.** 6.5 **33.** $1\frac{1}{2}$
34. $\frac{5}{12}$ **35.** 0.4 **36.** $4\frac{1}{2}$ **37.** 1.6 **38.** 9 **39.** $x = 9$ **40.** $y = 9$
41. $n = 26$ **42.** $b = 20$ **43.** $a = 3.5$ **44.** $c = 7.5$ **45.** $x = 11$
46. $y = 2$ **47.** $w = 1\frac{1}{2}$ **48.** $s = \frac{1}{3}$ **49.** $c = 6\frac{3}{4}$ **50.** $p = 11\frac{2}{3}$
51. $m = 5$ **52.** $n = 0$ **53.** $c = 78$ **54.** $y = 90$ **55.** $n = 11$
56. $x = 25$ **57.** $x = 31.0485$ **58.** $m = 26.6225$ **59.** $n - 19 = 35$
60. $a - 37 = 234$ **61.** $9 + n = 15\frac{1}{2}$ **62.** $n + 26 = 30\frac{1}{3}$ **63.** $2y = 16$
64. $25t = 175$ **65.** $34 = \frac{n}{19}$ **66.** $17 = \frac{z}{13}$ **67.** $\frac{1}{3}n = 27$ **68.** $\frac{2}{5}n = 4$
69. a. No **b.** Yes **c.** Yes **d.** No **70. a.** Yes **b.** No **c.** No **d.** Yes
71. $x = 5$ **72.** $t = 2$ **73.** $a = 105$ **74.** $n = 54$ **75.** $y = 9$
76. $r = 10$ **77.** $w = 90$ **78.** $x = 100$ **79.** $y = 20$ **80.** $a = 120$
81. $n = 32$ **82.** $b = 32$ **83.** $m = 3.15$ **84.** $z = 0.57$
85. $x = \frac{2}{5}$, or 0.4 **86.** $t = \frac{1}{2}$, or 0.5 **87.** $m = 1.2$ **88.** $b = 9.8$
89. $x = 12.5$ **90.** $x = 1.4847$ **91.** $2h$ degrees; 6 degrees
92. $\frac{d}{20}$ dollars per hr; \$9.55 per hr **93.** $\$0.89p$; \$2.67
94. $(3{,}000 + d)$ dollars; \$3,225 **95.** $x + 238 = 517$; \$279
96. $225 = x + 50$; 175 **97.** $2.9x = 100$; 34 L

98. $\frac{1}{4}x = 500{,}000$; 2,000,000 people   **99.** $\frac{x}{6} = 30$; 180 lb
100. $2.5x = 3{,}000{,}000{,}000{,}000$; $1,200,000,000,000 or $1.2 trillion
101. $98.6 + x = 101$; 2.4°F   **102.** $x - 256 = 8{,}957$; 9,213 applications

Chapter 4   Posttest, p. 246

1. Possible answer: x plus $\frac{1}{2}$ **2.** Possible answer: the quotient of a and 3
3. $n - 10$ **4.** $\frac{8}{p}$ **5.** 0   **6.** $\frac{1}{4}$ **7.** $x - 6 = 4\frac{1}{2}$ **8.** $\frac{y}{8} = 3.2$ **9.** $x = 0$
10. $y = 12$ **11.** $n = 27$ **12.** $a = 738$ **13.** $m = 7.8$ **14.** $n = 50$
15. $x = \frac{11}{20}$ **16.** $n = 760$ **17.** $1\frac{3}{4} + x = 2\frac{1}{4}$; $\frac{1}{2}$ lb   **18.** $\frac{1}{4}x = 500$;
2,000 wolves   **19.** $1.5x = 9$; 6 billion   **20.** $x - 19.8 = 7.6$; 27.4°C

Chapter 4   Cumulative Review, pp. 247–248

1. 314,200   **2.** c   **3.** 23,316   **4.** 1,030   **5.** $\frac{84}{96}$ **6.** $1\frac{2}{5}$ **7.** $5\frac{3}{8}$
8. Five and two hundred thirty-nine thousandths   **9.** $<$ **10.** 3.89
11. 0.0075   **12.** Yes   **13.** $n = 7.8$ **14.** $x = 32$ **15.** 7,200 images
16. He got back $\frac{2}{7}$ of his money, which is less than $\frac{1}{3}$.
17. $\frac{3}{5}x = 300{,}000{,}000$; 500 million tons   **18.** 92.4 lb   **19.** 55,000
beehives   **20. a.** $4.5x = 2{,}900{,}000$ **b.** 600,000 personnel

CHAPTER 5

Chapter 5   Pretest, p. 250

1. $\frac{3}{4}$ **2.** $\frac{2}{5}$ **3.** $\frac{5}{3}$ **4.** $\frac{19}{51}$ **5.** $\frac{16\text{ gal}}{5\text{ min}}$ **6.** $\frac{5\text{ mg}}{3\text{ hr}}$ **7.** $\frac{2\text{ dental assistants}}{1\text{ dentist}}$
8. $\frac{1\text{ calculator}}{1\text{ student}}$ **9.** $\frac{\$230}{\text{box}}$ **10.** $\frac{\$0.50}{\text{bottle}}$ **11.** True   **12.** False   **13.** $x = 9$
14. $x = 31\frac{1}{2}$ **15.** $x = 16$ **16.** $x = 160$ **17.** $\frac{4}{5}$ **18.** 200 lb/min
19. 4.5 in.   **20.** 76 mi

Section 5.1   Practices, pp. 251–255

1, p. 251: $\frac{2}{3}$ **2, p. 252:** $\frac{9}{5}$ **3, p. 252:** $\frac{20}{19} \approx 1.05 > 1$; yes
4, p. 253: a. $\frac{5\text{ mL}}{2\text{ min}}$ **b.** $\frac{3\text{ lb}}{2\text{ wk}}$ **5, p. 253: a.** 48 ft/sec **b.** 0.375 hit per time at
bat   **6, p. 254:** 1.5 min/city block   **7, p. 254: a.** $174/flight
b. $2.75/hr **c.** $0.99/download   **8, p. 255:** The 150-caplet bottle

Exercises 5.1, pp. 256–260

1. quotient   **3.** simplest form   **5.** denominator   **7.** $\frac{2}{3}$ **9.** $\frac{2}{3}$ **11.** $\frac{11}{7}$
13. $\frac{3}{2}$ **15.** $\frac{1}{4}$ **17.** $\frac{4}{3}$ **19.** $\frac{1}{1}$ **21.** $\frac{5}{3}$ **23.** $\frac{7}{24}$ **25.** $\frac{20}{1}$ **27.** $\frac{8}{7}$ **29.** $\frac{4}{5}$
31. $\frac{5\text{ calls}}{2\text{ days}}$ **33.** $\frac{36\text{ cal}}{5\text{ min}}$ **35.** $\frac{1\text{ million hits}}{3\text{ mo}}$ **37.** $\frac{17\text{ baskets}}{30\text{ attempts}}$ **39.** $\frac{37\text{ points}}{2\text{ games}}$
41. $\frac{100\text{ sq ft}}{\$329}$ **43.** $\frac{16\text{ males}}{3\text{ females}}$ **45.** $\frac{8\text{ Democrats}}{7\text{ Republicans}}$ **47.** $\frac{1\text{ lb}}{8\text{ servings}}$ **49.** $\frac{307\text{ flights}}{3\text{ days}}$
51. $\frac{1\text{ lb}}{200\text{ sq ft}}$ **53.** 225 revolutions/min   **55.** 8 gal/day   **57.** 0.3 tank/acre
59. 1.6 yd/dress   **61.** 2 hr/day   **63.** 0.25 km/min   **65.** 70 fat calories/tbsp
67. $0.45/bar   **69.** $2.95/roll   **71.** $66.67/plant   **73.** $99/night
75.

Number of Units	Total Price	Unit Price
30	$1.69	$0.06
100	$5.49	$0.05

100 cough drops

77.

Number of Units (Sheets)	Total Price	Unit Price
500	9.69	$0.019
2,500	$42.99	$0.017

2,500 sheets of paper

79.

Number of Units	Total Price	Unit Price
14	$8.49	$0.61
25	$11.49	$0.46
28	$7.49	$0.27

28 trash bags

81. $0.16/oz   **83.** 2 tutors/15 students   **85.** $\frac{5}{1}$ **87.** $\frac{2}{3}$ **89.** 170 cal/oz
91. $0.03 per page   **93.** $\frac{1}{2}$ **95.** $\frac{1}{6}$ **97.** In the Senate   **99. a.** $\frac{63}{68}$ **b.** $\frac{8}{9}$
101. 0.51 to 1

Section 5.2   Practices, pp. 261–265

1, p. 261: Yes   **2, p. 261:** Not a true proportion   **3, p. 262:** No
4, p. 263: $x = 8$ **5, p. 263:** $x = 12$ **6, p. 264:** 64,000 flowers
7, p. 264: Mach 1.06   **8, p. 265:** 300 faculty members

Exercises 5.2, pp. 266–269

1. proportion   **3.** as   **5.** True   **7.** False   **9.** True   **11.** False
13. True   **15.** True   **17.** $x = 20$ **19.** $x = 38$ **21.** $x = 4$
23. $x = 13$ **25.** $x = 8$ **27.** $x = 4$ **29.** $x = 20$ **31.** $x = 15$
33. $x = 21$ **35.** $x = 13\frac{1}{3}$ **37.** $x = 100$ **39.** $x = 1.8$ **41.** $x = 21$
43. $x = 280$ **45.** $x = 300$ **47.** $x = 20$ **49.** $x = 10$ **51.** $x = 5.4$
53. $x = \frac{1}{5}$ **55.** $x = 0.005$ **57.** $x = \frac{6}{5}$ **59.** $x = 1\frac{3}{5}$ **61.** False
63. Not the same   **65.** $1\frac{7}{8}$ gal   **67.** 54.5 g   **69.** 100 oxygen atoms
71. $41\frac{2}{3}$ in.   **73.** 0.25 ft   **75.** $600   **77.** 12,000 fish   **79.** 280 times
81. 90 mg and 50 mg   **83. a.** 92 g **b.** 4 g   **85.** 835,000 gal

Chapter 5   Review Exercises, pp. 271–272

1. is not; possible answer: when simplifying a ratio, drop the units if the
ratio has like quantities   **2.** is; possible answer: it is a comparison of two
unlike quantities   **3.** is not; possible answer: the denominator is not 1
4. is; possible answer: it is the price of one foot   **5.** is not; possible answer: a proportion must have an equal sign   **6.** are: possible answer: cross
products are found by multiplying diagonally   **7.** $\frac{2}{3}$ **8.** $\frac{1}{2}$ **9.** $\frac{3}{4}$ **10.** $\frac{25}{8}$
11. $\frac{8}{5}$ **12.** $\frac{3}{4}$ **13.** $\frac{44\text{ ft}}{5\text{ sec}}$ **14.** $\frac{9\text{ applicants}}{2\text{ positions}}$ **15.** 0.0025 lb/sq ft
16. 500,000,000 calls/day   **17.** 8 yd/down   **18.** 400 sq ft/gal
19. 10,500,000 vehicles/yr   **20.** 76,000 commuters/day   **21.** $118.75/
night   **22.** $3.89/rental   **23.** $1,250/station   **24.** $93.64/share
25.

Number of Units	Total Price	Unit Price
47	$39.95	$0.85
94	$69.95	$0.74

94 issues

26.

Number of Units	Total Price	Unit Price
100	$13.95	$0.14
250	$37.95	$0.15

100 checks

27.

Number of Units	Total Price	Unit Price
30	$16.95	$0.57
90	$44.85	$0.50
180	$77.70	$0.43

180 capsules

28.

Number of Units (fluid ounces)	Total Price	Unit Price
4	$2.78	$0.70
14	$3.92	$0.28
20	$3.74	$0.19

20 fl oz

29. True   **30.** False   **31.** False   **32.** True   **33.** $x = 6$ **34.** $x = 3$
35. $x = 32$ **36.** $x = 30$ **37.** $x = 2$ **38.** $x = 8$ **39.** $x = \frac{7}{10}$
40. $x = \frac{2}{5}$ **41.** $x = 67\frac{1}{2}$ **42.** $x = 45$ **43.** $x = \frac{3}{4}$, or 0.75   **44.**
$x = \frac{3}{20}$, or 0.15   **45.** $x = 28$ **46.** $x = 0.14$ **47.** $\frac{1}{15}$ **48.** $\frac{23}{45}$
49. $90/day   **50.** 0.125 in./mo   **51.** $\frac{2}{3}$ **52.** 50,000 books   **53.** No
54. $2\frac{1}{7}$ hr   **55.** 55 cc   **56.** 1.25 in.   **57.** 0.68 g/cc   **58.** 0.07 admitted
students per applicant

Chapter 5 Posttest, p. 273

1. $\frac{2}{3}$ **2.** $\frac{5}{14}$ **3.** $\frac{55}{31}$ **4.** $\frac{12}{1}$ **5.** $\frac{13\text{ revolutions}}{12\text{ sec}}$ **6.** $\frac{1\text{ cm}}{25\text{ km}}$ **7.** 68 mph
8. 8 m/sec **9.** \$136/day **10.** \$0.80/greeting card **11.** False
12. True **13.** $x = 25$ **14.** $x = 6$ **15.** $x = 28$ **16.** $x = 1$
17. 5 million e-mail addresses **18.** $\frac{9}{8}$ **19.** 25 ft **20.** 48 beats/min

Chapter 5 Cumulative Review, p. 274

1. \$108,411 **2.** 189 **3.** 52 **4.** $2^3 \cdot 3 \cdot 7$ **5.** $\frac{2}{5}$ **6.** $\frac{4}{39}$ **7.** $\frac{3}{4}$
8. 8,200 **9.** Possible answer: 3 **10.** $x = 2.5$ **11.** $n = 70$ **12.** $\frac{1}{4}$
13. \$4 per yd **14.** $x = \frac{3}{4}$ **15.** 2,106 sq ft **16.** \$445.88 **17.** 0.19 in.
18. $r \cdot t$ miles; 260 mi **19.** 7.5 in. **20.** $\frac{1}{29}$

CHAPTER 6

Chapter 6 Pretest, p. 276

1. $\frac{1}{20}$ **2.** $\frac{3}{8}$ **3.** 2.5 **4.** 0.03 **5.** 0.7% **6.** 800% **7.** 67%
8. 110% **9.** $37\frac{1}{2}$ ft **10.** 55 **11.** 32 **12.** 250 **13.** 40% **14.** 250%
15. \$10.50 **16.** 8% **17.** $\frac{6}{25}$ **18.** 25% **19.** \$61.11 **20.** \$10,000

Section 6.1 Practices, pp. 278–284

1, *p. 278:* $\frac{21}{100}$ **2,** *p. 278:* $\frac{9}{4}$, or $2\frac{1}{4}$ **3,** *p. 279:* $\frac{2}{300}$ **4,** *p. 279:* $\frac{1}{8}$
5, *p. 279:* $\frac{14}{25}$ **6,** *p. 280:* 0.31 **7,** *p. 280:* 0.05 **8,** *p. 281:* 0.482
9, *p. 281:* 0.6225 **10,** *p. 281:* 1.637 **11,** *p. 282:* 2.5% **12,** *p. 282:* 9%
13, *p. 282:* 70% **14,** *p. 282:* 300% **15,** *p. 283:* 71% **16,** *p. 283:*
Nitrogen; 78% > 0.93%, or 0.78 > 0.0093. **17,** *p. 284:* 16%
18, *p. 284:* True. $\frac{2}{3} \approx 67\% > 60\%$ **19,** *p. 284:* 27%

Exercises 6.1, pp. 285–288

1. percent **3.** left **5.** $\frac{2}{25}$ **7.** $2\frac{1}{4}$ **9.** $\frac{33}{100}$ **11.** $\frac{9}{50}$ **13.** $\frac{7}{50}$ **15.** $\frac{13}{20}$
17. $\frac{3}{400}$ **19.** $\frac{3}{1,000}$ **21.** $\frac{3}{40}$ **23.** $\frac{1}{7}$ **25.** 0.06 **27.** 0.72 **29.** 0.001
31. 1.02 **33.** 0.425 **35.** 5 **37.** 1.069 **39.** 0.035 **41.** 0.009
43. 0.0075 **45.** 31% **47.** 17% **49.** 30% **51.** 4% **53.** 12.5%
55. 129% **57.** 290% **59.** 287% **61.** 101.6% **63.** 900%
65. 30% **67.** 10% **69.** 16% **71.** 90% **73.** 6% **75.** $55\frac{5}{9}$%
77. $11\frac{1}{9}$% **79.** 600% **81.** 150% **83.** $216\frac{2}{3}$% **85.** < **87.** <
89. 44% **91.** 225%

93.

Fraction	Decimal	Percent
$\frac{1}{3}$	0.333 ...	$33\frac{1}{3}$%
$\frac{2}{3}$	0.666 ...	$66\frac{2}{3}$%
$\frac{1}{4}$	0.25	25%
$\frac{3}{4}$	0.75	75%
$\frac{1}{5}$	0.2	20%
$\frac{2}{5}$	0.4	40%
$\frac{3}{5}$	0.6	60%

95. $1\frac{1}{25}$ **97.** $316\frac{2}{3}$% **99.** 0.275 **101.** 310% **103.** 254% **105.** 0.96
107. $\frac{17}{50}$ **109.** $\frac{1}{10}$ **111.** 1,005% **113.** $1\frac{7}{20}$ **115.** 0.515 **117.** Among
men; $\frac{1}{4} = 25\% < 42\%$ **119. a.** 0.4% **b.** 99.6% **121.** 69%

Section 6.2 Practices, pp. 291–297

1, *p. 291:* **a.** $x = 0.7 \cdot 80$ **b.** $0.5 \cdot x = 10$ **c.** $x \cdot 40 = 20$ **2,** *p. 291:* 8
3, *p. 291:* 12 **4,** *p. 292:* 200 **5,** *p. 292:* 51 workers **6,** *p. 293:* 50
7, *p. 293:* 7.2 **8,** *p. 293:* 2,500,000 sq ft **9,** *p. 294:* $83\frac{1}{3}$%
10, *p. 294:* $112\frac{1}{2}$% **11,** *p. 295:* 30% **12,** *p. 295:* 270 **13,** *p. 296:* 1,080
14, *p. 296:* $33\frac{1}{3}$% **15,** *p. 296:* \$98 **16,** *p. 297:* \$340,000
17, *p. 297:* 105% **18,** *p. 297:* \$5.97

Exercises 6.2, pp. 298–301

1. base **3.** percent **5.** 6 **7.** 23 **9.** 2.87 **11.** \$140 **13.** 0.62
15. 0.045 **17.** 0.1 **19.** 4 **21.** \$18.32 **23.** 32 **25.** \$120 **27.** 2.5
29. \$250 **31.** 45 **33.** 1.75 **35.** 4,600 **37.** 3,000 **39.** \$49,230.77
41. 50% **43.** 75% **45.** $83\frac{1}{3}$% **47.** 25% **49.** 150% **51.** $112\frac{1}{2}$%
53. 62.5% **55.** 50% **57.** 31% **59.** 60 **61.** $66\frac{2}{3}$% **63.** 175 mi
65. 5% **67.** \$500 **69.** 10 **71.** $66\frac{2}{3}$% **73.** 40 questions **75.** \$600
77. 18,750,000 people **79.** 72 free throws **81.** 10.2 gal
83. \$30,000,000 **85.** \$9,000 **87.** 30% **89.** 6.8 million **91.** 5,100
employees **93. a.** 10 million **b.** 80%

Section 6.3 Practices, pp. 302–307

1, *p. 302:* 300% **2,** *p. 303:* 1929 **3,** *p. 304:* \$462.50
4, *p. 304:* **a.** \$1,125 **b.** \$2,625 **5,** *p. 305:* \$69.60 **6,** *p. 305:* \$1,450
7, *p. 306:* \$1,792 **8,** *p. 307:* \$2,524.95

Exercises 6.3, pp. 308–312

1. original **3.** discount

5.

Original Value	New Value	Percent Increase or Decrease
\$10	\$12	20% increase
\$10	\$8	20% decrease
\$6	\$18	200% increase
\$35	\$70	100% increase
\$14	\$21	50% increase
\$10	\$1	90% decrease
\$8	\$6.50	$18\frac{3}{4}$% decrease
\$6	\$5.25	$12\frac{1}{2}$% decrease

7.

Selling Price	Rate of Sales Tax	Sales Tax
\$30.00	5%	\$1.50
\$24.88	3%	\$0.75
\$51.00	$7\frac{1}{2}$%	\$3.83
\$196.23	4.5%	\$8.83

9.

Sales	Rate of Commission	Commission
\$700	10%	\$70.00
\$450	2%	\$9.00
\$870	$4\frac{1}{2}$%	\$39.15
\$922	7.5%	\$69.15

11.

Original Price	Rate of Discount	Discount	Sale Price
\$700.00	25%	\$175.00	\$525.00
\$18.00	10%	\$1.80	\$16.20
\$43.50	20%	\$8.70	\$34.80
\$16.99	5%	\$0.85	\$16.14

13.

Principal	Interest Rate	Time (in years)	Interest	Final Balance
$300	4%	2	$24.00	$324.00
$600	7%	2	$84.00	$684.00
$500	8%	2	$80.00	$580.00
$375	10%	4	$150.00	$525.00
$1,000	3.5%	3	$105.00	$1,105.00
$70,000	6.25%	30	$131,250.00	$201,250.00

15.

Principal	Interest Rate	Time (in years)	Final Balance
$500	4%	2	$540.80
$6,200	3%	5	$7,187.50
$300	1%	8	$324.86
$20,000	4%	2	$21,632.00
$145	3.8%	3	$162.17
$810	2.9%	10	$1,078.05

17.

Original Value	New Value	Percent Decrease
$5	$4.50	10%

19.

Original Price	Rate of Discount	Discount	Sale Price
$87.33	40%	$34.93	$52.40

21.

Selling Price	Rate of Sales Tax	Sales Tax
$200	7.25%	$14.50

23.

Principal	Interest Rate	Kind of Interest	Time (in years)	Interest	Final Balance
$3,000	5%	simple	5	$750.00	$3,750.00

25. 28% **27.** 550% **29.** 300% **31.** $84.95 **33.** 6.5% **35.** $2,700
37. $9 **39.** 15% **41.** $259.35 **43.** $150 **45.** $250 **47. a.** $144
b. $152.64 **49.** $3,244.80 **51.** 5,856

Chapter 6   Review Exercises, pp. 315–318

1. are; possible answer: a percent can be written as a fraction with denominator 100   **2.** are not; possible answer: $\frac{1}{2}$% is one-hundredth of $\frac{1}{2}$
3. is; possible answer: 8 is the number that we are taking the percent of
4. is not; possible answer: the amount (4) is the percent (50%) of the base (8)
5. is not; possible answer: when the percent is greater than 100%, the base is smaller than the amount   **6.** is; possible answer: if the number were smaller than or equal to 20, then 5% of it would be still smaller   **7.** is; possible answer: taking 100% of a number is the same as multiplying it by 1   **8.** is not; possible answer: the difference between the new and the original values is 100% of the original value

9.

Fraction	Decimal	Percent
$\frac{1}{4}$	0.25	25%
$\frac{7}{10}$	0.7	70%
$\frac{3}{400}$	0.0075	$\frac{3}{4}$%
$\frac{5}{8}$	0.625	62.5%
$\frac{41}{100}$	0.41	41%
$1\frac{1}{100}$	1.01	101%
$2\frac{3}{5}$	2.6	260%
$3\frac{3}{10}$	3.3	330%
$\frac{3}{25}$	0.12	12%
$\frac{2}{3}$	0.66…	$66\frac{2}{3}$%
$\frac{1}{6}$	0.166…	$16\frac{2}{3}$%

10.

Fraction	Decimal	Percent
$\frac{3}{8}$	0.375	37.5%
$\frac{49}{100}$	0.49	49%
$\frac{1}{1,000}$	0.001	0.1 %
$1\frac{1}{2}$	1.5	150%
$\frac{7}{8}$	0.875	87.5%
$\frac{5}{6}$	0.833…	$83\frac{1}{3}$%
$2\frac{3}{4}$	2.75	275%
$1\frac{1}{5}$	1.2	120%
$\frac{3}{4}$	0.75	75%
$\frac{1}{10}$	0.1	10%
$\frac{1}{3}$	0.33…	$33\frac{1}{3}$%

11. 12   **12.** 120%   **13.** 50%   **14.** 20   **15.** 43.75%   **16.** 5.5
17. $6   **18.** 20%   **19.** 0.3   **20.** 460   **21.** $70   **22.** 1,000   **23.** 2000%
24. 25%   **25.** $200   **26.** $44\frac{4}{9}$%   **27.** $12   **28.** $1,600   **29.** 17%
30. 42.42

31.

Original Value	New Value	Percent Decrease
24	16	$33\frac{1}{3}$%

32.

Original Value	New Value	Percent Decrease
360 mi	300 mi	$16\frac{2}{3}$%

33.

Selling Price	Rate of Sales Tax	Sales Tax
$50	6%	$3.00

ANSWERS

34.

Sales	Rate of Commission	Commission
$600	4%	$24

35.

Original Price	Rate of Discount	Discount	Sale Price
$200	15%	$30	$170

36.

Principal	Interest Rate	Time (in years)	Simple Interest	Final Balance
$200	4%	2	$16	$216

37. 10,000 hr **38.** 48% **39.** The agent that charges 11% **40.** $7,200
41. 20% **42.** Paper **43.** $\frac{1}{4}$ **44.** 64% **45.** 40% **46.** 15%
47. 0.0629 **48.** Possible estimate: 80 in. **49.** 45% **50.** $207
51. No **52.** Yes **53.** 180 seats **54.** 20% **55.** 63 first serves
56. 83% **57.** $165 **58.** 320 tons **59.** 70,000 mi **60.** $599
61. $51,500 **62.** $30,000 **63.** $7,791.18 **64.** 22%
65.

Quarter Ending	Income (in million of dollars)	Percent of Total Income (rounded to the nearest tenth of a precent)
June 30, 2009	260	12.3%
Sept 30, 2009	538	25.5%
Dec 31, 2009	655	31.0%
Mar 31, 2010	658	31.2%
Total	2,111	100.0%

66. Individual income taxes: $1,125 billion; Social Security taxes: $900 billion; corporate income taxes: $300 billion; excise taxes: $75 billion; other: $100 billion

Chapter 6   Posttest, p. 319

1. $\frac{1}{25}$ **2.** $\frac{11}{40}$ **3.** 1.74 **4.** 0.08 **5.** 0.9% **6.** 1,000% **7.** 83%
8. 220% **9.** 7.5 mi **10.** 48 **11.** 300 **12.** 200 **13.** 60%
14. 250% **15.** $200 **16.** 6 spaces **17.** 5% **18.** 4 pt
19. $217.80 **20.** $3\frac{1}{3}\%$

Chapter 6   Cumulative Review, p. 320

1. 10^7 **2.** 109 **3.** $5\frac{7}{10}$ **4.** 27.57 **5.** 0.7 **6.** 0.83 **7.** 7.32
8. $x - 6.7$ **9.** $23\frac{3}{5}$ **10.** 7.5 **11.** $8.19/hr **12.** 14 **13.** $\frac{2}{11}$
14. $1,000 **15.** $\frac{1}{8}$
16.

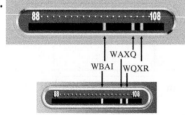

17. 15 times **18.** 715 adults **19.** 278 thousand **20.** 425%

CHAPTER 7

Chapter 7   Pretest, p. 322

1. +7 **2.** −4 **3.** −17 **4.** 0 **5.** −7 **6.** 0 **7.** −75 **8.** −64
9. $-\frac{1}{2}$ **10.** $\frac{1}{4}$ **11.** 2 **12.** 2 **13.** 8 **14.** 8 **15.** 36 **16.** −7
17. 58°F **18.** −$17.50 **19.** 23.6 degrees **20.** 25 centuries

Section 7.1   Practices, pp. 324–327

1, p. 324: (number line showing −3.1, −1, 0, $1\frac{9}{10}$ from −4 to 4)

2, p. 324: **a.** −9 **b.** $4\frac{9}{10}$ **c.** 2.9 **d.** −31 **3, p. 325:** **a.** 9 **b.** $1\frac{3}{4}$
c. 4.1 **d.** 5 **4, p. 325:** **a.** Sign: −; absolute value: 4 **b.** Sign: +;
absolute value: $6\frac{1}{2}$ **5, p. 326:** **a.** 0 **b.** −5 **c.** −4 **6, p. 327:**
+2 yd **7, p. 327:** Sirius

Exercises 7.1, pp. 328–331

1. positive number **3.** signed number **5.** opposites
7. smaller **9.** (number line showing −2, 2.5, 3 from −4 to 4)

11. (number line showing $-\frac{1}{2}$, 0, $1\frac{4}{5}$ from −4 to 4)

13. −8 **15.** −10.2 **17.** 25 **19.** $5\frac{1}{2}$ **21.** 4.1 **23.** −0.5 **25.** 6
27. $\frac{4}{5}$ **29.** 2 **31.** 0.6 **33.** Sign: +; Absolute value: 8
35. Sign: −; Absolute value: 4.3 **37.** Sign: −; Absolute value: 7
39. Sign: +; Absolute value: $\frac{1}{5}$ **41.** Two; −5 and 5 **43.** No **45.** −4
47. 12 **49.** 2 **51.** $-2\frac{1}{3}$ **53.** −2 **55.** 9 **57.** −2 **59.** −7
61. −8.3 **63.** $-3\frac{1}{2}$ **65.** T **67.** T **69.** T **71.** T **73.** F **75.** T
77. −3, 0, 3 **79.** −9, −4.5, 9 **81.** −$150 **83.** +14.5°C
85. (number line showing −3.9, $2\frac{1}{2}$ from −4 to 4) **87.** **a.** −$10.98 **b.** $100

89. **a.** 0.5 **b.** 11 **91.** **a.** < **b.** > **93.** Mariana Trench
95. Decreased by 25 mg **97.** No **99.** Mars
101. **a.** (number line from −4 to 4)

While the player is in the game, the number of goals scored by his team is equal to the number scored by the other team **b.** In the first period.

Section 7.2   Practices, pp. 333–336

1, p. 333: −25 **2, p. 334:** $-4\frac{1}{2}$ **3, p. 334:** 7 **4, p. 334:** 0
5, p. 335: −1.3 **6, p. 335:** 0 **7, p. 335:** 456 m **8, p. 336:** −2.478

Exercises 7.2, pp. 337–339

1. right **3.** larger **5.** 1 **7.** 3 **9.** −11 **11.** 0 **13.** 0 **15.** −5
17. 200 **19.** 6 **21.** −150 **23.** −5 **25.** −27 **27.** 0 **29.** 4.9
31. 0.1 **33.** 59.5 **35.** −5.9 **37.** −14.5 **39.** −6 **41.** $-\frac{3}{5}$ **43.** $1\frac{3}{5}$
45. $-\frac{1}{10}$ **47.** −102 **49.** −10 **51.** 9 **53.** $-7\frac{1}{2}$ **55.** 7 **57.** 3
59. 0 **61.** −6.9 **63.** 7.58 **65.** −4.914 **67.** 4.409
69. 3   Move 9 units to the right

71. 0 **73.** −4 **75.** 19,340 ft **77.** −238 employees **79.** −1
81. −6 yr (6 yr ago) **83.** −6 yd **85.** **a.** −1.0 million **b.** 14.7 million

Section 7.3   Practices, pp. 340–342

1, p. 340: −2 **2, p. 341:** 18 **3, p. 341:** −21.1 **4, p. 341:** −10
5, p. 342: 6 **6, p. 342:** 2,100 yr

Exercises 7.3, pp. 343–345

1. opposite **3.** order of operations **5.** 7 **7.** −4 **9.** −14 **11.** 44
13. −25 **15.** −19 **17.** 6 **19.** −38 **21.** −26 **23.** 26 **25.** −15
27. 1,000 **29.** −1.52 **31.** 9.7 **33.** 0 **35.** 10.5 **37.** −0.5 **39.** −5
41. $7\frac{3}{4}$ **43.** $-7\frac{1}{4}$ **45.** $7\frac{1}{4}$ **47.** 7 **49.** −5 **51.** −1.9 **53.** $-\frac{1}{2}$
55. −15 **57.** −3 **59.** −3.842 **61.** −16.495 **63.** −25 **65.** 0
67. 1 **69.** 1,000 mi **71.** 22,965 ft **73.** −$1.4 million
75. **a.** −6.2 ft **b.** 55.8 ft **77.** **a.** 8.30 in. **b.** −6.80 in.

Section 7.4   Practices, pp. 346–348

1, p. 346: 32 **2, p. 347:** −10 **3, p. 347:** **a.** 1 **b.** −1 **4, p. 347:** $\frac{4}{15}$
5, p. 347: −20 **6, p. 348:** −48 **7, p. 348:** 169 **8, p. 348:** No

Exercises 7.4, pp. 349–351

1. positive **3.** even **5.** −10 **7.** −10 **9.** 25 **11.** 306 **13.** −16 **15.** −8,163 **17.** −40 **19.** −176 **21.** 800 **23.** −7,200 **25.** −5 **27.** −10 **29.** 5.52 **31.** −8 **33.** $-\frac{5}{27}$ **35.** $-\frac{5}{6}$ **37.** −25 **39.** 10,000 **41.** 0.25 **43.** −0.001 **45.** $\frac{9}{16}$ **47.** −1 **49.** 0.094864 **51.** −216 **53.** −60 **55.** 0 **57.** 5 **59.** $-\frac{32}{135}$ **61.** 0.14652 **63.** 5 **65.** −26 **67.** 0 **69.** −28 **71.** 1.25 **73.** −12 **75.** 9 **77.** −10.8 **79.** 289 **81.** 41 **83. a.** 5 **b.** 2 **c.** −1 **d.** −4 **e.** −7 **85.** −4,830 **87.** −0.0001 **89.** −8 **91.** −72 mm **93.** −$4,425 **95.** −160° C **97.** −64 ft **99. a.** −$900 **b.** $100

Section 7.5   Practices, pp. 352–354

1, *p. 352:* 12 **2,** *p. 353:* $-\frac{3}{5}$ **3,** *p. 353:* −0.3 **4,** *p. 353:* $-\frac{1}{6}$ **5,** *p. 354:* **a.** 0 **b.** −1 **6.** *p. 354:* −50 sq mi/mo **7,** *p. 354:* 0 degrees

Exercises 7.5, pp. 355–357

1. positive **3.** equal **5.** 5 **7.** 0 **9.** −5 **11.** −2 **13.** 25 **15.** −25 **17.** 7 **19.** −2 **21.** 17 **23.** 6 **25.** −0.3 **27.** −20 **29.** 16 **31.** $-\frac{5}{6}$ **33.** −21 **35.** −16 **37.** 6.172 **39.** −3.5 **41.** $-\frac{1}{5}$ **43.** 1 **45.** $-\frac{2}{5}$ **47.** $5\frac{1}{2}$ **49.** $4\frac{1}{4}$ **51.** $\frac{3}{4}$ **53.** −8 **55.** −4 **57.** 5 **59.** 1 **61.** −16 **63.** −3 **65.** −0.06 **67.** −4 **69.** −33 **71.** 2 **73.** −7 **75.** $9 \div (1 - 4) = -3$ **77.** $6 \div (3 - 1) - 4 = -1$ **79.** $(8 - 10) \cdot 2 - (-5 + 13) \div 4 = -6$ **81.** $-\frac{6}{5}$ **83.** $-3\frac{1}{6}$ **85.** $-\frac{4}{27}$ **87.** −6,098.9 **89.** −3.5 thousand **91.** −1,000 ft/min **93.** Yes. **95. a.** Thursday; Saturday **b.** 0°F

Chapter 7   Review Exercises, pp. 359–361

1. is; possible answer: a positive sign is understood **2.** is; possible answer: it lies to the left of 0 on the number line **3.** is not; possible answer: the integers are the numbers . . . −4, −3, −2, −1, 0, 1, 2, 3, 4 . . . continuing indefinitely in both directions **4.** are; possible answer: they are the same distance from 0 on the number line but on opposite sides of it **5.** is not; possible answer: all absolute values are either positive or 0 **6.** is not; possible answer: adding −1 on the number line means moving one unit to the left

7., 8.

9. −6 **10.** 4 **11.** $7\frac{1}{2}$ **12.** −10.1 **13.** 10 **14.** 2.5 **15.** $1\frac{1}{5}$ **16.** 7 **17.** −11 **18.** 10 **19.** 9 **20.** −2 **21.** −8, −3.5, 8 **22.** −9.7, −6, 9 **23.** −2.9, $-2\frac{1}{2}$, 0 **24.** −4, $-1\frac{1}{4}$, 0 **25.** +10 ft **26.** −$350 **27.** −20 **28.** −2 **29.** $6\frac{1}{2}$ **30.** −1 **31.** −4.1 **32.** −2 **33.** −7 **34.** $-\frac{1}{4}$ **35.** 0 **36.** 28 **37.** −10 **38.** −11 **39.** 3 **40.** $-4\frac{1}{8}$ **41.** 100 **42.** −45 **43.** $-\frac{20}{33}$ **44.** −7.35 **45.** 72 **46.** −30 **47.** $\frac{1}{16}$ **48.** 0.49 **49.** 36 **50.** −81 **51.** 5 **52.** −10 **53.** −5 **54.** $\frac{1}{32}$ **55.** −50 **56.** 2 **57.** 15 **58.** 114 **59.** −100 **60.** 1 **61.** 2.73 **62.** −2.62 **63.** 104 **64.** 21 **65.** 10 **66.** −2 **67.** 225 **68.** 400 **69.** −$400 **70.** Yes **71.** −$2,820 **72.** $1,649.83 **73.** 28°F **74.** 7 questions **75.** −$1.20 **76.** 2,010 years apart **77.** Yes **78.** 90 feet below the surface **79.** 5 under par **80.** 100 ft above the point of release (+100 ft) **81. a.** Alabama **b.** 14°F **82. a.** −$116.4 million **b.** −$38.8 billion

Chapter 7   Posttest, p. 362

1. −10 **2.** $-\frac{1}{2}$ **3.** 0 **4.** −0.5 **5.** −49 **6.** 0 **7.** −207 **8.** −0.1 **9.** −144 **10.** $\frac{1}{16}$ **11.** −4 **12.** $-\frac{1}{8}$ **13.** 4 **14.** 21 **15.** 40 **16.** −18 **17.** −51 lb **18.** −$550/yr **19.** BP, Exxon Mobil, Royal Dutch Shell, Conoco Phillips, Chevron **20.** 76°C

Chapter 7   Cumulative Review, p. 363

1. 3,000 **2.** −4 **3.** 10 **4.** 14 **5.** 3.108 **6.** 3.44 **7.** $x = 1.5$ **8.** $\frac{5}{9}x = 40$ **9.** $n = 65$ **10.** 112.5% **11.** 20% **12.** −6.04 **13.** 0.5 **14.** $-\frac{5}{9}$ **15.** $2\frac{2}{3}$ innings **16.** 80 mg **17.** 4:1 **18.** 25% **19.** −89°C **20.** A liquid

CHAPTER 8

Chapter 8   Pretest, pp. 365–366

1. Yes **2.** 31 **3.** 11 min **4.** 52 millimeters **5.** 3.1 **6.** 1960, 1970, 1980, 1990, and 2010 **7.** 1990–1992 and 1999–2005 **8.** 1,100,000 newspapers **9.** 406 thousand **10.** 41%

Section 8.1   Practices, pp. 368–372

1, *p. 368:* Reggie Jackson **2,** *p. 369:* Above; the exam average is 87. **3,** *p. 370:* **a.** 7 **b.** 4 **4,** *p. 370:* **a.** $16 million **b.** The median for the six movies was $2 million less. **5,** *p. 371:* **a.** 2 **b.** 4 and 9 **c.** No mode **6,** *p. 371:* 12 hr **7,** *p. 372:* 7 **8,** *p. 372:* $3.40

Exercises 8.1, pp. 373–375

1. statistics **3.** weighted **5.** mode

7.

Numbers	Mean	Median	Mode(s)
a. 8, 2, 9, 4, 8	6.2	8	8
b. 3, 0, 0, 3, 10	3.2	3	0 and 3
c. 4, 6, 9, 1, 1, 3	4	3.5	1
d. 7.5, 9, 8.5, 5.5, 8.1	7.7	8.1	None
e. $3\frac{1}{2}, 3\frac{3}{4}, 4, 3\frac{1}{2}, 3\frac{1}{4}$	$3\frac{3}{5}$	$3\frac{1}{2}$	$3\frac{1}{2}$
f. 4, −2, −1, 0, −1	0	−1	−1

9. $12,266.67

11.

Numbers	Range
a. 20, 11, 3, 4, 16	17
b. 2.3, 5.7, 10.2, 6.1, 0.9	9.3
c. $6\frac{5}{6}, 5\frac{1}{2}, \frac{1}{3}, 8, 5\frac{3}{4}$	$7\frac{2}{3}$
d. −2, 6, −4, −1, −4	10

13. No; the student's GPA was 3.25, which is less than 3.5. **15.** The mean amount is $100,000. We can't compute the median amount because we don't know the actual amount given to each grandchild. **17.** Indiana, North Carolina, and Tennessee **19. a.** $50,921 **b.** $32,927 **21. a.** 31,000 mi **b.** 20,000 mi **c.** 8,000 mi **d.** 86,000 mi **23.** 25 pieces of mail

Section 8.2   Practices, pp. 377–384

1, *p. 377:* **a.** $4.95 **b.** $5.95 **c.** $5.45 **2,** *p. 378:* **a.** 10 million passengers **b.** Atlanta **c.** 60 million passengers **3,** *p. 379:* **a.** Dairy products **b.** $2.9 billion **c.** $1 billion **4,** *p. 380:* **a.** 11% **b.** 10% **5,** *p. 381:* **a.** 25 presidents **b.** No **c.** 34 presidents **6,** *p. 382:* **a.** July **b.** 27°F **c.** In Chicago, mean temperatures increase from January through July and then decrease from July through December. **7,** *p. 383:* **a.** In Orlando **b.** 5 in. **c.** Possible answer: In Orlando, the average precipitation increases steadily from January through October. In Seattle, it peaks in January, dips in April and in July, and increases in October. **8,** *p. 384:* **a.** $\frac{3}{50}$ **b.** 38% **c.** 9 times as great

Exercises 8.2, pp. 385–388

1. table **3.** rows **5.** bar graph **7.** line graph **9. a.** $60 **b.** $100 **c.** She will pay a lower commission if she sells 400 shares in a single deal; 400 shares in a single deal will cost her $70 or $90, whereas two deals of 200 shares will cost her between $100 and $120. **11. a.** 1,556 mi **b.** 1,020 mi **c.** The blanks mean that there is no distance between a city and itself. **13. a.** Health care and social assistance **b.** 12.5 million workers **15. a.** Milk, lemon juice, and vinegar **b.** 8 **c.** Pure water **17. a.** More than 89 minutes **b.** 92 applicants **c.** 70 applicants **19. a.** 270 million subscribers **b.** 2005 **c.** Every year, the number of cell phone subscribers increased. **21. a.** Democrats **b.** $\frac{2}{5}$ **c.** 600

Chapter 8   Review Exercises, pp. 392–395

1. cannot; possible answer: the mean is the sum of the numbers divided by the number of numbers   2. can; possible answer: there may be two or more numbers that occur with the highest frequency   3. is; possible answer: the difference between the largest and smallest numbers in each set is the same   4. does; possible answer: reading a graph generally involves estimating   5. is not; possible answer: they are difficult to distinguish on a pictograph   6. is not; possible answer: it is used to represent parts of a whole
7.

List of Numbers	Mean	Median	Mode	Range
6, 7, 4, 10, 4, 5, 6, 8, 7, 4, 5	6	6	4	6
1, 3, 4, 4, 2, 3, 1, 4, 5, 1	2.8	3	1 and 4	4

8. a. The husbands (83 yr) lived longer than the wives (70 yr). b. 13 yr
c. 23 yr   9. a. Half of the people who listen to NPR are younger than 55, and half are older. b. 30 years below the median   10. This machine is reliable because the range is 1.7 fl oz.   11. Since the average was 13,109, the zoo was profitable.   12. a. 70,720,000 tons b. Beaumont, TX
c. 41,440,000 tons more d. All except the Port of South Louisiana
13. a. 830,000 monthly domestic flights b. In 2005 c. 80,000 more monthly domestic flights   14. a. 10 million volumes b. 5 million volumes more
c. Harvard University and the Boston Public Library   15. a. 61 million licensed drivers b. 10% c. Possible answer: It increases for younger age groups, peaks for 40–44, and decreases for older age groups.   16. a. Run number 3 b. Approximately 3 min c. With practice, the rat ran through the maze more quickly.   17. a. 2003 b. $\frac{1}{2}$ c. Both out-of-pocket expenditures and insurance expenditures increased each year from 2000 through 2010 (with the exception of the period 2005–2006).   18. a. 27,578 transplants
b. 4,429 more liver transplants c. 58%   19. 76   20. Internet users

Chapter 8   Posttest, pp. 396–397

1. 3.2   2. 162   3. 77   4. Mode: 200 lb; range: 90 lb   5. Toyota Prius, Ford Fusion Hybrid, Mercury Milan Hybrid, and Nissan Altima Hybrid   6. 30% greater   7. 3 million more victims   8. a. 2007
b. Overall music purchases are the sum of digital track and album sales. $600 million + $600 million = $1,200 million, or $1.2 billion, in sales for overall music purchases in the year 2006   9. 60%   10. 1961–1975; U.S. scientists received approximately 40 and U.K. scientists received approximately 20 Nobel prizes.

Chapter 8   Cumulative Review, pp. 398–399

1. 23   2. $\frac{4}{5}$ 3. $1\frac{87}{100}$ 4. 40   5. 2.81   6. 3,010   7. $x = 17\frac{1}{4}$ 8. No
9. $n = 21$ 10. $4\frac{3}{8}$ 11. 2   12. Negative; $\frac{7}{4}$ 13. -18 14. Mean: 3.7; median: 3.8; mode: 3.9; range: 0.6   15. 10.6 times   16. 8 jobless people per opening   17. 2%   18. 5,000 yr   19. Higher in the American League; the medians were 48 and 50.   20. Males, age 45–54

Section 11.6   Practices, pp. 515–518

1, p. 515: a. 7 b. 12   2, p. 515: Between 6 and 7   3, p. 516: a. 7.48
b. 3.46   4, p. 517: 10 in.   5, p. 517: 3.5 ft   6, p. 518: Approximately 12.8 ft

Exercises 11.6, pp. 519–522

1. square root   3. perfect square   5. hypotenuse   7. 3   9. 4   11. 9
13. 13   15. 20   17. 16   19. 7 and 8   21. 8 and 9   23. 6 and 7
25. 3 and 4   27. 2.2   29. 6.1   31. 11.8   33. 99   35. $a = 16\,cm$
37. $c \approx 3.2\,m$ 39. b. 7 m   41. b. 8 ft   43. c. 20 m   45. c. 11.4 cm
47. a. 8.7 ft   49. 14   51. $x = 10\,in.$ 53. $n \approx 9.8\,cm$ 55. 16 ft
57. 240 ft   59. Approximately 37.4 ft

APPENDIX

Appendix   Practices, pp. 539–542

1, p. 539: 25,390,000   2, p. 540: 8.0×10^{12}, or 8×10^{12}
3, p. 541: 0.0000000043   4, p. 541: 7.1×10^{-11}
5, p. 542: a. 2.464×10^2 b. 8.35×10^{11}

Exercises p. 543

1. 317,000,000   3. 0.000001   5. 0.00004013   7. 4×10^8
9. 3.5×10^{-6} 11. 3.1×10^{-10} 13. 9×10^7 15. 2.075×10^{-4}
17. 1.25×10^{10} 19. 4×10^1

Section 5.2   Practices, pp. 360–368

1, p. 360: a. $2^6 = 64$ b. $\frac{1}{7^3} = \frac{1}{343}$ c. q^8 d. $\frac{-1}{p^{15}} = -\frac{1}{p^{15}}$
2, p. 361: a. $49a^2$ b. $-64x^3$ c. $-64x^3$ 3, p. 361: a. $36a^{18}$
b. $q^{16}r^{20}$ c. $-2a^3b^{21}$ d. $\frac{49}{a^2c^{10}}$ 4, p. 362: a. $\frac{y^2}{9}$ b. $\frac{u^{10}}{v^{10}}$ c. $\frac{y^2}{9}$
d. $\frac{100a^{10}}{9b^4c^2}$ e. $125x^3y^6$ 5, p. 363: a. $\frac{a^2}{25}$ b. $\frac{v}{4u}$ c. $\frac{b^6}{a^{10}}$ 6, p. 364: 253.9
7, p. 364: 0.0000000043   8, p. 365: 8×10^{12} 9, p. 365: 7.1×10^{-11}
10, p. 365: a. 2.464×10^2 b. 4×10^{11} 11, p. 366: 9×10^{14}
12, p. 367: 1×10^{-3}, or 0.001   13, p. 367: 2.5E−17 (Answers may vary.)   14, p. 368: 7.3E−10 (Answers may vary.)
15, p. 368: 4.6×10^8, or 460,000,000

Exercises 5.2, pp. 369–373

1. factors   3. raise each factor to that power   5. raise the reciprocal of the quotient   7. left   9. 2^8, or 256   11. 5^4, or 625   13. 10^{10}, or 10,000,000,000   15. $\frac{1}{4^4}$, or $\frac{1}{256}$ 17. x^{24} 19. y^8 21. $\frac{1}{x^6}$ 23. n^4
25. $64x^3$ 27. $64y^2$ 29. $-64n^{15}$ 31. $64y^8$ 33. $\frac{1}{9a^2}$ 35. $\frac{1}{p^7q^7}$
37. $r^{12}t^6$ 39. $4p^{10}q^2$ 41. $-2m^{12}n^{24}$ 43. $-\frac{64m^{15}}{n^{30}}$ 45. $\frac{1}{a^{12}b^8}$
47. $\frac{16y^6}{x^4}$ 49. $\frac{125}{b^3}$ 51. $\frac{c^2}{b^2}$ 53. $-\frac{a^7}{b^7}$ 55. $\frac{a^6}{27}$ 57. $-\frac{p^{15}}{q^{10}}$ 59. $\frac{4}{a}$ 61. $\frac{8x^{15}}{y^6}$
63. $\frac{1}{p^5q^5}$ 65. $81x^4y^{12}$ 67. $\frac{v^4}{16u^4}$ 69. $\frac{y^4z^{16}}{16x^8}$ 71. $\frac{t^{12}}{r^{10}}$ 73. $\frac{b^6}{8a^{12}}$
75. 317,000,000   77. 0.000001   79. 6,200,000   81. 0.00004025
83. 4.2×10^8 85. 3.5×10^{-6} 87. 2.17×10^{11} 89. 7.31×10^{-9}
91.

Standard Notation	Scientific Notation (written)	Scientific Notation (displayed on a calculator)
975,000,000	9.75×10^8	9.75E8
487,000,000	4.87×10^8	4.87E8
0.0000000001652	1.652×10^{-10}	1.652E−10
0.000000067	6.7×10^{-8}	6.7E−8
0.0000000000001	1×10^{-13}	1E−13
3,281,000,000	3.281×10^9	3.281E9

93. 9×10^7 95. 2.075×10^{-4} 97. 1.68×10^1 99. 1.25×10^{10}
101. 3×10^2 103. 3×10^8 105. 0.0003067
107.

Standard Notation	Scientific Notation (written)	Scientific Notation (displayed on a calculator)
428,000,000,000	4.28×10^{11}	4.28E11
3,240,000	3.24×10^6	3.24E6
0.000005224	5.224×10^{-6}	5.224E−6
0.000000057	5.7×10^{-8}	5.7E−8
0.000000682	6.82×10^{-7}	6.82E−7
48,360,000	4.836×10^7	4.836E7

109. $\frac{9b^{10}}{a^4}$ **111.** $-\frac{1}{64y^3}$ **113.** $-\frac{16y^{12}}{x^8z^4}$ **115.** 7×10^{-8}

117. The larger volume is 8 times the smaller volume.

119. 4,000,000,000 bytes and 17,000,000,000 bytes

121. 7×10^{-7} m   **123.** 2×10^{11} cells

125. 0.00000000000000000000000017 g   **127.** 7,600,000,000

129. 1.6×10^{13} red blood cells   **131.**   a. 1.86×10^5 mi/sec

b. About 8.495×10^8 sec, or about 27 yr

Glossary

The numbers in brackets following each glossary term represent the section in which that term is discussed.

absolute value [7.1] The absolute value of a number is its distance from zero on the number line. The absolute value of a number is represented by the symbol | |.

acute angle [11.1] An acute angle is an angle whose measure is less than 90°.

acute triangle [11.1] An acute triangle is a triangle with three *acute* angles.

addends [1.2] In an addition problem, the numbers being added are called addends.

algebraic expression [4.1] An algebraic expression is an expression that combines variables, constants, and arithmetic operations.

amount (percent) [6.2] The amount is the result of taking the percent of the base.

angle [11.1] An angle consists of two rays that have a common endpoint.

area [11.3] Area is the number of square units that a figure contains.

associative property of addition [1.2] The associative property of addition states that when adding three numbers, regrouping the addends gives the same sum.

associative property of multiplication [1.3] The associative property of multiplication states that when multiplying three numbers, regrouping the factors gives the same product.

average (or mean) [1.5, 8.1] The average of a set of numbers is the sum of those numbers divided by however many numbers are in the set.

bar graph [8.2] A bar graph is a graph in which quantities are represented by thin, parallel rectangles called bars. The length of each bar is proportional to the quantity that it represents.

base (exponent) [1.5] The base is the number that is a repeated factor when written with an exponent.

base (percent) [6.2] The base is the number that we are taking the percent of. It always follows the word *of* in the statement of the problem.

circle [11.1] A circle is a closed plane figure made up of points that are all the same distance from a fixed point called the center.

circle graph [8.2] A circle graph is a graph that resembles a pie (the whole amount) that has been cut into slices (the parts).

circumference [5.1, 11.2] The distance around a circle is called its circumference.

commission [6.3] Salespeople may work on commission instead of receiving a fixed salary. This means that the amount of money that they earn is a specified percent of the total sales for which they are responsible.

commutative property of addition [1.2] The commutative property of addition states that changing the order in which two numbers are added does not affect the sum.

commutative property of multiplication [1.3] The commutative property of multiplication states that changing the order in which two numbers are multiplied does not affect the product.

complementary angles [11.1] Two angles are complementary if the sum of their measures is 90°.

composite figure [11.2] A composite figure is the combination of two or more basic geometric figures.

composite number [2.1] A composite number is a whole number that has more than two factors.

constant [4.1] A constant is a known number.

corresponding sides [11.5] Corresponding sides are the sides opposite the equal angles in similar triangles.

cube [11.4] A cube is a solid in which all six faces are squares.

cylinder [11.4] A cylinder is a solid in which the bases are circles and are perpendicular to the height.

decimal [3.1] A decimal is a number written with three parts: a whole number, the decimal point, and a fraction whose denominator is a power of 10.

decimal place [3.1] The decimal places are the places to the right of the decimal point.

denominator [2.2] The number below the fraction line in a fraction is called the denominator. It stands for the number of parts into which the whole is divided.

diameter [5.1, 11.1] A diameter is a line segment that passes through the center of a circle and has both endpoints on the circle.

difference [1.2] The result of a subtraction problem is called the difference.

digits [1.1] Digits are the numbers 0, 1, 2, 3, 4, 5, 6, 7, 8, and 9.

discount [6.3] In buying or selling merchandise, the term *discount* refers to a reduction on the merchandise's original price.

distributive property [1.3] The distributive property states that multiplying a factor by the sum of two numbers gives the same result as multiplying the factor by each of the two numbers and then adding.

dividend [1.4] In a division problem, the number being divided is called the dividend.

divisor [1.4] In a division problem, the number that is being used to divide another number is called the divisor.

equation [4.2] An equation is a mathematical statement that two expressions are equal.

equilateral triangle [11.1] An equilateral triangle is a triangle with three sides equal in length.

equivalent fractions [2.2] Equivalent fractions are fractions that represent the same quantity.

evaluate [4.1] To evaluate an algebraic expression, substitute the given value for each variable and carry out the computation.

exponent (or power) [1.5] An exponent (or power) is a number that indicates how many times another number is used as a factor.

exponential form [1.5] Exponential form is a shorthand method for representing a repeated multiplication of the same factor.

factors [1.3, 2.1] In a multiplication problem, the numbers being multiplied are called factors.

formula [9.3] A formula is an equation that indicates how the variables are related to one another.

fraction [2.2] A fraction is any number that can be written in the form $\frac{a}{b}$, where a and b are whole numbers and b is nonzero.

fraction line [2.2] The fraction line separates the numerator from the denominator and stands for "out of" or "divided by."

graph [8.2] A graph is a picture or diagram of the data in a table.

gram [10.2] A unit of weight or, more precisely, of mass.

hexagon [11.1] A hexagon is a polygon with six sides and six angles.

histogram [8.2] A histogram is a graph of a frequency table.

hypotenuse [11.6] In a right triangle, the hypotenuse is the side opposite the right angle.

identity property of addition [1.2] The identity property of addition states that the sum of a number and zero is the original number.

identity property of multiplication [1.3] The identity property of multiplication states that the product of any number and 1 is that number.

improper fraction [2.2] An improper fraction is a fraction greater than or equal to 1, that is, a fraction whose numerator is greater than or equal to its denominator.

integers [7.1] The integers are the numbers . . . , $-4, -3, -2, -1, 0, +1, +2, +3, +4, . . .$, continuing indefinitely in both directions.

intersecting lines [11.1] Intersecting lines are two lines that cross.

isosceles triangle [11.1] An isosceles triangle is a triangle with two or more sides equal in length.

least common denominator (LCD) [2.2] The least common denominator (LCD) for two or more fractions is the least common multiple of their denominators.

least common multiple (LCM) [2.1] The least common multiple (LCM) of two or more whole numbers is the smallest nonzero whole number that is a multiple of each number.

legs [11.6] In a right triangle, the legs are the two sides that form the right angle.

like fractions [2.2] Like fractions are fractions with the same denominator.

like quantities [5.1] Like quantities are quantities that have the same unit.

like terms [9.2] Like terms are terms that have the same variables with the same exponents.

line [11.1] A line is a collection of points along a straight path that extends endlessly in both directions. A line has only one dimension.

line graph (broken-line graph) [8.2] A line graph (broken-line graph) is a graph in which quantities are represented as points connected by straight line segments. The position of any point on a line graph is read against the vertical axis and the horizontal axis.

line segment [11.1] A line segment is part of a line having two endpoints. Every line segment has a length.

liter [10.2] A unit of capacity, that is, of liquid volume.

magic square [1.2] A magic square is a square array of numbers in which the sum of every row, column, and diagonal is the same number.

mean (average) [1.5, 8.1] The mean of a set of numbers is the sum of those numbers divided by however many numbers are in the set.

median [8.1] In a set of numbers arranged in numerical order, the median of the numbers is the number in the middle. If there are two numbers in the middle, the median is the mean of the two middle numbers.

meter [10.2] A unit of length, which gives the metric system its name.

minuend [1.2] In a subtraction problem, the number from which we subtract from is called the minuend.

mixed number [2.2] A mixed number is a number greater than 1 with a whole number part and a proper fraction part.

mode [8.1] The mode of a set of numbers is the number (or numbers) occurring most frequently in the set.

multiplication property of 0 [1.3] The multiplication property of 0 states that the product of any number and 0 is 0.

negative number [7.1] A negative number is a number less than 0.

numerator [2.2] The number above the fraction line in a fraction is called the numerator. It tells us how many parts of the whole the fraction contains.

obtuse angle [11.1] An obtuse angle is an angle whose measure is more than 90° and less than 180°.

obtuse triangle [11.1] An obtuse triangle is a triangle with one obtuse angle.

opposites [7.1] Two numbers that are the same distance from 0 on the number line but on opposite sides of 0 are called opposites.

parallel lines [11.1] Parallel lines are two lines in the same plane that do not intersect.

parallelogram [11.1] A parallelogram is a quadrilateral with both pairs of opposite sides parallel. Opposite sides are equal in length, and opposite angles have equal measures.

percent (or rate) [6.1] A percent is a ratio or fraction with denominator 100. A number written with the % sign means "divided by 100."

percent decrease [6.3] In a percent problem, if the quantity is decreasing, it is called a percent decrease.

percent increase [6.3] In a percent problem, if the quantity is increasing, it is called a percent increase.

perfect square [1.5, 11.6] A perfect square is a number that is the square of any whole number.

perimeter [1.2, 11.2] The perimeter of a polygon is the distance around it.

period [1.1] A period is a group of three digits, which are separated by commas, when writing a large whole number in standard form.

perpendicular lines [11.1] Perpendicular lines are two lines that intersect to form right angles.

pictograph [8.2] A pictograph is a kind of graph in which images such as people, books, coins, etc., are used to represent and to compare quantities.

place value [1.1] Each of the digits in a whole number in standard form has place value.

plane [11.1] A plane is a flat surface that extends endlessly in all directions.

point [11.1] A point is an exact location in space. A point has no dimension.

polygon [11.1] A polygon is a closed plane figure made up of line segments.

positive number [7.1] A positive number is a number greater than 0.

prime factorization [2.1] Prime factorization of a whole number is the number written as the product of its prime factors.

prime number [2.1] A prime number is a whole number that has exactly two different factors: itself and 1.

principal [6.3] The principal is the amount of money borrowed.

product [1.3] The result of a multiplication problem is called the product.

proper fraction [2.2] A proper fraction is a fraction less than 1, that is, a fraction whose numerator is smaller than its denominator.

proportion [5.2] A proportion is a statement that two ratios are equal.

Pythagorean theorem [11.6] The Pythagorean theorem states that for every right triangle, the sum of the squares of the lengths of the two legs equals the square of the length of the hypotenuse. That is, $a^2 + b^2 = c^2$, where a and b are the legs, and c is the hypotenuse.

quadrilateral [11.1] A quadrilateral is a polygon with four sides.

quotient [1.4] The result of a division problem is called the quotient.

radius [11.1] A radius is a line segment with one endpoint on the circle and the other at the center.

range [8.1] The range of a set of numbers is the difference between the largest and the smallest number in the set.

rate [5.1] A rate is a ratio of unlike quantities.

ratio [5.1] A ratio is a comparison of two quantities expressed as a quotient.

ray [11.1] A ray is a part of a line having only one endpoint.

reciprocal [2.4] The reciprocal of the fraction $\frac{a}{b}$ is $\frac{b}{a}$.

rectangle [11.1] A rectangle is a parallelogram with four right angles.

rectangular solid [11.4] A rectangular solid is a solid in which all six faces are rectangles.

right angle [11.1] A right angle is an angle whose measure is 90°.

right triangle [11.1] A right triangle is a triangle with one right angle.

rounding [1.1] Rounding is the process of approximating an exact answer by a number that ends in a given number of zeros.

scalene triangle [11.1] A scalene triangle is a triangle with no sides equal in length.

signed number [7.1] A signed number is a number with a sign that is either positive or negative.

similar triangles [11.5] Similar triangles are triangles that have the same shape but not necessarily the same size.

simplified form (or written in lowest terms) [2.2] A fraction is said to be in simplified form when the only common factor of its numerator and denominator is 1.

solution [9.1] A solution to an equation is a value of the variable that makes the equation a true statement.

solve [9.1] To solve an equation means to find all solutions of the equation.

sphere [11.4] A sphere is a three-dimensional figure made up of all points a given distance from the center.

square [11.1] A square is a rectangle with four sides equal in length.

square root [11.6] The (principal) square root of a number n, written $\sqrt{n}$, is the positive number whose square is n.

statistics [8.1] Statistics is the branch of mathematics that deals with ways of handling large quantities of information.

straight angle [11.1] A straight angle is an angle whose measure is 180°.

subtrahend [1.2] In a subtraction problem, the number that is being subtracted is called the subtrahend.

sum [1.2] The result of an addition problem is called the sum.

supplementary angles [11.1] Two angles are supplementary if the sum of their measures is 180°.

table [8.2] A table is a rectangular display of data.

tessellation [11.1] A tessellation is any repeating pattern of interlocking shapes.

trapezoid [11.1] A trapezoid is a quadrilateral with only one pair of opposite sides parallel.

triangle [11.1] A triangle is a polygon with three sides.

unit fraction [2.3] A fraction with 1 as the numerator is called a unit fraction.

unit price [5.1] The unit price is the price of one item, or one unit.

unit rate [5.1] A unit rate is a rate in which the number in the denominator is 1.

unlike fractions [2.2] Unlike fractions are fractions with different denominators.

unlike quantities [5.1] Unlike quantities are quantities that have different units.

unlike terms [9.2] Unlike terms are terms that do not have the same variables with the same exponents.

variable [4.1] A variable is a letter that represents an unknown number.

vertex [11.1] A vertex is the common endpoint of an angle.

vertical angles [11.1] Vertical angles are two opposite angles with equal measure formed by two intersecting lines.

volume [11.4] Volume is the number of cubic units required to fill a three-dimensional figure.

weighted average [8.1] A weighted average is a special kind of average (mean) used when some numbers in a set count more heavily than others.

written in lowest terms (or simplified) [2.2] A fraction is said to be written in lowest terms when the only common factor of its numerator and denominator is 1.

Index

A

Absolute value, 325, 333
Addends, 14
Addition
    associative property of, 15
    commutative property of, 15
    of decimals, 173–174
        on a calculator, 178
    equations involving, 224–227
    estimating sums in, 22–23, 123, 176–177
    identity property of, 15
    of like fractions, 109–111
    meaning and properties of, 14–15
    of mixed numbers, 113–116, 122
    in order of operations, 57
    repeated, 32
    of signed numbers, 333–336
    of unlike fractions, 111–113
    of whole numbers, 15–17
        on a calculator, 23–24
Algebra
    defined, 215
    importance of, 215
    pressure and, 213
Algebraic expressions, 215
    defined, 216
    evaluating, 217–218
    translating phrases to, 215–217
Amount, 290
    finding, 291–292
Analogies, 269
Apparent magnitude, 327
Area, 36
Arithmetic mean, 368
The Art of Tenths (Stevin), 172
Associative property
    of addition, 15
    of multiplication, 33
Astronomical unit (AU), 209
Augustus, 289
Averages, 59, 368–372
    mean in, 368–369
    median in, 368, 369–370
    mode in, 368, 371
    weighted, 369

B

Balance scale, 222
Bar graphs, 378–380
    double, 379
Base
    for an exponent, 55
    of a percent, 290
        finding, 292–293
Blood tests, decimals and, 157

Brackets in order of operations, 57
Brahmagupta, 332
Broken-line graph, 382
Business applications of percents, 303–307

C

Caesar, Julius, 289
Calculator
    addition of
        decimals on a, 178
        whole numbers on a, 23–24
    division of
        decimals on, 200
        whole numbers on a, 51
    multiplication of
        decimals on, 187
        whole numbers of a, 38
    order of operations on, 60
    percents on a, 297
    powers on a, 60
    scientific notation and, 367–368
    signed numbers on a, 336
    subtraction of
        decimals on, 178
        whole numbers on a,
            23–24
Capacity
Celsius scale, 332
Chemistry, signed numbers
            and, 321
Circle graphs, 384
Circles
    circumference of, 260
    diameter of, 260
Circumference of a circle, 260
Class frequencies, 381
Class intervals, 381
Commissions, 304
Commutative property
    of addition, 15
    of multiplication, 33
Comparison of decimals, 163–165
Composite numbers, 86
Compound interest, 305, 306–307
Connecticut Compromise, ratio, proportion and, 249
Constant, defined, 215, 216
Cubed, 55
Cultural notes, 43, 147, 172, 222, 255, 289,
            332, 367

D

Decimal coinage, 172
Decimal places, 159–160
Decimals

addition of, 173–174
    on a calculator, 178
blood tests and, 157
changing
    to fractions, 160–163
    to percents, 281–283
changing percents to, 280–281
comparing, 163–165
division of, 192–198
equivalent
    change percents to, 280
    changing fractions to the, 192–194
fractional part of, 159
multiplication of, 183–185
    on a calculator, 187
numbers written as, 159
repeating, 194
rounding of, 165–167
subtraction of, 174–175
    on a calculator, 178
whole-number part of, 159
Denominator, 93
    least common, 101–102
Diameter of a circle, 260, 471
Differences, 14. *See also* Subtraction
    estimating, 22–23, 123, 176–177
Digit notation, 43
Digits, 3
Discounts, 305
Distributive property, 33
Dividend, 44
Divisibility, 83
    tests for, 84
Division
    of decimals, 192–198
        on a calculator, 200
    equations involving, 232–237
    estimating quotients in, 49–50, 139,
            199–200
    of fractions, 135–137
    meaning and properties of, 44–45
    of mixed numbers, 137–138
    in order of operations, 57
    of signed numbers, 352–354
    of whole numbers, 45–49
        on a calculator, 51
Divisor, 44, 136
Double-bar graphs, 379
Drawing a picture, as strategy in solving word
            problems, 67–68

E

Equations
    defined, 223
    involving addition and subtraction,
            224–227

involving multiplication and division, 232–237
isolation of variables in, 22
as mathematical models, 226
translating sentences to, 223–224, 232
Equivalent decimals
change percents to, 280
changing fractions to the, 192–194
Equivalent fractions, 96–98
changing decimals to, 161
changing percents to, 278
Equivalent percent, 281, 283
Estimating
differences in subtraction, 22–23, 123, 176–177
products in multiplication, 36–37, 139, 186
quotients in division, 49–50, 139, 199–200
sums in addition, 22–23, 123, 176–177
Expanded form, writing whole numbers in, 5–6
Exponential form, 55
Exponents
defined, 55
laws of, 360–363
power rule of, 360–361

F

Factors, 32, 83
finding, 83–85
Factor tree, 86–87
Feet, 432
Filibuster, 81
Fraction diagrams, 93–94
Fraction line, 93
Fractions
addition of like, 109–111
addition of unlike, 111–113
changing, to percents, 283–284
changing decimals to, 160–163
changing percents to, 278–279
changing to the equivalent decimal, 192–194
comparing, 100–102
defined, 93
denominator of a, 93
division of, 135–137
equivalent, 96–98
changing decimals to, 161
changing percents to, 278
improper, 94–96
like, 100
multiplication by, 130–132
numerator of a, 93
proper, 93
subtraction of like, 109–111
subtraction of unlike, 111–113
unit, 129
unlike, 100
writing, 147
in simplest form, 98–100

Frequency table, 381
Fundamental theorem of arithmetic, 86

G

Goldbach, Christian, 92
Golden ratio, 260
Golden rectangle, 260
Grams, 113
Graphs, 376, 378–384
bar, 378–380
circle, 384
double-bar, 379
histograms as, 381–382
line, 382–383
pictographs as, 378
Graunt, John, 367
Grouping symbols in order of operations, 57

H

Headings in tables, 376
Hindu symbols, 43
Histograms, 381–382
Hypotenuse, 516

I

Identity property
of addition, 15
of multiplication, 33
Improper fractions, 94–96
changing, to a mixed number, 96
Integers, 323
Interest
compound, 305, 306–307
simple, 305–306
Intersecting lines, 466
Inverting, 136

K

Karim, Jawed, 1
Khwarazmi, Muhammad ibn Musa al-, 230
Kiloliters, 113

L

Lattice method of multiplication, 42
Law, statistics and, 364
Laws of exponents, 360–363
Least common denominator (LCD), 101–102
Least common multiple, finding the, 87–89
Legs, 516
Like fractions, 100
addition of, 109–111
subtraction of, 109–111
Like quantities, 251
Line graphs, 382–383
broken, 382

Liquid-in-glass thermometers, 332
Liters, 113

M

Mathematical models, equations as, 226
Mean, 59, 368–369
Median, 368, 369–370
Milligrams, 113
Milliliters, 113
Mindstretchers, 13, 31, 42, 54, 65, 92, 108, 129, 144, 172, 182, 191, 204, 222, 231, 241, 260, 269, 289, 301, 312, 331, 339, 345, 351, 357, 373, 375, 522
Minuend, 18
Mixed numbers, 94–96
addition of, 113–116, 122, 123
changing decimals to, 161
changing improper fraction to, 96
division of, 137–138, 139
multiplication by, 133–135, 139
subtraction of, 116–122, 123
Mode, 368, 371
Multiple, least common, 87–89
Multiplication
associative property of, 33
commutative property of, 33
of decimals, 183–185
on a calculator, 187
equations involving, 232–237
estimating products in, 36–37, 139, 186
of fractions, 130–132
identity property of, 33
lattice method of, 42
meaning and properties of, 32–33
of mixed numbers, 133–135
in order of operations, 57
of signed numbers, 346–348
of whole numbers, 33–38
on a calculator, 38
Multiplication property of zero, 33

N

Natural and Political Observations upon the Bills of Mortality (Graunt), 367
Negative numbers, 323, 326
absolute value of, 325, 333
on a calculator, 336
Negative power, raising a quotient to a, 363
Notation
scientific, 363–368
Number line, 323–324, 326
representing whole numbers on, 3
Numbers
absolute value of, 325, 333
addition of mixed, 113–116
composite, 86
mixed, 94–96
negative, 323, 325, 326
positive, 323, 325, 326

prime, 86
   substituting simpler, in solving word
      problems, 68–69
   subtraction of mixed, 116–122
Number theory, 63
Numerator, 93

O

Operations, opposite, 225
Opposite operations, 225
Opposites, 324
Order of operations, 57–58
   on a calculator, 60

P

Parentheses
   in order of operations, 57
Part, 290
Percent increase or decrease, finding, 302–303
Percent problems
   proportion method for solving, 295–297
   translation method for solving, 290–295
   types of, 290
Percents
   base of, 290
   business applications of, 303–307
   on a calculator, 297
   changing
      to decimals, 280–281
      to fractions, 278–279
   changing decimals to, 281–283
   changing fractions to, 283–284
   defined, 277
   equivalent, 281, 283
   finding, 294–295
   importance of, 277–278
   political polls and, 275
Perfect square, 65, 515
Perimeter, 17, 36
Periods, 3
Phrases, translating, to the algebraic
      expressions, 215–217
Pi (p), 163
Pictographs, 378
Picture, drawing, as strategy in solving word
      problems, 67–68
Placeholders, 4
Place value, 3
Plus/minus statistic, 331
Political polls, percents and, 275
Positive numbers, 323, 326
   absolute value of, 325
   on a calculator, 336
Power rule of exponents, 360–361
Power(s)
   on a calculator, 60
   defined, 55
   in order of operations, 57
   raising a product to a, 361–362
   raising a quotient to a, 362–363

raising a quotient to a negative, 363
   raising signed numbers to a, 347
Powers of 10
   multiplication of decimal by a, 185
Pressure, algebra and, 213
Price, unit, 254
Prime factorization, finding of a number, 86–87
Prime numbers, 86
Products, estimating, 36–37, 139
   in multiplication, 186
Proper fraction, 93
Proportion method, 295–297
Proportions
   defined, 261
   ratio, and the Connecticut Compromise,
      249
   solving, 262–265
   writing, 261–262
Pythagoras, 255, 322
Pythagorean theorem, 516–517
Pythagorean triple, 63

Q

Question, breaking up, in solving word
      problems, 68
Quotient, raising
   to a negative power, 363
   to a power, 362–363
Quotients, 44
   estimating, 49–50, 139, 199–200

R

Range, 372
Rate, 252, 290
   simplifying a, 253
   unit, 253
Ratios
   defined, 251
   golden, 260
   importance of, 251
   proportion, and the Connecticut
      Compromise, 249
   simplifying a, 253
Reciprocal, 136
Rectangles, 461, 470, 479
   golden, 260
Regroup, 15, 18
Repeated addition, 32
Repeating decimals, 194
Return on investment (ROI), 259
   hypotenuse of, 516
   legs of, 516
Rounding, 6
   of decimals, 165–167
   of whole numbers, 6–8

S

Scale, balance, 222
Scientific notation, 363–367

calculators and, 367–368
Sentences, translating, to equations,
      223–224, 232
Signed numbers, 321–363
   addition of, 333–336
   applications of, 323
   on a calculator, 336
   chemistry and, 321
   comparison of, 326–327
   defined, 323
   division of, 352–354
   multiplication of, 346–348
   raising to a power, 347
   subtraction of, 340–342
Simple interest, 305–306
Simplest form, writing fraction in, 98–100
Squared, 55
Square roots
   defined, 515
   finding, 515–516
Standard form, 3
   writing whole numbers in, 5
Standard notation, 43
Statistics, 364–399
   averages in, 368–372
   defined, 367
   graphs in, 376, 378–384
   importance of, 367
   law and, 364
   range in, 372
   tables in, 376–377
Stevin, Simon, 172
Subtraction
   of decimals, 174–175
      on a calculator, 178
   equations involving, 224–227
   estimating differences in, 22–23, 123,
      176–177
   of like fractions, 109–111
   of mixed numbers, 116–122
   in order of operations, 57
   of signed numbers, 340–342
   of unlike fractions, 111–113
   of whole numbers, 17–21
      on a calculator, 23–24
Subtrahend, 14, 18
Sums, 14. See also Addition
   estimating, in addition, 22–23, 123,
      176–177

T

Tables, 376–377
   frequency, 381
   making, in solving word problems, 69
Taxes, 303–304
Thermometers, liquid-in-glass, 332
Total, 14
Translation method, 290–295
Trapezoids, 118
Triangles
   right, 516

U

Unit fractions, 129
Unit price, 254
Unit rate, 253
Unlike fractions, 100
      addition of, 111–113
      subtraction of, 111–113
Unlike quantities, 252

W

Weighted averages, 369
Whole numbers
      addition of, 15–17
            on a calculator, 23–24
      division of, 45–49
            on a calculator, 51

finding prime factorization of,
      86–87
multiplication of, 33–38
      on a calculator, 38
properties of, 3
reading and writing, 3–6
representing, on number line, 3
rounding, 6–8
square of, 65
subtraction of, 17–21
      on a calculator, 23–24
writing, 6–8
      in expanded form, 5–6
Word problems
      choosing strategy
            breaking up the question, 68
            drawing a picture, 67–68

making a table, 69
substituting simpler numbers, 68–69
reading, 66–67
solving, 66

Y

Young's Rule, 59
YouTube, 1

Z

Zero, 326
      multiplication property of, 33

Geometric Formulas

For the following, P = perimeter $\quad A$ = area

C = circumference $\quad V$ = volume

Triangle

$P = a + b + c$

$A = \frac{1}{2}bh$

Rectangle

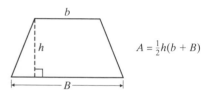

$P = 2l + 2w$

$A = lw$

Square

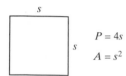

$P = 4s$

$A = s^2$

Parallelogram

$A = bh$

Trapezoid

$A = \frac{1}{2}h(b + B)$

Circle

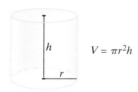

$C = \pi d = 2\pi r$

$A = \pi r^2$

Rectangular Solid

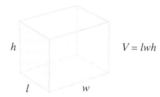

$V = lwh$

Cube

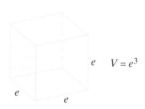

$V = e^3$

Cylinder

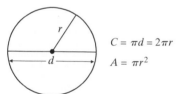

$V = \pi r^2 h$

Sphere

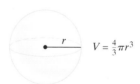

$V = \frac{4}{3}\pi r^3$

Pythagorean Theorem

For every right triangle, the sum of the squares of the two legs equals the square of the hypoteneuse.

$$a^2 + b^2 = c^2$$

Sum of Angle Measures in a Triangle

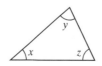

The sum of the measures of all three angles in a triangle is 180°.

$$x + y + z = 180°$$

ISBN-13: 978-1-256-78452-4
ISBN-10:   1-256-78452-4

90000>

9 781256 784524

www.pearsonlearningsolutions.com